MODERN PLANE GEOMETRY FOR COLLEGE STUDENTS

Modern Plane Geometry
for College Students

HERMAN R. HYATT and **CHARLES C. CARICO**
Department of Mathematics, Los Angeles Pierce College

THE MACMILLAN COMPANY, NEW YORK
COLLIER-MACMILLAN LIMITED, LONDON

First Printing

Library of Congress catalog card number: 67–15538

THE MACMILLAN COMPANY, NEW YORK
COLLIER-MACMILLAN CANADA, LTD., TORONTO, ONTARIO

Printed in the United States of America

PREFACE

This book is designed for use in a one-semester course in plane geometry for college students. Geometry may be a terminal course for many students; however, material in this text is covered in sufficient depth to permit those who complete the course to continue their study of mathematics. Although it is assumed that the student has a knowledge of elementary algebra, a brief review of prerequisite material is included in Chapter 2.

The development of the material is based on recent curriculum recommendations of national study groups. In line with these recommendations, a careful distinction is made between geometric entities and their measures, which are elements of the set of real numbers. Both direct and indirect proofs are discussed thoroughly. In the early chapters proofs are presented formally, using the statement-reason format. In later chapters proofs are also given informally—in paragraph form that is easy for the student to follow.

Definitions, axioms, and theorems are clearly identified by number and introduced throughout the text as they are required. For easy reference, complete lists of these theorems, axioms, and definitions are printed in the Appendix. Students may also use these lists as a study guide for review purposes. The basic criterion for the selection of the theorems to be included in the text has been that of "future need." Thus the list of numbered theorems has been kept to an optimum length. However, other theorems traditionally included have been introduced in exercises, and are available if desired.

The majority of the symbols in the text are algebraic, and most students will recognize them as those used in previous algebra courses. A minimum number of new symbols has been introduced. A list of these symbols and abbreviations is furnished in the front of the book for convenient reference.

The design of the problem sets will enable the instructor to use this text for courses which are given for different numbers of hours. The (A) sets may be used for a three-semester-hour course, the (A) and (B) sets for a five-semester-hour course. The (B) sets are also a source of more challenging problems for more highly motivated students.

Answers to most odd-numbered problems are provided in the Appendix. An answer booklet containing selected even-numbered answers is available from the publisher.

Our gratitude goes to Mr. William Wooton and Mr. Irving Drooyan of our mathematics department who were lavish in assistance and advice. Special thanks are in order to Miss Janet Cook of Fullerton College, Mr. Robert Steinbach of Grossmont College, and Mr. John Cockrill of Venice High School for their helpful comments and criticisms. To our patient wives and especially to our hard-working typist, Mrs. Irene Hyatt, we dedicate this book.

H. R. H.
C. C. C.

SYMBOLS AND ABBREVIATIONS

SYMBOL	MEANING	PAGE
$\{\ \}$	set	8
$\in$	is an element of	9
/	negation; for example, $\notin$: is *not* an element of	9
$R \subset S$	set R is a subset of set S	9
iff	if and only if	10
$A = B$	set A is equal to set B	10
$A \cap B$	intersection of sets A and B	10
$A \cup B$	union of sets A and B	10
$\varnothing$	the empty, or null, set	10
$\ldots$	and so on	11
$\approx$	is approximately equal to	12
$>$	is greater than	18
$<$	is less than	18
$=$	is equal to	18
$\geq$	is greater than or equal to	18
$\leq$	is less than or equal to	18
$\sqrt{x}$	the nonnegative square root of x	24
$\lvert x \rvert$	the absolute value of x	25
AB	the distance between points A and B	28
$\overleftrightarrow{AB}$	the line determined by points A and B	31
$\overline{AB}$	the segment with endpoints A and B	32
$\overrightarrow{AB}$	the ray through B with endpoint A	32
$\angle$	angle	45
$\triangle$	triangle	47
$m\angle ABC = r$	the measure of $\angle ABC$ is r	51
$\cong$	is congruent to	57

SYMBOL	MEANING	PAGE
$\perp$	is perpendicular to	60
$\therefore$	therefore	74
Ax.	Axiom	74
Thm.	Theorem	74
Def.	Definition	74
$ABC \leftrightarrow DEF$	the correspondence that matches A with D, B with E, and C with F	96
SAS Ax.	Axiom 5–2	100
ASA Ax.	Axiom 5–3	101
SSS Ax.	Axiom 5–4	101
$\parallel$	is parallel to	162
$\square$	parallelogram	191
area(R)	the area of polygonal region R	213
$\sim$	is similar to	239
AA Similarity Corollary	Corollary 10–3.1	255
SAS Similarity Thm.	Theorem 10–6	260
SSS Similarity Thm.	Theorem 10–7	260
$\sin r°$	sine of $\angle A$ if $m\angle A = r$	288
$\cos r°$	cosine of $\angle A$ if $m\angle A = r$	288
$\tan r°$	tangent of $\angle A$ if $m\angle A = r$	288
$\overset{\frown}{AB}$	the arc whose endpoints are A and B	310
$m\overset{\frown}{AB}$	the degree measure of $\overset{\frown}{AB}$	311
$P(x, y)$	x and y are the coordinates of point P	383

CONTENTS

1. INTRODUCTION   1

2. SETS: ALGEBRAIC AND GEOMETRIC   8
  2–1: SETS AND SYMBOLS   8
  2–2: SETS OF NUMBERS   12
  2–3: SETS OF POINTS (POINT, LINE, PLANE)   14
  2–4: ORDER AND THE NUMBER LINE   18
  2–5: ALGEBRAIC AXIOMS AND FIELD PROPERTIES   20
  2–6: SQUARE ROOTS AND ABSOLUTE VALUE   24
  2–7: THE RULER AXIOM AND BETWEENNESS   26
  2–8: LINES, SEGMENTS, AND RAYS   31
  2–9: MIDPOINT   36

3. ANGLES   40
  INTRODUCTION   40
  3–1: AXIOMS, DEFINITIONS I   40
  3–2: AXIOMS, DEFINITIONS II   43
  3–3: ANGLES   45
  3–4: MEASUREMENT OF ANGLES   49
  3–5: SPECIAL ANGLE DEFINITIONS AND RELATIONSHIPS   54
  3–6: PERPENDICULARITY   59

4. ANATOMY OF PROOF   64
  INTRODUCTION   64
  4–1: INDUCTIVE REASONING   65
  4–2: THEOREMS   67
  4–3: DEDUCTIVE REASONING   68
  4–4: ELEMENTARY THEOREMS, INFORMAL PROOFS   71

4–5: FORMAL PROOFS   74
4–6: WRITING ORIGINAL PROOFS   82

5. TRIANGLES. CONGRUENCE RELATION   89
   5–1: SOME USEFUL THEOREMS   89
   5–2: CONGRUENCE   94
   5–3: CONGRUENT TRIANGLES   100
   5–4: CLASSIFICATION OF TRIANGLES   105
   5–5: SUGGESTIONS FOR WRITING PROOFS   111
   5–6: OTHER SEGMENTS   117

6. FURTHER ANATOMY OF PROOF   124
   6–1: INDIRECT PROOF   124
   6–2: PERPENDICULARS   128
   6–3: AUXILIARY SETS   140

7. INEQUALITIES: ALGEBRAIC AND GEOMETRIC   145
   7–1: ALGEBRA OF INEQUALITIES   145
   7–2: EXTERIOR ANGLES   148
   7–3: THEOREMS AND CONVERSES   152
   7–4: THE TRIANGLE INEQUALITY   156
   7–5: INEQUALITIES FOR TWO TRIANGLES   159

8. QUADRILATERALS AND PARALLELOGRAMS   162
   8–1: PARALLEL LINES   162
   8–2: ANGLES RELATED TO PARALLEL LINES   167
   8–3: FURTHER PROPERTIES OF TRIANGLES   179
   8–4: POLYGONS   186
   8–5: QUADRILATERALS   191
   8–6: MANY PARALLEL LINES   199
   8–7: RIGHT TRIANGLE THEOREMS   205

9. AREA OF POLYGONAL REGIONS   212
   9–1: POLYGONAL REGIONS   212
   9–2: AREAS OF TRIANGLES AND SOME QUADRILATERALS   219
   9–3: THE PYTHAGOREAN THEOREM   228

10. PROPORTION AND SIMILARITY   234
    10–1: INTUITIVE SIMILARITY   234
    10–2: SIMILAR POLYGONS   239
    10–3: PROPORTIONAL DIVISION OF SEGMENTS   246
    10–4: TRIANGLE SIMILARITY THEOREMS I   253
    10–5: TRIANGLE SIMILARITY THEOREMS II   259
    10–6: RIGHT-TRIANGLE SIMILARITIES   274
    10–7: AREAS OF SIMILAR TRIANGLES   281

10–8: TRIGONOMETRIC RATIOS   287
10–9: NUMERICAL TRIGONOMETRY AND TABLES   292

11. CIRCLES AND RELATED SETS   298
11–1: DEFINITIONS   298
11–2: TANGENT LINES   300
11–3: ARCS AND CENTRAL ANGLES   310
11–4: OTHER ANGLES   316
11–5: TANGENT AND SECANT SEGMENTS   325

12. CHARACTERIZATIONS, CONCURRENCE, AND   331
CONSTRUCTIONS
INTRODUCTION   331
12–1: CHARACTERIZATION OF SETS   331
12–2: CONCURRENCE THEOREMS   338
12–3: FURTHER CONCURRENCE THEOREMS   345
12–4: CONSTRUCTIONS   350
12–5: ELEMENTARY CONSTRUCTIONS I   352
12–6: ELEMENTARY CONSTRUCTIONS II   356
12–7: ELEMENTARY CONSTRUCTIONS III   359
12–8: INSCRIBED AND CIRCUMSCRIBED CIRCLES   361

13. AREA OF CIRCULAR REGIONS   366
13–1: REGULAR POLYGONS   366
13–2: THE CIRCUMFERENCE OF A CIRCLE   369
13–3: AREA OF A CIRCLE AND SECTOR   375

14. ANALYTIC GEOMETRY   381
INTRODUCTION   381
14–1: COORDINATE SYSTEMS IN THE PLANE   381
14–2: SLOPE   387
14–3: PARALLEL AND PERPENDICULAR LINES   395
14–4: THE DISTANCE FORMULA   399
14–5: THE MIDPOINT FORMULA   401
14–6: PROOFS BY COORDINATE METHODS   404
14–7: THE GRAPH OF A CONDITION   408
14–8: DESCRIPTION OF A LINE BY AN EQUATION   410

APPENDIX
TABLE OF TRIGONOMETRIC FUNCTIONS   417
TABLE OF SQUARE ROOTS OF NUMBERS 1–300   418
LIST OF DEFINITIONS   419
LIST OF THEOREMS AND COROLLARIES   425
LIST OF AXIOMS   430
ANSWERS TO SELECTED ODD-NUMBERED PROBLEMS   435

INDEX   447

Chapter 1

INTRODUCTION

The rudiments of geometry were used by the Egyptians almost four thousand years ago. The annual overflow of the Nile River left deposits of mud when the river receded, and boundary lines were obliterated. Because land area was taxable, it was important to be able to resurvey the land with some degree of precision. Further, the orientation of temples with respect to direction was a matter of great practical (as well as religious) importance. Temple priests kept the calendar, which advised of planting and harvesting times and predicted the time of flooding. Thus accurate north-south lines and east-west lines at right angles to them were crucial. These needs were met by a collection of crude formulas and working rules.

The Egyptians were not concerned with the reasoning behind the formulas they used, nor with the possibility of generalizing the knowledge they possessed. They merely knew they could lay out a right angle by using ropes 3, 4, and 5 cubits long, as shown in Figure 1–1.

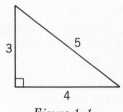

Figure 1–1

As we shall see, there are many other trios of numbers that will accomplish the same result, but this fact apparently held no significance for the Egyptians.

The credit for the actual study and development of geometry as a mathematical science falls to the ancient Greeks, a people who delighted in the pursuit of intellectual activities solely for the mental discipline and satisfaction this afforded, and who—it must be confessed—spurned any practical applications thereof. The best-known name among the early Greek mathematicians is that of Euclid (*ca.* 300 B.C.). His work, called *Elements*, consists of thirteen volumes, five of which deal with plane geometry and three with solid geometry. The remaining five offer geometric treatments of what we would call algebraic problems. These books were in use as texts for nearly two thousand years. Only in comparatively recent times have major changes been made—and those changes often involved merely the rearrangement and reorganization of existing material.

The fundamental difference between the Egyptian and Greek geometries was that of "approach." The Egyptians had amassed much knowledge by making many measurements and observations for hundreds of years. This may have been a practical approach, but it was time consuming and not always correct. Further, the knowledge so painfully accumulated was seldom in a form that could be applied to new problems. The Greeks, on the other hand, did not place much reliance on observation, but set about organizing all that they knew into a methodically arranged system, seeing to it that further ideas followed, in some manner, from earlier ones. To this very day mathematicians strive to develop mathematics within the framework of a system. That particular branch of the system concerning geometry is the one we shall study.

Modern point of view does not unduly emphasize the practical aspects of geometry, nor does it wholly ignore them. Rather it seeks to build an appreciation and understanding of a mathematical system and the nature of a mathematical "proof," as well as a reasonable amount of familiarity with rules and formulas that are of practical and theoretical use. In most fields of mathematics the major emphasis is on theory; if practical applications result, they are, of course, welcomed.

Let us consider an admittedly superficial system, which will probably be somewhat familiar to you. Our purpose is to illustrate and examine some of the structures and features of a system, in preparation for the study of a mathematical system. You are cautioned that no attempt at completeness is being made; rather we deliberately choose for discussion only those portions that serve our needs.

Consider an athletic system called "basketball." We begin with certain words, words that we shall need but may not be able to define explicitly. We require:

(1) A ball.
(2) Players.
(3) Iron hoops.
(4) A large flat court.

The ball, players, hoops, and court are more or less familiar to us from everyday experience; however, some additional descriptive information might help to clarify their meaning. The hoops are circular and about 18 in. in diameter. The ball is spherical, like any other ball, and is about 30 in. in circumference. The court is just like a floor. These statements do not make completely clear what each of the various objects actually is, so we content ourselves by saying, "everyone knows what a hoop, ball, and floor look like," and proceed from there.

A set of Rules of Operation would help clarify the system further. We list a representative few:

(1) There shall be two opposing teams, with exactly five players each.

(2) Two points may be earned by throwing the ball through one of the hoops.

(3) The ball may not be moved along the court unless it is thrown from one player to another, or bounced on the floor by the player as he runs along the court.

(4) The team scoring the greater number of points is declared to be the winner.

Now, using these rules (as well as many others not listed above), we develop methods of play to assist in the scoring of points. All such methods must of course abide by the rules, and consist of allowed activities, forming what we shall call a "strategy." One such strategy might be:

IF: 1. A team has many more points than its opponent.

2. Very little time for playing remains.

THEN: Each player on that team will keep moving and passing the ball rapidly from one player to another, thus preventing the opposing team from gaining possession of the ball and having the opportunity to score points.

Thus our system contains words naming the objects in use, rules that must be followed, and strategies that are developed by use of the rules. While this much may be sufficient for playing the game, we also have further refinements. For identification purposes each player might have a number assigned, and each team might adopt its own color scheme for clothing. Also we might use certain tools: rubber-soled shoes, heavy knit socks, athletic shorts, etc. While it may be possible to play without some of these tools, their use does facilitate the play and adds to the enjoyment.

A question may have occurred by now to the alert reader: Why should we have undefined words? Surely any good dictionary should suffice to avoid such an awkward situation. Let us consider the nature of a definition for a given word. Perhaps we could find a simpler synonym for the word—this would suffice as an acceptable definition. Sometimes we find a few descriptive phrases, using only previously defined words, that form an acceptable definition. Such words as *and, the, if,* and so forth, are most often defined by giving grammatical rules for their usage. Certainly any form of a definition must be couched in words that are already defined and—it is hoped—simpler to understand than the word being defined. This leads to the basic question: How can we define our very *first* word? If it is the first, no other words are available; thus we are forced to choose words that we cannot define, and begin with them. It is desirable to keep the number of such words to a minimum, and, in fact, later we shall choose just three such undefined words.

Rules of operation in mathematics are usually called "axioms," "postulates," or "assumptions." (We choose to use the word *axioms* only.) We are not free to choose a set of axioms at random; in particular, they must not be contradictory; that is, they must not imply that any statement is *both* true and false. We could not state that the ball must be bounced as it is moved along the court, and at the same time permit a player to run with the ball. It is also desirable to keep the number of axioms as small as possible, although the set of axioms chosen for our study of geometry of necessity will not be the smallest. Also, with respect to geometry, we shall try to choose axioms that conform to our everyday experiences. For example, it seems evident that if two straight streets cross, they can do so only once. We shall later choose as one of our axioms that two straight lines can intersect in at most one point.

Once we have chosen some undefined words and a set of axioms, we will be ready to develop "strategies." In mathematics we prefer to use the word *theorem* rather than strategy. Theorems must be established using any previously available material—words, axioms, and any earlier theorems that may exist. We have no desire to minimize the number of such theorems; on the contrary, we wish to obtain as many nontrivial ones as possible.

Finally, our system will also require words that are definable, and we shall introduce such words, with their definitions, as the need for them arises.

Returning to our basketball system, we note the convenience of having players identified by number, and teams identified by color. Such simple devices do not suffice in mathematics. We shall have to invent many types of notation as we proceed, so that we can clearly identify whatever entities may be under consideration. Thus we shall choose "line" as one of our undefined terms; then we have to decide how to name lines so that we may be able to distinguish one line from another.

Taking a last look at basketball, we note again the specialized equipment. In like manner our mathematics system requires specialized equipment. In particular we make use of arithmetic, algebra, and some set theory. This information will be reviewed and discussed in Chapter 2.

To recapitulate: our purpose is to construct a mathematical system called *Geometry*. To accomplish this we require:

(1) A set of undefined terms.
(2) A set of axioms.
(3) A set of terms to be introduced and carefully defined as the need arises.
(4) An agreed-upon set of notational devices and symbols.

(5) Any and all mathematical tools that we may already possess, or that we may acquire as we proceed with our study.

(6) Some specialized equipment: straightedge, compass, and protractor.

We end this introduction with some words of advice. There are, basically, three broad areas of concentration in the learning of mathematics, and it is essential to pay full and thorough attention to all three.

1. Definitions: In mathematics, words in ordinary usage are assigned very special and often severely restricted meanings. You should make every effort to master these meanings precisely, and read neither more nor less into a definition than is actually there. For example, the word *factor* has many meanings: (1) an agent in commercial transactions; (2) a steward of an estate; (3) a substance involved in a physiological process (vitamin, hormone, etc.). None of these apply, however, to algebraic usage. Commonly we define **factor** to mean any numbers which are to be multiplied together to form a product. If one is unaware of precise meanings, ambiguity and confusion are certain to ensue.

2. Notation: You must become thoroughly familiar with all the symbols and abbreviations employed. To illustrate (without at this time going deeply into meanings), AB, $\overline{AB}$, and $\overleftrightarrow{AB}$ each will mean something different, despite the presence of exactly the same letters in each symbol. A conscious effort at memorization on your part is called for so that recognition of symbols, and the meanings they convey, shall be as immediate and automatic as possible. Notation is not a trivial matter, and its study must not be slighted.

3. Theory: This, of course, is the actual subject matter of mathematics—the *body* itself. Obviously you should make a major effort to master as much theory as possible. Past experience indicates that students all too frequently concentrate on theory, and neglect definitions and notation.

Zealous pursuit of the mastery of all three of the above areas is essential for deep understanding of, and success in, mathematics.

Exercise 1–1

1. Look up a definition for "and." Do you find the definition as a synonym, a descriptive phrase, or grammatical instructions?
2. Look up definitions for "length," "measure," and "dimension." Is each of these words defined without the use of the others?

For problems 3 to 7, consider the following system:

    I. Undefined terms: tree, row, lies in.
   II. Axioms
      (a) Two rows have one and only one tree in common.
      (b) Every tree in the system lies in two and only two rows.
      (c) There are exactly four rows in the system.

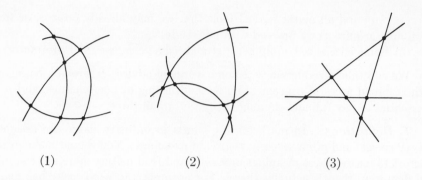

(1)   (2)   (3)

3. Which of the above diagrams does *not* illustrate the system? Why?

4. Rewrite the three axioms using *line* for row, and *point* for tree.

5. Rewrite the axioms using *game* for point and *team* for line. Should you change "lies in" so that your new system has meaning?

6. Reasoning from diagram (3), can you conjecture a theorem that will be valid for the system using points and lines?

7. Using the axioms with trees and rows, try to show that at least four trees must exist in this system.

For problems 8 to 22, consider the system:

    I. Undefined terms: city, highway.

   II. Axioms

      (a) There are at least two cities.

      (b) Any two cities are on exactly one highway.

      (c) Not all the cities are on the same highway.

      (d) On each highway there are at least two cities.

In the diagrams of problems 8 to 17, the dots represent cities, the lines (straight or curved) represent highways. State whether or not each of the diagrams violates any of the axioms.

8.   **9.**   **10.**

11.   **12.**   **13.**

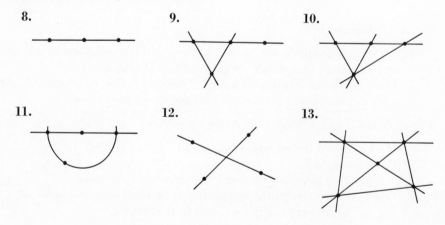

14.

15.

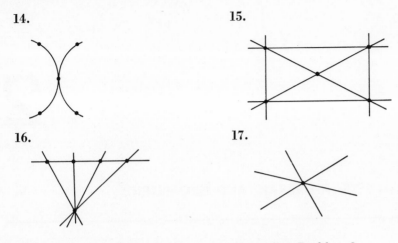

16.

17.

For problems 18 to 22, reread the axioms preceding Problem 8.

18. If there are three cities:
   (a) What is the least number of highways possible?
   (b) What is the greatest number of highways possible?
19. If there are four cities, answer questions (a) and (b) of problem 18.
20. If there are five cities, answer (a) and (b) of problem 18.
21. Can you show that there must be at least three cities?
22. Can you show that there must be at least three highways?

Chapter 2

SETS: ALGEBRAIC AND GEOMETRIC

2–1 SETS AND SYMBOLS

Throughout this text we will need to use concepts and methods of elementary algebra. The next few pages contain a brief review of these ideas. If you find yourself in need of a more intensive review, you should consult any recent textbook on elementary algebra.

In Chapter 1 we stated that it is not possible to define every word we will be using, and that for the development of our geometry we shall choose three undefined terms—point, line, and plane. As we progress, we will introduce undefined terms from algebra as the need arises. In particular, let us now consider the idea of a **set.** The word *set* itself can conveniently be taken as an undefined term, since there seems to be no simpler term available with which to define it. Intuitively, you can think of any collection of objects as a set. Each of the objects in the set is called a **member** or an **element** of the set. The objects themselves can be almost anything: numbers, books, automobiles, etc. For example, we might speak of the set of all positive even integers less than 10. The members (elements), of this set are the numbers 2, 4, 6, and 8. Since sets are often named with capital letters, we will use the letter A to name this particular set.

One method of specifying a set is to list all the members of the set between a pair of braces. Thus $\{2, 4, 6, 8\}$ represents the set A described above. This is known as the **listing** method.

Another notation commonly used, particularly when it is inconvenient (or perhaps impossible) to list all the members of the set, is called **set-builder** notation. The symbolism for set A, using set-builder notation, is $\{x \mid x$ is a positive even integer less than 10$\}$. This is read, "the set of *all* x such that x is a positive even integer less than 10." (The vertical bar $\mid$ is read as "such that.") The word "all" is italicized to emphasize that the set contains all of the elements described to the right of the vertical bar.

The set E of all even integers is an example of a set for which the listing method is not satisfactory. This set is called an **infinite set** since it contains an infinite number of elements, and so all of them could never be listed. Set-builder notation, however, is quite adequate: $\{x \mid x = 2n,\ n$ is any integer$\}$.

In algebra we speak of the solution set of an equation. For example, the solution set of $3x - 5 = 7$ is $\{4\}$, meaning that 4 is the only solution of the equation. An alternate notation for this solution set is $\{x \mid 3x - 5 = 7\}$. Again, the solution set of $x^2 - x - 6 = 0$ is $\{3, -2\}$. Alternatively, $\{x \mid x^2 - x - 6 = 0\}$.

The symbol $\in$ is read "is a member of" or "is an element of." For example, $2 \in A$, $2 \in E$, $1000 \in E$. The symbol $\notin$ is read "is not a member of" or "is not an element of." For example, $3 \notin A$, $3 \notin E$, $1000 \notin A$, $\frac{1}{2} \notin E$.

Having taken the undefined term "set," we can now use it to define other terms. One very useful concept is that of *subset:*

Definition 2–1:   A set R is a **subset** of the set S if and only if every element of R is also an element of S. (Notation: $R \subset S$.)

Thus:
$$\{2\} \subset \{1, 2, 3\}$$
$$\{3, 4\} \subset \{1, 3, 4, 5\}$$
$$\{2, 4, 6, 8\} \subset \{x \mid x = 2n, n \text{ an integer}\}$$
$$\{3\} \subset \{x \mid x^2 - x - 6 = 0\}$$
$$S \subset S \quad \text{(since every element of } S \text{ \textit{is} in } S)$$
$$\{3, 4\} \subset \{3, 4\}$$

As illustrated above ($\notin$), negation bars such as / or | are very commonly used symbols to indicate the negation of a relation; thus $\neq$ (*not* equal to), $\notin$ (not a member of), and $\not\subset$ (not a subset of), are examples of its use.

We now wish to call your attention to the phrase "if and only if" as used in Definition 2–1, and in definitions generally. In nontechnical language, this phrase implies that the reverse of a definition (or statement) is always true. That is, Definition 2–1 really tells us two things:

(1) *If* every element of R is also an element of S, *then* R is a subset of S.
(2) *If* R is a subset of S, *then* every element in R is also an element in S.

This important property of a definition—reversibility—can be used to distinguish between definitions and would-be definitions, even though the statement itself might not actually include the phrase "if and only if." For example, "a dog is an animal" would not be an acceptable definition since the reverse, "an animal is a dog," is not necessarily true. On the other hand, we could define "catboat" by saying that "a catboat is a sailboat having a cat rig" because the reverse of this statement, "a sailboat having a cat rig is a catboat," is always true. Because the phrase "if and only if" is used so frequently in mathematical writing, mathematicians often use the abbreviation *iff* to stand for the entire phrase. When you see "iff" in subsequent definitions, there is no error being made; it means "if and only if."

Definition 2–2: Two sets, A and B, are **equal** iff the two sets contain exactly the same elements. (Notation: $A = B$.)

By the definition, each of the sets $\{2, 3\}$, $\{3, 2\}$, $\{x \mid x$ is an integer between $1\frac{1}{2}$, and $3\frac{1}{2}\}$, and $\{y \mid y$ is a natural number greater than 1 and less than 4$\}$ is equal to each of the others. This example illustrates the fact that sets may be equal although their descriptions may seem quite different.

Definition 2–3: The **intersection** of two sets, R and S, is the set whose elements are all of the elements common to both R and S. (Notation: $R \cap S$.)

Definition 2–4: The **union** of two sets, R and S, is the set whose elements are all of the elements in R or in S or in both. (Notation: $R \cup S$.)

EXAMPLES

Let $A = \{2, 4, 6, 8\}$, $B = \{1, 2, 3, 4\}$, $C = \{1, 3, 5, 7\}$.
Then

$$A \cap B = \{2, 4\} \qquad A \cup B = \{1, 2, 3, 4, 6, 8\}$$
$$B \cap C = \{3, 1\} \qquad B \cup C = \{1, 2, 3, 4, 5, 7\}$$

Observe in the above examples that the sets A and C have no elements in common. Despite this, there are times when we need to give a meaning to $A \cap C$.

Definition 2–5: The set with *no* elements is called the **empty** or **null set.** (Notation: $\varnothing$.)

Then we may write $A \cap C = \varnothing$. A word of caution: The set $\{0\}$ is *not* empty, it has one element—zero. Thus $\{0\}$ and $\varnothing$ are not symbols for the same set. Note also that the symbol $\varnothing$ is not enclosed in braces—$\varnothing$ and $\{\varnothing\}$ are not the same—the symbol $\{\varnothing\}$ is incorrect if you mean the null set. The symbol $\{\varnothing\}$ represents a set with only one member; that member is the null set itself.

EXAMPLES

1. If $A = \{1, 2, 3\}$, $B = \{3, 5, 4\}$, and $C = \{a, b\}$, describe the following sets by the listing method:
   (a) $A \cup B$ (b) $A \cap B$ (c) $A \cap \varnothing$ (d) $(A \cap B) \cup C$

Solution
(a) $A \cup B = \{1, 2, 3, 4, 5\}$ (b) $A \cap B = \{3\}$ (c) $A \cap \varnothing = \varnothing$
(d) Since $A \cap B = \{3\}$, $(A \cap B) \cup C = \{3\} \cup \{a, b\} = \{3, a, b\}$.

2. List all the subsets of $C = \{a, b, c\}$.
Solution: The subsets are: $\varnothing$, $\{a\}$, $\{b\}$, $\{c\}$, $\{a, b\}$, $\{a, c\}$, $\{b, c\}$, $\{a, b, c\}$.
(Note that the set itself, and the empty set, are both subsets of a given set.)

3. Indicate the set 5, 10, 15, 20, . . . using set-builder notation. (The three dots at the end indicate that the numbers continue indefinitely.)
Solution: Since each listed integer is a multiple of 5, we assume that this is the underlying pattern. The set may be indicated by:

$$\{x \mid x = 5n, \ n \text{ any positive integer}\}$$

or

$$\{x \mid x \text{ is a positive integer exactly divisible by 5}\}$$

Exercise 2-1

If $A = \{2, 4, 6\}$, $B = \{1, 3, 5\}$, $C = \{6, 7\}$, $D = \{5, 6\}$, describe the sets in problems 1 to 14 by the listing method.

1. $A \cup B$ 2. $A \cap B$ 3. $A \cap C$
4. $A \cup C$ 5. $A \cup D$ 6. $A \cap D$
7. $(B \cup D) \cap C$ 8. $(B \cup D) \cup C$ 9. $(A \cup C) \cup B$
10. $(A \cup C) \cap B$ 11. $(A \cap B) \cap C$ 12. $(A \cap B) \cap D$
13. $\{x \mid x \in A \text{ and } x \notin C\}$ 14. $\{x \mid x \in C \text{ and } x \notin D\}$

15. List all subsets of $\{a, b, c, d\}$.

If E, F, and G indicate nonempty, unequal sets, indicate whether each statement in problems 16 to 30 is *always* true, *sometimes* true, or *never* true.

16. $E \cap F = E$ 17. $E \cup F = E$ 18. $E \cup F = F$
19. $E \cap F = F$ 20. $E \cup G = \varnothing$ 21. $E \cap G = \varnothing$
22. $F \cap G = G \cap F$ 23. $F \cup E = E \cup F$ 24. $E \cup F = G$
25. $(E \cup F) \cup G = E \cup (F \cup G)$ 26. $(E \cup F) \cap G = E \cup (F \cap G)$
27. $E \cap \varnothing \neq \varnothing$ 28. $\varnothing \subset E$ 29. $E \subset \varnothing$ 30. $\varnothing \subset (E \cap F)$

Indicate the sets in problems 31 to 34 using set-builder notation.

31. The set whose members are 4, 8, 12, 16, . . . (As stated in example 3, the three dots mean that the numbers continue indefinitely.)
32. The set whose members are 3, 6, 9, 12, ...
33. The set whose members are 1, 4, 9, 16, 25, ...
34. The set whose members are 1, 4, 7, 10, 13, ...

For the sets described in problems 35 to 38, does $A = B$?

35. $A = \{$All whole numbers between $\frac{1}{2}$ and $2\frac{1}{4}\}$; $B = \{1, 2\}$.
36. $A = \{a, c\}$; $B = \{a\} \cup \{c\}$.
37. $A = \{1, 3, 5\}$; $B = \{1, 3\} \cap \{3, 5\}$.
38. $A = \{1, 2\} \cap \{2, 3, 4\}$; $B = \{$All even whole numbers from 1 to 3$\}$.

2-2 SETS OF NUMBERS

In developing a geometric system by the method we intend using, many of the facts relating to the system of real numbers that you studied in your earlier algebra course will be needed. We begin our review with the set of natural numbers.

The **natural numbers** are the members of the set N where $N = \{1, 2, 3, 4, \ldots\}$; as usual the three dots indicate that the elements continue indefinitely. Thus N is an infinite set.

The **integers** are the members of the set J where

$$J = \{\ldots, -3, -2, -1, 0, 1, 2, 3, \ldots\},$$

the three dots at either end having the same meaning as above. Thus the set of integers contains all of the natural numbers, as well as the negatives of the natural numbers, and zero.

The **rational numbers** are the members of the set Q where

$$Q = \left\{\frac{p}{q} \,\middle|\, p \in J, q \in J, \text{ and } q \neq 0\right\}.$$

In words, the rationals are all numbers that can be expressed in the form $\frac{p}{q}$, p and q integers, and $q \neq 0$. The following are rational numbers:

$$5 \text{ or } \frac{5}{1}, \quad 5.27 \text{ or } \frac{527}{100}, \quad -8 \text{ or } \frac{-8}{1}, \quad 0 \text{ or } \frac{0}{1}, \quad \sqrt{4} \text{ or } \frac{2}{1}$$

The **irrational numbers** are the members of the set of all real numbers that *cannot* be expressed as the quotient $\frac{p}{q}$ of two integers. Numbers such as $\pi, \sqrt{2}, (4 + \sqrt{3})$ are irrational, since they cannot be expressed as a quotient of two integers. You may have used $\frac{22}{7}$ for π, and 1.414 for $\sqrt{2}$ in the past; the numbers named by these common and decimal fractions are only approximations that are frequently used in computations in place of the irrational numbers. A frequently used notation is $\sqrt{2} \approx 1.414$, and $\pi \approx \frac{22}{7}$, where the symbol $\approx$ is read "is approximately equal to."

The **real numbers** are the members of the set formed by the union of the sets of rational and irrational numbers. Every number mentioned thus far in this text has been a real number. Observe that the sets of natural numbers, integers, rational numbers, and irrational numbers are all subsets of the set of real numbers. *Throughout this book we will use R when referring to the set of real numbers; further, by the word* **number** *in this book we shall mean* **real number.**

EXAMPLES

If $N = \{$Natural numbers$\}$, $J = \{$Integers$\}$, $R = \{$Real numbers$\}$, $Q = \{$Rational numbers$\}$, and $H = \{$Irrational numbers$\}$, are the following *true* or *false*?

1. $J \subset H$ 2. $N \cup Q = Q$

Solutions

1. *False*, because any integer *can* be expressed as a quotient of two integers $\left(\text{for example, } 5 = \dfrac{5}{1}\right)$, while the set H contains only those numbers that *cannot* be so expressed.

2. *True*, because N is a subset of Q. Remembering that the union of N and Q is a set whose members are elements of N or Q or both, we see that the set N contributes no new elements to the collection we already have in the set Q.

Exercise 2–2

In the following problems, $N = \{$Natural numbers$\}$, $J = \{$Integers$\}$, $H = \{$Irrational numbers$\}$, $R = \{$Real numbers$\}$, and $Q = \{$Rational numbers$\}$.

For problems 1 to 9, state whether *true* or *false*.

1. $N \cap J = J$ 2. $N \cup J = J$ 3. $N \cap Q = N$ 4. $Q \cap H = Q$
5. $J \cap R = J$ 6. $Q \cup R = R$ 7. $J \subset Q$ 8. $N \subset J$
9. $H \subset R$

For problems 10 to 13, $A = \{-5, -\frac{5}{2}, 0, 1, 2.3, 5\frac{1}{3}, \pi, -\sqrt{2}, \sqrt{4}\}$.

10. List all natural numbers x such that $x \in A$.
11. List all integers y such that $y \in A$.
12. List all rational numbers n such that $n \in A$.
13. List all irrational numbers m such that $m \in A$.

For problems 14 to 20, state whether *true* or *false*.

14. Negative numbers are real numbers.
15. All negative numbers are integers.
16. $(-x)$ is a negative number for all numbers x.

17. If x is a negative number, then $-x$ is a positive number.
18. If x is a positive number, then $-x$ is a negative number.
19. If $-x$ is a negative number, then x is a positive number.
20. If $-x$ is a positive number, then x is a negative number.

For problems 21 to 34, select the best word (*never*, *sometimes*, or *always*) that will make the statement true, and give at least one example to support your conclusion.

21. The sum of two natural numbers is _____ a natural number.
22. The product of two natural numbers is _____ a natural number.
23. If $a \in N$ and $b \in N$, then $(a - b)$ is _____ a member of N.
24. If a and b are integers, then $(a + b)$ is _____ an integer.
25. If a and b are integers, then ab is _____ an integer.
26. If a and b are integers, then $(a - b)$ is _____ an integer.

27. If $a \in J$ and $b \in J$, then $\dfrac{a}{b}$ is _____ a member of J.

28. If $a \in Q$ and $b \in Q$, then $(a + b)$ is _____ a member of Q.

29. If $a \in Q$ and $b \in Q$, then ab is _____ a member of Q.

30. If $a \in Q$ and $b \in Q$, then $\dfrac{a}{b}$ is _____ a member of Q.

31. If $a \in H$ and $b \in H$, then $(a + b)$ is _____ a member of H.
32. If $a \in H$ and $b \in H$, then ab is _____ a member of H.
33. If $a \in R$ and $b \in R$, then $(a + b)$, $(a - b)$, and ab are _____ real numbers.

34. If $a \in R$ and $b \in R$, then $\dfrac{a}{b}$ is _____ a real number.

2–3 SETS OF POINTS (POINT, LINE, PLANE)

We now identify the three basic undefined geometric terms which we shall use: point, line, and plane. We begin with the term **point,** and indicate what a point is *not*. A point is not a dot made on a piece of paper with a pencil, nor on a chalkboard with a piece of chalk. Such marks are intended only to represent points under discussion. Also, such marks have some measurable dimension—width or diameter—whereas a point has no dimensions at all. Euclid attempted to define a point as "that which has position but no magnitude." This definition substitutes *two* undefined terms—position and magnitude—in place of *one* undefined word—point—and this is plainly of no advantage. A point must then be considered as a mathematical idea, rather than as a physical entity.

Similarly, the **lines** we draw on paper or chalkboard are not really lines, but marks used to represent lines under discussion. As illustrated in

Figure 2-1, there are three basic types of lines with which we will be concerned. Of these, we will be particularly interested in the straight line, and we assume that such a concept does have an intuitive significance for you. Physical models of straight lines are the tightly stretched strings of a piano or guitar. Another example is the mark we make on a piece of paper when we run the point of a pencil along the edge of a ruler. *Throughout this book, unless otherwise stated, the word* **line** *shall be understood to mean* **straight line.**

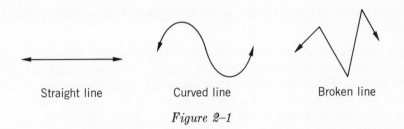

| Straight line | Curved line | Broken line |

Figure 2-1

A **plane** is often described as a "flat surface." If we decide to accept this as a definition of a plane, we are again, as in Euclid's definition for a point, replacing one undefined word, *plane*, with *two* undefined words, *flat* and *surface*. Instead we choose to take the word *plane* as undefined.

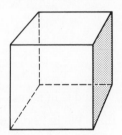

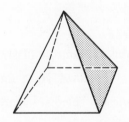

The six faces of a cube are portions of different planes.

The five faces of this pyramid are portions of different planes.

Figure 2-2

We list here, informally, some ways of thinking about points, lines, and planes that are often very useful:

(1) A line may be considered a set of points.

(2) A line may be considered as being traced out by a moving point. (Think of the point of a pencil tracing out a line as it moves over the surface of a piece of paper.)

(3) A plane may be considered a set of points.

(4) A plane may be considered a set of lines. (Consider the result if you attempt to picture as many straight lines as possible, all passing through the same point on a piece of paper (see Figure 2-3).

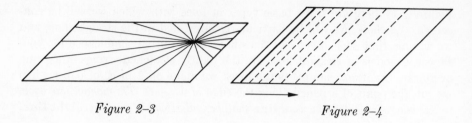

Figure 2-3   *Figure 2-4*

(5) A plane can be thought of as being traced by a moving line (see Figure 2-4).

We now need to agree on methods for naming points, lines, and planes. At this time we will discuss the naming of points, and defer lines and planes until later. We choose always to name points with upper case (capital) letters (see Figure 2-5). In Figure 2-5, points A, B, and C are three points in a plane, points P and Q are two points in a line, and S is the point of intersection of two lines.

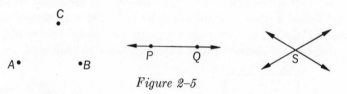

Figure 2-5

EXAMPLES

1. Make a figure to illustrate the following:

Points A, B, C, and D, with points A, B, and C in a line.

Solution: There are many ways to illustrate this. We indicate two:

(a)

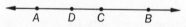

(b) The instructions do not restrict the position of D. D may also be on the line, and the figure could be:

2. Write a description of the adjoining figure.

Solution: Five points, A, B, C, D, and E, and five lines such that each line passes through two and only two points.

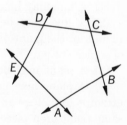

Exercise 2–3

1. Make a dot on your paper. Using a straightedge, draw a line through the dot. Draw another line. Another. How many lines can be drawn through one dot?
2. Make two distinct dots on your paper. Draw a straight line containing both dots. Can you draw a second (distinct) line through both dots?
3. Locate a set of three distinct dots on your paper. Can you draw a straight line through all three dots?
4. Make three distinct dots on your paper. How many lines can you draw connecting them two at a time?
5. Make four distinct dots on your paper. How many lines can you draw connecting them two at a time?

Make a figure to illustrate each of the following (6 to 13):

6. Point A in each of two lines.
7. Points A and B in one line.
8. Points A, B, and C, with points A and B in the same line, but point C not in the line.
9. Points A, B, and C in the same line.
10. Points A, B, C, and D so that no three points are in the same line.
11. Points P, Q, R, S, and T so that P, T, and R are in one line, and S, T, and Q in another line.
12. Points A, B, C, and D and four lines, so that each line passes through at least two points, and B, C, and D are in the same line.
13. Points A, B, C, and D and six lines, so that each line contains exactly two points.

Write a description of each of the figures of problems 14 to 19, similar to those given for problems 6 to 13:

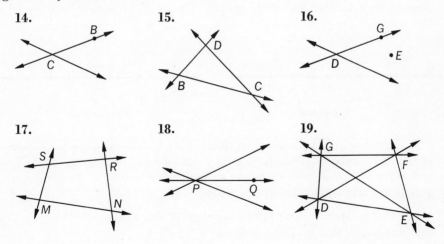

14.   15.   16.

17.   18.   19.

2–4 ORDER AND THE NUMBER LINE

A convenient way to illustrate many of the relations between the various sets of numbers we have been discussing is by the use of a *number line*. A **number line** is a straight line, the points of which have been paired with the real numbers in some way. The following is one way in which the points of the number line and the real numbers can be paired. We begin by selecting any convenient point on the line, and assigning to it the number zero. This point we call the **origin** (Figure 2–6). Next we arrange the integers successively to the right and left of the origin, assigning each integer to a point (Figure 2–7). Usually the positive integers are assigned to points on the right of the origin, and the negative integers to points on the left.

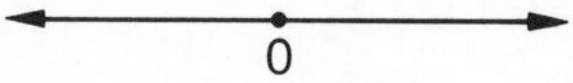

Figure 2–6 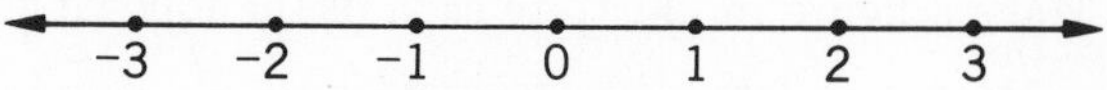   *Figure 2–7*

Now we assign the remaining rational numbers to points. Figure 2–8 shows some of these new numbers on the number line.

It can be shown that the irrational numbers can also be assigned to points of the line in such a way that when combined with the rational numbers, every real number is assigned to a point, and conversely. That is, there will be no point which has no number assigned to it, nor will there be any real number which is not assigned to a point. Furthermore, there will be just *one* number assigned to any particular point and just *one* point paired with any particular number. This situation is described by saying that there is a **one-to-one correspondence** between the points on a line and the set of real numbers. The points are called the **graphs** of the numbers, and the numbers are called **coordinates** of the points. (Figure 2–9 shows the approximate location on a number line of the graphs of some real numbers between zero and one.)

Figure 2–8   *Figure 2–9*

The number line is a convenient device by which to visualize the *ordering* of the real numbers. By **ordering** we mean: if points corresponding to two real numbers, x and y, are selected at random on a number line, there are exactly three possibilities that can occur:

(1) The number x might fall to the right of the number y. If so, we say that x is *greater than* y. (Notation: $x > y$.)

(2) The number x might fall to the left of the number y. If so, we say that x is *less than* y. (Notation: $x < y$.)

(3) The numbers x and y might fall on the same point. Then we say x equals y. (Notation: $x = y$.)

As a matter of notation, we point out that $x > y$ has exactly the same meaning as $y < x$; these symbols may be read in either direction.

There are two other symbols of use to us: $\leq$ (read "less than or equal to") and $\geq$ (read "greater than or equal to"). When we write $x \leq y$, it is interpreted as meaning that one of two relations is true: *either $x < y$ or $x = y$.* An analogous interpretation can be made of $x \geq y$. Each of the following is true: $5 \leq 6$ because $5 < 6$; $7 \geq 5$ because $7 > 5$; and $4 \leq 4$ because $4 = 4$.

The inequality symbols are also often used in this manner: $a < b < c$ (or $c > b > a$) which is read "*b* is less than *c* and greater than *a*." Interpreted on a number line, this places the point

Figure 2–10

corresponding to b between the points corresponding to a and c (see Figure 2–10). (Note that the symbols a, b, and c represent *numbers* that are coordinates of points, not labels for points. If we intended to label the points we would have used A, B, and C.) To illustrate:

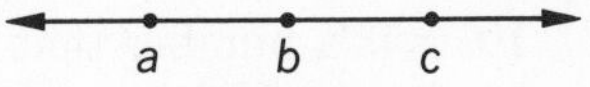

$$0 < 4 < 5, \quad 3 < 7 \leq 8, \quad -4 \leq -4 \leq -2,$$
$$5 > 2 > 1, \quad -3 > -5 \geq -6$$

EXAMPLES

1. In what order would $2\frac{1}{2}$, $2\frac{1}{3}$, $2\frac{9}{16}$, and $2\frac{15}{32}$ be arranged on a number line?

Solution: They would be arranged, with the smallest to the left, as follows: $2\frac{1}{3}$, $2\frac{15}{32}$, $2\frac{1}{2}$, $2\frac{9}{16}$.

2. Restate $a \leq b < c$ in words.

Solution: There is more than one way. One possibility is: b is less than c and greater than, or equal to, a.

3. If $x \geq y$, is it always true that $x - y < 0$?

Solution: $x \geq y$ states that either $x > y$ or $x = y$. Let us try some particular values for x and y. Suppose, for example, $x = 5$ and $y = 4$. Then $x - y = 1$, which is certainly not less than zero; hence the statement $x - y < 0$ is not always true.

Exercise 2–4

In what order would the points corresponding to the numbers in each of problems 1 to 4 be arranged on a number line?

1. $3.1, 3.07, 3.029, \sqrt{10}$

2. $\frac{5}{4}, 1\frac{1}{8}, 1\frac{3}{8}$

3. $\frac{5}{6}, -1, -\frac{3}{4}$

4. $-2.4, -1.9, -0.6, -\sqrt{2}$

Restate problems 5 to 10 in words.

5. $x < y$ **6.** $a \geq b$ **7.** $p < q < r$
8. $k \leq 0$ **9.** $5 > n \geq 3$ **10.** $r \leq s \leq 4$

If x and y are real numbers such that $x \geq y$, $y \neq 0$, indicate whether the following are true *always*, *sometimes*, or *never* (11 to 16):

11. $x \neq y$ **12.** $x - y > 0$ **13.** $y - x > 0$
14. $\left(\dfrac{x}{y}\right) > 1$ **15.** $\left(\dfrac{y}{x}\right) > 1$ **16.** $x \geq y \geq 0$

Rewrite problems 17 to 20, using symbols for order ($<$, $\geq$, etc.).

17. y is a positive number.
18. x is a number between 2 and 4.
19. n is a number that is not negative.
20. r is a number between -3 and 3 inclusive.

Write equivalent statements for problems 21 to 26 using symbols for order, but *without* the negation bar.

21. $a \not> b$ **22.** $x \not< y$ **23.** $5 \not\leq 4$
24. $8 \not\geq 10$ **25.** $3 \not< x < 5$ **26.** $3 < x \not< 5$

Write equivalent statements for problems 27 to 30 *with* the negation bar.

27. $a > b$ **28.** $a < b$ **29.** $a \geq b$ **30.** $a \leq b$

2–5 ALGEBRAIC AXIOMS AND FIELD PROPERTIES

Statements such as $x = y$, $x + 5 = 8$, and $x + 3y - 5 = 0$ are called equations, while such statements as $x < y$, $x + 5 \geq 8$, and $x + 3y - 5 < 0$ are called inequalities. In our work with equations and inequalities we will use some algebraic axioms.

EQUALITY AXIOMS

E–1 (Reflexive Axiom): $a = a$.

E–2 (Symmetric Axiom): If $a = b$, then $b = a$.

E–3 (Transitivity Axiom): If $a = b$ and $b = c$, then $a = c$.

E–4 (Addition Axiom): If $a = b$ and $c = d$, then $a + c = b + d$.

E–5 (Subtraction Axiom): If $a = b$ and $c = d$, then $a - c = b - d$.

E–6 (Multiplication Axiom): If $a = b$ and $c = d$, then $ac = bd$.

E–7 (Division Axiom): If $a = b$ and $c = d \neq 0$, then $\dfrac{a}{c} = \dfrac{b}{d}$.

ORDER AXIOMS

O–1 (Trichotomy Axiom): **For every pair of real numbers, a and b, exactly one of the following is true: $a < b$, $a = b$, $a > b$.**

O–2 (Addition Axiom): **If $a < b$ and $c \leq d$, then $a + c < b + d$.**

O–3 (Multiplication Axiom): **If $a < b$ and $c > 0$, then $ac < bc$.**

O–4 (Transitivity Axiom): **If $a < b$ and $b < c$, then $a < c$.**

This next axiom is very useful; it cannot really be classified, however, as either an equality or an order axiom:

S–1 (Substitution Axiom): **If x and y are two symbols for the same real number, then either may be substituted for the other in any equation or inequality, without changing the truth or falsity of the statement.**

The next set of axioms (commonly called *laws*) describes some of the properties of the real numbers. These properties are frequently referred to as the "field properties." As stated earlier, R denotes the set of real numbers.

F–1 (Closure Law for Addition): **If $a, b \in R$, then $a + b \in R$.**

F–2 (Associative Law for Addition): **If $a \in R$, $b \in R$, and $c \in R$, then $(a + b) + c = a + (b + c)$.**

F–3 (Commutative Law for Addition): **If $a, b \in R$, then $a + b = b + a$.**

F–4 (Additive Identity Law): **There exists a real number 0 (zero), such that if $a \in R$, then $0 + a = a$.**

F–5 (Additive Inverse Law): **If $a \in R$, then there exists an element $(-a) \in R$ such that $a + (-a) = 0$.**

F–6 (Closure Law for Multiplication): **If $a, b \in R$, then $ab \in R$.**

F–7 (Associative Law for Multiplication): **If $a, b,$ and $c \in R$, then $(ab)c = a(bc)$.**

F–8 (Commutative Law for Multiplication): **If $a, b \in R$, then $ab = ba$.**

F–9 (Multiplicative Identity Law): **There exists a real number, 1 (one), such that if $a \in R$, then $1 \cdot a = a$.**

F–10 (Multiplicative Inverse Law): **If $a \in R$, $a \neq 0$, then there exists an element $\frac{1}{a} \in R$, such that $a \cdot \frac{1}{a} = 1$.**

F–11 (Distributive Law): **If $a, b,$ and $c \in R$, then $a(b + c) = ab + ac$.**

EXAMPLES

Which of the axioms listed in this section may be used to justify each of the following statements?

1. If $x - 5 = 1$, then $x = 6$.

Solution: Since the second equation is obtained from the first by adding 5 to each member of the first equation, the Addition Axiom (E–4) applies.

Alternatively, it is also true that if (-5) is subtracted from each member, we are led to the same result. Thus the Subtraction Axiom (E–5) also applies.

2. If $3y = 12$, then $y = 4$.

Solution: If each member of the first equation is divided by 3, we obtain the second equation. Thus the Division Axiom (E–7) applies.

Alternatively, the same result is obtained if both members of the first equation are multiplied by $\frac{1}{3}$. Thus the Multiplication Axiom (E–6) also applies.

3. Justify each step in solving the following equation by naming one of the axioms in this section:

Solutions

$4x - 6 = 2(x + 3)$			
$4x - 6 = 2x + 6$	(step 1)	Distributive law	
$4x = 2x + 12$	(step 2)	Addition Axiom (E–4)	
$2x = 12$	(step 3)	Subtraction Axiom (E–5)	
$x = 6$	(step 4)	Division Axiom (E–7)	

4. Write the additive and multiplicative inverses of each of the following numbers:

Solutions

NUMBER	ADDITIVE INVERSE	MULTIPLICATIVE INVERSE
5	-5	$\dfrac{1}{5}$
0	0	None
a	$-a$	$\dfrac{1}{a}$
-8	8	$-\dfrac{1}{8}$
$\dfrac{2}{3}$	$-\dfrac{2}{3}$	$\dfrac{3}{2}$
$\sqrt{2}$	$-\sqrt{2}$	$\dfrac{1}{\sqrt{2}}$
$\dfrac{2}{\sqrt{3}}$	$-\dfrac{2}{\sqrt{3}}$	$\dfrac{\sqrt{3}}{2}$

Exercise 2–5

Which of the axioms listed in this section may be used to justify the statements in problems 1 to 15? (There may be more than one correct answer.) Assume all letters represent numbers.

1. If $a + 3 = 4$, then $a = 1$.
2. If $\dfrac{b}{5} = 5$, then $b = 25$.
3. If $2x - 5 = 3$, then $2x = 8$.
4. If $2x = 8$, then $x = 4$.
5. If $3(y + 4) = 15$, then $3y + 12 = 15$.
6. If $3y + 12 = 15$, then $3y = 3$.
7. If $3y = 3$, then $y = 1$.
8. If $r \neq s$ and $r \not< s$, then $r > s$.
9. If $x - 2 > 5$, then $x > 7$.
10. $5 \times \sqrt{2}$ is a real number.
11. $7 \cdot (\frac{1}{7}) = 1$.
12. If $x = y$ and $y = 4$, then $x = 4$.
13. $(-3 + \sqrt{5})$ is a real number.
14. If $x < a$ and $a < b$, then $x < b$.
15. $(9 \times 37) \times \frac{1}{9} = (37 \times 9) \times \frac{1}{9}$.

Write the additive inverse of each of the following (16 to 19):

16. 7	**17.** -4	**18.** $-5\frac{1}{2}$	**19.** $3\frac{1}{4}$

Write the multiplicative inverse of each of the following (20 to 23):

20. 7	**21.** -4	**22.** $-5\frac{1}{2}$	**23.** $3\frac{1}{4}$

Name the field property illustrated by each of the following (24 to 29):

24. $x + y = y + x$ **25.** $b + (-b) = 0$ **26.** $r(s + t) = rs + rt$
27. $a(bc) = (ab)c$ **28.** $(r + s) + t = r + (s + t)$ **29.** $0 + x = x$

Name an axiom from this section to justify each of the numbered steps in problems 30 to 33.

30. $12 - x = 20 - 5x$

$12 + 4x = 20$	(step 1)
$4x = 8$	(step 2)
$x = 2$	(step 3)

31. $4x - 5 = 7 + x$

$3x - 5 = 7$	(step 1)
$3x = 12$	(step 2)
$x = 4$	(step 3)

32. $3(y + 5) = 27 + y$

$3y + 15 = 27 + y$	(step 1)
$2y + 15 = 27$	(step 2)
$2y = 12$	(step 3)
$y = 6$	(step 4)

33. $5(y + 1) = 17 + y$

$5y + 5 = 17 + y$	(step 1)
$4y + 5 = 17$	(step 2)
$4y = 12$	(step 3)
$y = 3$	(step 4)

Write the additive inverse and the multiplicative inverse for each of the following irrational numbers (34 to 37):

34. $\sqrt{7}$ **35.** $\dfrac{9}{\sqrt{5}}$ **36.** π **37.** $-\dfrac{\sqrt{3}}{2}$

2–6 SQUARE ROOTS AND ABSOLUTE VALUE

There is a technical point about the notation for square roots that sometimes causes a little confusion. To help clarify this, we begin by stating that: x is a square root of a if and only if $x \cdot x = a$. Thus 5 is a square root of 25, since $5 \cdot 5 = 25$; (-5) is also a square root of 25, since $(-5) \cdot (-5) = 25$. Now, it is true that every nonnegative real number, except zero, has *two* real square roots, one positive and one negative (zero has only one square root— zero itself); however in our work in geometry we will be concerned primarily with the positive square root.

The symbol for the *nonnegative* square root of the number x is $\sqrt{x}$. Thus $\sqrt{25} = 5$, $\sqrt{36} = 6$, $\sqrt{144} = 12$; moreover $\sqrt{25} \neq -5$, $\sqrt{36} \neq -6$, and $\sqrt{144} \neq -12$. If we wish to indicate the negative square root we must use such notation as $-\sqrt{25} = -5$, $-\sqrt{36} = -6$, and $-\sqrt{144} = -12$. In other words, the symbol $\sqrt{x}$ represents a number that is either zero $(\sqrt{0} = 0)$ or positive, but never negative. This leads to a formal definition for square root:

Definition 2–6: If $x \in R$, then

$$\sqrt{x^2} = x \qquad \text{iff } x \geq 0$$

and
$$\sqrt{x^2} = -x \qquad \text{iff } x < 0$$

This definition tells us that $\sqrt{4^2} = 4$ (since $4 \geq 0$) and $\sqrt{(-4)^2} = -(-4) = 4$ (since $-4 < 0$).

An alternate and somewhat useful definition is: $\sqrt{x^2}$ represents the *greater* of the pair of numbers x and $-x$. Thus $\sqrt{(-4)^2} = -(-4)$, since $[-(-4)] > (-4)$.

To complete this line of thought, we make the assumption that the set of real numbers has the following property:

Axiom R–1: Every positive number has a positive square root.

As a result of Axiom R–1, we can now introduce another equality axiom:

Axiom E–8: If $a = b$ and $b > 0$, then $\sqrt{a} = \sqrt{b}$.

The symbol $|x|$ is read "the absolute value of x," and always represents a real number greater than, or equal to, zero. Using more formal language, we state this as follows:

Definition 2-7: If $x \in R$, then

$$|x| = x \qquad \text{iff } x \geq 0$$

and
$$|x| = -x \qquad \text{iff } x < 0$$

Thus $|3| = 3$, $|-3| = -(-3) = 3$, and $|0| = 0$.

It should now become apparent that $|x|$ and $\sqrt{x^2}$ are different symbols for the same number. That is, $|x| = \sqrt{x^2}$, or by the symmetric law of equality, $\sqrt{x^2} = |x|$.

EXAMPLES

1. Is $|x - 2| = (x - 2)$ always a true statement?

Solution: By definition, $|x - 2| = (x - 2)$ if $x - 2 \geq 0$ or, by Axiom 0-2, $x \geq 2$. That is, $|x - 2| = (x - 2)$ *is* true when $x \geq 2$. However, also by definition, $|x - 2| = -(x - 2)$ when $(x - 2) < 0$, or $x < 2$. Therefore, when $x < 2$, $|x - 2| \neq (x - 2)$. Hence the statement is not always true.

Complete the following statements:

2. $\sqrt{5^2} = ?$ *Solution:* $\sqrt{5^2} = |5| = 5$
3. $\sqrt{(-5)^2} = ?$ *Solution:* $\sqrt{(-5)^2} = |-5| = 5$
4. $\sqrt{(y - 5)^2} = ?$
Solution: (a) If $y \geq 5$, then $\sqrt{(y - 5)^2} = |y - 5| = y - 5$.
(b) If $y < 5$, then $\sqrt{(y - 5)^2} = |y - 5| = -(y - 5)$.

Exercise 2-6

Write the absolute value of the following (1 to 8):

1. -4
2. 4.3
3. x^2
4. $-x^2$
5. x,   if $x \geq 0$
6. x,   if $x < 0$
7. $(x - 1)$,   if $x \geq 1$
8. $(x - 1)$,   if $x < 1$

9. For what value(s) of x does $|x + 1| = x + 1$?
10. For what value(s) of x does $|x + 1| = -(x + 1)$?
11. $\sqrt{16} = ?$ 12. $-\sqrt{25} = ?$ 13. $\sqrt{a^2} = ?$
14. $\sqrt{(x - 1)^2} = ?$ (if $x \geq 1$)
15. $\sqrt{(x - 1)^2} = ?$ (if $x < 1$)
16. For what value(s) of x does $\sqrt{(x - 2)^2} = x - 2$?
17. For what value(s) of x does $\sqrt{(x - 2)^2} = -(x - 2)$?

Which of the following are true (18 to 23)?

18. $|-5| < 4$ 19. $|-6| > 10$ 20. $|-4| \leq |-5|$

21. $|-7| \geq |-5|$ **22.** $\sqrt{4} > |-2|$ **23.** $\sqrt{16} > |-4|$

In each of the following sets of numbers, arrange the elements in order, with the smallest first (24 to 27).

24. $\sqrt{7}$, 3, 2.   **25.** 4, $\sqrt{11}$, 2.
26. $\sqrt{(-3)^2}$, -4, 0.   **27.** $\sqrt{(-5)^2}$, -6, 0.

For what value (or values) of x is each of the following true (28 to 33)?

28. $|x| > -1$ **29.** $|x| > -4$
30. $|x| < -1$ **31.** $|x| < -4$
32. $|x| = -1$ **33.** $|x| = -4$

2–7 THE RULER AXIOM AND BETWEENNESS

In much of geometry we are concerned with the distance between two points, which frequently implies the need for some method of measuring. Such measurements are made, in physical situations, with a ruler of some type—perhaps a yardstick. Now we are aware, of course, that you have used such measuring devices; nevertheless we will examine in some detail exactly how a ruler is used to measure distance.

First we point out that a ruler is a physical representation of a subset of the number line. One mark on the ruler corresponds to the origin, and successive integers are used to label successive units. Various units are in use: the yardstick uses the inch (in.); the meterstick uses the centimeter (cm.).

To measure the distance between points A and B, we could proceed as follows: place the ruler on the line so that the endpoint, corresponding to the origin, falls on A (or B); the number on the ruler corresponding to the point falling on B (or A) is the distance between the two points.

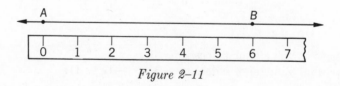

Figure 2–11

In Figure 2–11, the number 6 tells us how many units are contained in the distance from A to B (or from B to A, since the distance is the same regardless of the direction chosen to measure). The actual number itself depends upon the units being used. If the distance between two points measured by a yardstick is 10 (in.), the same distance will be approximately 25.4 (cm.) as measured by a meterstick. A distance of 10 in. is approximately *equivalent* to a distance of 25.4 cm.

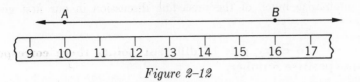

Figure 2–12

A second method for measuring the distance between two points (and the one method we shall use) is to place the ruler so that any convenient point falls on A (or B). Then the distance between A and B is the *absolute value* of the difference between the numbers corresponding to A and B. In Figure 2–12, the distance from A to B (or B to A) is $|16 - 10| = 6$. Note the result is exactly the same if we consider $|10 - 16| = |-6| = 6$.

Remembering that the yardstick may be said to represent a subset of the number line, let us replace the yardstick by the complete number line. If you then interpret the number line as an infinite ruler, Figure 2–13 illustrates some of the situations that could occur. In each case the distance between A and B is given by $|x - y|$, where x is the number corresponding to A, and y is the number corresponding to B. The result can be verified by counting the number of units between A and B.

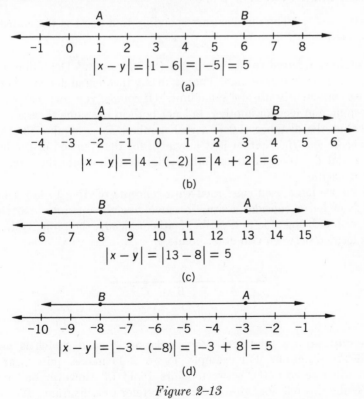

Figure 2–13

We summarize much of the preceding discussion in our first geometric axioms:

Axiom 2–1: To every pair of different points there corresponds a unique positive number.

Definition 2–8: The **distance** between two points on a line is the unique positive number of Axiom 2–1. (If the points are A and B, this distance is denoted by the symbol AB, or BA.)

Axiom 2–2 (The Ruler Axiom): The points of a line can be placed in correspondence with the real numbers in such a way that:
  (1) To every point of the line there corresponds exactly one real number, and
  (2) To every real number there corresponds exactly one point of the line, and
  (3) The distance between two points equals the absolute value of the difference between the corresponding numbers.

Definition 2–9: A correspondence of the sort described in the Ruler Axiom is a **coordinate system** on a line.

Definition 2–10: The number corresponding to a point is the **coordinate** of the point.

The number referred to in Axiom 2–1 (the *distance* of Definition 2–8), is *unique* for a given choice of unit. That is, in any theorem under consideration, you must consistently use the same unit. Of course, you may use yards for one theorem, and feet for another, but not both in the same theorem.

Note that the distance AB is a real number, *not* a symbol for the line containing A and B. Neither is it a symbol for that portion of the line between A and B. We will choose other symbols to indicate these particular geometric entities.

Thus far we have been concerned with concepts relating to *two* points on a line. Now let us consider a situation involving three points—particularly the question of being able to describe, mathematically, the property that one point is located between two other points.

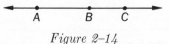

Figure 2–14

Betweenness is a relatively simple relation when a sketch is used to illustrate the situation. For example, Figure 2–14 makes quite clear what we mean when we say: "B is between points A and C." However, our problem is to describe this relation without having to refer to a diagram. We accom-

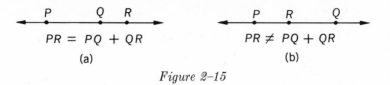

$$PR = PQ + QR$$

(a)

$$PR \neq PQ + QR$$

(b)

Figure 2-15

plish this by using the definition of the distance between two points, as in the definition:

Definition 2-11: The point Q is **between** the points P and R iff (1) P, Q, and R are three different points on a line, and (2) $PR = PQ + QR$. (Figure 2-15.)

EXAMPLES

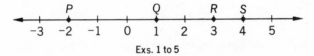

Exs. 1 to 5

1. What is the coordinate of P?   *Answer:* -2.

Let p, q, r, and s represent the coordinates of points P, Q, R, and S:

2. $p - q = ?$ *Solution:* $p - q = -2 - 1 = -3$

3. $|p - q| = ?$ *Solution:* $|p - q| = |-2 - 1| = |-3| = 3$

4. $PQ = ?$
Solution: By definition, the distance from P to Q is given by $PQ = |p - q| = 3$

5. Why is Q between P and R?
Solution: Q is between P and R because:

(a) P, Q, and R are three distinct points on a line.

(b) $PR = |-2 - 3| = |-5| = 5$; $PQ = |-2 - 1| = |-3| = 3$; and $QR = |1 - 3| = |-2| = 2$. Hence $PR = PQ + QR$.

6. Let 4 be the coordinate of A and x be the coordinate of B. Find all values of x so that $AB = |x - 4|$ will have the following value: $|x - 4| = 3$.

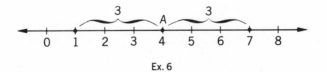

Ex. 6

Solution: From the sketch, it is apparent that if the coordinate of B were 1 or 7, then $AB = 3$. Hence $x = 1$ or $x = 7$.

Exercise 2–7

Problems 1 to 24 refer to the figure below.

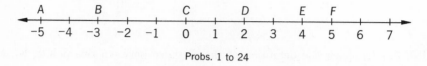

Probs. 1 to 24

For problems 1 to 6, list the coordinate of the indicated point.

1. A **2.** B **3.** C **4.** D **5.** E **6.** F

For problems 7 to 12, let a, b, c, d, e, and f represent the coordinates of points A, B, C, D, E, and F, then:

7. $a - b = ?$ **8.** $b - d = ?$ **9.** $|a - b| = ?$
10. $|b - d| = ?$ **11.** $AB = ?$ **12.** $BD = ?$

In problems 13 to 16, state which point is *between* the other two, and state *why*:

13. A, D, C **14.** E, B, C **15.** F, C, A **16.** D, C, B

17. What is the coordinate of a point at a distance 5 to the left of D?
18. What is the coordinate of a point at a distance 4 to the left of C?
19. A point P is located so that $AP = PD$. What is the coordinate of P?
20. A point Q is located so that $BQ = QE$. What is the coordinate of Q?
21. Point D is located midway between two points. One has the coordinate 6. What is the coordinate of the other?
22. Point E is located midway between two points. One has the coordinate -1. What is the coordinate of the other point?
23. If P were located on the line so that $PA = 2(PC)$, what would be the coordinate of P?
24. If P were located on the line so that $PC = 3(PB)$, what would be the coordinate of P?

Given the three points R, S, and T, with S located between R and T, complete the following table (25 to 30):

	RS	ST	RT
25.	5	3	?
26.	2	10	?
27.	?	8	12
28.	?	7	13
29.	5	?	11.4
30.	8	?	8.07

Let 5 be the coordinate of A, and x the coordinate of B. Find all values of x so that $AB = |x - 5|$ will have the following values (31 to 36):

31. $|x - 5| = 1$ **32.** $|x - 5| = 3$ **33.** $|x - 5| = 7$
34. $|x - 5| = 8$ **35.** $|x - 5| = 903$ **36.** $|x - 5| = 876$

A problem related to problems 31 to 36 is the following:

Let a be the coordinate of A, and x the coordinate of B. Find all values of x so that $AB < c$ ($c \geq 0$) or $|x - a| < c$. For example, suppose $|x - 5| < 2$. From the sketch it should be clear that if the coordinate of B is 3 or 7, then $AB = |x - 5| = 2$. Therefore, if we want $|x - 5| < 2$, the coordinate of B must be between 3 and 7, or the solution set of $|x - 5| < 2$ is $\{x \mid 3 < x < 7\}$.

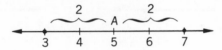

Find all values of x so that each of the following is true (37 to 50):

37. $|x - 1| < 2$ **38.** $|x - 1| < 4$ **39.** $|x - 3| \leq 1$
40. $|x - 3| \leq 2$ **41.** $|x + 1| < 2$ **42.** $|x + 1| < 4$
43. $|x + 3| < 1$ **44.** $|x + 3| < 2$ **45.** $|x - 2| < \frac{2}{3}$
46. $|x - 4| < \frac{5}{6}$ **47.** $|x - 3| < \sqrt{2}$ **48.** $|x - 5| < \sqrt{7}$
49. $|x - 2| > 3$ **50.** $|x - 3| > 5$

2-8 LINES, SEGMENTS, AND RAYS

In this section we consider lines and two subsets of a line: segments and rays. We begin with:

Axiom 2-3: For every two distinct points there is exactly one line that contains both points.

This axiom is sometimes stated as: Two points determine one and only one line. Note that this axiom really says *two* things:

(1) There *does exist* one line that contains the two given points.
(2) The word *exactly* means that there is *only one* such line. There cannot be two or more distinct lines containing the given two points.

If the points determining the line are B and C, the line containing them is usually represented by the symbol $\overleftrightarrow{BC}$ or $\overleftrightarrow{CB}$. A straight line may also be identified by using a single lowercase letter. Thus the line in Figure 2-16 may be referred to as $\overleftrightarrow{BC}$, $\overleftrightarrow{CB}$, or line m.

Figure 2-16

A line is to be thought of as extending indefinitely in both directions, as the arrowheads on each end are meant to indicate. If we wish to discuss some subset of a line that does not extend indefinitely in both directions, we must use another name and symbol. We introduce two: a *line segment* (more simply, *segment*) and a *ray*.

Definition 2–12: The **segment** $\overline{XY}$, or $\overline{YX}$, is the set of points whose elements are the points X and Y, together with all the points of the line $\overleftrightarrow{XY}$ that lie between X and Y.

Definition 2–13: The points X and Y are the **endpoints** of $\overline{XY}$.

Figure 2–17 (a) shows $\overline{XY}$ as part of $\overleftrightarrow{XY}$, while Figure 2–17 (b) shows segment $\overline{XY}$ alone.

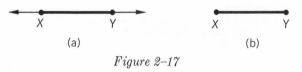

(a)   (b)

Figure 2–17

We now have three different symbols to be used when discussing lines and line segments, and each symbol has a different meaning:

(1) $\overleftrightarrow{XY}$ is the line containing (or determined by) X and Y.

(2) $\overline{XY}$ is the segment having X and Y as endpoints.

(3) XY is a real number indicating the distance between X and Y.

Definition 2–14: The number XY is the **length** of $\overline{XY}$, or the **measure** of $\overline{XY}$. (Symbol: $m(\overline{XY})$ or XY.)

Definition 2–15: Two points, B and C, are on the **same side of point** A iff A, B, and C are distinct points on the same line, and A is **not** between B and C.

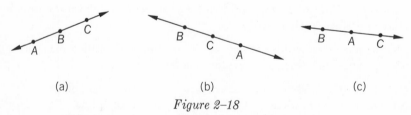

(a)   (b)   (c)

Figure 2–18

Figure 2–18 (a) and (b) illustrate Definition 2–15: B and C are on the same side of A. In Figure 2–18 (c), however, B and C are not on the same side of A, since A is between B and C.

Finally we consider another possible subset of a line:

Definition 2–16: **Ray** $\overrightarrow{AB}$ is the set of points which is the union of A and all points on the same side of A as B. (Notation: $\overrightarrow{AB}$ or $\overleftarrow{BA}$.)

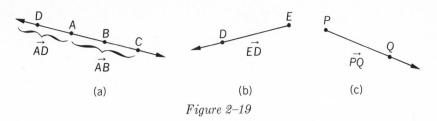

Figure 2–19

Definition 2–17: The point A is the **endpoint** of $\overrightarrow{AB}$.

Definition 2–18: Two rays are **opposite rays** iff they are subsets of the same line, and their intersection consists of a single point.

In Figure 2–19 (a) $\overrightarrow{AB}$ and $\overrightarrow{AD}$ are opposite rays; their intersection consists of a single point, their common endpoint A.

A ray may be said to have **direction.** The ray $\overrightarrow{AB}$ can be thought of as starting at A, the endpoint, and continuing in a straight line through B (Figure 2–20). On the other hand, $\overrightarrow{BA}$ can be thought of as starting at B, and continuing through A. Unlike the symbols for line and line segment, the letters used in the symbol for a ray can be reversed only if the arrow is also reversed; that is, $\overrightarrow{AB}$ and $\overrightarrow{BA}$ represent the same ray, while $\overrightarrow{AB}$ and $\overrightarrow{BA}$ represent two overlapping rays.

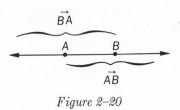

Figure 2–20

To summarize: A straight line extends indefinitely in two directions and has *no* endpoints; a ray extends indefinitely in one direction and has *one* endpoint; and a segment has finite length and has *two* endpoints.

EXAMPLES

1. Draw line $\overleftrightarrow{AB}$. On the line $\overleftrightarrow{AB}$ locate segments $\overline{CD}$ and $\overline{EF}$ so that $\overline{AB} \cap \overline{CD} = \overline{CB}$ and $\overline{AB} \cap \overline{EF} = \varnothing$.

Solution: There are many ways to do this; here are two:

2. Draw $\overleftrightarrow{AB}$ and $\overleftrightarrow{CD}$ intersecting at P.

Solution

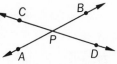

3. Draw a figure to illustrate each of these statements:
   (a) $\overleftrightarrow{PQ} \cap \overleftrightarrow{RS} = \{T\}$ (b) $\overleftrightarrow{PQ} \cap \overleftrightarrow{RS} = \varnothing$

Solution

(a) 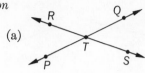   (b)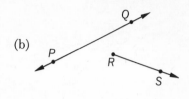

Exercise 2–8

1. Into how many rays does a point on a line divide the line?
2. Draw two intersecting lines. How many rays are formed with the point of intersection as their endpoint?
3. What are the differences between a line, a ray, and a line segment?
4. Do two points determine exactly one line? Do two points determine exactly one ray?

For problems 5 to 11, given the figure $\overleftrightarrow{PQ}$:

5. Do P, Q, and A lie on the same line?
6. Does $\overrightarrow{PA}$ pass through Q?
7. Does $\overleftarrow{PA}$ pass through Q?
8. Do $\overrightarrow{PA}$ and $\overrightarrow{AP}$ represent the same ray?
9. Can we say: $\overline{PA} + \overline{AQ} = \overline{PQ}$? Why?
10. Name a pair of opposite rays.
11. Write an expression for the ray with endpoint P, passing through Q.

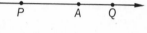

Probs. 5 to 11

12. (a) Copy the following paragraph. Fill in appropriate missing symbols, if any, over each letter pair:

    AC contains points B and D, but AC contains neither B nor D. D belongs to AC, but B does not. $BC + CD = BD$.

    (b) Make a sketch showing the relative positions of the four points.

Draw a line. On it locate A, B, C, D, E, or F so that the following are true (13 to 26): (Draw a different line for each problem.)

13. $\overline{AB} \cap \overline{CD} = \overline{AD}$ 14. $\overline{AB} \cap \overline{CD} = \varnothing$ 15. $\overline{AB} \cup \overline{CD} = \overline{CD}$
16. $\overline{AB} \cup \overline{CD} = \overline{AB}$ 17. $\overline{AB} \cup \overline{CD} = \overline{AD}$ 18. $\overline{AB} \cup \overline{CD} = \overline{BC}$
19. $\overline{AB} \subset \overline{EF}$ 20. $\overline{AB} \not\subset \overline{EF}$ 21. $(\overline{AB} \cap \overline{CD}) \subset \overline{EF}$
22. $(\overline{AB} \cup \overline{CD}) \subset \overline{EF}$ 23. $\overline{AB} \subset \overrightarrow{AC}$ 24. $\overline{AB} \cap \overline{CD} = \overline{AB}$
25. $\overline{AB} \cap \overline{CD} = \overline{CB}$ 26. $\overline{AB} \cap \overleftrightarrow{CD} = \overline{AC}$

Indicate which of the points P, Q, R, S, or T in the figure is a member of the following sets (27 to 38):

27. $\overrightarrow{PQ}$ 28. $\overrightarrow{PQ}$ 29. $\overleftrightarrow{PQ}$ 30. $\overline{PQ}$ 31. $\overline{QR}$ 32. $\overrightarrow{QR}$
33. $\overrightarrow{RS}$ 34. $\overrightarrow{RQ}$ 35. $\overleftrightarrow{QT}$ 36. $\overrightarrow{SQ}$ 37. $\overleftrightarrow{TS}$ 38. $\overrightarrow{PT}$

Probs. 27 to 38

Probs. 39 to 46

From the figure for problems 39 to 46, complete the following:

39. $\overleftrightarrow{AB} \cap \overrightarrow{AC} =$
40. $\overrightarrow{AB} \cap \overrightarrow{CB} =$
41. $\overleftrightarrow{AB} \cap \overleftrightarrow{CE} =$
42. $\overleftrightarrow{AF} \cap \overrightarrow{DB} =$
43. $\overleftrightarrow{AF} \cap \overleftrightarrow{AC} \doteq$
44. $\overleftrightarrow{CE} \cap \overleftrightarrow{BD} =$
45. $\{A\} \cup \overrightarrow{AB} =$
46. $\{C\} \cup \overrightarrow{CB} =$

Draw a figure to illustrate each of the following (47 to 55):

47. Line q and $\overline{AB} \not\subset q$.
48. $\{P \mid P \in \overline{ST}\}$
49. $\overline{AB}$, $\overline{BC}$, and $\overline{AC}$ such that $\overline{AB} \cap \overline{BC} = \{B\}$ and $\overline{AC} \cap \overline{BC} = \{C\}$.
50. Line q, $\overrightarrow{AB}$, $\overrightarrow{AC}$, and $\overrightarrow{BC}$ such that $\overrightarrow{AB} \cap q \neq \varnothing$, $\overrightarrow{AC} \cap q \neq \varnothing$, and $\overrightarrow{BC} \cap q = \varnothing$.
51. $\overline{AB}$, $\overline{BC}$, $\overline{AC}$, and $\overrightarrow{DE}$ such that $\overline{AB} \cap \overrightarrow{DE} = \varnothing$, $\overline{BC} \cap \overrightarrow{DE} = \varnothing$ and $\overline{AC} \cap \overrightarrow{DE} \neq \varnothing$.
52. $\overline{AB} \cup \overline{BC} \cup \overline{CA}$
53. $\overleftrightarrow{AB} \cup \overleftrightarrow{BC} \cup \overleftrightarrow{CA}$
54. $\overleftrightarrow{AB} \cup \overleftrightarrow{AC}$
55. $\overrightarrow{AB} \cup \overrightarrow{AC} \cup \overrightarrow{AD}$, if $\overrightarrow{AD}$ is opposite to $\overrightarrow{AC}$.

Write a description of each of the figures of problems 56 to 65, using symbols for rays, lines, segments, union or intersection of sets.

56. **57.** **58.**

59. **60.** **61.**

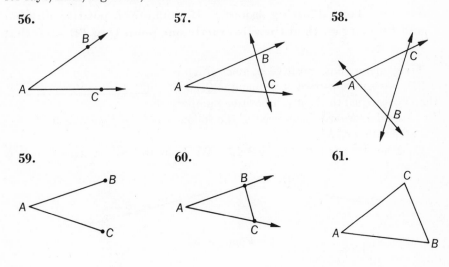

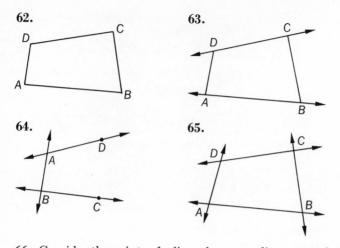

62. **63.**

64. **65.**

66. Consider the points of a line whose coordinates are described as follows:

(a) $x < 2$ (b) $x = 3$ (c) $x > 3$
(d) $x \leq 2$ (e) $x = -4$ (f) $|x| \leq 4$
(g) $|x| > 1$ (h) $|x| \geq 0$

Which of the above sets is a ray? A point? A line? A segment? None of these?

2–9 MIDPOINT

At times—for example, in making a drawing—it is necessary to have a segment of some given length. Our next axiom assures us that, given a number, we can obtain a segment with that number as its given length.

Axiom 2–4 (Point-Plotting Axiom): If x denotes a positive number and $\overrightarrow{PR}$ is a ray, then there is exactly one point Q of $\overrightarrow{PR}$ such that $PQ = x$.

Thus, given some positive number (Figure 2–21), we can construct a segment $\overline{PQ}$ such that PQ is equal to the given positive number. In particular, we will have need of the following application of Axiom 2–4.

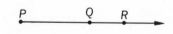

Figure 2–21

Consider $\overline{AB}$ and $\overrightarrow{CD}$ (Figure 2–22). We desire to locate a point B' on $\overrightarrow{CD}$

Figure 2–22

such that $CB' = AB$. Since AB (the measure of $\overline{AB}$) represents a unique positive number, Axiom 2–4 assures us that B' can be located.

Definition 2–19: Q is the **midpoint** of $\overline{PR}$ iff Q is between P and R, and $PQ = QR$.

Axiom 2–5: **Every segment has exactly one midpoint.**

Definition 2–20: A point **bisects** a segment iff it is the midpoint of the segment.

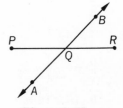

More generally, any figure whose intersection with a segment is the midpoint of the segment is said to bisect the segment. In Figure 2–23, if Q is the midpoint of $\overline{PR}$, then Q, $\overleftrightarrow{AB}$, $\overrightarrow{AB}$, $\overrightarrow{BA}$, and $\overline{AB}$ are all said to bisect $\overline{PR}$.

Figure 2–23

EXAMPLES

If B is the midpoint of $\overline{AC}$, complete this table:

	Coordinate of A	Coordinate of B	Coordinate of C
1.	1	?	4
2.	-5	-1	?
3.	?	1	6

Solutions: Sketching a number line for each example, we have:

1. By counting units, we see that B lies midway between 2 and 3, that is, at $2\frac{1}{2}$.

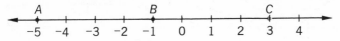

2. Since $AB = BC$, we see that C must lie 4 units to the right of B, hence at 3.

3. As in example 2, A must lie 5 units to the left of B, hence at -4.

Exercise 2–9

Use a number line to complete the following table (1 to 7):

	Coordinate of A	Coordinate of B	Coordinate of Midpoint of $\overline{AB}$
1.	3	?	4
2.	2	6	?
3.	−1	5	?
4.	−4	−2	?
5.	1	?	3
6.	?	−2	2
7.	−2	?	−4

8. In a more complete study of coordinate geometry, it is shown that if a and b are coordinates of A and B respectively, then $\frac{1}{2}(a + b)$ is the coordinate of the midpoint of $\overline{AB}$. For example, if $a = 3$, and $b = 5$, then the coordinate of the midpoint is $\frac{1}{2}(3 + 5)$ or 4. Use this formula to check the results of problems 1 to 7.

Use the formula of problem 8 to complete the table for problems 9 to 16.

	Coordinate of A	Coordinate of B	Coordinate of Midpoint of $\overline{AB}$
9.	5	$7\frac{1}{2}$	
10.	−8	102	
11.	0	−12	
12.	$x - 4$	$x + 4$	
13.	$y + 5$	$y - 5$	
14.	15	0	
15.	$x + c$	$x - c$	
16.	$y - c$	$y + c$	

17. From the figure, if $AM = MB$, name a point, a segment, a ray, and a line, each of which may be said to bisect $\overline{AB}$.

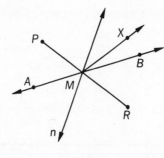

Prob. 17

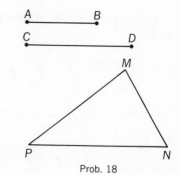

Prob. 18

18. Using a ruler, draw the following segments: $\overline{AB}$ such that $AB = 1$ in., $\overline{CD}$ such that $CD = 1\frac{1}{2}$ in. Copy $\triangle MNP$ at least as large as the given diagram. On $\overline{MN}$ locate a point B' such that $MB' = AB$. On $\overline{MP}$ locate a point D' such that $MD' = CD$.

Probs. 19 to 23

19. Can $AB = AC$? Why?   **20.** Can $AB = CD$? Why?

21. Can B and C both be midpoints of $\overline{AD}$? Why?

22. Can B be the midpoint of AD? Why?

23. Can C be the midpoint of $\overline{AB}$? Why?

24. A is a point on a line, and c is a number greater than zero. How many points of the line are at a distance c from A?

25. Could this be a definition of midpoint of a segment? "M is a midpoint of $\overline{AB}$ iff $AM = MB$." Why?

26. (a) If A, B, C are three distinct points and $AB + BC = AC$, what is the relationship of the three points?

   (b) If A, B, C are three distinct points, can $AB + BC > AC$ be true? Can you make a sketch illustrating this?

Chapter 3

ANGLES

INTRODUCTION

Heretofore we have considered certain properties of points on a line, and particularly the concept of length as the distance between two points. Geometry must consider relationships between more than one line, as well as between lines, points, and planes, generally. In this chapter we establish some of the beginning concepts we shall need for such study. As usual, these concepts will be presented in the form of axioms, definitions, and theorems. At this stage we shall not be deeply concerned with proofs; you are urged to consider carefully the meaning of each of the basic concepts presented.

Although our undefined terms are still point, line, and plane, it is useful, as stated earlier, to conceive of lines and planes as sets of points. Extending this idea, we have:

Definition: The set of all points is called **space.**

Thus any geometric entity made up of points, lines, and planes constitutes a subset of the set of all points that we call space.

3–1 AXIOMS, DEFINITIONS I

Consider the sketch of a room (Figure 3–1), and satisfy yourself as to the truth of the following statements:

(1) Points A, K, B lie on a single line, $\overleftrightarrow{AB}$.
(2) Points B, J, C lie on a single line, $\overleftrightarrow{BC}$.
(3) Points A, B, C lie in the same plane.
(4) Points F, G, H lie in the same plane.

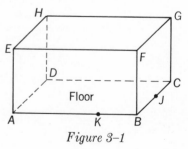

Figure 3–1

(Other such statements can be made, but the above will suffice for our present purposes.) Statements (1) and (2) illustrate:

Definition 3–1: A set of points is **collinear** iff all the points of the set lie on the same straight line.

Observe that A, B, and D do not form a collinear set, and are thus called **noncollinear.** Statements (3) and (4) illustrate:

Definition 3–2: A set of points is **coplanar** iff all the points of the set lie in the same plane.

Note that A, B, F, and G do not all lie in the same plane, and are thus called **noncoplanar.**

Axiom 3–1: If two different lines intersect, they intersect in at most one point.

In set language, Axiom 3–1 states that the intersection of two sets of points (each set constituting a distinct straight line) contains at most one point. This axiom does not require that the intersection *must* contain one point—in fact the intersection may be empty—but it cannot contain more than one point.

EXAMPLES

1. Sketch $\overrightarrow{AB} \cup \overrightarrow{CD}$ where A and C are the same point.
Solution: Two possibilities are:

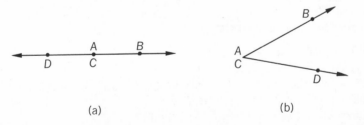

(a)   (b)

2. Sketch four noncollinear points A, B, C, and D, and all possible segments joining them in pairs.
Solution: Four noncollinear points could imply:

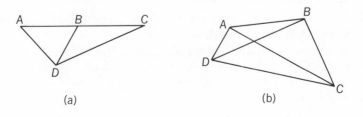

(a)   (b)

Exercise 3–1

1. In Definition 3–1, the symbol *iff* is used. Rewrite the definition as two separate statements, without using iff.
2. If two different lines, q_1 and q_2, intersect at a point A and also at point B, what conclusion must you reach about A and B? State an axiom as a reason for your conclusion.
3. Must two distinct points be collinear? Coplanar? Must three distinct points be collinear? Coplanar? Explain.

Illustrate each of the following by drawing a diagram (4 to 6):

4. $\overrightarrow{AB} \cup \overrightarrow{AC}$, A, B, C are noncollinear.
5. $\overrightarrow{AB} \cup \overrightarrow{AC}$, A, B, C are collinear.
6. $\overrightarrow{AB} \cup \overrightarrow{AC}$, B and C are the same point.

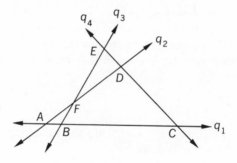

Probs. 7 to 11

In the figure for problems 7 to 11:

7. Which points lie on line q_1?
8. Which points lie on line q_2?
9. State whether or not the following sets are collinear: $\{A, F, D\}$; $\{E, F, A\}$; $\{B, F, E\}$; and $\{B, F, D\}$.
10. Lines q_2 and q_4 intersect at which point?
11. Can we be certain that q_2 and q_4 intersect at no point other than D? Why?

12. If three points are collinear, how many different planes do you think could contain all three points?
13. If three points are not collinear, how many different planes do you think could contain all three points?
14. If we consider a line and a point not on the line, how many different planes do you think could contain the line and the point?
15. If two lines intersect, how many different planes do you think could contain both lines?

16. If two different planes intersect, how would you describe the set of points in the intersection?

3–2 AXIOMS, DEFINITIONS II

In order to insure that a plane shall contain many points, and also be essentially *flat*, we state:

Axiom 3–2: If two points lie in a plane, then the line determined by the two points lies entirely in the plane.

The Ruler Axiom (Axiom 2–2) states that to each number there is associated a point on the line. Since there are indefinitely many numbers, there must be indefinitely many points on the line, and thus the plane contains indefinitely many points. Also, since no part of the line can lie out of the plane, the plane is basically *flat*.

Just as we say: "two points determine a line," these next axioms determine planes:

Axiom 3–3: Any three points lie in at least one plane; if the three points are noncollinear, they lie in exactly one plane.

A convenient restatement of this axiom is: "Three noncollinear points determine a plane."

Axiom 3–4: A line and a point not on the line determine exactly one plane.

Axiom 3–5: If two different lines intersect, they determine exactly one plane.

You will be pleased to know that we introduce no other axioms for the determination of a plane, and conclude this section with:

Axiom 3–6: If two different planes intersect, then their intersection is a straight line.

Exercise 3–2

1. Why will three-legged stools or tables, camera tripods, transit stands, etc., always be steady on a surface, while four-legged tables and chairs frequently rock?

2. If two distinct points A and B lie in one plane, what can be said about $\overleftrightarrow{AB}$?

3. How many planes can contain two given points? Three given points?

4. Just as we name a line using any two distinct points on it, how many distinct points must we use to name a plane?

5. How would you describe the intersection of a wall and ceiling in your classroom? What axiom does this illustrate?

6. Take a sheet of paper, and consider it to be a portion of a plane. Draw a line t across the sheet from one edge to the other, about halfway down. In the upper half of the sheet draw a noncollinear set $\{A, B, C\}$, and in the lower half draw a noncollinear set $\{M, N, P\}$.
   (a) Draw $\overline{AB}$, $\overline{AC}$, $\overline{BC}$. Do any of these segments intersect line t?
   (b) Draw $\overline{MN}$, $\overline{MP}$, $\overline{NP}$. Do any of these segments intersect line t?
   (c) Draw another point X anywhere in the plane (your sheet of paper). Draw $\overline{XA}$, $\overline{XB}$, $\overline{XC}$. Do any of these segments intersect t? Draw $\overline{XM}$, $\overline{XN}$, $\overline{XP}$. Do any of these segments intersect t? Could you use your results to help decide on which "side" of the line t the point X lies?

7. Points P and Q both lie in each of two planes. The line of intersection of the two planes is $\overleftrightarrow{AB}$. Justify the statement that P and Q lie in $\overleftrightarrow{AB}$.

8. Are all triangles plane figures?

9. How many planes are determined by four noncoplanar points?

10. How many planes are determined by the four different lines $\overleftrightarrow{PA}$, $\overleftrightarrow{PB}$, $\overleftrightarrow{PC}$, and $\overleftrightarrow{PD}$, no three of which are coplanar?

How many plane surfaces are required to form each of the solids pictured for problems 11 to 13?

11.   12.

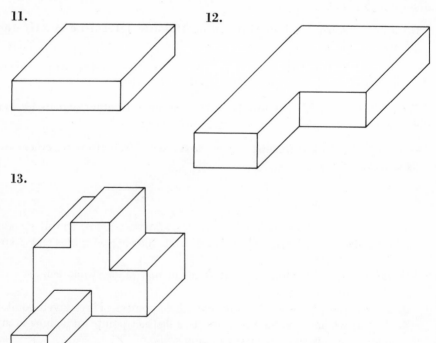

13.

3-3 ANGLES

Definition 3-3: A figure is an **angle** iff it is the union of two rays with the same endpoint. The two rays are the **sides** of the angle, and their common endpoint is the **vertex.**

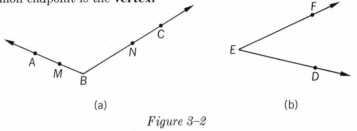

(a)   (b)

Figure 3-2

In Figure 3-2(a), the vertex is B, the sides are $\overrightarrow{BA}$ and $\overrightarrow{BC}$. The sides are also the rays $\overrightarrow{BM}$ and $\overrightarrow{BN}$, and in fact we may use B and any pair of points, one from each ray, and distinct from B. In Figure 3-2(b), E is the vertex, and we may use $\overrightarrow{ED}$ and $\overrightarrow{EF}$ as the names for the sides.

Notation: There are many acceptable notations used to denote an angle. The symbol $\angle$ stands for the word *angle*, and we usually follow it by three letters which distinguish the vertex and the sides. Thus in Figure 3-2 (a) we could write $\angle ABC$, $\angle CBA$, or $\angle MBN$. Observe that the order of the first and last letters is unimportant, but we must always write the vertex letter as the middle letter. While this three-letter notation avoids ambiguity, it is perhaps somewhat lengthy, particularly if we have many angles to write about. If no possibility for confusion can arise, we are willing to write $\angle B$ (the vertex letter alone) in place of $\angle ABC$. Figure 3-3 illustrates a diagram where such single letter notation must *not* be used. Here $\angle E$ could mean $\angle AEB$, $\angle AEC$, $\angle CED$, or several others.

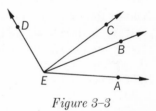

Figure 3-3

Other acceptable notations for angles are illustrated by Figures 3-4 and 3-5. From Figure 3-4 we write $\angle 1$ and $\angle 2$, and from Figure 3-5 we write $\angle m$ and $\angle n$. Keep in mind that notation is our servant, not our master: the guiding principle in choosing proper notation is that of avoiding the possibility of more than one meaning. Subject to this requirement, we choose the simplest form of notation that will serve.

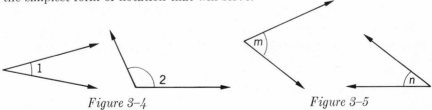

Figure 3-4   *Figure 3-5*

Our next task is to assign some sort of "measure" to these geometric entities called angles. This we shall do in a later paragraph; we must first introduce some preliminary concepts.

Figure 3–6 shows a line with a single point P on it. We say that the point P divides the line into three disjoint sets of points (no two sets having any points in common): one set on one side of P, a second set on the opposite side of P, and a third set including just P alone. Whether two points are on opposite sides or the same side of P can be determined by observing whether the dividing point P is or is not between the two points.

Just as a point divides a line into three disjoint sets, a line divides a plane into three disjoint sets. The points of the line form one of the sets, and the two remaining sets are called **half-planes.**

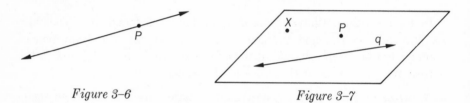

Figure 3–6   Figure 3–7

In Figure 3–7, the line q (called the **edge** of *both* half-planes) forms one set of points, the set of all points on one side of q is a second set constituting one of the half-planes, and the set of all points on the other side of the edge is the set forming the second half-plane. The method of determining when points are on the same or opposite sides of the edge is somewhat more involved than on the line. Consider (Figure 3–7) any two distinct points, P and X, in the plane, neither of which lie on q. If $\overline{XP}$ intersects q, then X and P are on opposite sides of q; if $\overline{XP}$ does not intersect q, then X and P lie on the same side of q. We note that the edge serves as the edge for both half-planes, but its points are not contained in either.

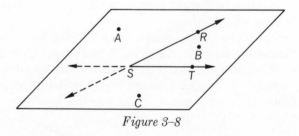

Figure 3–8

In Figure 3–8, the points A and B lie in the same half-plane (with edge $\overleftrightarrow{ST}$), while C lies in the opposite half-plane. We also use such statements as:

"A and B lie on the same side of $\overleftrightarrow{ST}$."

"A and C lie on opposite sides of $\overleftrightarrow{ST}$."

Definition 3-4: The **interior** of $\angle RST$ is the set of all points B such that B and R lie on the same side of $\overleftrightarrow{ST}$ and B and T lie on the same side of $\overleftrightarrow{SR}$. (See Figure 3-8.)

Definition 3-5: The set of all points not in the interior of an angle nor on the angle, is the **exterior** of the angle.

In Figure 3-8, B is in the interior of $\angle RST$, while A and C are in the exterior.

Another possible approach to this concept is to define the interior of an angle as the intersection of two half-planes as in Figure 3-9, where the doubly cross-hatched area (excluding the points on the two lines) represents all the points of the interior of $\angle RST$.

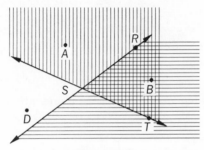

Figure 3-9

Definition 3-6: The union of segments $\overline{AB}$, $\overline{AC}$, and $\overline{BC}$ is a **triangle** iff A, B, and C are any three noncollinear points. (Notation: $\triangle ABC$.) A, B, and C are **vertices;** $\overline{AB}$, $\overline{AC}$, and $\overline{BC}$ are **sides.**

In Figure 3-10, A, B, and C are vertices, and $\overline{AB}$, $\overline{AC}$, and $\overline{BC}$ are the three sides of $\triangle ABC$.

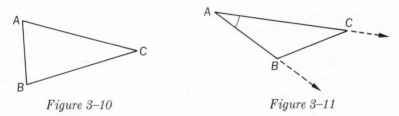

Figure 3-10   *Figure 3-11*

In accordance with our definition for angle, which requires a union of two rays to form its sides, care must be taken when talking about the angles associated with a triangle. Suppose we extended $\overline{AB}$ and $\overline{AC}$ to form rays $\overrightarrow{AB}$ and $\overrightarrow{AC}$ (Figure 3-11); then we could talk about $\angle CAB$ (or $\angle A$). In like manner we could introduce $\angle B$ and $\angle C$. In this sense a triangle determines three angles. These angles are generally called the *interior* angles of the triangle. It would be rather awkward if we had to follow such a procedure each time we wished to consider the angles associated with a given triangle. Instead, we agree that given any triangle we may freely refer to, and work with, any or all of its three interior angles, without having to extend its sides.

Definition 3–7: A point lies in the **interior** of a triangle iff it is an element of the set of all points lying in the intersection of the interiors of the three angles of the triangle. A point lies in the **exterior** of a triangle iff it is an element of the set of all points neither in the interior nor on the triangle.

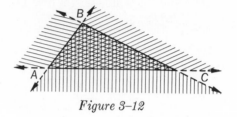

Figure 3–12

The triply hatched region of Figure 3–12 represents the interior of △ABC.

Exercise 3–3

1. Name the sides and vertices of △ABD; of △BCD.
2. Find a third (different) triangle in the figure, and name its sides and vertices.
3. Name the angles determined by the sides of the triangle of problem 2. Use three-letter notation where needed, otherwise use the vertex letter only.
4. Name the angles determined by △DBC.
5. Name the angles in the figure. Which angles permit the use of single-letter notation?
6. (a) Name all the triangles in the figure. (There are at least four.)
   (b) Name all the angles determined by the figure with common vertex at A. (There are at least four.)

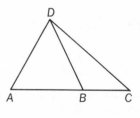

Probs. 1 to 4

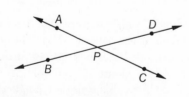

Prob. 5

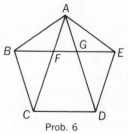

Prob. 6

7. (a) Illustrate, with a sketch, a point P which lies in the exterior of $\triangle ABC$, and in the interior of $\angle ACB$.

  (b) Illustrate a point Q which lies in the exterior of $\triangle ABC$, but not in the interior of any of the three angles determined by $\triangle ABC$.

8. Without referring to your text, write a definition for: angle; sides of an angle; vertex of an angle.

9. Without looking in your text, write a definition for: triangle; sides of a triangle; vertices of a triangle.

10. Draw $\triangle ABC$. Could we describe $\triangle ABC$ as the union of $\angle B$ and $\angle C$? Explain.

11. Draw $\triangle ABC$. Are the sides $\overline{AB}$ and $\overline{BC}$ the same as the sides of $\angle B$? Explain.

12. $\angle B$ may be named $\angle CBE$ or $\angle FBD$. Name $\angle B$ in four more ways, without using the same three letters more than once.

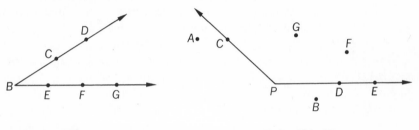

Prob. 12   Probs. 13 to 15

13. Name the points of the figure which are in the interior of $\angle CPD$.

14. Name the points of the figure in the exterior of $\angle CPD$.

15. Name the points of the figure neither in the interior nor the exterior of $\angle CPD$.

16. Given $\triangle ABC$ and a point P in the interior of $\angle A$ and also in the interior of $\angle B$. Make a sketch. What can you conclude about P?

3-4 MEASUREMENTS OF ANGLES

A glance at various angles indicates the existence of angles of different *sizes*, where, for the present, we interpret this statement to mean only that the angles we have seen differ in some manner. In order to measure the *size* of an angle numerically, we need a *unit*. For this we choose the familiar and much-used **degree**. Thus the measure of an angle will be the number of degrees in it. The notation $m\angle ABC = r$ shall mean there are r degrees in $\angle ABC$.

Just as line segments may be measured with a ruler, angles may be measured with a protractor (Figure 3-13). This device has a semicircular scale ruled in degrees, and a straight-line portion with a center point called

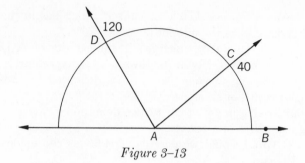

Figure 3-13

the "index" marked on it in some way (an arrowhead, a cross mark, a small straight line, or perhaps just a small hole). On the semicircular scale you can read numbers from 0 to 180. (Some protractors have scales printed so that they can be read in both directions, clockwise and counterclockwise.)

To use a protractor, place the index on the vertex of the angle to be measured, with the zero mark falling on one side of the angle ($\overrightarrow{AB}$ in Figure 3–13). Then read the number on the circular scale where the second side of the angle ($\overrightarrow{AC}$ in Figure 3–13) intersects the scale. Thus $m\angle BAC = 40$, and $m\angle BAD = 120$. Note that we do not require the degree symbol after the number, since we have already agreed that the measure of an angle is a number of degrees. We do, however, speak of $\angle BAC$ as a 40° angle, and $\angle BAD$ as a 120° angle. Finally, observe that $m\angle CAD$ cannot be read directly, but we can compute it by taking $120 - 40 = 80$, the difference between the two readings.

Recall that earlier (Chapter 2) we set up a one-to-one correspondence between the real numbers and the points on a number line. Having done so we were able to define the measure of a line segment. A somewhat similar approach leads to a formal definition of the measure of an angle.

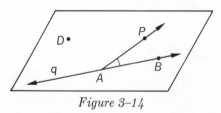

Figure 3-14

In Figure 3–14, consider $\overrightarrow{AB}$ lying on line q, where q is the edge of a half-plane. If we construct any other ray with A as endpoint, such that the ray extends into the half-plane containing D, an angle is formed, $\angle BAP$. To each ray drawn in such a manner we assign a number between 0 and 180, inclusive. Conversely, to every number r ($0 \leq r \leq 180$) there corresponds one ray with its endpoint at A, extending into the half-plane containing D.

Thus, a one-to-one correspondence between a set of rays (each of which, with $\overrightarrow{AB}$, determines an angle) and the set of numbers from 0 to 180 inclusive, is established.

The ray corresponding to 0 requires some separate discussion. The two rays forming a 0° angle would coincide, and the result would not seem to be an angle. Regardless of appearance, we accept the existence of a 0° angle, and further we agree that the interior of the 0° angle is the empty set, $\varnothing$.

Having established this correspondence between numbers and angles, we sum up the above discussion, formally:

Axiom 3–7 (Angle Measurement Axiom): To every angle there corresponds a real number from 0 to 180 inclusive.

Definition 3–8: The number specified by the Angle Measurement Axiom is the **measure** of the angle. (Notation: $m\angle ABC$.)

Axiom 3–8 (Angle Construction Axiom): Let $\overrightarrow{AB}$ be a ray on the edge of a half-plane. For every number r $(0 < r < 180)$, there is exactly one ray $\overrightarrow{AP}$, with P in that half-plane, such that $m\angle PAB = r$. For $r = 0$, P lies on $\overrightarrow{AB}$; for $r = 180$, P lies on the ray opposite to $\overrightarrow{AB}$.

Axiom 3–9 (Angle Addition Axiom): If P is a point in the interior of $\angle ABC$, then $m\angle ABC = m\angle ABP + m\angle PBC$.   (Figure 3–15.)

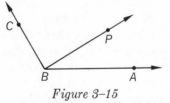

Figure 3–15

Since the measure of an angle is a number, the operations and axioms for numbers apply to angle measures. For instance, we may now add and subtract measures of angles: If $m\angle ABP = 38$ and $m\angle PBC = 108$, then $m\angle ABC = 38 + 108 = 146$.   If $m\angle ABC = 140$ and $m\angle PBC = 112$, then $m\angle ABP = 140 - 112 = 28$.   Hence the Angle Addition Axiom (Axiom 3–9) implies that: $m\angle ABP = m\angle ABC - m\angle PBC$, and also, $m\angle PBC = m\angle ABC - m\angle ABP$.

Exercise 3–4

Note: In drawing figures, it is suggested that most line segments be *at least* $1\frac{1}{2}$ inches in length.

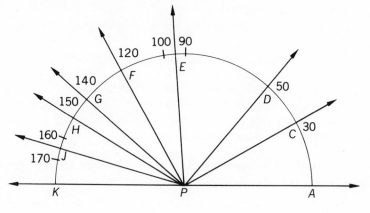

Probs. 1 to 11

From the figure for problems 1 to 11, find the value of each of the following:

1. $m\angle APD$ 2. $m\angle CPA$
3. $m\angle FPA$ 4. $m\angle HPD$
5. $m\angle JPH$ 6. $m\angle KPA$
7. $m\angle DPE + m\angle EPF$ 8. $m\angle GPF + m\angle FPD$
9. $m\angle HPD - m\angle EPD$ 10. $m\angle FPA - m\angle CPA$
11. $m\angle JPD - m\angle JPG$

12. Using a protractor, draw an angle of measure:
    (a) 30   (b) 90   (c) 45   (d) 120   (e) 180
13. Draw $\overrightarrow{AP}$. Locate B on $\overrightarrow{AP}$ such that $(AB) = 2\frac{1}{2}$ inches. At A, use a protractor to construct $\angle BAC$ such that $m\angle BAC = 40$. Let $AC = 2$ in. Draw $\overline{CB}$. Measure $\angle ABC$ and $\angle BCA$ and find the sum of the three angles determined by $\triangle ABC$. (Try to compare your answer with others who may do the problem.)

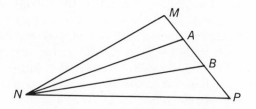

Probs. 14 to 17

Using the figure for problems 14 to 17, complete the following:

14. $m\angle MNA + m\angle ANB = m\angle$ _____
15. $m\angle ANB + m\angle BNP + m\angle MNA = m\angle$ _____

16. $m\angle ANP - m\angle BNP = m\angle$ _____

17. $m\angle MNP - m\angle MNA = m\angle$ _____

18. With a little practice, you should be able to judge the measure of an angle by eye. Do not use a protractor to work out your answers. Match each *angle* in the figure with one of the following *measures*. (Check your answers with a protractor.)

(1) $70 < x < 90$ (2) $35 < x < 55$ (3) $130 < x < 150$

(4) $160 < x < 180$ (5) $10 < x < 30$

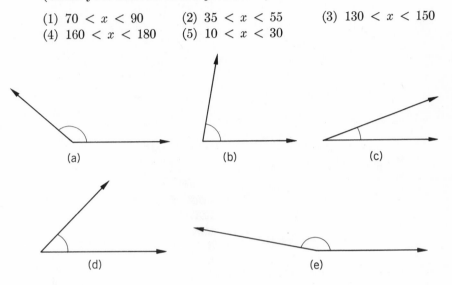

Prob. 18

19. Without a protractor, sketch angles whose measures are approximately 30, 45, 60, 90, 135, 150, and 180. Use a protractor to check your results.

20. (a) Given a ray $\overrightarrow{AC}$ lying in the edge of a *half-plane*, and a number, 45, in how many ways can you construct a ray $\overrightarrow{AP}$ lying in the half-plane such that $m\angle CAP = 45$?

(b) Given a ray $\overrightarrow{AC}$ lying in a *plane*, and a number, 45, in how many ways can you construct $\overrightarrow{AP}$ in the plane such that $m\angle CAP = 45$?

For problems 21 to 26, given $m\angle MPT = 60$, $m\angle TPS = 95$, $m\angle MPQ = 180$, and $m\angle SPR = m\angle RPQ$:

21. $m\angle SPM = ?$

22. $m\angle SPQ = ?$

23. $m\angle SPR = ?$

24. $m\angle RPQ = ?$

25. $m\angle TPR = ?$

26. $m\angle TPQ = ?$

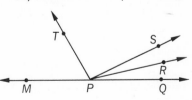

Probs. 21 to 26

For problems 27 to 29, given $\overleftrightarrow{AD}$, $m\angle APB = r$, $m\angle BPE = 110$, $m\angle BPC = s$, and $m\angle APD = 180$, using symbols s and r, write expressions for:

27. $m\angle APC$ **28.** $m\angle DPC$ **29.** $m\angle CPE$

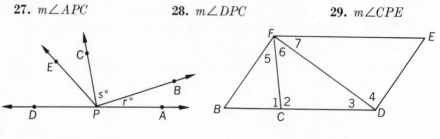

Probs. 27 to 29   Probs. 30 to 33

For problems 30 to 33, given $C \in \overline{BD}$, and $m\angle BFD = 90$:

30. If $m\angle 3 = 45$, and $m\angle 4 = 85$, find $m\angle BDE$.
31. If $m\angle 2 = 60$, find $m\angle 1$.
32. If $m\angle 5 = 15$, find $m\angle 6$.
33. If $m\angle 7 = 42$, find $m\angle BFE$.

3–5   SPECIAL ANGLE DEFINITIONS AND RELATIONSHIPS

Definition 3–9: An angle is **acute** iff its measure is less than 90.

Definition 3–10: An angle is a **right angle** iff its measure is 90.

Definition 3–11: An angle is **obtuse** iff its measure is greater than 90, but less than 180.

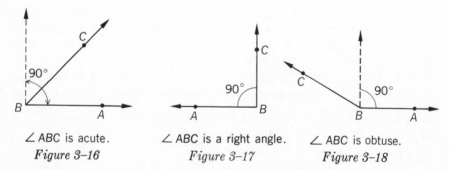

∠ABC is acute.   ∠ABC is a right angle.   ∠ABC is obtuse.
Figure 3–16   *Figure 3–17*   *Figure 3–18*

Definition 3–12: An angle is a **straight angle** iff its measure is 180.

Definition 3–12 (Alternate): An angle is a **straight angle** iff its sides are opposite rays.

In Figure 3–19, $\overrightarrow{BA}$ and $\overrightarrow{BC}$ are the opposite rays forming the sides of $\angle ABC$.

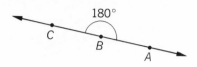

$\angle ABC$ is a straight angle.

Figure 3–19

The concept of *straight angle* is sometimes puzzling. Looking at Figure 3–19, the alert reader may well ask, "How does a straight angle differ from a straight line?" The distinguishing feature is the point serving as the vertex (B in Figure 3–19). A vertex is an essential part of an angle, but not of a line. We can always select a point on a line to be a vertex; once this has been done we *do* have a union of two opposite rays, and by definition such a configuration determines an angle. Since the sides of a straight angle lie in a line, and the line is the edge of two half-planes, either half-plane may be considered to be the interior of the straight angle.

Definition 3–13: Two angles are **adjacent** iff they lie in the same plane, have a common vertex and a common side, and the intersection of their interiors is empty. The sides *not common* to both angles are the **exterior sides.**

In Figure 3–20, $\angle 1$ and $\angle 2$ are adjacent.

Definition 3–14: Two angles formed by two intersecting straight lines are **vertical angles** iff their sides form two pairs of opposite rays.

In Figure 3–21, $\angle 1$ and $\angle 2$ are vertical angles.

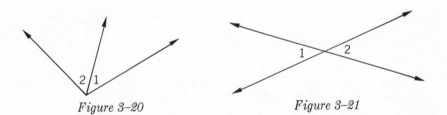

Figure 3–20   *Figure 3–21*

Definition 3–15: Two angles are **complementary angles** iff the sum of their measures is 90. Each angle is the **complement** of the other.

Definition 3–16: Two angles are **supplementary angles** iff the sum of their measures is 180. Each angle is the **supplement** of the other.

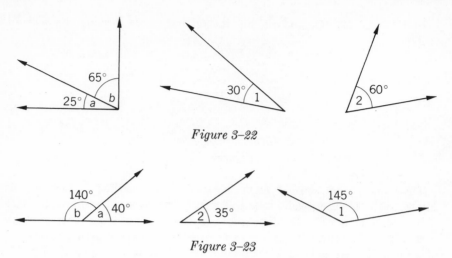

Figure 3-22

Figure 3-23

In Figure 3-22, ∠a and ∠b are complementary, as are ∠1 and ∠2. In Figure 3-23, ∠a and ∠b are supplementary, as are ∠1 and ∠2. We wish to emphasize two aspects of the complementary and supplementary relationships:

(1) The definitions apply to *two* angles at a time.

(2) The definitions do not specify any special position of the two angles with respect to each other. In particular, the two angles *may* be, but do not have to be, adjacent.

Definition 3–17: Two angles are **congruent** iff their measures are equal. (Notation: ∠ABC ≅ ∠PQR.)

Thus if $m\angle ABC = 40$ and $m\angle PQR = 40$, then $\angle ABC \cong \angle PQR$. The symbol ≅ is read, "is congruent to."

EXAMPLES

Given $\overleftrightarrow{AD}$, $\overleftrightarrow{BE}$, $\overleftrightarrow{FC}$, and $m\angle APF = 90$:

1. From the figure, name two angles that are (a) acute, (b) right, (c) obtuse, (d) straight.
Solution: (a) ∠EPD, ∠BPC. (b) ∠APF, ∠CPD. (c) ∠APE, ∠BPF. (d) ∠APD, ∠FPC.
2. From the figure, find a pair of angles that are: (a) complementary, (b) supplementary, (c) vertical.
Solution: (a) ∠APB, ∠BPC. (b) ∠BPF, ∠FPE. (c) ∠APB, ∠EPD.
3. What is the measure of an angle whose measure is twice the measure of its complement?

Solution: Let $m\angle A = x$ and $m\angle B = 2x$. Since $\angle A$ and $\angle B$ are complementary, by Definition 3–15 we have:

$$m\angle A + m\angle B = 90$$
$$x + 2x = 90$$
$$3x = 90$$
$$x = 30 \quad \text{and} \quad m\angle B = 60$$

Exercise 3–5

1. If two lines intersect, how many pairs of vertical angles are formed? How many pairs of adjacent angles? Draw and label a diagram to illustrate this, and name the pairs of adjacent and the vertical angles.
2. Determine the measure of an angle complementary to each of the following:
   (a) 20°   (b) 70°   (c) $33\frac{1}{2}°$ (d) $x°$ (e) $(90 - x)°$
3. Determine the measure of an angle supplementary to each of the following:
   (a) 50°   (b) 120°   (c) $22\frac{1}{2}°$ (d) $x°$ (e) $(180 - x)°$
4. (a) If two angles with the same measure are supplementary, what is the measure of each?
   (b) If two angles with the same measure are complementary, what is the measure of each?

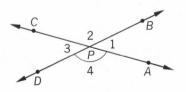

Prob. 5

5. Given $\overleftrightarrow{CA}$, $\overleftrightarrow{DB}$ intersect at P, and $m\angle 1 = 50$:
   (a) Name a straight angle with $\overrightarrow{PA}$ as one side.
   (b) What is the measure of the angle named in part (a)?
   (c) $m\angle 1 + m\angle 2 = m\angle$ _____.
   (d) Name an angle adjacent to $\angle 1$ such that their common side shall be in the same half-plane as B.
   (e) Why are angles 1 and 2 supplementary?

(f) If $m\angle 1 = 50$, what is the measure of $\angle 2$?
(g) Why is $\angle DPB$ a straight angle?
(h) Are angles 2 and 3 supplementary? Why?
(i) Using your answer to part (f), what is the measure of $\angle 3$?
(j) Are angles 3 and 4 supplementary?
(k) What is the measure of $\angle 4$?
(l) Name two pairs of vertical angles.
(m) What conclusion can you reach about each of these pairs of vertical angles?

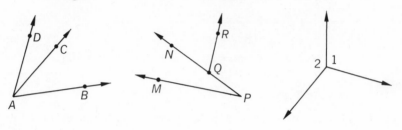

Probs. 6 to 10

State whether the following pairs of angles *are* or *are not* adjacent. For each answer state *why* (6 to 10):

6. $\angle BAC$ and $\angle CAD$
7. $\angle BAC$ and $\angle BAD$
8. $\angle CAD$ and $\angle BAD$
9. $\angle MPQ$ and $\angle NQR$
10. $\angle 1$ and $\angle 2$

11. Write the definition of supplementary angles in two parts, without using iff.
12. Write the definition of congruent angles without using iff.
13. Write the *alternate* definition of straight angle without using iff.
14. Given $\overleftrightarrow{AE}$, $\angle APB \cong \angle BPC$, $\angle EPD \cong \angle DPC$, and $P \in \overleftrightarrow{AE}$, find $m\angle BPD$.

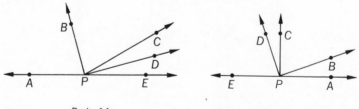

Prob. 14   Probs. 15 to 17

For problems 15 to 17, given $m\angle CPE = 90$, $m\angle CPA = 90$, $\overleftrightarrow{EA}$, and $P \in \overleftrightarrow{EA}$:

15. Identify each of the following angles as acute, obtuse, right, or straight:

$\angle APB$, $\angle BPC$, $\angle APC$, $\angle APD$, $\angle EPA$, $\angle BPE$, $\angle CPE$, $\angle CPD$.

16. Name two pairs of complementary angles.

17. Name two pairs of supplementary angles.

18. What is the measure of an angle whose measure is $\frac{2}{3}$ the measure of its complement?

19. What is the measure of an angle whose measure is 5 times the measure of its complement?

20. What is the measure of an angle whose measure is 5 times the measure of its supplement?

21. Is there an angle the measure of whose supplement is twice the measure of its complement? If so, find it.

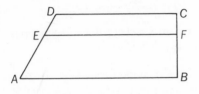

Probs. 22 to 24

22. Name four angles in the figure which seem to be right angles.

23. Name two acute angles. **24.** Name two obtuse angles.

3-6 PERPENDICULARITY

A most useful and important concept can be developed from a consideration of the figure formed by two intersecting lines. In Figure 3-24, $\overleftrightarrow{AB}$ intersects $\overleftrightarrow{CD}$ at P. We state the following:

(1) $\overrightarrow{PA}$, $\overrightarrow{PB}$, $\overrightarrow{PC}$, and $\overrightarrow{PD}$ are rays determined by these lines.

(2) $\overline{AB}$ and $\overline{CD}$ intersect at P.

(3) $\angle APD$, $\angle DPB$, $\angle BPC$, and $\angle CPA$ may be said to be determined either by the two intersecting *lines* or by the two intersecting *segments*.

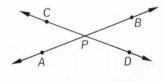

Figure 3-24

We can have two intersecting lines forming a pair of noncongruent angles. Figure 3-24 illustrates such a situation ($\angle DPB$ and $\angle BPC$). If the angles are not congruent, their measures are not equal, hence, by the Trichotomy Axiom (Axiom O-1), the measure of one of the angles must be smaller than the measure of the other. We choose $m\angle DPB$ to be less than $m\angle BPC$. Now we appeal to the imagination, and suggest that you imagine the effect of allowing the line $\overleftrightarrow{AB}$ to rotate about the point P in a counterclockwise direction. It is evident that $m\angle DPB$ increases while at the same time

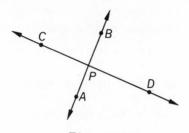

Figure 3–25

$m\angle DPC$ decreases. It should also be evident that at some intermediate position $\angle DPB \cong \angle BPC$ (see Figure 3–25).

Definition 3–18: Two intersecting lines are **perpendicular** iff they form congruent adjacent angles. (Notation: $\overrightarrow{AB} \perp \overrightarrow{CD}$.)

Consider next the straight angle formed by the opposite rays $\overrightarrow{PD}$ and $\overrightarrow{PC}$, and recall that the measure of a straight angle is 180. If two equal measures sum to 180, then each must be 90; thus the measures of each of the congruent angles formed by perpendicular lines must be 90.

Definition 3–18 (Alternate): Two intersecting lines are **perpendicular** iff they form a right angle.

Taking advantage of the three statements made at the beginning of this section, note the following use of language:

(1) $\overrightarrow{PD} \perp \overrightarrow{PB}$, and $\overrightarrow{PB} \perp \overrightarrow{PD}$:   in words, the two rays are perpendicular, each to the other.

(2) $\overline{AB} \perp \overline{CD}$, and $\overline{CD} \perp \overline{AB}$:   the two segments are perpendicular, each to the other.

(3) $\overleftrightarrow{AB} \perp \overleftrightarrow{CD}$, and $\overleftrightarrow{CD} \perp \overleftrightarrow{AB}$:   the two lines are perpendicular, each to the other.

In any given situation, we use whichever one of these statements suits our particular need, as well as statements concerning lines perpendicular to rays, rays to segments, lines to segments, and lines to rays.

In the case where a figure involves nonintersecting rays or segments, or combinations of nonintersecting rays and segments, perpendicularity is determined by whether the lines containing the rays or segments are perpendicular.

Exercise 3–6

1. Restate Definition 3–18 as two separate statements, without using iff. Do the same for Definition 3–18 (Alternate).

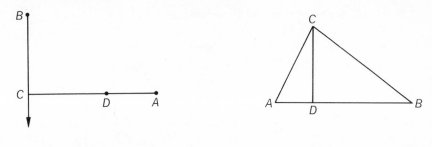

Prob. 2   Prob. 3

2. In the figure, $m\angle BCD = 90$. Which of the following statements are true? (Reason *entirely* from the given diagram.)
   (a) $\overline{AD} \perp \overline{BC}$ (b) $\overline{AD} \perp \overleftrightarrow{BC}$ (c) $\overrightarrow{AD} \perp \overline{BC}$ (d) $\overleftrightarrow{AD} \perp \overleftrightarrow{BC}$
   (e) $\overleftrightarrow{AD} \perp \overline{BC}$

3. Given $\overline{CD}$, $\triangle ABC$, and $\angle ADC \cong \angle BDC$:
   (a) Justify that there exists a line segment with endpoints A and B.
   (b) Is $\overline{CD} \perp \overline{AB}$? Why?
   (c) $m\angle BDC =$ _____. $m\angle ADC =$ _____. Why?

4. Given $q_1 \perp q_2$:
   (a) Why is one of the angles in the figure a right angle?
   (b) Suppose $\angle 1$ is the right angle of part (a). Is $\angle 2$ adjacent to $\angle 1$? What then must be true about $\angle 2$? Why?
   (c) Is $\angle 3$ adjacent to $\angle 2$? What then must be true about $\angle 3$? Why?
   (d) Is $\angle 4$ adjacent to $\angle 3$? What then must be true about $\angle 4$? Why?
   (e) If two lines are perpendicular, how many right angles are determined?

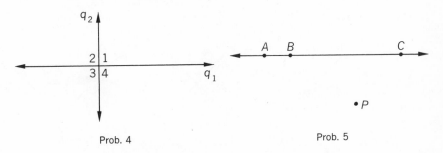

Prob. 4   Prob. 5

5. Copy the diagram as closely as you can. Draw $\overline{AP}$, $\overline{BP}$, and $\overline{CP}$. Now, by eye, draw as nearly as you can, $\overline{PX}$ such that $\overline{PX} \perp \overleftrightarrow{AC}$.
   (a) Find, by measuring with a ruler, AP, BP, and CP.
   (b) Find, by measuring with a ruler, PX.
   (c) Which of the four measurements is the smallest?
   (d) Which of these measurements do you feel most closely fits the idea of "the distance from point P to line $\overleftrightarrow{AC}$"?

6. If $\overleftrightarrow{AB} \perp \overrightarrow{PC}$, how is $\angle APC$ related to $\angle BPC$?

7. If $\angle APC \cong \angle BPC$, how is $\overrightarrow{PC}$ related to $\overleftrightarrow{AB}$?

8. If $\overleftrightarrow{AB} \perp \overrightarrow{PC}$, what is the measure of $\angle APC$?

9. If $\angle BPC$ is a right angle, how is $\overleftrightarrow{AB}$ related to $\overrightarrow{PC}$?

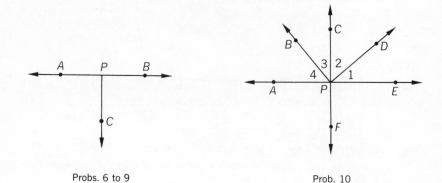

Probs. 6 to 9   Prob. 10

10. Given $\overleftrightarrow{CF} \perp \overleftrightarrow{AE}$, $\overrightarrow{PD} \perp \overrightarrow{PB}$, and $m\angle 1 = 40$, find $m\angle 2$, $m\angle 3$, and $m\angle 4$.

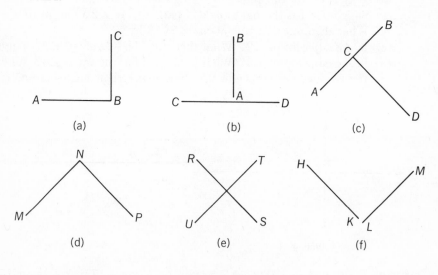

(a)   (b)   (c)

(d)   (e)   (f)

Prob. 11

11. In the figures, segments that look perpendicular are meant to be perpendicular. Name pairs of perpendicular segments. If you decide a pair is not perpendicular, state why.

For problems 12 to 15, given $\overleftrightarrow{AB}$, $P \in \overleftrightarrow{AB}$, and $\overrightarrow{PD} \perp \overrightarrow{PE}$:

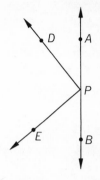

12. Name a pair of perpendicular rays, if any.

13. Name a pair of complementary angles, if any.

14. Name a pair of supplementary angles, if any.

15. Name a pair of congruent angles, if any.

Probs. 12 to 15

Chapter 4

ANATOMY OF PROOF

INTRODUCTION

In one sense, the mathematical system we are studying, geometry, consists of an orderly list of statements or assertions. Until now, we have examined only the beginning of this list: the definitions and axioms discussed in the previous chapters. One might suggest that we continue in this manner—making assumptions and defining new terms—and thus construct a useful and meaningful branch of mathematics. We propose to indicate briefly why the prospects for success of such an approach are not at all bright. To do this, certain properties of axiomatic systems must be considered. We will not need to analyze these properties deeply, just enough to shed some light on why the course of action suggested above is not desirable.

There are three basic requirements that an axiomatic system must meet if it is to be mathematically acceptable, the first of which is **independence.** A set of axioms is said to be independent if no axiom is a logical consequence of the others. While independence of a set of axioms is *mathematically* desirable, it is not necessarily desirable for a beginning study of geometry. We do not require this property for our system, and in fact, our chosen set of axioms is *not* independent.

A second requirement, and for our immediate purposes the least useful, is **completeness.** Completeness requires that, using only the agreed upon terms, no *new* axiom can be formulated that is independent of the given set of axioms. This property is usually not easy to verify, and is not of major concern to us.

The most important requirement is **consistency.** A set of axioms cannot lead to fruitful results if the use of any combination of those axioms leads to inconsistent (contradictory) statements. As an example, we would not want $\angle ABC \cong \angle DEF$ and $\angle ABC \not\cong \angle DEF$ at the same time.

The procedure we follow, to increase our list of assertions, is to choose a consistent set of axioms, and develop new assertions by use of chains of reasoning and rules of logic.

4-1 INDUCTIVE REASONING

One method of convincing people of the truth of an assertion is that of presenting a quantity of evidence in its favor. For example, most of us would be willing to agree that the sun will rise tomorrow morning, even if we know of no law that guarantees that this must happen. The pattern that has been observed for thousands of years reinforces our belief that, since the sun has always risen in the morning, it will continue to do so. This mode of thinking —reasoning from specific instances to a general conclusion—is called **inductive reasoning,** and is used in science, the business world, and in numerous everyday affairs. Unfortunately, such reasoning does not always lead to valid results!

Consider the following assertion: "If a symbol represents a real number, then that real number is less than 1,000,001." We offer *one million* examples as evidence to support the truth of this assertion: 1 is less than 1,000,001; 2 is less than 1,000,001; $3 < 1,000,001; \ldots; 1,000,000 < 1,000,001$. The numbers from 1 to 1,000,000 all support the truth of the assertion. Surely such a wealth of evidence should be convincing. Just as surely, the assertion is false.

A useful concept may be gleaned from the above example. Note that if we had begun our consideration with the number 1,000,002, the assertion would have been *disproved* immediately. Thus, even though *any* number of supporting examples cannot prove an assertion, only *one* counterexample is enough to disprove the statement.

Notwithstanding its disadvantages, inductive reasoning has its uses. Often it points the way to the discovery of a new idea or concept, physical as well as mathematical. If an event is observed to occur a great number of times, we are led to surmise that there may be some "natural law" in operation. The discovery of such natural laws is one occupation of the scientist. Similar situations occur in mathematics. There is a famous assertion known as the *Goldbach Conjecture*, which states that every even number greater than 2 is the sum of two prime numbers. (A **prime number** is a number that is exactly divisible—that is, with no remainder—only by itself and one.) Thus $6 = 3 + 3$, and $54 = 47 + 7$, are examples. No one has ever found an even number greater than 2 that could *not* be written as the sum of two prime numbers—at the same time no one has as yet succeeded in establishing the mathematical truth of the Goldbach Conjecture.

Exercise 4–1

1. A teacher has given his class a test each Friday of the first seven weeks of the semester. Make a conjecture based on this information.
2. A naturalist found blue eggs in twenty nests. The nests were all made by robins. Make a conjecture based on this information.
3. Draw four different appearing triangles, large enough so that you can measure the angles. For each triangle, measure its three angles and find their sum. Make a conjecture based on the information you found.
4. Draw four separate diagrams, each consisting of a pair of intersecting lines. Measure the vertical angles in each figure. Make a conjecture based on the information you found.

In problems 5 and 6, study the given information, make a conjecture as to the underlying pattern, and use it to complete the statements.

EXAMPLE

$$1^3 + 2^3 = \frac{2^2}{4}(2+1)^2 = 9$$

$$1^3 + 2^3 + 3^3 = \frac{3^2}{4}(3+1)^2 = 36$$

$$1^3 + 2^3 + 3^3 + 4^3 = \frac{4^2}{4}(4+1)^2 = 100$$

(a) $1^3 + 2^3 + 3^3 + 4^3 + 5^3 = \,?$
(b) $1^3 + 2^3 + 3^3 + 4^3 + 5^3 + 6^3 + 7^3 + 8^3 = \,?$
(c) $1^3 + 2^3 + 3^3 + \cdots + n^3 = \,?$

Solutions

(a) $1^3 + 2^3 + 3^3 + 4^3 + 5^3 = \frac{5^2}{4}(5+1)^2 = 225$

(b) $1^3 + 2^3 + 3^3 + 4^3 + 5^3 + 6^3 + 7^3 + 8^3 = \frac{8^2}{4}(8+1)^2 = 1296$

(c) $1^3 + 2^3 + 3^3 + \cdots + n^3 = \frac{n^2}{4}(n+1)^2$

5. $1 + 2 = \dfrac{2(1+2)}{2} = 3;\quad 1 + 2 + 3 = \dfrac{3(1+3)}{2} = 6;$

$1 + 2 + 3 + 4 = \dfrac{4(1+4)}{2} = 10$

(a) $1 + 2 + 3 + 4 + 5 = \,?$

    (b) $1 + 2 + 3 + \cdots + 39 + 40 = ?$

    (c) $1 + 2 + 3 + \cdots + n = ?$

6. $1^2 + 2^2 = \frac{2}{6}(2 + 1)(2 \cdot 2 + 1) = 5$

    $1^2 + 2^2 + 3^2 = \frac{3}{6}(3 + 1)(2 \cdot 3 + 1) = 14$

    $1^2 + 2^2 + 3^2 + 4^2 = \frac{4}{6}(4 + 1)(2 \cdot 4 + 1) = 30$

    (a) $1^2 + 2^2 + 3^2 + 4^2 + 5^2 + 6^2 = ?$

    (b) $1^2 + 2^2 + 3^2 + \cdots + 10^2 + 11^2 = ?$

    (c) $1^2 + 2^2 + 3^2 + \cdots + n^2 = ?$

For problems 7 and 8 copy each of the diagrams as closely as you can, and large enough so that you can measure each of the angles with a protractor.

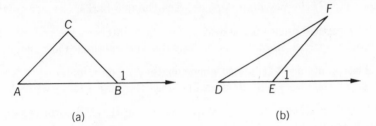

      (a)   (b)

Fill out the following table:

Figure (a)	*Figure (b)*
$m\angle 1 = $ _____	$m\angle 1 = $ _____
$m\angle A = $ _____	$m\angle D = $ _____
$m\angle C = $ _____	$m\angle F = $ _____

7. In each figure, which of the listed angles has the greatest measure?

8. Can you make a conjecture concerning a relationship between $m\angle 1$ and the measures of the other two angles?

4-2 THEOREMS

Let us consider next, with closer attention to detail, the nature of the assertions with which we are concerned. Our major interest centers upon statements which can be classified as *true* or *false*. Statements such as: "It is raining," and "Point P is in the interior of $\triangle ABC$," are usually verifiable; as opposed to a statement such as: "Poetry is food for the soul." This last statement is too subjective for our purposes; its truth or falsity depends entirely upon individual tastes in such matters.

Our assertions will most frequently be written in the If–Then form, presenting a statement that is verifiable. Example of such assertions are: "*If* it rains, *then* the ground will get wet," and "*If* two lines intersect, *then* they intersect in exactly one point." By *mathematically* true (or false), we mean: Does (or does not) the assertion follow logically from the given set of axioms, definitions, and previous assertions? The assertions that we prove will be called **Theorems.**

It will sometimes be necessary for you to rephrase an assertion into the If–Then form. There is no rule that we can give that tells exactly how to do this; you must try to rewrite in such a manner that the resulting language, as well as the mathematics, makes sense.

EXAMPLES

Rewrite in If–Then form:

1. The dog barks whenever the postman appears.
Solution: *If* the postman appears, *then* the dog barks.

2. The vertical angles formed when two lines intersect are congruent.
Solution: *If* two lines intersect, *then* the vertical angles are congruent.

3. Two points are 4 ft. apart whenever they lie on a line.
Solution: *If* two points lie on a line, *then* they are 4 ft. apart.

Note that a statement may be written in the If–Then form regardless of its truth or falsity.

Exercise 4–2

Rewrite in the If–Then form:

1. I get wet whenever I go outdoors during a rainstorm.
2. Reading without sufficient light causes eyestrain.
3. The product of two even integers is an even integer.
4. Every polynomial equation of degree four has at least one root.
5. Two intersecting lines are not parallel.
6. A triangle with all three sides congruent has all three angles congruent.
7. A triangle with all three angles congruent has all three sides congruent.
8. Two adjacent angles with their exterior sides contained in a straight line are supplementary.
9. Two perpendicular lines form four right angles.
10. Two noncongruent angles are not vertical angles.
11. The product is positive whenever two numbers are multiplied together.

4–3 DEDUCTIVE REASONING

We now consider the method most commonly used in proofs, deductive reasoning. To start, we must be *given* some information. This given information is the IF part of the assertion, and is called the **hypothesis.** From this given hypothesis, as well as all axioms, definitions, and previously established theorems, we attempt to reach a conclusion by a valid chain of reasoning. The **conclusion** (or conclusions) is the THEN part of the assertion. If we succeed, then the theorem is proved, and may be used in all later work.

To illustrate the preceding discussion, imagine a pseudo-mathematical system as follows:

Undefined terms: member, committee, belongs to.
Axioms:
(1) There are at least two members.
(2) Any two members are together on exactly one committee.
(3) Not all members belong to the same committee.

We now make an assertion, verify that this assertion follows logically from the given information, and thus prove the truth of a theorem.

Theorem I: *If* there is one member, *then* there are at least three members.

Proof: Since we are at the very beginning of the pseudo-system, no previous theorems are available, and we can use only the given axioms. Axiom (1) assures us of the existence of at least two members; let us name two of them A and B. Axiom (2) states that these two members are together on exactly one committee. As an aid to our thinking it is convenient, when possible, to have a diagram. Let us represent members by points, and committees by lines. Figure 4–1 shows A and B belonging to the same committee. Axiom (3) tells us that *not all* the members belong to the same committee. If Figure 4–1 represented our entire system, then axiom (3) would be violated, since then all the members (A and B) would be on the same committee. Thus it follows that there must be a member not belonging to the same committee with A and B. Let us call this member C. But now we have *three* members in existence, which is the desired conclusion.

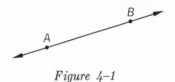

Figure 4–1

Now that one theorem is available, let us see how it may be used in developing our pseudo-system further.

Theorem II: *If* there is one member, *then* there are at least three committees.

Proof: If there is one member, then we know, from Theorem I (proved above), that there are at least three members. Let us name the members A, B, and C as before. Axiom (2) tells us that each pair of members belongs to exactly one committee. With three members we can form three different pairs: (A, B), (A, C), and (B, C). Since each such pair determines exactly one committee, we count three committees, thus proving Theorem II.

Finally, let us emphasize the important distinction between inductive and deductive reasoning. Inductive reasoning attempts to arrive at a general conclusion from specific cases; deductive reasoning begins with general statements and arrives at conclusions that are applicable to all specific cases. For example, suppose we meet Mr. M and are told he is a member. From Theorem I we may immediately state that there are at least two more members, even though Mr. M was not explicitly mentioned in the theorem.

The so-called "theorems" of this section are, of course, superficial, and not to be learned for future use. In the remainder of this chapter we prove theorems to be used throughout all of geometry.

EXAMPLE

Identify the *hypothesis* and the *conclusion* of the following: Two non-congruent angles are not vertical angles.

Solution: Rewrite the statement in If–Then form: If two angles are not congruent, then they are not vertical angles.

    Hypothesis: Two angles are not congruent.
    Conclusion: They are not vertical angles.

Exercise 4–3

List the *hypothesis* and *conclusion* for each of problems 1 to 3.

1. If a student is registered with the admissions office, and has filed his complete program, then he may attend classes.
2. If two acute angles are adjacent, and their exterior sides are contained in two perpendicular lines, then they are complementary.
3. If two of the angles of a triangle are congruent, then the sides opposite these angles are congruent.
4. *Theorem:* If the sum of the digits of an integer is divisible by 3, then the integer is itself divisible by 3. (For example, 1323 is divisible by 3 since $1 + 3 + 2 + 3 = 9$, and 9 is divisible by 3.)

To which of the following numbers does the conclusion of this theorem apply?

    (a) 12,345   (b) 203,333,333
    (c) 123,097,625   (d) 218,375,421,906,342,111

5. *Theorem:* If two angles are adjacent, and their exterior sides are contained in a straight line, then the angles are supplementary.

Examine the following figures. (Assume that any line that looks like a straight line *is* a straight line.) If the conclusion of the theorem applies to $\angle 1$ and $\angle 2$, write *yes*. If not, write *no* and state why not.

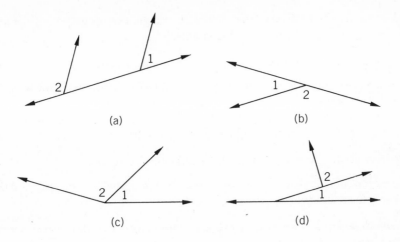

(a)   (b)

(c)   (d)

Prob. 5

For problems 6 to 10, list the hypothesis and conclusion of the indicated problem of Exercise 4–2.

6. Problem 3.   **7.** Problem 5.   **8.** Problem 6.
9. Problem 7.   **10.** Problem 9.

4–4 ELEMENTARY THEOREMS, INFORMAL PROOFS

The actual details encountered in writing a proof require some comment. While many methods are used, we use two: the *informal* proof—a running discourse or paragraph type; and the *formal* proof—requiring two columns and certain features to be illustrated below. In this section we use the informal method of proof to establish several theorems.

Theorem 4–1: Every angle is congruent to itself.

Proof: The definition of congruence of angles states that two angles are congruent iff their measures are equal. Let $\angle A$ represent any angle. Then $m\angle A$ is, by Axiom 3–7, some number between 0 and 180 inclusive, say, $m\angle A = r$. But by the reflexive property of equality of numbers (Axiom E–1), $r = r$; that is, the measure of any angle is always equal to itself. Therefore, since $m\angle A = m\angle A$, we conclude that $\angle A \cong \angle A$.

Perhaps the thought occurred: Why wasn't the theorem stated in If–Then form? We could have written: "If a figure is an angle, then it is congruent to itself." Such wording seems rather awkward, and not too desirable. In fact, theorems are stated as simply as possible with respect to the English language as well as with respect to geometry; further, if a particular form is excessively awkward and serves no useful purpose, we shall refrain from employing it. We will use the If–Then arrangement as much as possible, but depart from it when it seems desirable.

Theorem 4–2: Any two right angles are congruent.

Proof: An angle is a right angle, by definition, iff its measure is 90. If each of two angles is a right angle, then the measure of each is 90. By the reflexive property of equality of real numbers, $90 = 90$. Thus, since their measures are equal, the two right angles are congruent.

Theorem 4–3: Any two straight angles are congruent.

The proof of this theorem so closely parallels the proof of Theorem 4–2 that we leave it as an exercise.

Theorem 4–4: If two angles are congruent and supplementary, then each angle is a right angle.

Proof: If two angles are congruent, their measures are equal. Let r denote the measure of each of the angles. Since two angles are supplementary iff the sum of their measures is 180, we may write $r + r = 2r = 180$, and thus, by either the Multiplication Axiom (E–6) or the Division Axiom (E–7), $r = 90$. Therefore each of the two angles is a right angle.

Theorem 4–5: If two angles are adjacent, and their exterior sides are contained in two perpendicular lines, then they are complementary.

Proof: Let $\overleftrightarrow{AB}$ and $\overleftrightarrow{CD}$ be the perpendicular lines, and $\angle 1$ and $\angle 2$ be the adjacent angles. $\angle CPB$ is a right angle by definition of perpendicular lines. Let Q be a point on the side common to $\angle 1$ and $\angle 2$, hence in the interior of $\angle CPB$. Then $m\angle 1 + m\angle 2 = m\angle CPB$ by the Angle Addition Axiom (3–9). Since $m\angle CBP = 90$, $m\angle 1 + m\angle 2 = 90$, by the Transitivity Axiom of Equality (E–3). Hence $\angle 1$ and $\angle 2$ are complementary.

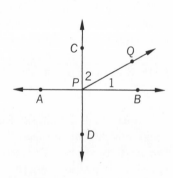

Theorem 4–6: If two angles are adjacent, and their exterior sides are contained in a straight line, then they are supplementary.

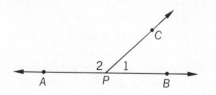

Proof: Let $\angle 1$ and $\angle 2$ be the adjacent angles, with their exterior sides (opposite rays $\overrightarrow{PA}$ and $\overrightarrow{PB}$) contained in $\overleftrightarrow{AB}$. Then $m\angle 1 + m\angle 2 = m\angle APB$. But $m\angle APB = 180$. Therefore, $m\angle 1 + m\angle 2 = 180$, by the Transitivity Axiom (Axiom E–3), and $\angle 1$ and $\angle 2$ are supplementary.

EXAMPLE

Given $\overleftrightarrow{AB}$, $\triangle ABC$, and $m\angle 1 = 5(m\angle 2)$, find $m\angle 1$.

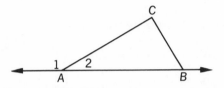

Solution: $\angle 1$ and $\angle 2$ are adjacent angles, and their exterior sides lie in $\overleftrightarrow{AB}$. By Theorem 4–5:

$$m\angle 1 + m\angle 2 = 180 \quad \text{or} \quad m\angle 2 = 180 - m\angle 1$$

Now
$$m\angle 1 = 5(m\angle 2)$$
$$m\angle 1 = 5(180 - m\angle 1)$$
$$m\angle 1 = 900 - 5(m\angle 1)$$
$$6(m\angle 1) = 900$$
$$m\angle 1 = 150$$

Exercise 4–4

For problems 1 to 15, write an *axiom, definition,* or *theorem* to justify each statement. State whether you are quoting an axiom, definition, or theorem.

EXAMPLES

(a) $AB = AB$.   *Solution:* Reflexive Axiom of Equality (E–1).

(b) If $CD = EF$ and $EF = AB$, then $CD = AB$.   *Solution:* Transitivity Axiom of Equality (E–3).

(c) $\angle ABC \cong \angle ABC$.   *Solution:* Every angle is congruent to itself (Theorem 4–1).

1. If $m\angle A + m\angle B = m\angle A + m\angle C$, then $m\angle B = m\angle C$.
2. If $2(m\angle A) + 2(m\angle B) = 180$, then $m\angle A + m\angle B = 90$.
3. If $m\angle A = 36$, and $m\angle B = 54$, then $\angle A$ and $\angle B$ are complementary.
4. If $AB = CD$ and $MN = PQ$, then $AB + MN = CD + PQ$.
5. If $\angle A$ is a right angle, and $\angle B$ is a right angle, then $\angle A \cong \angle B$.
6. If $m\angle D = 41$, then $\angle D$ is an acute angle.
7. If $AB > BC$, then $AB \neq BC$.
8. If $AC = CB$, then C is the midpoint of $\overline{AB}$.
9. If $m\angle X = 177$, then $\angle X$ is an obtuse angle.

Prob. 8

10. If $MN = PQ$, then $\frac{1}{2}(MN) = \frac{1}{2}(PQ)$.

11. If $m\angle 1 = m\angle 2$ and $m\angle 2 = 90$, then $m\angle 1 = 90$.

12. If $m\angle X = 180$ and $m\angle Y = 180$, then $\angle X \cong \angle Y$.

13. If $m\angle A = m\angle B$ and $m\angle A + m\angle B = 180$, then $\angle A$ and $\angle B$ are both right angles.

14. If $\overleftrightarrow{AB}$ intersects $\overleftrightarrow{CD}$ at P such that $\angle APD$ is a right angle, then $\overleftrightarrow{AB} \perp \overleftrightarrow{CD}$.

15. $m\angle B = m\angle B$.

16. Prove Theorem 4–3 using an informal proof.

For problems 17 to 20, given $\triangle ABC$, $\overleftrightarrow{AB}$:

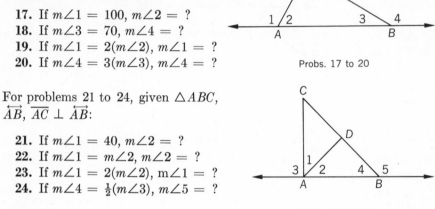

17. If $m\angle 1 = 100$, $m\angle 2 = ?$

18. If $m\angle 3 = 70$, $m\angle 4 = ?$

19. If $m\angle 1 = 2(m\angle 2)$, $m\angle 1 = ?$

20. If $m\angle 4 = 3(m\angle 3)$, $m\angle 4 = ?$

Probs. 17 to 20

For problems 21 to 24, given $\triangle ABC$, $\overleftrightarrow{AB}$, $\overline{AC} \perp \overleftrightarrow{AB}$:

21. If $m\angle 1 = 40$, $m\angle 2 = ?$

22. If $m\angle 1 = m\angle 2$, $m\angle 2 = ?$

23. If $m\angle 1 = 2(m\angle 2)$, $m\angle 1 = ?$

24. If $m\angle 4 = \frac{1}{2}(m\angle 3)$, $m\angle 5 = ?$

Probs. 21 to 24

4–5   FORMAL PROOFS

In this section we introduce you to the structure of the formal proof. A helpful way to learn the requirements of this type of proof is to study proofs in the text carefully. Below are several theorems, with proofs illustrating the formal approach. Not only is a study of the *form* required, but the content of each theorem must be mastered as well, since these theorems are all basic tools for future use.

Two comments on notation:

(1) The symbol $\therefore$ stands for the word *therefore*.

(2) We shall use the following abbreviations: *Ax.* for axiom, *Thm.* for theorem, and *Def.* for definition.

Theorem 4–7:   Complements of the same angle are congruent.

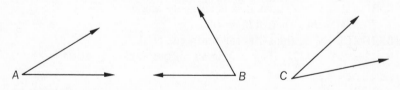

GIVEN: $\angle A$ and $\angle B$ are complementary; $\angle C$ and $\angle B$ are complementary.
PROVE: $\angle A \cong \angle C$.

Proof

STATEMENTS	REASONS
1. $\angle A$ and $\angle B$ are complementary; $\angle C$ and $\angle B$ are complementary.	1. Given.
2. $m\angle A + m\angle B = 90$; $m\angle C + m\angle B = 90$.	2. Two angles are complementary iff the sum of their measures is 90 (Def. 3–15).
3. $m\angle A + m\angle B = m\angle C + m\angle B$.	3. Transitivity Ax. (E–3).
4. $\angle B \cong \angle B$.	4. Every angle is congruent to itself (Thm. 4–1).
5. $m\angle B = m\angle B$.	5. Def. of congruent angles.
6. $m\angle A = m\angle C$.	6. Subtraction Ax. (E–5). (Subtract $m\angle B$ from both members of step 3.)
7. $\therefore \angle A \cong \angle C$.	7. Def. of congruent angles.

Theorem 4–8: Supplements of congruent angles are congruent.

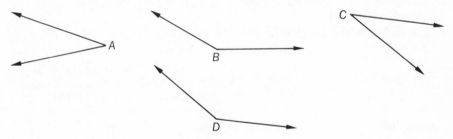

GIVEN: $\angle A$ and $\angle B$ are supplementary; $\angle C$ and $\angle D$ are supplementary; $\angle B \cong \angle D$.
PROVE: $\angle A \cong \angle C$.

Proof

STATEMENTS	REASONS
1. $\angle A$ and $\angle B$ are supplementary; $\angle C$ and $\angle D$ are supplementary.	1. Given.
2. $m\angle A + m\angle B = 180$; $m\angle C + m\angle D = 180$.	2. Def. of supplementary angles.
3. $m\angle A + m\angle B = m\angle C + m\angle D$.	3. Transitivity Ax. (E–3).
4. $\angle B \cong \angle D$.	4. Given.
5. $m\angle B = m\angle D$.	5. Def. of congruent angles.
6. $m\angle A = m\angle C$.	6. Subtraction Ax. (E–5).
7. $\therefore \angle A \cong \angle C$.	7. Def. of congruent angles.

Theorem 4–9: Complements of congruent angles are congruent.

Theorem 4–10: Supplements of the same angle are congruent.

The proofs of Theorems 4–9 and 4–10 are left as exercises.

Theorems 4–7 and 4–9 are frequently combined as follows: **Complements of the same or congruent angles are congruent.** Similarly, Theorems 4–8 and 4–10 are combined as: **Supplements of the same or congruent angles are congruent.**

Theorem 4–11: If two lines intersect, then the vertical angles formed are congruent.

GIVEN: $\overleftrightarrow{AB}$ and $\overleftrightarrow{CD}$ intersect at P.
PROVE: $\angle 1 \cong \angle 2$ and $\angle 3 \cong \angle 4$.

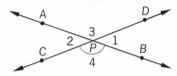

Proof

STATEMENTS	REASONS
1. $\overleftrightarrow{AB}$ and $\overleftrightarrow{CD}$ intersect at P.	1. Given.
2. $\angle 1$ and $\angle 3$ are adjacent, $\angle 2$ and $\angle 3$ are adjacent.	2. Def. of adjacent angles.
3. $\angle 1$ and $\angle 3$ are supplementary, $\angle 2$ and $\angle 3$ are supplementary.	3. Adjacent angles with exterior sides contained in a straight line are supplementary (Thm. 4–6).
4. $\angle 1 \cong \angle 2$.	4. Supplements of the same angle are congruent (Thm. 4–10).

Proof that $\angle 3 \cong \angle 4$ is left as an exercise.

Theorem 4–12: If two intersecting lines are perpendicular, then they form four right angles.

GIVEN: $\overleftrightarrow{AB} \perp \overleftrightarrow{CD}$, with $\angle 1$ a right angle.*
PROVE: $\angle 2$, $\angle 3$, and $\angle 4$ are right angles.

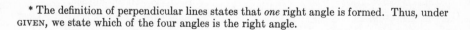

* The definition of perpendicular lines states that *one* right angle is formed. Thus, under GIVEN, we state which of the four angles is the right angle.

Proof

STATEMENTS	REASONS
1. $\overleftrightarrow{AB} \perp \overleftrightarrow{CD}$ with $\angle 1$ a right angle.	1. Given.
2. $\angle 1 \cong \angle 3$.	2. Vertical angles are congruent (Thm. 4–11).
3. $m\angle 1 = m\angle 3$.	3. Def. of congruent angles.
4. $m\angle 1 = 90$.	4. Def. of right angle.
5. $m\angle 3 = 90$.	5. Transitivity Ax. (E–3).
6. $\therefore \angle 3$ is a right angle.	6. Def. of right angle.
7. $m\angle 1 + m\angle 2 = 180$.	7. Thm. 4–6 and Def. of supplementary angles.
8. $90 + m\angle 2 = 180$.	8. Substitution Ax. (S–1).
9. $m\angle 2 = 90$.	9. Subtraction Ax. (E–5).
10. $\therefore \angle 2$ is a right angle.	10. Def. of right angle.
11. In the same manner, $\angle 4$ is a right angle.	11. As in steps 2, 3, 4, and 5; using $\angle 2$ and $\angle 4$.

This is the longest proof we have encountered so far, but the number of steps in a proof is not a measure of the difficulty of the proof. Frequently the same theorem may be proved in different ways, some longer than others. The really important criterion is not length, but validity—is your proof correct?

A rereading of the proof of Theorem 4–12 will disclose that $\angle 3$ and $\angle 4$ were both shown to be right angles in the same way. Statements 2, 3, 4, and 5 were used to establish that $\angle 3$ was a right angle, and a similar chain of reasoning established that $\angle 4$ was a right angle. We took advantage of this situation in the following manner: first we wrote the proof that $\angle 3$ was a right angle, then we stated, "In the same manner $\angle 4$ is a right angle." You must of course be certain that the similar chain of reasoning really does accomplish what you seek to accomplish.

A most useful way to shorten a proof is to use more powerful theorems. As an example, we could establish the following theorem: "If one of two vertical angles is a right angle, then the other is also a right angle." The proof of this theorem would require little more than steps 2, 3, 4, and 5, and we would not have to repeat this sequence of steps in future proofs. (This particular theorem is not included in our list only because the list will eventually be quite extensive, and we try to include among the theorems to be *remembered* those that we feel are most useful.) As we proceed, more and more theorems will be proved, and you will have many more with which to work.

A last word of caution: Do not look for ways to shorten a proof merely because you desire that it be shorter. It is too easy to leave out a significant step in the mistaken belief that it is not needed. If you are in doubt as to whether a step should really be included, then it most probably should!

EXAMPLES

1. Given $\overleftrightarrow{AB}$ and $\overleftrightarrow{CD}$ intersect at P, $\overrightarrow{PR} \perp \overleftrightarrow{AB}$, and $m\angle APD = 170$, find $m\angle 1$, $m\angle 2$, $m\angle 3$, and $m\angle 4$.

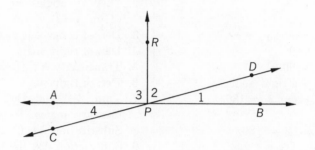

Solution: Since $\overrightarrow{PR} \perp \overleftrightarrow{AB}$, $\angle 3$ is a right angle, hence $m\angle 3 = 90$. $m\angle APD = m\angle 3 + m\angle 2$. Since $m\angle APD = 170$, by substitution, $170 = m\angle 3 + m\angle 2$, and $170 = 90 + m\angle 2$. Thus $m\angle 2 = 80$.

Since $\overrightarrow{PR} \perp \overleftrightarrow{AB}$, $\angle RPB$ is a right angle. Then $\angle 1$ and $\angle 2$ are complementary. Therefore $m\angle 2 = 90 - 80 = 10$.

Finally, $\angle 1$ and $\angle 4$ are vertical angles and are therefore congruent. Therefore $m\angle 1 = m\angle 4 = 10$.

2. Write a formal proof:

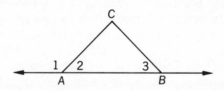

GIVEN: $\angle 1$ and $\angle 3$ are supplementary; $\overleftrightarrow{AB}$.
PROVE: $\angle 2 \cong \angle 3$.

Proof

STATEMENTS	REASONS
1. $\angle 1$ and $\angle 3$ are supplementary.	1. Given.
2. $\overleftrightarrow{AB}$ a straight line.	2. Given.
3. $\angle 1$ and $\angle 2$ are supplementary.	3. Two adjacent angles with their exterior sides contained in a straight line are supplementary (Thm. 4–6).
4. $\angle 2 \cong \angle 3$.	4. Supplements of the same angle are congruent (Thm. 4–8).

Exercise 4-5

1. If $\overrightarrow{MA} \perp \overrightarrow{MB}$, $\overrightarrow{NC} \perp \overrightarrow{ND}$, $\angle 1 \cong \angle 3$, and $m\angle 1 = 25$, find $m\angle 3$, $m\angle 2$, and $m\angle 4$.

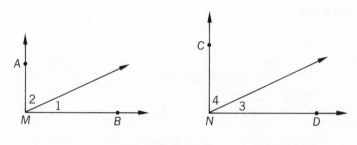

Prob. 1

2. If $m\angle 1 = 30$, and $\angle 1 \cong \angle 2$, find the measure of each of angles 2, 3, 4, 5, 6, 7, and 8.

3. If $\overleftrightarrow{CD} \perp \overleftrightarrow{EF}$, and $\angle 3 \cong \angle 5$, find the measure of each of angles 1, 2, 3, 4, 5, and 6.

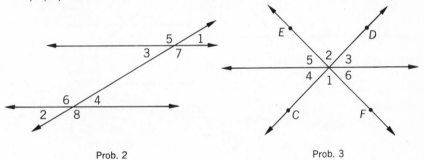

Prob. 2   Prob. 3

4. If $\overline{AD} \perp \overline{AB}$, $\overline{AB} \perp \overline{BC}$, $m\angle 2 = 70$, and $\angle 1 \cong \angle 3$, find $m\angle 1$, $m\angle 3$, and $m\angle 4$.

5. Given $\overleftrightarrow{AD}$, $\overrightarrow{PB} \perp \overrightarrow{PC}$:
   (a) Name a right angle.
   (b) Name a pair of complementary angles.
   (c) Name two pairs of supplementary angles.

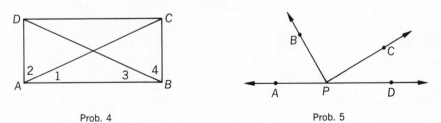

Prob. 4   Prob. 5

6. Write a formal proof for Theorem 4–9.

7. Write a formal proof for Theorem 4–10.

8. Using the same beginning information for Theorem 4–11, write a formal proof to show that $\angle 3 \cong \angle 4$.

9. Write a formal proof: "If one of two vertical angles is a right angle, then the other is also a right angle."
GIVEN: $\overleftrightarrow{AB} \perp \overleftrightarrow{CD}$; $\angle 1$ is a right angle.
PROVE: $\angle 2$ is a right angle.

10. GIVEN: $\overrightarrow{AC}$ and $\overrightarrow{AB}$; $\overrightarrow{CB}$; $m\angle 1 = m\angle 2$.
PROVE: $m\angle 3 = m\angle 4$.

11. GIVEN: Lines q_1, q_2, and t; $\angle 1 \cong \angle 2$.
PROVE: $\angle 3 \cong \angle 4$.

12. GIVEN: Lines q_1, q_2, and t; $\angle 1 \cong \angle 2$.
PROVE: $\angle 5 \cong \angle 6$.

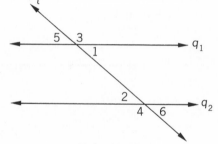

Prob. 9

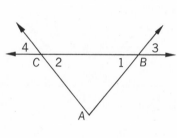

Prob. 10

Probs. 11, 12

13. GIVEN: $\overleftrightarrow{AB}$; $\angle 2 \cong \angle 3$; $\triangle ABC$.
PROVE: $\angle 1 \cong \angle 4$.

14. GIVEN: $\overleftrightarrow{AB}$, $\overleftrightarrow{CD}$, and $\overleftrightarrow{EF}$; $\overleftrightarrow{CD} \perp \overleftrightarrow{AB}$.
PROVE: $\angle 1$ and $\angle 2$ are complementary.

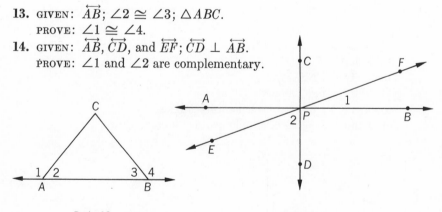

Prob. 13

Prob. 14

15. GIVEN: $\overleftrightarrow{AC}$; $\overrightarrow{BD}$ and $\overrightarrow{BE}$; $\angle 1$ and $\angle 3$ are complementary.
PROVE: $\overrightarrow{BD} \perp \overrightarrow{BE}$.

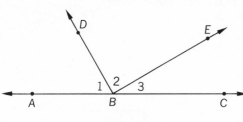

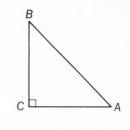

Prob. 15

Prob. 16

In problems 16 and 17, statements of the proof are supplied. Write the reason for each step.

16. GIVEN: $\triangle ABC$; $\angle C$ a right angle; $m\angle A + m\angle B + m\angle C = 180$.
　　PROVE: $\angle A$ and $\angle B$ are complementary.

Proof

STATEMENTS	REASONS
1. $m\angle A + m\angle B + m\angle C = 180$.	1.
2. $\angle C$ is a right angle.	2.
3. $m\angle C = 90$.	3.
4. $m\angle A + m\angle B + 90 = 180$.	4.
5. $m\angle A + m\angle B = 90$.	5.
6. $\angle A$ and $\angle B$ are complementary.	6.

17. GIVEN: $\overleftrightarrow{AD}$; $P \in \overleftrightarrow{AD}$; $\overrightarrow{PB} \perp \overrightarrow{PC}$.
　　PROVE: $m\angle 1 + m\angle 2 = 90$.

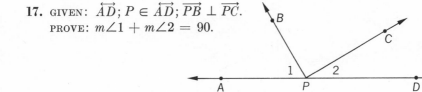

Prob. 17

Proof

STATEMENTS	REASONS
1. $\angle APC$ and $\angle 2$ are supplementary.	1.
2. $m\angle APC + m\angle 2 = 180$.	2.
3. $m\angle APC = m\angle 1 + m\angle BPC$.	3.
4. $\overrightarrow{PB} \perp \overrightarrow{PC}$.	4.
5. $\angle BPC$ is a right angle.	5.
6. $m\angle BPC = 90$.	6.
7. $m\angle APC = m\angle 1 + 90$.	7.
8. $m\angle 1 + 90 + m\angle 2 = 180$.	8. (*Hint:* See statement 2.)
9. $m\angle 1 + m\angle 2 = 90$.	9.

18. GIVEN: $\overleftrightarrow{BC}$; $\triangle ABC$; $m\angle 1 + m\angle 2 + m\angle 3 = 180$.
   PROVE: $m\angle x = m\angle 2 + m\angle 3$.

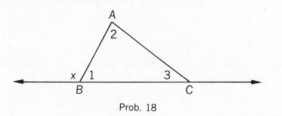

Prob. 18

19. GIVEN: $\angle 1 \cong \angle 3$; t intersects q_1 and q_2 at A and B, respectively.
   PROVE: $\angle 1$ and $\angle 2$ are supplementary.

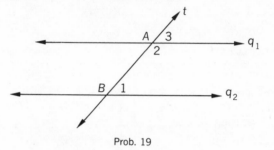

Prob. 19

20. GIVEN: $\triangle ABC$; $\angle ACB$ a right angle; $m\angle 1 + m\angle 2 = 90$.
   PROVE: $\angle 1 \cong \angle 3$.

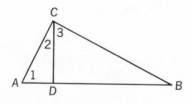

Prob. 20

4-6 WRITING ORIGINAL PROOFS

Now that you have had the opportunity to examine several formal proofs, you may well raise the question: How does one originate these proofs? There is no simple answer, but there are ways in which you may develop your ability to attack original problems. Experience—getting as much practice as possible—is probably the most useful way to develop skill. Many of the problems that you do will contain ideas and chains of thought that may be used in future problems. Following this section is a set of exercises, each of which makes use of techniques that will be used again in future problems. Careful study of these techniques will repay your efforts.

We have need of one further definition:

Definition 4–1: Two line segments are **congruent** iff their measures are equal. (Notation: $\overline{AB} \cong \overline{CD}$.)

Thus $\overline{AB} \cong \overline{CD}$ iff $m\overline{AB} = m\overline{CD}$. We do not generally use the "m" notation for segments; rather we prefer the simpler notation $AB = CD$.

EXAMPLES

1. GIVEN: $\overline{AC} \cong \overline{DB}$; C between A and D; D between C and B.
   PROVE: $\overline{AD} \cong \overline{CB}$.

$$\overset{\displaystyle\bullet}{A} \quad\overset{\displaystyle\bullet}{C}\qquad\qquad\overset{\displaystyle\bullet}{D}\quad\overset{\displaystyle\bullet}{B}$$

Proof

STATEMENTS	REASONS
1. $\overline{AC} \cong \overline{DB}$, C between A and D, D between C and B.	1. Given.
2. $AC = DB$.	2. Def. of congruent segments.
3. $CD = CD$.	3. Reflexive Ax. (E–1).
4. $AC + CD = DB + CD$.	4. Addition Ax. (E–4).
5. $AD = AC + CD$, $CB = DB + CD$.	5. Def. of betweenness.
6. $AD = CB$	6. Substitution Ax. (S–1).
7. $\therefore \overline{AD} \cong \overline{CB}$.	7. Def. of congruent segments.

2. GIVEN: $\overline{AB} \cong \overline{AC}$; P is the midpoint of $\overline{AB}$; Q is the midpoint of $\overline{AC}$.
   PROVE: $\overline{AP} \cong \overline{AQ}$.

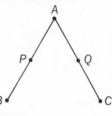

Proof

STATEMENTS	REASONS
1. $\overline{AB} \cong \overline{AC}$.	1. Given.
2. $AB = AC$.	2. Def. of congruent segments.
3. $AB = AP + PB$, $AC = AQ + QC$.	3. Def. of betweenness.
4. $AP + PB = AQ + QC$.	4. Substitution Ax. (S–1).
5. P the midpoint of $\overline{AB}$, Q the midpoint of $\overline{AC}$.	5. Given
6. $AP = PB$, $AQ = QC$.	6. Def. of midpoint of segment.
7. $2(AP) = 2(AQ)$	7. Substitution Ax. (S–1): AP for PB, and AQ for QC in statement 4.
8. $AP = AQ$.	8. Division Ax. (E–7).
9. $\therefore \overline{AP} \cong \overline{AQ}$.	9. Def. of congruent segments.

Another approach to discovering proofs is by way of *analyzing* the problem. Basically, analyzing the problem means beginning with the required conclusion, and considering a chain of reasoning designed to lead back to the hypothesis. The method is best explained by considering examples.

EXAMPLES

1. GIVEN: $\triangle ADE$; $\angle 2 \cong \angle 3$.
   PROVE: $\angle 1 \cong \angle 4$.

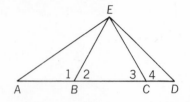

Analysis: We start by looking at what we are being asked to prove. In this problem we are asked to prove that two angles are congruent. We ask: "How can we prove that two angles are congruent?" To answer this, you must search among all the definitions, axioms, and theorems, and examine those that refer to the congruence of angles. There is, for example, the definition of angle congruence which requires equal measures. In this problem we have no information about measures, so the definition does not look encouraging. There may come to mind a theorem: Supplements of congruent angles are congruent. This seems hopeful because we *do* have a pair of congruent angles. Further, we note that the angles we are trying to prove congruent ($\angle 1$ and $\angle 4$) are related to the given angles ($\angle 2$ and $\angle 3$) by way of being adjacent in pairs. Thus we might now think: We could show $\angle 1 \cong \angle 4$ if we knew that they were supplements of $\angle 2$ and $\angle 3$, respectively. The pairs *would* be supplementary, if each pair were adjacent, with their exterior sides contained in a straight line. We see that they *are* adjacent; also, $\overline{AD}$ determines a straight line since it is a side of $\triangle ADE$, and $\overleftrightarrow{AD}$ does contain the exterior sides of the angles in question. Thus we discover a proof.

Proof

STATEMENTS	REASONS
1. $\triangle ADE$.	1. Given.
2. Endpoints A and D determine a line.	2. Def. of segment, and Ax. 2–1. (Two points determine exactly one line.)
3. $\angle 1$ and $\angle 2$ are adjacent, $\angle 3$ and $\angle 4$ are adjacent.	3. Def. of adjacent angles.
4. $\angle 1$ and $\angle 2$ are supplementary, $\angle 3$ and $\angle 4$ are supplementary.	4. Thm. 4–6.
5. $\angle 2 \cong \angle 3$.	5. Given.
6. $\angle 1 \cong \angle 4$.	6. Supplements of congruent angles are congruent (Thm. 4–8).

2. GIVEN: $\overleftrightarrow{AB}$ intersects $\overleftrightarrow{CD}$ at P; $\angle 1 \cong \angle 4$; $\angle 3 \cong \angle 2$; $\overrightarrow{PM}, \overrightarrow{PN}$.
PROVE: $\overleftrightarrow{CD} \perp \overleftrightarrow{AB}$.

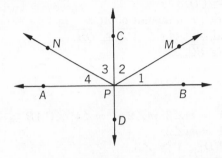

Analysis: We again begin with the conclusion: How can we show that two lines are perpendicular? We have two definitions; either show that the two lines intersect to form a right angle, or that the two lines intersect to form two equal adjacent angles. A look at the diagram suggests—by its very appearance—the Angle Addition Axiom (Ax. 3–9): $m\angle 1 + m\angle 2 = m\angle CPB$ and $m\angle 3 + m\angle 4 = m\angle CPA$. We could show that $\angle CPA \cong \angle CPB$ if their measures were equal—we *can* show this because we are given two sets of congruent angles, and our thinking above suggests the use of the Angle Addition Axiom. Thus we write a proof.

Proof

STATEMENTS	REASONS
1. $\angle 1 \cong \angle 4$; $\angle 2 \cong \angle 3$.	1. Given.
2. $m\angle 1 = m\angle 4$; $m\angle 2 = m\angle 3$.	2. Def. of congruent angles.
3. $m\angle 1 + m\angle 2 = m\angle 3 + m\angle 4$.	3. Addition Ax. (E–4).
4. $m\angle APC = m\angle 3 + m\angle 4$; $m\angle BPC = m\angle 1 + m\angle 2$.	4. Angle Addition Ax. (Ax. 3–9).
5. $m\angle BPC = m\angle APC$.	5. Substitution Ax. (S–1).
6. $\angle BPC \cong \angle APC$.	6. Def. of congruent angles.
7. $\overleftrightarrow{CD} \perp \overleftrightarrow{AB}$.	7. Def. of perpendicular lines.

Exercise 4–6

Write formal proofs for the following problems. Try to think of an analysis for each problem before writing a proof.

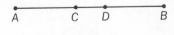

1. GIVEN: $\overline{AD} \cong \overline{CB}$.
   PROVE: $\overline{AC} \cong \overline{DB}$.

Prob. 1

2. GIVEN: $\triangle ABC$; P midpoint of $\overline{AC}$;
  Q midpoint of $\overline{CB}$; $\overline{AC} \cong \overline{BC}$.
  PROVE: $\overline{CP} \cong \overline{CQ}$.

3. GIVEN: $\triangle ABC$; P midpoint of $\overline{AC}$;
  Q midpoint of $\overline{CB}$; $\overline{PA} \cong \overline{QB}$.
  PROVE: $\overline{AC} \cong \overline{BC}$.

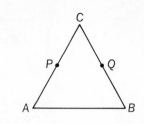

Probs. 2, 3

4. GIVEN: $m\angle 1 = m\angle 3$; $m\angle 2 = m\angle 4$; $\angle CAB \cong \angle ACB$.
  PROVE: $m\angle 1 = m\angle 2$.

5. GIVEN: $\triangle AED$; $\angle 1 \cong \angle 3$.
  PROVE: $\angle AEC \cong \angle DEB$.

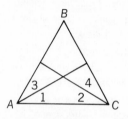

Prob. 4

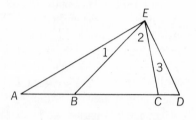

Prob. 5

6. GIVEN: $\angle 1 \cong \angle 3$; $\angle 2 \cong \angle 4$.
  PROVE: $\angle ABC \cong \angle ADC$.

7. GIVEN: $\angle 3 \cong \angle 1$; $\angle ABC \cong \angle ADC$.
  PROVE: $m\angle 2 = m\angle 4$.

8. GIVEN: $\overleftrightarrow{AB}$; $P \in \overleftrightarrow{AB}$; $\overrightarrow{PD} \perp \overleftrightarrow{AB}$; $\angle 1 \cong \angle 3$.
  PROVE: $\overrightarrow{PC} \perp \overrightarrow{PE}$.

9. GIVEN: $\overleftrightarrow{AB}$; $P \in \overleftrightarrow{AB}$; $\overrightarrow{PD} \perp \overleftrightarrow{AB}$; $\overrightarrow{PC} \perp \overrightarrow{PE}$.
  PROVE: $\angle 1 \cong \angle 3$.

10. GIVEN: $\overleftrightarrow{AB}$; $P \in \overleftrightarrow{AB}$; $\overrightarrow{PC} \perp \overrightarrow{PE}$; $\angle 1 \cong \angle 3$.
  PROVE: $\overrightarrow{PD} \perp \overleftrightarrow{AB}$.

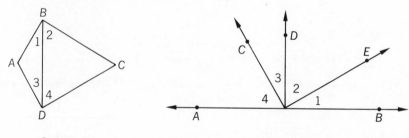

Probs. 6, 7

Probs. 8 to 10

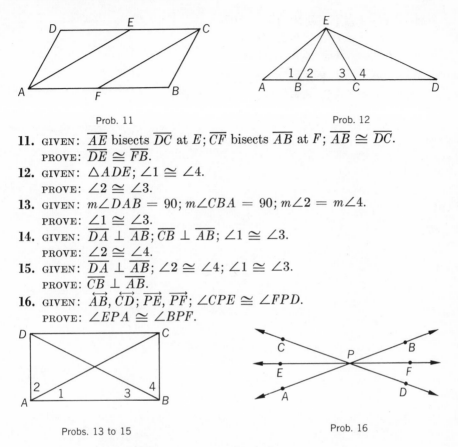

Prob. 11

Prob. 12

11. GIVEN: $\overline{AE}$ bisects $\overline{DC}$ at E; $\overline{CF}$ bisects $\overline{AB}$ at F; $\overline{AB} \cong \overline{DC}$.
    PROVE: $\overline{DE} \cong \overline{FB}$.

12. GIVEN: $\triangle ADE$; $\angle 1 \cong \angle 4$.
    PROVE: $\angle 2 \cong \angle 3$.

13. GIVEN: $m\angle DAB = 90$; $m\angle CBA = 90$; $m\angle 2 = m\angle 4$.
    PROVE: $\angle 1 \cong \angle 3$.

14. GIVEN: $\overline{DA} \perp \overline{AB}$; $\overline{CB} \perp \overline{AB}$; $\angle 1 \cong \angle 3$.
    PROVE: $\angle 2 \cong \angle 4$.

15. GIVEN: $\overline{DA} \perp \overline{AB}$; $\angle 2 \cong \angle 4$; $\angle 1 \cong \angle 3$.
    PROVE: $\overline{CB} \perp \overline{AB}$.

16. GIVEN: $\overleftrightarrow{AB}$, $\overleftrightarrow{CD}$; $\overrightarrow{PE}$, $\overrightarrow{PF}$; $\angle CPE \cong \angle FPD$.
    PROVE: $\angle EPA \cong \angle BPF$.

Probs. 13 to 15

Prob. 16

17. GIVEN: $\overleftrightarrow{AD}$, $\overleftrightarrow{BE}$, $\overleftrightarrow{PC}$; $\angle 1$ and $\angle 2$ are complementary.
    PROVE: $\angle BPA$ is a right angle.

18. GIVEN: $\overline{AB}$ and $\overline{CD}$ intersect at P; $\angle 1$ and $\angle 3$ are complementary.
    PROVE: $\angle 2$ and $\angle 3$ are complementary.

19. GIVEN: $\overleftrightarrow{AB}$, $\overleftrightarrow{CD}$; $\triangle APC$, $\triangle PBD$; $\angle 1$ and $\angle 3$ are complementary;
    $\angle 2$ and $\angle 4$ are complementary.
    PROVE: $\angle 3 \cong \angle 4$.

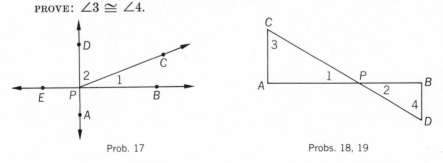

Prob. 17

Probs. 18, 19

20. GIVEN: $\overline{DA} \perp \overline{AB}$; $\overline{DC} \perp \overline{CB}$;
            $\angle 1 \cong \angle 2$.
    PROVE: $\angle 3 \cong \angle 4$.

21. GIVEN: $\overline{DA} \perp \overline{AB}$; $\angle 1 \cong \angle 2$;
            $\angle 3 \cong \angle 4$.

    PROVE: $\overline{DC} \perp \overline{CB}$.

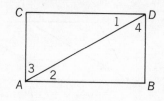

Probs. 20, 21

TRIANGLES: CONGRUENCE RELATION

5–1 SOME USEFUL THEOREMS

The following theorems are particularly useful in shortening many proofs. Essentially they are a list of properties of the congruence relation as applied to segments and angles. Some of the proofs will be furnished, the others will be left as exercises.

THEOREMS FOR SEGMENTS

Theorem 5–1 (Reflexive Property): Every segment is congruent to itself.

GIVEN: $\overline{AB}$.
PROVE: $\overline{AB} \cong \overline{AB}$.

Proof

STATEMENTS	REASONS
1. $AB = AB$.	1. Reflexive Ax. (E–1).
2. $\overline{AB} \cong \overline{AB}$.	2. Def. of congruent segments.

Theorem 5–2 (Symmetry Property): If $\overline{AB} \cong \overline{CD}$, then $\overline{CD} \cong \overline{AB}$.

Theorem 5–3 (Transitive Property): If $\overline{AB} \cong \overline{CD}$ and $\overline{CD} \cong \overline{EF}$, then $\overline{AB} \cong \overline{EF}$.

Theorem 5–4 (Addition Property): If B is between A and C, S is between R and T, $\overline{AB} \cong \overline{RS}$ and $\overline{BC} \cong \overline{ST}$, then $\overline{AC} \cong \overline{RT}$. (Figure 5–1.)

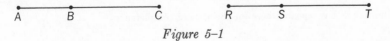

Figure 5–1

GIVEN: $\overline{AB} \cong \overline{RS}$, $\overline{BC} \cong \overline{ST}$, B between A and C, S between R and T.
PROVE: $\overline{AC} \cong \overline{RT}$.

Proof

STATEMENTS	REASONS
1. $\overline{AB} \cong \overline{RS}$, $\overline{BC} \cong \overline{ST}$.	1. Given.
2. $AB = RS$, $BC = ST$.	2. Def. of congruent segments.
3. $AB + BC = RS + ST$.	3. Addition Ax. (E–4).
4. S between R and T, B between A and C.	4. Given.
5. $AC = AB + BC$, $RT = RS + ST$.	5. Def. of betweenness.
6. $AC = RT$.	6. Substitution Ax. (S–1) (steps 3, 5).
7. $\overline{AC} \cong \overline{RT}$.	7. Def. of congruent segments.

Theorem 5–5 (Subtraction Property): If $\overline{AC} \cong \overline{RT}$, B is between A and C, S is between R and T, and $\overline{AB} \cong \overline{RS}$ then $\overline{BC} \cong \overline{ST}$. (Figure 5–1.)

THEOREMS FOR ANGLES

Theorem 4–1 (Reflexive Property): Every angle is congruent to itself.*

Theorem 5–6 (Symmetry Property): If $\angle A \cong \angle B$, then $\angle B \cong \angle A$.

Theorem 5–7 (Transitive Property): If $\angle A \cong \angle B$ and $\angle B \cong \angle C$, then $\angle A \cong \angle C$.

Theorem 5–8 (Addition Property): If D is in the interior of $\angle ABC$, P is in the interior of $\angle RST$, $\angle ABD \cong \angle RSP$ and $\angle DBC \cong \angle PST$, then $\angle ABC \cong \angle RST$. (Figure 5–2.)

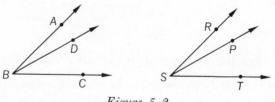

Figure 5–2

Theorem 5–9 (Subtraction Property): If $\angle ABC \cong \angle RST$, D is in the interior of $\angle ABC$, P is in the interior of $\angle RST$, and $\angle ABD \cong \angle RSP$, then $\angle DBC \cong \angle PST$. (Figure 5–2.)

*Theorem 4–1 is repeated here for the sake of completeness.

GIVEN: $\angle ABC \cong \angle RST$; $\angle ABD \cong \angle RSP$; D in interior of $\angle ABC$; P in interior of $\angle RST$. (Figure 5–2.)

PROVE: $\angle DBC \cong \angle PST$.

Proof

STATEMENTS	REASONS
1. $\angle ABC \cong \angle RST$; $\angle ABD \cong \angle RSP$; D in interior of $\angle ABC$; P in interior of $\angle RST$.	1. Given.
2. (a) $m\angle ABC = m\angle RST$; (b) $m\angle ABD = m\angle RSP$.	2. Def. of angle congruence.
3. $m\angle ABC = m\angle ABD + m\angle DBC$; $m\angle RST = m\angle RSP + m\angle PST$.	3. Angle Addition Ax. (Ax. 3–9).
4. $m\angle ABD + m\angle DBC = m\angle RSP + m\angle PST$.	4. Substitution Ax. (S–1) (steps 2a, 3).
5. $\therefore m\angle DBC = m\angle PST$.	5. Subtraction Ax. (E–5) (steps 2b, 4).
6. $\therefore \angle DBC \cong \angle PST$.	6. Def. of angle congruence.

THEOREMS CONCERNING BISECTION

Theorem 5–10: **If $\overline{AC} \cong \overline{RT}$, B is the midpoint of $\overline{AC}$, and S is the midpoint of $\overline{RT}$, then $\overline{AB} \cong \overline{RS}$.**

GIVEN: $\overline{AC} \cong \overline{RT}$; B the midpoint of $\overline{AC}$; S the midpoint of $\overline{RT}$.

PROVE: $\overline{AB} \cong \overline{RS}$.

Proof

STATEMENTS	REASONS
1. $\overline{AC} \cong \overline{RT}$; B the midpoint of $\overline{AC}$; S the midpoint of $\overline{RT}$.	1. Given.
2. $AC = RT$.	2. Def. of congruent segments.
3. $AB = BC$; $RS = ST$.	3. Def. of midpoint of segment.
4. $AC = AB + BC$; $RT = RS + ST$.	4. Def. of betweenness.
5. $AC = AB + AB = 2(AB)$; $RT = RS + RS = 2(RS)$.	5. Substitution Ax. (S–1) (steps 3, 4).
6. $2(AB) = 2(RS)$.	6. Substitution Ax. (S–1) (steps 2, 5).
7. $AB = RS$.	7. Division Ax. (E–7).
8. $\overline{AB} \cong \overline{RS}$.	8. Def. of congruent segments.

Definition 5–1: $\overrightarrow{BD}$ is the **bisector** of $\angle ABC$ iff D is in the interior of $\angle ABC$ and $\angle ABD \cong \angle DBC$. (Figure 5–3.)

Axiom 5–1: **Every angle has exactly one bisector.**

Theorem 5–11: **If $\angle ABC \cong \angle RST$, $\overrightarrow{BD}$ is the bisector of $\angle ABC$, and $\overrightarrow{SP}$ is the bisector of $\angle RST$, then $\angle ABD \cong \angle RSP$.** (Figure 5–3.)

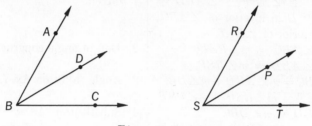

Figure 5–3

The proof of Theorem 5–11 follows the same pattern as that of Theorem 5–10 and is left as an exercise.

One practical implication of Theorems 5–10 and 5–11 is that if each of two congruent segments (or angles) is bisected, each of the resulting four segments (or angles) is congruent to each of the others. Thus, in Theorem 5–10, $\overline{AB} \cong \overline{RS}$, $\overline{AB} \cong \overline{ST}$, $\overline{BC} \cong \overline{RS}$, and $\overline{BC} \cong \overline{ST}$. (Of course, bisection implies that $\overline{AB} \cong \overline{BC}$ and $\overline{RS} \cong \overline{ST}$.) A similar set of congruences results from Theorem 5–11. In any individual proof, you may choose whichever congruence (or congruences) serves the purpose at hand.

EXAMPLES

1. GIVEN: $\angle AFC \cong \angle BFD$.
   PROVE: $\angle AFB \cong \angle CFD$.

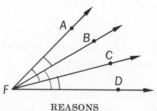

Proof

STATEMENTS	REASONS
1. $\angle AFC \cong \angle BFD$.	1. Given.
2. $\angle BFC \cong \angle BFC$.	2. Reflexive property of congruent angles (Thm. 4–1).
3. $\therefore \angle AFB \cong \angle CFD$.	3. Subtraction property (Thm. 5–9).

2. GIVEN: $\overline{AB} \cong \overline{CD}$.
   PROVE: $\overline{AC} \cong \overline{BD}$.

Proof

STATEMENTS	REASONS
1. $\overline{AB} \cong \overline{CD}$.	1. Given.
2. $\overline{BC} \cong \overline{BC}$.	2. Reflexive property of congruent segments (Thm. 5–1).
3. $\therefore \overline{AC} \cong \overline{BD}$.	3. Addition property (Thm. 5–4).

Exercise 5–1

(A)

1. Using the drawing and the hypothesis in the text for Thm. 5–11, list all pairs of congruent angles.

Justify each of the statements of problems 2 to 21 with an appropriate definition, axiom, or theorem.

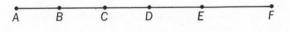

Probs. 2 to 11

2. $\overline{AB} \cong \overline{BA}$.　　　　　　　　**3.** If $\overline{CE} \cong \overline{DF}$, then $\overline{DF} \cong \overline{CE}$.

4. If $\overline{AC} \cong \overline{BD}$, then $\overline{AB} \cong \overline{CD}$.

5. If $\overline{BC} \cong \overline{DE}$ and $\overline{DE} \cong \overline{AB}$, then $\overline{BC} \cong \overline{AB}$.

6. If $\overline{AB} \cong \overline{CD}$ and $\overline{CD} \cong \overline{EF}$, then $\overline{AB} \cong \overline{EF}$.

7. If $\overline{BD} \cong \overline{CE}$, then $\overline{BC} \cong \overline{DE}$.　　**8.** If $\overline{AB} \cong \overline{BC}$, then $\overline{BC} \cong \overline{AB}$.

9. If $\overline{AB} \cong \overline{CD}$ and $\overline{BC} \cong \overline{DE}$, then $\overline{AC} \cong \overline{CE}$.

10. If $\overline{CD} \cong \overline{EF}$ and $\overline{BC} \cong \overline{DE}$, then $\overline{BD} \cong \overline{DF}$.

11. $\overline{BD} \cong \overline{DB}$.　　　　　　　　**12.** $\angle BAC \cong \angle CAB$.

13. If $\angle BAC \cong \angle DAE$, then $\angle DAE \cong \angle BAC$.

14. If $\angle BAD \cong \angle CAE$,
then $\angle BAC \cong \angle DAE$.

15. If $\angle EAF \cong \angle CAD$
and $\angle CAD \cong \angle FAG$,
then $\angle EAF \cong \angle FAG$.

16. If $\angle BAD \cong \angle DAF$
and $\angle DAF \cong \angle EAG$,
then $\angle BAD \cong \angle EAG$.

17. If $\angle DAF \cong \angle EAG$,
then $\angle DAE \cong \angle FAG$.

18. If $\angle CAE \cong \angle EAG$,
then $\angle EAG \cong \angle CAE$.

Probs. 12 to 21

19. If $\angle BAC \cong \angle DAE$ and $\angle CAD \cong \angle EAF$, then $\angle BAD \cong \angle DAF$.

20. If $\angle CAD \cong \angle EAF$ and $\angle DAE \cong \angle FAG$, then $\angle CAE \cong \angle EAG$.

21. $\angle EAF \cong \angle FAE$.

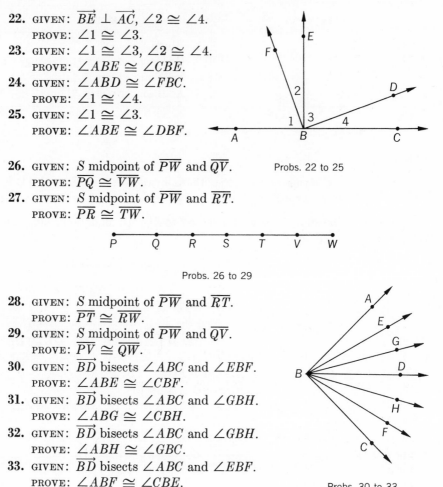

22. GIVEN: $\overrightarrow{BE} \perp \overrightarrow{AC}$, $\angle 2 \cong \angle 4$.
    PROVE: $\angle 1 \cong \angle 3$.
23. GIVEN: $\angle 1 \cong \angle 3$, $\angle 2 \cong \angle 4$.
    PROVE: $\angle ABE \cong \angle CBE$.
24. GIVEN: $\angle ABD \cong \angle FBC$.
    PROVE: $\angle 1 \cong \angle 4$.
25. GIVEN: $\angle 1 \cong \angle 3$.
    PROVE: $\angle ABE \cong \angle DBF$.

26. GIVEN: S midpoint of $\overline{PW}$ and $\overline{QV}$.   Probs. 22 to 25
    PROVE: $\overline{PQ} \cong \overline{VW}$.
27. GIVEN: S midpoint of $\overline{PW}$ and $\overline{RT}$.
    PROVE: $\overline{PR} \cong \overline{TW}$.

Probs. 26 to 29

28. GIVEN: S midpoint of $\overline{PW}$ and $\overline{RT}$.
    PROVE: $\overline{PT} \cong \overline{RW}$.
29. GIVEN: S midpoint of $\overline{PW}$ and $\overline{QV}$.
    PROVE: $\overline{PV} \cong \overline{QW}$.
30. GIVEN: $\overrightarrow{BD}$ bisects $\angle ABC$ and $\angle EBF$.
    PROVE: $\angle ABE \cong \angle CBF$.
31. GIVEN: $\overrightarrow{BD}$ bisects $\angle ABC$ and $\angle GBH$.
    PROVE: $\angle ABG \cong \angle CBH$.
32. GIVEN: $\overrightarrow{BD}$ bisects $\angle ABC$ and $\angle GBH$.
    PROVE: $\angle ABH \cong \angle GBC$.
33. GIVEN: $\overrightarrow{BD}$ bisects $\angle ABC$ and $\angle EBF$.
    PROVE: $\angle ABF \cong \angle CBE$.

Probs. 30 to 33

(B)

34. Prove Thm. 5–2.   35. Prove Thm. 5–3.
36. Prove Thm. 5–5.   37. Prove Thm. 5–6.
38. Prove Thm. 5–7.   39. Prove Thm. 5–8.
40. Prove Thm. 5–11.

5–2 **CONGRUENCE**

Consider the geometric figures of Figure 5–4. Appealing to the imagination, it appears that if it were possible to move these figures about (perhaps if they were formed of rigid wire), figure (c) would "fit" figure (a), and figure (d) would "fit" figure (e). Here the word *fit* carries the meaning of "having the same size and shape." Intuitively speaking, geometric figures are congruent if they have the same size and shape. (This is not intended as a definition, but simply as a description of the relative appearance of a pair of figures.)

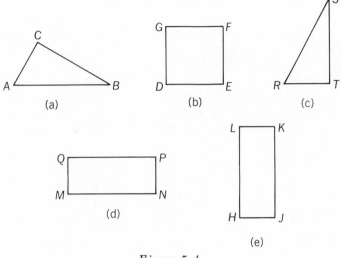

Figure 5–4

We need to describe, in some manner, *how* to "fit" two figures together. This can be done by indicating which points go where. For example, for Figure 5–4(a) and (c), we indicate that point R goes to point A, S goes to B, and T goes to C, by writing:

$$R \leftrightarrow A \qquad S \leftrightarrow B \qquad T \leftrightarrow C$$

For Figure 5–4(d) and (e) we could match:

$$H \leftrightarrow Q \qquad J \leftrightarrow M \qquad K \leftrightarrow N \qquad L \leftrightarrow P$$

Each such matching scheme is called a one-to-one correspondence between vertices. A correspondence may establish an exact fit; that is, the figures may be congruent. On the other hand, examine the matching scheme between Figure 5–4(b) and (d):

$$D \leftrightarrow M \qquad E \leftrightarrow N \qquad F \leftrightarrow P \qquad G \leftrightarrow Q$$

This is a one-to-one correspondence, but does not seem to lead to a pair of congruent figures.

Let us focus our attention upon pairs of triangles, and see what properties cause two triangles to appear to have the same size and shape. We shall appeal to our definitions of congruence for angles and segments because it is true that two triangles will have the same shape only if certain pairs of angles are congruent, and the same size only if certain pairs of sides are

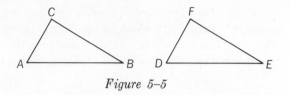

Figure 5-5

congruent. The proper selection of these certain pairs of angles and sides is to be examined below.

Consider now a pair of congruent triangles with the correspondence $A \leftrightarrow D$, $B \leftrightarrow E$, and $C \leftrightarrow F$ (Figure 5-5). We now introduce a convenient shorthand to indicate correspondences in a more concise manner; $ABC \leftrightarrow DEF$ shall mean the same as $A \leftrightarrow D$, $B \leftrightarrow E$, and $C \leftrightarrow F$. It must be remembered, when using this notation, that the names for corresponding vertices occupy corresponding positions, as shown:

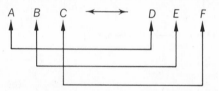

The matched congruent pairs (corresponding sides, corresponding angles) are:

$$\angle A \cong \angle D \qquad \overline{AB} \cong \overline{DE}$$
$$\angle B \cong \angle E \qquad \overline{BC} \cong \overline{EF}$$
$$\angle C \cong \angle F \qquad \overline{CA} \cong \overline{FD}$$

We are now prepared to give a mathematical (rather than an intuitive) definition of congruence.

Definition 5-2: A one-to-one correspondence between the vertices of two triangles is a **congruence between the triangles** iff every pair of corresponding sides are congruent, and every pair of corresponding angles are congruent.

Note that the same correspondence can be expressed in different ways, Thus $ABC \leftrightarrow DEF$ may also be written as $BCA \leftrightarrow EFD$, $ACB \leftrightarrow DFE$. or $BAC \leftrightarrow EDF$, for example. Note further that correspondences do not have to be congruences. If we write $ABC \leftrightarrow EDF$, this is no longer a congruence relation. To indicate a congruence, it is essential that the matching of congruent pairs be carefully indicated by arranging the letters in correct order.

If a congruence can be found between two triangles, we shall say that the triangles are congruent, and write $\triangle ABC \cong \triangle DEF$, where the order of the letters is the same as the order used in the congruence $ABC \leftrightarrow DEF$.

It is obvious that a congruence can always be established between a triangle and itself. For example, consider $\triangle RST$ (Figure 5–6). Clearly $RST \leftrightarrow RST$ is a congruence (the **identity** congruence), since each side corresponds to itself, forming a congruent pair; and each angle corresponds to itself, forming a congruent pair (Theorems 5–1 and 4–1). Note however that $RTS \leftrightarrow RST$ is *not* necessarily a congruence, since $\angle T$ is not necessarily congruent to $\angle S$, hence we cannot say $\triangle RTS \cong \triangle RST$.

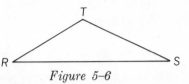

Figure 5–6

A useful way of indicating the matched pairs in two congruent triangles is illustrated in Figure 5–7. In each case, the corresponding (congruent) pairs of the two triangles are indicated with the same number of marks. Notice particularly the special mark used to indicate a right angle; $\angle C$ and $\angle C'$ are right angles.

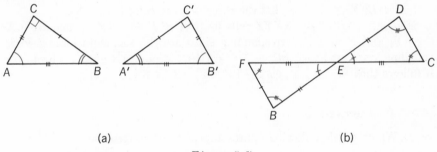

(a)   (b)

Figure 5–7

To finish this section we clarify some language that is commonly used in geometry:

Definition 5–3: An **angle** is **included between two sides** of a triangle iff the two sides of the triangle are subsets of the sides of the angle.

Definition 5–4: A **side** of a triangle is **included between two angles** of the triangle iff the endpoints of the side are the vertices of the angles.

Definition 5–5: An **angle** of a triangle is **opposite a side** of a triangle (and that **side is opposite the angle**) iff the vertex of the angle is not an endpoint of the side.

In Figure 5–8, $\angle D$ is included between $\overline{DF}$ and $\overline{DE}$; $\overline{EF}$ is included between $\angle F$ and $\angle E$; $\angle F$ is opposite $\overline{DE}$; and $\overline{DF}$ is opposite $\angle E$. Of course, other such relations can be stated for $\triangle DEF$; further practice is provided in the exercises.

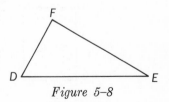

Figure 5–8

EXAMPLES

1. If $\triangle ABC \cong \triangle DEF$, complete the following statements:

    (a) $A\_B \leftrightarrow$ _____   *Solution:* $ACB \leftrightarrow DFE$
    (b) $\angle A \cong$ _____   *Solution:* $\angle A \cong \angle D$
    (c) $\angle F \cong$ _____   *Solution:* $\angle F \cong \angle C$
    (d) $\overline{BC} \cong$ _____   *Solution:* $\overline{BC} \cong \overline{EF}$
    (e) $DF \cong$ _____   *Solution:* $\overline{DF} \cong \overline{AC}$

The order of the letters used in stating the congruence tells us that $A \leftrightarrow D$, $B \leftrightarrow E$, and $C \leftrightarrow F$. The solutions follow directly from this.

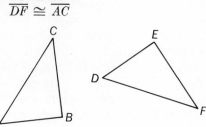

2. If $\triangle BCF \cong \triangle XYZ$, list the three pairs of congruent sides.

Solution: $\triangle BCF \cong \triangle XYZ$ tells us that $BCF \leftrightarrow XYZ$. Then $B \leftrightarrow X$, $C \leftrightarrow Y$, and $F \leftrightarrow Z$. Corresponding sides are the segments joining corresponding vertices; hence $\overline{BC} \leftrightarrow \overline{XY}$, $\overline{CF} \leftrightarrow \overline{YZ}$, and $\overline{FB} \leftrightarrow \overline{ZX}$. From this it follows that $\overline{BC} \cong \overline{XY}$, $\overline{CF} \cong \overline{YZ}$, and $\overline{FB} \cong \overline{ZX}$.

Exercise 5–2

1. Which of the following figures appear to be congruent?

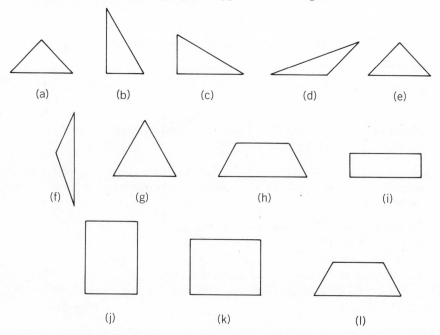

In each of the figures for problems 2 to 9 there is at least one pair of congruent triangles. Identify at least one congruence, using the proper notation.

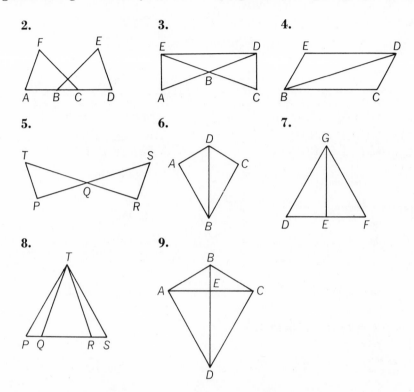

2.

3.

4.

5.

6.

7.

8.

9.

In the following (10 to 23), a triangle is indicated. Write the angle (or side) opposite the indicated side (or angle).

10. $\angle B$ **11.** $\angle C$ **12.** $\angle D$ **13.** $\overline{BC}$ **14.** $\overline{CD}$ **15.** $\overline{BD}$

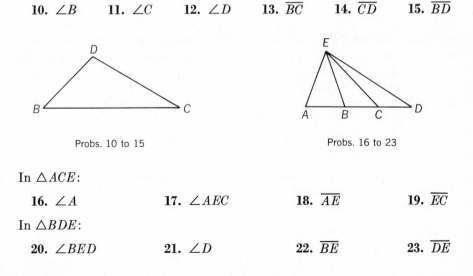

Probs. 10 to 15

Probs. 16 to 23

In $\triangle ACE$:

16. $\angle A$ **17.** $\angle AEC$ **18.** $\overline{AE}$ **19.** $\overline{EC}$

In $\triangle BDE$:

20. $\angle BED$ **21.** $\angle D$ **22.** $\overline{BE}$ **23.** $\overline{DE}$

In the following pairs of congruent triangles, state the pairs of corresponding parts (24 to 35):

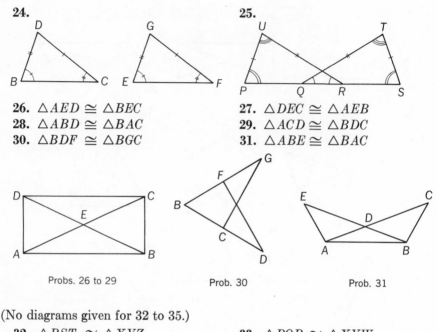

24.

25.

26. $\triangle AED \cong \triangle BEC$

27. $\triangle DEC \cong \triangle AEB$

28. $\triangle ABD \cong \triangle BAC$

29. $\triangle ACD \cong \triangle BDC$

30. $\triangle BDF \cong \triangle BGC$

31. $\triangle ABE \cong \triangle BAC$

Probs. 26 to 29   Prob. 30   Prob. 31

(No diagrams given for 32 to 35.)

32. $\triangle RST \cong \triangle XYZ$ **33.** $\triangle PQR \cong \triangle XYW$

34. $\triangle RST \cong \triangle YZX$ **35.** $\triangle PQR \cong \triangle YWX$

5–3 CONGRUENT TRIANGLES

Definition 5–3 states that a congruence between two triangles exists iff the corresponding sides and angles of the two triangles are congruent. As discussed earlier, this involves six statements of congruence—three pairs of corresponding sides, and three pairs of corresponding angles. Fortunately, it is not necessary to establish all six congruences in order to show that two triangles are congruent. If we choose our information properly, we can prove two triangles congruent by establishing only *three* congruences. We emphasize —the three congruences must be *properly* selected. The next three axioms indicate some of the selections.

Axiom 5–2 (The SAS Axiom): Two triangles are congruent if two sides and the included angle of one are congruent to the corresponding sides and included angle of the second.

Figure 5–9 shows $\triangle BCD \cong \triangle EFG$ by the SAS Axiom.

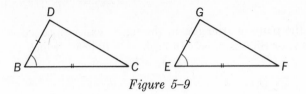

Figure 5-9

Axiom 5-3 (The ASA Axiom): Two triangles are congruent if two angles and the included side of one are congruent to the corresponding angles and included side of the second.

Figure 5-10 shows $\triangle CDE \cong \triangle GFH$ by the SAS Axiom.

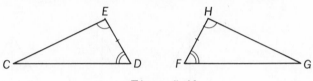

Figure 5-10

Axiom 5-4 (The SSS Axiom): Two triangles are congruent if three sides of one are congruent to the corresponding sides of the second.

Figure 5-11 shows $\triangle PRS \cong \triangle ZXY$ by the SSS Axiom.

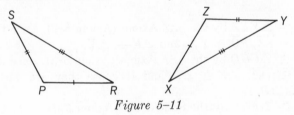

Figure 5-11

Notice that each of the three axioms contains the requirement that at least *one pair of* corresponding *sides* be congruent. If the three angles only of one triangle are known to be congruent to the corresponding angles of another, the triangles are not necessarily congruent. They could be described as having the same shape, but not necessarily being the same size (Figure 5-12). Such triangles are said to be *similar,* a relationship to be studied in detail in Chapter 10.

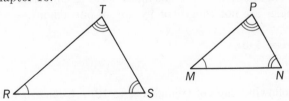

Figure 5-12

Which of the pairs of triangles in the figure can be proved congruent by the SAS, ASA, or SSS axioms? In each case indicate which axiom applies.

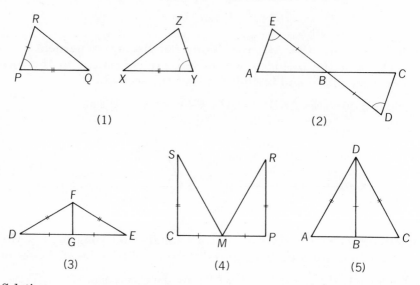

Solutions

1. $\triangle PQR \cong \triangle YXZ$ by the SAS Axiom (Axiom 5–2), since the markings indicate $\overline{PR} \cong \overline{YZ}$, $\overline{PQ} \cong \overline{YX}$, and $\angle P \cong \angle Y$.

2. $\triangle ABE \cong \triangle CBD$ by the ASA Axiom (Axiom 5–3), since the markings indicate $\overline{EB} \cong \overline{DB}$, $\angle E \cong \angle D$ and (because they are vertical angles) $\angle ABE \cong \angle CBD$.

3. $\triangle DGF \cong \triangle EGF$ by the SSS Axiom (Axiom 5–4), since the markings indicate $\overline{GD} \cong \overline{GE}$, $\overline{DF} \cong \overline{EF}$ and (by the Reflexive Axiom, E–1, for congruent segments) $\overline{FG} \cong \overline{FG}$.

4. $\triangle CMS$ and $\triangle PMR$ can not be proved congruent without more information. If we knew that $\overline{SM} \cong \overline{RM}$, the triangles would be congruent by the SSS Axiom (Axiom 5–4); or if we knew that $\angle C \cong \angle P$, the triangles would be congruent by the SAS Axiom (Axiom 5–2). Even though $\overline{CS}$ and $\overline{PR}$ may each *appear* to be perpendicular to $\overline{CP}$, and $\overline{SM}$ and $\overline{RM}$ may *look* as if they are congruent, we must not make these assumptions.

5. The triangles are not congruent by any of our axioms.

Exercise 5–3

(A)

Which of the following pairs of triangles (1 to 12) are congruent by the SAS, ASA, or SSS axiom? Indicate which axiom, if any, applies.

1. **2.**

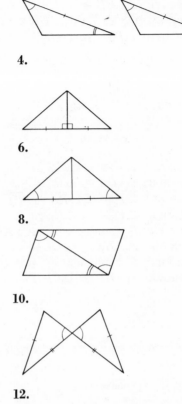

3. **4.**

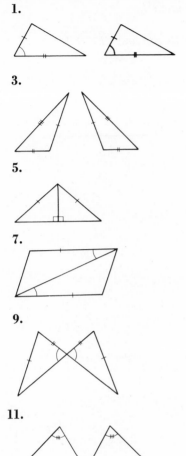

5. **6.**

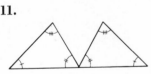

7. **8.**

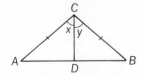

9. **10.**

11. **12.**

13. GIVEN: $\triangle ABC$; $\overline{CD}$ bisects $\angle ACB$; $\overline{AC} \cong \overline{BC}$.
PROVE: $\triangle ADC \cong \triangle BDC$.

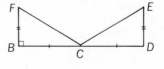

Prob. 13   Prob. 14

14. GIVEN: $\overline{BF} \perp \overline{BD}$; $\overline{DE} \perp \overline{BD}$; $\overline{BC} \cong \overline{CD}$; $\overline{BF} \cong \overline{DE}$.
PROVE: $\triangle BCF \cong \triangle DCE$.

15. GIVEN: $\overline{FB} \cong \overline{DB}$; $\overline{CB} \cong \overline{BE}$; $\overline{FD}$ and $\overline{CE}$.
    PROVE: $\triangle FBE \cong \triangle DBC$.

16. GIVEN: $\overline{CB} \cong \overline{BE}$; $\angle FCB \cong \angle DEB$; $\overline{FD}$ and $\overline{CE}$.
    PROVE: $\triangle FCB \cong \triangle DEB$.

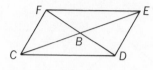   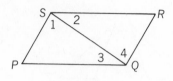

Probs. 15, 16   Probs. 17, 18

17. GIVEN: $\angle 1 \cong \angle 4$; $\angle 2 \cong \angle 3$.
    PROVE: $\triangle PQS \cong \triangle RSQ$.

18. GIVEN: $\angle 1 \cong \angle 4$; $\overline{PS} \cong \overline{RQ}$.
    PROVE: $\triangle PQS \cong \triangle RSQ$.

19. GIVEN: B is midpoint of $\overline{AC}$; $AE = CD$; $m\angle A = m\angle C$.
    PROVE: $\triangle ABE \cong \triangle CBD$.

20. GIVEN: B is midpoint of $\overline{AC}$; $BE = BD$; $AE = CD$.
    PROVE: $\triangle ABE \cong \triangle CBD$.

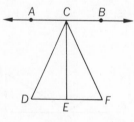   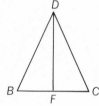

Probs. 19, 20

21. GIVEN: $\overline{DF}$ bisects $\overline{BC}$; $\overline{DB} \cong \overline{DC}$.   Probs. 21, 22
    PROVE: $\triangle BFD \cong \triangle CFD$.

22. GIVEN: $\overline{DF}$ bisects $\overline{BC}$; $\overline{DF} \perp \overline{BC}$.
    PROVE: $\triangle BFD \cong \triangle CFD$.

Prob. 23   Prob. 24

23. GIVEN: $\overleftrightarrow{AB} \perp \overline{CE}$; $\overline{CD} \cong \overline{CF}$; $\angle ACD \cong \angle BCF$.
    PROVE: $\triangle DEC \cong \triangle FEC$.

24. GIVEN: $\overleftrightarrow{PR}$; $\angle x \cong \angle y$; $\overline{QR} \cong \overline{SR}$.
    PROVE: $\triangle PQR \cong \triangle PRS$.

(B)

25. GIVEN: $\overline{AD} \cong \overline{BD}$; F is midpoint of $\overline{AD}$; C is midpoint of $\overline{BD}$; $\overline{AC} \cong \overline{BF}$.
    PROVE: $\triangle ABC \cong \triangle BAF$.
26. GIVEN: $\overline{AD} \cong \overline{BD}$; F is midpoint of $\overline{AD}$; C is midpoint of $\overline{BD}$.
    PROVE: $\triangle BFD \cong \triangle ACD$.

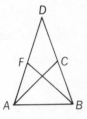   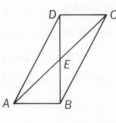

Probs. 25, 26   Prob. 27

27. GIVEN: $\overline{BD} \perp \overline{DC}$; $\overline{BD} \perp \overline{AB}$; $\overline{AC}$ bisects $\overline{BD}$.
    PROVE: $\triangle ABE \cong \triangle CDE$.
28. GIVEN: $\overline{AF} \perp \overline{AC}$; $\overline{ED} \perp \overline{BD}$; $\overline{AB} \cong \overline{CD}$; $\overline{AF} \cong \overline{DE}$.
    PROVE: $\triangle ACF \cong \triangle DBE$.

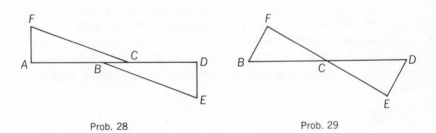

Prob. 28   Prob. 29

29. GIVEN: $\overline{BD}$ and $\overline{FE}$ bisect each other.
    PROVE: $\triangle BCF \cong \triangle DCE$.
30. GIVEN: $\overline{SP} \cong \overline{RQ}$; $\overline{SQ} \cong \overline{RP}$.
    PROVE: $\triangle PRS \cong \triangle QSR$.

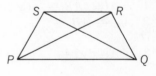

Prob. 30

5–4 CLASSIFICATION OF TRIANGLES

The following definitions classify triangles with respect to certain properties of their sides and angles.

Definition 5–6: A triangle is **scalene** iff no two sides are congruent.

Definition 5–7: A triangle is **isosceles** iff at least two sides are congruent. The **vertex** is the common endpoint of the two congruent sides. The

vertex angle is the angle included between the two congruent sides. The **base** is the side opposite the vertex angle. The **base angles** are the angles opposite the congruent sides.

The words *vertex, base,* and *angle* may be used with respect to any triangle. You should note that these words take on special meanings (as defined in Definition 5–7) when they are being used in relation to an *isosceles* triangle. (Another definition for *base* is given in Chapter 9.)

Definition 5–8:   A triangle is **equilateral** iff its three sides are congruent.

Definition 5–9:   A triangle is **equiangular** iff its three angles are congruent.

Definition 5–10:   A triangle is **acute** iff each of its angles is acute.

Definition 5–11:   A triangle is **obtuse** iff one of its angles is obtuse.

Theorem 5–12: If two sides of a triangle are congruent, the angles opposite these sides are congruent.

GIVEN: $\triangle ABC$; $\overline{AB} \cong \overline{AC}$.
PROVE: $\angle B \cong \angle C$.

The proof of this theorem is of such a nature that a few comments are in order. We will show that the correspondence $ABC \leftrightarrow ACB$ is a congruence, and therefore $\triangle ABC$ is congruent to itself *with the particular order of vertices* indicated by $ABC \leftrightarrow ACB$; $\triangle ABC \cong \triangle ACB$. (Note: This is *not* the identity congruence.)   Since $\angle B$ and $\angle C$ are then corresponding angles, they are congruent.

Proof

STATEMENTS	REASONS
1. $\triangle ABC$, $\overline{AB} \cong \overline{AC}$.	1. Given.
2. $\overline{AC} \cong \overline{AB}$.	2. Symmetric property of congruent segments (Thm. 5–2).
3. $\angle A \cong \angle A$.	3. Reflexive property of congruent angles (Thm. 4–1).
4. $\triangle ABC \cong \triangle ACB$.	4. SAS Ax. (Ax. 5–2).
5. $\angle B \cong \angle C$.	5. Def. of congruence.

Theorem 5–12 is sometimes stated: "The base angles of an isosceles triangle are congruent."

We now introduce our first corollary. A **corollary** is a theorem that is closely allied to some previous theorem. The two are usually so related that the previous theorem constitutes a major part of the proof of the corollary.

Corollary 5–12.1: **Every equilateral triangle is equiangular.**

GIVEN: $\triangle DEF$, $\overline{DE} \cong \overline{EF}$, $\overline{EF} \cong \overline{FD}$, $\overline{FD} \cong \overline{DE}$.
PROVE: $\angle D \cong \angle E$, $\angle E \cong \angle F$, $\angle D \cong \angle F$.

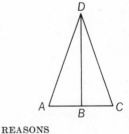

Proof

STATEMENTS	REASONS
1. $\overline{DE} \cong \overline{EF}$, $\overline{EF} \cong \overline{FD}$, $\overline{FD} \cong \overline{DE}$.	1. Given.
2. $\angle D \cong \angle E$.	2. Thm. 5–12 ($\overline{EF} \cong \overline{FD}$).
3. $\angle E \cong \angle F$.	3. Thm. 5–12 ($\overline{FD} \cong \overline{DE}$).
4. $\angle D \cong \angle F$.	4. Transitive property of congruent angles (Thm. 5–7) (steps 2 and 3).

Theorem 5–13: **If two angles of a triangle are congruent, the sides opposite these angles are congruent.**

The proof of Theorem 5–13 is analogous to the proof of Theorem 5–12, using the ASA Axiom (Axiom 5–3), and is left as an exercise.

Corollary 5–13.1: **Every equiangular triangle is equilateral.**

The proof is left as an exercise.

EXAMPLES

1. GIVEN: Isosceles $\triangle ACD$; $\overline{AD} \cong \overline{CD}$; $\overline{DB}$ bisects $\angle ADC$.
   PROVE: $\triangle ABD \cong \triangle CBD$.

Proof

STATEMENTS	REASONS
1. $\overline{AD} \cong \overline{CD}$; $\overline{DB}$ bisects $\angle ADC$.	1. Given.
2. $\angle ADB \cong \angle CDB$.	2. Def. of angle bisector.
3. $\angle A \cong \angle C$.	3. Thm. 5–12.
4. $\triangle ADB \cong \triangle CDB$.	4. ASA Ax. (Ax. 5–3).

The proof above could be revised so that steps 3 and 4 read:

3. $\overline{DB} \cong \overline{DB}$	3. Reflexive property of congruent segments (Thm. 5–1).
4. $\triangle ADB \cong \triangle CDB$.	4. SAS Ax. (Ax. 5–2).

2. GIVEN: $\overline{AC} \cong \overline{BD}, \overline{BE} \cong \overline{CE}$.
   PROVE: $\triangle ABE \cong \triangle DCE$.

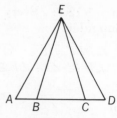

Proof

STATEMENTS	REASONS
1. $\overline{AC} \cong \overline{BD}$; $\overline{BE} \cong \overline{CE}$	1. Given.
2. $\angle EBC \cong \angle ECB$.	2. Thm. 5–12.
3. $\angle EBA$ and $\angle EBC$ are supplementary; $\angle ECD$ and $\angle ECB$ are supplementary.	3. Thm. 4–6 (Note that we are using the drawing to tell us that these angles are adjacent.)
4. $\therefore \angle EBA \cong \angle ECD$.	4. Thm. 4–8.
5. $\overline{BC} \cong \overline{BC}$.	5. Reflexive property of congruent segments (Thm. 5–1).
6. $\therefore \overline{AB} \cong \overline{CD}$.	6. Subtraction property of congruent segments (Thm. 5–5).
7. $\therefore \triangle ABE \cong \triangle DCE$.	7. SAS Ax. (Ax. 5–2).

Exercise 5–4

(A)

Classify each of the following triangles (1 to 9) as acute, obtuse, equiangular, scalene, isosceles, or equilateral. If more than one name applies, list all of them.

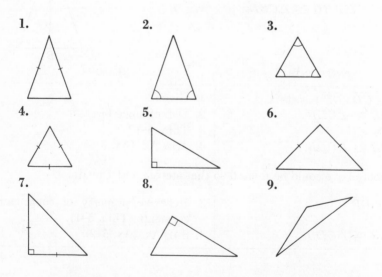

1.   2.   3.

4.   5.   6.

7.   8.   9.

10. GIVEN: $\triangle ABC$; $\angle A \cong \angle B$; D is midpoint of $\overline{AB}$.
PROVE: $\triangle ADC \cong \triangle BDC$.

11. GIVEN: $\overleftrightarrow{DE}$; $\angle x \cong \angle y$.
PROVE: $\triangle DEF$ is isosceles.

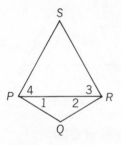

Prob. 10

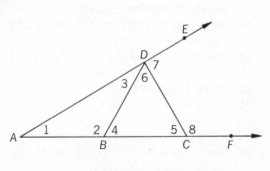

Prob. 11

12. GIVEN: $\overline{PQ} \cong \overline{RQ}$; $\overline{SP} \perp \overline{PQ}$; $\overline{SR} \perp \overline{RQ}$.
PROVE: $\triangle SPR$ is isosceles.

Prob. 12

Probs. 13, 14

13. If $AB = BD = DC = BC$, $m\angle 1 = 30$, and $m\angle 4 = 60$, find the measures of all the numbered angles.

14. If $AB = BD = DC$, $m\angle 1 = 20$, $m\angle 5 = 40$, and $m\angle 7 = 60$, find the measures of all the numbered angles.

15. GIVEN: $\triangle BCD$; $\overline{BD} \cong \overline{CD}$.
PROVE: $\angle x \cong \angle y$.

16. GIVEN: $\triangle BCD$; $\angle x \cong \angle y$.
PROVE: $\triangle BCD$ is isosceles.

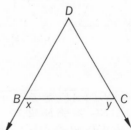

Probs. 15, 16

17. Given $\overleftrightarrow{DB}$, $\overleftrightarrow{AC}$, $\overline{DE} \cong \overline{EC}$, $\overline{AE} \cong \overline{BE}$, $m\angle 1 = 40$, $m\angle 3 = 100$, and $m\angle 7 = 40$, find measures of all numbered angles.

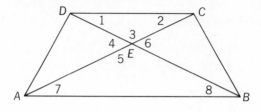

Probs. 17, 18

18. Given $\overleftrightarrow{DB}$, $\overleftrightarrow{AC}$, $\overline{DE} \cong \overline{EC}$, $\overline{AE} \cong \overline{BE}$, $m\angle 2 = 50$, $m\angle 6 = 100$, and $m\angle 8 = 50$, find measures of all numbered angles.

19. GIVEN: $\triangle PST$, $\overline{PT} \cong \overline{TS}$, $\overline{PR} \cong \overline{QS}$.
PROVE: $\triangle PRT \cong \triangle SQT$.

20. GIVEN: $\triangle PST$, $\overline{QT} \cong \overline{RT}$, $\overline{PQ} \cong \overline{RS}$.
PROVE: $\triangle PQT \cong \triangle SRT$.

21. GIVEN: $\triangle PST$; $\overline{QT} \cong \overline{RT}$; $\overline{PQ} \cong \overline{RS}$.
PROVE: $\triangle PRT \cong \triangle SQT$.

22. GIVEN: $\triangle PST$; $\overline{PT} \cong \overline{ST}$; $\overline{PQ} \cong \overline{RS}$.
PROVE: $\triangle PRT \cong \triangle SQT$.

23. Prove Theorem 5–13.

24. Prove Corollary 5–13.1.

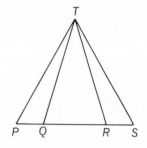

Probs. 19 to 22

(B)

25. GIVEN: $\triangle ACE$; $\overline{AE} \cong \overline{CE}$; B, D, and F midpoints of sides.
PROVE: $\triangle ABF \cong \triangle CBD$.

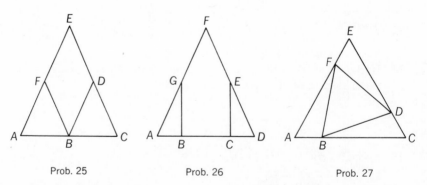

Prob. 25   Prob. 26   Prob. 27

26. GIVEN: $\triangle ADF$; $\overline{AF} \cong \overline{DF}$; $\overline{AC} \cong \overline{BD}$; $\overline{BG} \perp \overline{AD}$; $\overline{CE} \perp \overline{AD}$.
PROVE: $\triangle ABG \cong \triangle DCE$.

27. GIVEN: Equilateral $\triangle ACE$; $\overline{AB} \cong \overline{CD}$; $\overline{AB} \cong \overline{FE}$.
PROVE: (a) $\triangle ABF \cong \triangle CDB$ and (b) $\triangle ABF \cong \triangle EFD$.

28. GIVEN: $\triangle PQS$; $\angle SPQ \cong \angle SQP$; $\overline{ST} \cong \overline{SR}$.
  PROVE: $\triangle PRS \cong \triangle QTS$.
29. GIVEN: Equilateral $\triangle ABD$; $\angle 1 \cong \angle 2$; $B \in \overline{AC}$; $D \in \overline{BE}$.
  PROVE: $\triangle ACD \cong \triangle BEA$.
30. GIVEN: Equilateral $\triangle ABD$; $\angle 1 \cong \angle 2$; $B \in \overline{AC}$; $D \in \overline{BE}$.
  PROVE: $\triangle BCD \cong \triangle DEA$.

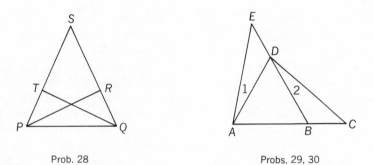

Prob. 28   Probs. 29, 30

31. PROVE: The bisector of the vertex angle of an isosceles triangle divides the isosceles triangle into two congruent triangles.
32. PROVE: The segment joining the vertex of an isosceles triangle to the midpoint of the base, divides the isosceles triangle into two congruent triangles.

5-5 SUGGESTIONS FOR WRITING PROOFS

In presenting problems for proof in geometry textbooks, it is common practice to supply part of the hypothesis (the "given" information) by means of a drawing. Consider the example:

GIVEN: $\triangle ADE$;
  $\overline{AC} \cong \overline{BD}$;
  $\overline{BE} \cong \overline{CE}$.
PROVE: $\triangle ABE \cong \triangle DCE$.

In addition to the information actually written as GIVEN, there are several (unstated) assumptions that can be made from the drawing. Since we are given that ADE is a triangle, we know that $\overline{AD}$ is a segment (the side of a triangle), and can therefore assume:

(1) A, B, C, and D are collinear.
(2) B is between A and C.
(3) C is between B and D.

Another example is:

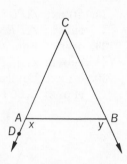

GIVEN: $\triangle ABC$; $\overline{AC} \cong \overline{BC}$.
PROVE: $\angle x \cong \angle y$.

In this case, without the drawing to indicate exactly where $\angle x$ and $\angle y$ are located, we would need
descriptions of this sort: "$\angle x$ is the angle formed
by $\overrightarrow{AD}$ and $\overrightarrow{AB}$, when $D \in \overrightarrow{CA}$ and A is between
C and D." To include such information in a proof
would make the proof unnecessarily complicated.
Instead, we will assume from the figure such things as betweenness, points
lying on a line, interior and exterior location of angles, and, in general, the
relative positions of lines, points, and planes. You must be careful, however,
not to assume *too* much from the appearance of the drawing. Do not infer
such things as congruence of angles or of segments, midpoints of segments,
angle bisectors, or perpendicular lines. All of these involve *measures* in some
way, and must be specifically indicated. Thus, in Figure 5–13, it would not
be correct to assume that $\overleftrightarrow{AB} \perp \overleftrightarrow{CD}$ or that $\overline{PR} \cong \overline{QR}$ simply because they
"look" that way.

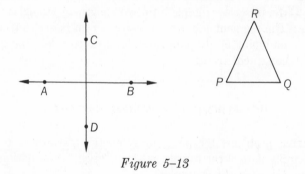

Figure 5–13

One last word of caution: a drawing is not sufficient evidence to guarantee
the collinearity of points. For example, in Figure 5–14(a), we must not assume that A, B, and C are collinear, or conclude that $\angle x$ and $\angle y$ are supplementary, unless we know that $\overleftrightarrow{AC}$ is a straight line. In Figure 5–14(b), we

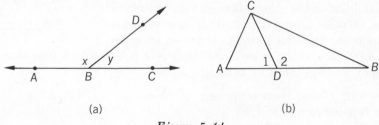

(a)   (b)

Figure 5–14

can assume from the figure that A, D, and B are collinear only if we know that ABC is a triangle and therefore $\overline{AB}$ is a segment.

EXAMPLES

1. Given $\triangle BDF$. What points are collinear, and which points lie between two named points?

Solution: B, C, and D are collinear. C is between B and D. We cannot reach any conclusion regarding A and E without further information. The drawing could be as below

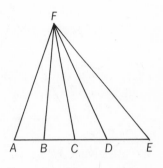

Exs. 1, 2

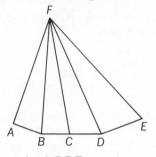

and still contain $\triangle BDF$.

2. Given $\triangle AEF$. Answer the questions above.

Solution: A, B, C, D, and E are collinear. B is between A and C, C is between B and D, D is between C and E. (Also, B is between A and D, A and E; C is between B and E, A and D, A and E; and D is between B and E, A and E.)

3. Given $\triangle BDE$ in this figure, which of the triangles are acute triangles?

Solution: We cannot answer this question. $\angle BED$ is a right angle, hence $\triangle BDE$ is not acute. $\angle BCE$ and $\angle DCE$ appear too much like right angles to say that either is acute. On the other hand, neither can we assume $\overline{EC} \perp \overline{BD}$.

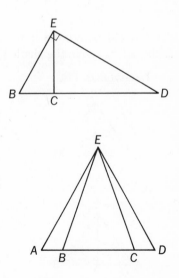

4. GIVEN: $\triangle ADE$; $\overline{AB} \cong \overline{CD}$; $\overline{AE} \cong \overline{DE}$.
   PROVE: $\triangle ACE \cong \triangle DBE$.

DISCUSSION: It sometimes helps to make separate sketches of the triangles we wish to prove congruent. In this problem:

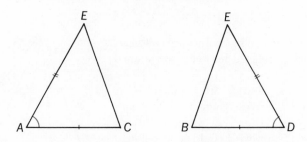

We are given $\overline{AE} \cong \overline{DE}$. If we can show $\overline{AC} \cong \overline{BD}$, and $\angle A \cong \angle D$, the triangles will be congruent by the SAS Axiom.

Proof

STATEMENTS	REASONS
1. $\overline{AB} \cong \overline{CD}$.	1. Given.
2. $\overline{BC} \cong \overline{BC}$.	2. Reflexive property of congruent segments (Thm. 5–1).
3. $\therefore \overline{AC} \cong \overline{BD}$.	3. Addition property of congruent segments (Thm. 5–4).
4. $\overline{AE} \cong \overline{DE}$.	4. Given.
5. $\therefore \angle A \cong \angle D$.	5. Thm. 5–12. (Using $\triangle ADE$.)
6. $\therefore \triangle ACE \cong \triangle DBE$.	6. SAS Ax. (Ax. 5–2) (steps 3, 4, 5).

Exercise 5–5

(A)

In 1 to 10 determine if the given information (including the drawing) is sufficient to prove the shaded triangles congruent.

1. Given $\triangle ABC$:

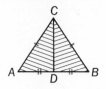

2. Given $\triangle ABC$:

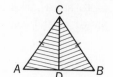

3. Given $\triangle ABC$:

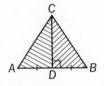

4. Given $\triangle ABC$:

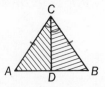

5. Given △*ABC*:

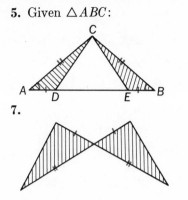

6.

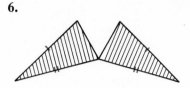

7.

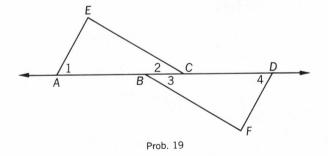

8. Given $\overleftrightarrow{AC}$ and $\overleftrightarrow{BD}$:

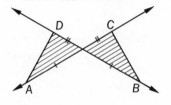

9.

10. Given △*ABC*:

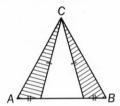

From the given information, which points, if any, are known to lie between two points? (11 to 18)

11. Given $\overrightarrow{CE}$ and $\overrightarrow{CA}$.

12. Given $\overrightarrow{DE}$ and $\overrightarrow{DA}$.

13. Given $\overrightarrow{BA}$ and $\overrightarrow{DE}$.

14. Given $\overrightarrow{BA}$ and $\overrightarrow{CE}$.

15. Given $\overrightarrow{CA}$ and $\overrightarrow{DE}$.

16. Given $\overrightarrow{CA}$ and $\overrightarrow{BE}$.

17. Given $\overrightarrow{DA}$ and $\overrightarrow{CE}$.

18. Given $\overrightarrow{DA}$ and $\overrightarrow{DC}$.

A   B   C   D   E

Probs. 11 to 18

Prob. 19

19. GIVEN: $\overleftrightarrow{AD}$; ∠1 ≅ ∠4; ∠2 ≅ ∠3, $\overline{AB}$ ≅ $\overline{CD}$.
  PROVE: △*ACE* ≅ △*DBF*.

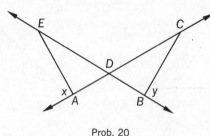

Prob. 20

20. GIVEN: $\overleftrightarrow{EB}$ and $\overleftrightarrow{AC}$; $\angle x \cong \angle y$, $\overline{AD} \cong \overline{DB}$.
PROVE: $\triangle ADE \cong \triangle BDC$.

21. GIVEN: $\overline{BD} \perp \overline{CF}$; $\overline{DF} \cong \overline{DA}$; $\angle m \cong \angle F$.
PROVE: $\triangle ACD \cong \triangle FBD$.

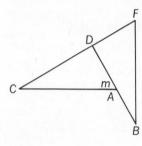

Prob. 21

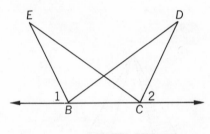

Prob. 22

22. GIVEN: $\overleftrightarrow{BC}$; $\angle 1 \cong \angle 2$; $\overline{BE} \cong \overline{CD}$.
PROVE: $\triangle BCE \cong \triangle CBD$.

23. GIVEN: $\overrightarrow{AC}$ bisects $\angle DAB$ and $\angle DCB$.
PROVE: $\triangle ACD \cong \triangle ACB$.

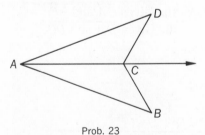

Prob. 23

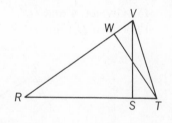

Prob. 24

24. GIVEN: $\overline{VS} \perp \overline{RT}$; $\overline{TW} \perp \overline{RV}$; $\overline{RW} \cong \overline{RS}$.
PROVE: $\triangle RSV \cong \triangle RWT$.

(B)

25. GIVEN: B is midpoint of $\overline{AC}$; $\angle 1 \cong \angle 2$; $\overline{BE} \cong \overline{BD}$.
PROVE: $\triangle ABD \cong \triangle CBE$.

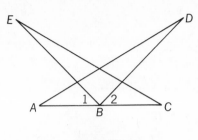
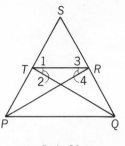

Prob. 25

Prob. 26

26. GIVEN: $\triangle PQS$; $\angle 1 \cong \angle 3$; $\angle 2 \cong \angle 4$.
PROVE: $\triangle PRS \cong \triangle QTS$.
27. GIVEN: $\triangle ABC \cong \triangle A'B'C'$; $\overline{BD}$ bisects $\overline{AC}$; $\overline{B'D'}$ bisects $\overline{A'C'}$.
PROVE: $\triangle ABD \cong \triangle A'B'D'$.
28. GIVEN: $\angle 1 \cong \angle 2$, $\overline{AE} \cong \overline{BC}$.
PROVE: $\triangle ACD \cong \triangle BED$.

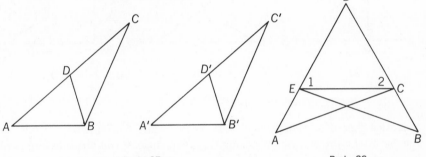

Prob. 27   Prob. 28

5–6 OTHER SEGMENTS

There are certain line segments, other than sides, associated with triangles, that are of concern to us.

Definition 5–12: A segment is a **median** of a triangle iff its endpoints are a vertex of the triangle and the midpoint of the opposite side.

Figure 5–15 illustrates two medians, $\overline{AE}$ and $\overline{BD}$, of $\triangle ABC$.

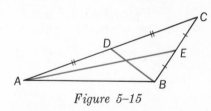

Figure 5–15

Definition 5–13: A segment is an **angle bisector of a triangle** iff it is a subset of the bisector of one of the angles of the triangle, and its endpoints are the vertex of the angle and the point of intersection of the angle bisector and the opposite side.

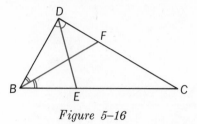

Figure 5-16

Figure 5-16 illustrates two angle bisectors, $\overline{BF}$ and $\overline{DE}$, of $\triangle BCD$.

Definition 5-14:   A segment is an **altitude** of a triangle iff it is a perpendicular from a vertex to the line containing the opposite side.

Figure 5-17 illustrates altitudes $\overline{CD}$, $\overline{FH}$, and $\overline{LJ}$ of the triangles.

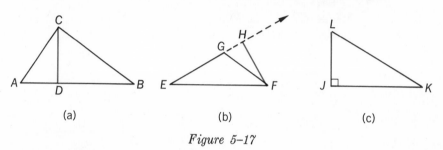

(a)   (b)   (c)

Figure 5-17

Notice that if a triangle is obtuse, as in Figure 5-17(b), an altitude need not lie in the interior of the triangle. Nevertheless, the altitude $\overline{FH}$ is perpendicular to the *line* containing the opposite side ($\overleftrightarrow{EG}$). Notice also that, in the case of a right triangle (c), the two legs are also altitudes, since each is a segment from a vertex, perpendicular to the opposite side.

The word *altitude* is also used for two other different, but related, concepts:

(1) The *line* containing an altitude is called "altitude."
(2) The *length* of an altitude is customarily referred to as an "altitude."

Thus, in Figure 5-18, $\overline{EF}$ and $\overleftrightarrow{EF}$ are each called an altitude. Further, if $EF = 5$, we say that the altitude from E is 5.

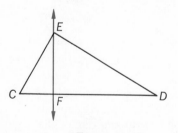

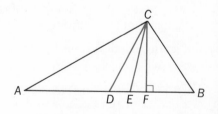

Figure 5-18   Figure 5-19

This multiple use of a word indicates the possibility of some misunderstanding. However, the context will generally indicate which meaning is intended.

Every triangle has three medians, three angle bisectors and three altitudes. In general, these nine segments are distinct (in Figure 5–19, median $\overline{CD}$, angle bisector $\overline{CE}$, altitude $\overline{CF}$), but it may happen in some cases that two or more coincide (see Chapter 6).

At this point we remind you that the definition of a congruence between triangles (Definition 5–2) requires that corresponding sides and corresponding angles be congruent. Many problems in which two segments, or two angles, are to be proved congruent, can be solved by first proving two triangles congruent. For example, from Figure 5–20, to prove $\overline{AC} \cong \overline{DB}$, we might first show $\triangle ADC \cong \triangle BCD$, or perhaps $\triangle ABD \cong \triangle BAC$. The important idea is that we choose two triangles of which $\overline{AC}$ and $\overline{DB}$ are corresponding parts.

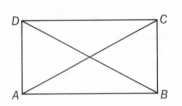

Figure 5–20

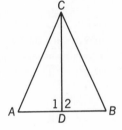

Figure 5–21

A rather common problem is that of proving two segments perpendicular, as $\overline{AB}$ and $\overline{CD}$ in Figure 5–21. This can sometimes be done by proving that the intersecting lines form congruent adjacent angles, such as $\angle 1$ and $\angle 2$ in Figure 5–21. The lines are then known to be perpendicular by Definition 3–18.

EXAMPLE

1. GIVEN: $\overline{AD} \cong \overline{BC}$; $\overline{AD} \perp \overline{DC}$;
   $\overline{BC} \perp \overline{CD}$.
   PROVE: $\overline{AC} \cong \overline{BD}$.

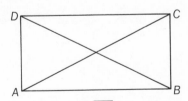

Analysis: $\overline{AC}$ is a side of $\triangle ADC$ and of $\triangle ABC$, and $\overline{BD}$ is a side of $\triangle ABD$ and $\triangle DCB$. We will select two triangles, such that $\overline{AC}$ and $\overline{BD}$ are corresponding sides, and try to prove the triangles congruent. $\overline{AC}$ and $\overline{BD}$ will then be congruent. Since we are given $\overline{AD}$ and $\overline{BC}$ perpendicular to $\overline{DC}$, thus forming congruent right angles at D and C, a reasonable choice would seem to be $\triangle ADC$ and $\triangle BCD$.

Proof

STATEMENTS	REASONS
1. $\overline{AD} \perp \overline{DC}$, $\overline{BC} \perp \overline{CD}$.	1. Given.
2. $\angle ADC$ is a right angle, $\angle BDC$ is a right angle.	2. Thm. 4–12.
3. $\angle ADC \cong \angle BCD$.	3. Thm. 4–2.
4. $\overline{DC} \cong \overline{DC}$.	4. Reflexive property of congruent segments (Thm. 5–1).
5. $\overline{AD} \cong \overline{BC}$.	5. Given.
6. $\triangle ADC \cong \triangle BCD$.	6. SAS Ax. (Ax. 5–2).
7. $\therefore \overline{AC} \cong \overline{BD}$.	7. Def. of congruence.

Exercise 5–6

(A)

1. GIVEN: $\overline{BD}$ bisects $\angle FBC$ and $\angle FDC$.
   PROVE: $\overline{BC} \cong \overline{BF}$.
2. GIVEN: Isosceles $\triangle RTS$; $\overline{TW}$ median to base.
   PROVE: $\overline{TW} \perp \overline{RS}$.

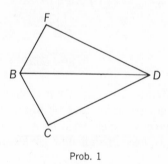

Prob. 1

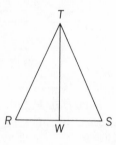

Prob. 2

3. GIVEN: $\overline{AC}$ and $\overline{DE}$ bisect each other at B.
   PROVE: $AE = CD$.

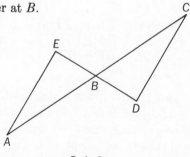

4. GIVEN: $\overline{JM} \cong \overline{KL}$; $\overline{JL} \cong \overline{KM}$.
   PROVE: $\angle MJK \cong \angle LKJ$.

Prob. 3

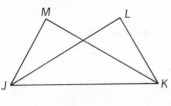

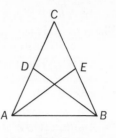

Prob. 4   Prob. 5

5. GIVEN: $\triangle ABC$; medians $\overline{AE}$ and $\overline{BD}$; $\overline{AC} \cong \overline{BC}$.
   PROVE: $\overline{AE} \cong \overline{BD}$.

6. GIVEN: $\triangle RST$; M, N, P midpoints of sides.
   PROVE: $\overline{PM} \cong \overline{NM}$.

7. GIVEN: $\triangle ABC$; $\overline{CB}$ bisects $\overline{DF}$; $\angle x \cong \angle y$.
   PROVE: $\overline{DF}$ bisects $\overline{CB}$.

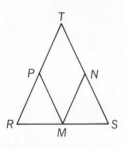

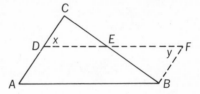

Prob. 6   Prob. 7

8. GIVEN: $\overline{PT} \cong \overline{QR}$; $\overline{PS} \cong \overline{QS}$.
   PROVE: $\angle P \cong \angle Q$.

9. GIVEN: $\triangle ABC \cong \triangle EFG$; $\overline{CD}$ bisects $\angle ACB$; $\overline{GH}$ bisects $\angle EGF$.
   PROVE: $\overline{CD} \cong \overline{GH}$.

10. GIVEN: $\triangle ABC \cong \triangle EFG$; $\overline{CD}$ and $\overline{GH}$ are medians.
   PROVE: $\overline{CD} \cong \overline{GH}$.

11. GIVEN: $\triangle ABC \cong \triangle EFG$; $\overline{CD}$ and $\overline{GH}$ are altitudes.
   PROVE: $\overline{CD} \cong \overline{GH}$.

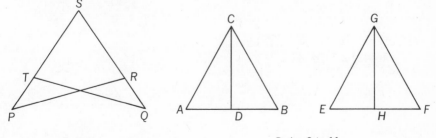

Prob. 8   Probs. 9 to 11

12. If $\triangle RST$ is equilateral, prove $\triangle RST \cong \triangle STR$.

13. PROVE: If the bisector of $\angle F$ in $\triangle DEF$ is perpendicular to the opposite side, then $\triangle DEF$ is isosceles.

14. PROVE: The median to the base of an isosceles triangle is also an altitude.

15. PROVE: The altitude to the base of an isosceles triangle is also a median.

16. PROVE: If the altitude to one side of a triangle is also a median, then the triangle is isosceles.

(B)

17. GIVEN: $\overline{RT} \perp \overline{PS}$; $\overline{RT}$ bisects $\overline{PS}$ at Q.
　　PROVE: $\triangle PTR \cong \triangle STR$.

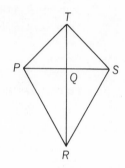

Prob. 17

18. GIVEN: $\triangle BDE$; $\overline{BE} \cong \overline{DE}$; $\overline{BF} \cong \overline{DF}$.
　　PROVE: $\overline{EC} \perp \overline{BD}$.

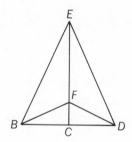

Prob. 18

19. GIVEN: $\overline{AC} \cong \overline{BC}$; $\overline{CD}$ bisects $\angle ACB$.
　　PROVE: $\angle 5 \cong \angle 6$.

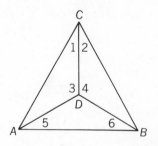

Prob. 19

20. GIVEN: $\angle 5 \cong \angle 6$; $\angle 3 \cong \angle 4$.
    PROVE: $\triangle ABC$ is isosceles.
21. GIVEN: $AD = DC$; $BA = BC$.
    PROVE: (a) $\overline{DB} \perp \overline{AC}$ and (b) $\overline{DB}$ bisects $\overline{AC}$.
22. GIVEN: $\overline{EC}$ and $\overline{AG}$ bisect each other at D; $D \in \overline{FB}$; $F \in \overline{EG}$; $B \in \overline{AC}$.
    PROVE: $\overline{BC} \cong \overline{FE}$.

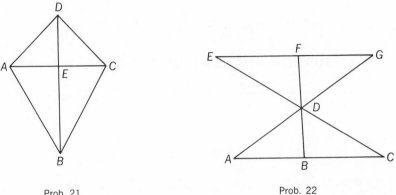

Prob. 21   Prob. 22

23. PROVE: The medians to the congruent sides of an isosceles triangle are congruent.
24. PROVE: If a point on the base of an isosceles triangle is equidistant from the midpoints of the congruent sides, the point bisects the base.
25. PROVE: If the angle bisectors of two adjacent angles form a 45° angle, the two adjacent angles are complementary.

Chapter 6

FURTHER ANATOMY OF PROOF

6-1 INDIRECT PROOF

Now that you have had the opportunity to write formal proofs, the structure of the deductive proof should be clearer. Starting with a given hypothesis, a chain of reasoning is established which leads to the desired conclusion. The deductive method is sometimes referred to as the *direct* method, as opposed to the *indirect* method, to be considered here.

A rigorous analysis of the indirect proof requires using the notation and principles of the study of logic. However, we will examine indirect proof somewhat less rigorously by studying examples. This method of proof is a very useful and powerful tool at all levels of mathematics, and you should become familiar with its principal features.

As a first example, consider the case of the misplaced photographs. Suppose we are certain that some photographs have been stored in one of three places: a desk drawer, an old trunk, or a safe-deposit box at a bank several miles from home. Since the bank is some distance away, we might be reluctant to check the safe-deposit box directly, so we proceed as follows. First, the desk drawer is opened and examined; the photographs are not there. Second, the trunk is opened and found to be empty. What conclusion can be reached? The photographs must be in the safe-deposit box!

The basic characteristics illustrated above are:

(1) We must know, and be able to state, all the alternative possibilities.

(2) The possibilities must be such that *exactly* one of them is true: that is, one of them must be true, but two or more cannot be simultaneously true.

(3) In some manner we must be able to show that all but one of the possibilities are false, and thus be able to conclude that the remaining possibility is true.

Statement (3) above raises the question "How do you prove that an assertion is *false?*" One answer is this procedure:

   I. Assume that the alternative to be tested is true.
  II. On the basis of this assumption show that a valid chain of reasoning
      leads to a conclusion that contradicts some previous theorem, axiom,
      definition, or the hypothesis.

To illustrate, let us examine in detail the reasoning of the example of the
missing photographs:

  1. The alternative possibilities are:
    (a) The photographs are in the drawer.
    (b) The photographs are in the trunk.
    (c) The photographs are in the safe-deposit box.
  2. We are certain that the photographs must be in *exactly one* of the three
    distinct locations.
  3. To show that two of the three alternatives are false:
    (a) Assume that it is true that the photographs are in the drawer.
       We state a theorem: "If we open the drawer, then we must find
       the photographs." We open the drawer, and do not find them.
       This contradicts the theorem.
    (b) Assume that the photographs are in the trunk. Theorem: "If the
       photographs are in the trunk, then we shall find them when the
       trunk is opened." The trunk is opened, and is empty. Again, the
       theorem is contradicted.

Since each of the first two alternative possibilities leads to a contradiction,
both are now known to be false; we conclude that the only remaining alternative—they are at the bank—is true.

Two thoughts may occur to the reader: What if you cannot reach a con-
tradiction? and How do you know which alternative to select for testing?
If you cannot reach a contradiction, you have no proof—perhaps you have
chosen the alternative that is actually true. Not reaching a contradiction,
however, does not allow you to conclude that the chosen alternative is true.
For instance, suppose I wish to prove that it rained during the night. I state:
"Either it rained, or it did not rain." Assume the first alternative is true.
Then, if I go outdoors before daylight, I should find a wet street. I go outdoors, and the street is wet. No contradiction has been reached, hence nothing
has been proven. I cannot conclude it rained—possibly a watering truck has
just gone by, wetting the street! If you do not arrive at a contradiction,
start over again with another alternative.

There is no unique answer to the question of which alternative to select
for testing. Often the problem on which we are working will offer some indi-
cation as to which alternative we should try to prove true, and we would
accordingly start with the *other* possibilities. Suppose it is desired to prove

that two numbers are equal, using an indirect method. The Trichotomy Axiom (Axiom O–1) tells us that for two numbers, a and b, either $a = b$, $a > b$, or $a < b$. We should show that each of the alternatives involving "greater than" and "less than" is false, and thus conclude that $a = b$ is true.

A special case that occurs frequently is the situation in which there are exactly two alternatives, and they are negations of each other. These two alternatives are the conclusion of an assertion, and the negation of that conclusion. Examples of such conclusions, and their negations, are:

(1) Two angles are congruent, or they are not congruent.

(2) A point is the midpoint of a segment, or it is not the midpoint.

(3) Two line segments do not have the same length, or they have the same length.

(4) Two lines are perpendicular, or they are not perpendicular.

As an illustration of such a special case, consider the assertion, "If no two angles of a triangle are congruent, then no two sides of the triangle are congruent."

Proof (Indirect): Either no two sides of the triangle are congruent, or two sides of the triangle are congruent. (These are the two alternatives.) Assume that "two of the sides are congruent." It follows, by Theorem 5–12, that the two angles opposite these sides are congruent. This contradicts the hypothesis that *no* two angles of the triangle are congruent. Therefore, it is false that "two of the sides are congruent," hence we conclude that no two of the sides are congruent.

EXAMPLES

1. Prove by an indirect method that if two angles are not congruent, then they are not both right angles.

Proof: The two angles are right angles, or they are not right angles. Assume they are right angles. Then, by Theorem 4–2, they are congruent. This contradicts the hypothesis which states the angles are not congruent. We conclude the two angles are not both right angles.

2. Prove by an indirect method that the bisector of any angle of a scalene triangle is not perpendicular to the opposite side.

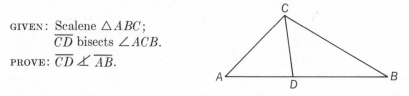

GIVEN: Scalene $\triangle ABC$;
      $\overline{CD}$ bisects $\angle ACB$.
PROVE: $\overline{CD} \not\perp \overline{AB}$.

(*Note:* It suffices to consider just one of the angles, say $\angle C$. Since we know just as much about each of the other angles as we do about $\angle C$, the reasoning that we apply to $\angle C$ will apply to each of the other angles as well.)

Proof: Either $\overline{CD} \perp \overline{AB}$, or $\overline{CD} \not\perp \overline{AB}$. Assume $\overline{CD} \perp \overline{AB}$. Then $\angle ADC$ and $\angle BDC$ are right angles, and are therefore congruent. Since $\overline{CD}$ is the angle bisector, $\angle ACD \cong \angle BCD$. Further, $\overline{CD} \cong \overline{CD}$. Hence $\triangle ADC \cong \triangle BDC$, and it follows that $\overline{CA} \cong \overline{CB}$. This contradicts the hypothesis that $\triangle ABC$ is scalene (no two sides congruent). Hence we conclude that $\overline{CD} \not\perp \overline{AB}$.

Exercise 6–1

Assume that each statement (1 to 4) below is to be proved by an indirect method. In each case, state the alternative possibilities. (Do not try to prove.)

(A)

1. $\sqrt{3}$ is not a rational number.
2. If no two angles of a triangle are congruent, the triangle is not equilateral.
3. If two lines intersect to form a pair of acute vertical angles, the lines are not perpendicular.
4. If a number is even, then its square is even.

In each of the following (5 to 8), what can you conclude from the given information?

5. $\angle R \not> \angle S$ and $\angle R \neq \angle S$.
6. Either $\overline{AB} \perp \overline{CD}$ or $\overline{AB} \not\perp \overline{CD}$. $m\angle BPC = 89$.

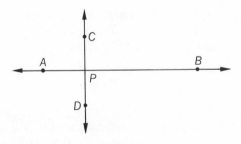

Prob. 6

7. Either $\overline{AC} \cong \overline{BC}$ or $\overline{AC} \not\cong \overline{BC}$. $m\angle A = 40$ and $m\angle B = 41$.
8. Either A, B, and C are collinear, or A, B, and C are not collinear. $m\angle CBP = 34$, $m\angle ABP = 145$.

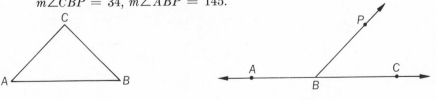

Prob. 7   Prob. 8

Prove each of the following (9 to 13) by an indirect method.

9. If two angles are not congruent, they are not both straight angles.

10. If two lines contain more than one point in common, they are not different lines.

11. If two angles are not congruent, they are not vertical.

12. If two lines intersect to form a pair of acute vertical angles, the lines are not perpendicular.

13. If no two sides of a triangle are congruent, no two of its angles are congruent.

(B)

14. GIVEN: $\overline{AC} \not\cong \overline{BC}, \overline{CM} \perp \overline{AB}$.
     PROVE: M is not the midpoint of $\overline{AB}$.

15. GIVEN: $\overline{AC} \cong \overline{AB}, \overline{CP} \not\cong \overline{PB}$.
     PROVE: $\overrightarrow{AP}$ is not the bisector of $\angle CAB$.

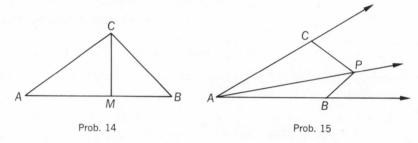

Prob. 14   Prob. 15

16. PROVE: A scalene triangle cannot have two congruent angles.

17. PROVE: The median to a side of a scalene triangle cannot be the altitude to that side.

6–2 PERPENDICULARS

Consider $\overleftrightarrow{AB}$ and P a given point contained in $\overleftrightarrow{AB}$ (Figure 6–1). With P as vertex we could construct (with a protractor) a right angle, $\angle BPC$. It follows that $\overleftrightarrow{PC}$, the line containing $\overrightarrow{PC}$, is perpendicular to $\overleftrightarrow{AB}$. Thus it appears possible to construct a line perpendicular to a given line at a given point on the given line. Two questions arise:

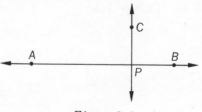

Figure 6–1

(1) Can this always be accomplished—that is, is there always a line perpendicular to a given line at a given point on the line?

(2) Is it possible, perhaps by use of some other method, to obtain another line, distinct from the first, perpendicular to the same given line at the same point?

The following theorem provides the answers:

Theorem 6–1: In a plane, through a given point on a given line, there is one and only one line perpendicular to the given line.

Note particularly the phrase "one and only one." This phrase is used in mathematics to imply *two* assertions. For Theorem 6–1, these are:

(1) An assertion that at least one perpendicular line **exists**—there **is** one line perpendicular to the given line at the given point.

(2) An assertion that the existing line referred to in (1) above is the **only** such line. The word *unique* is used to describe the property of being the *only one*.

Existence Proof (*Theorem 6–1*)

GIVEN: $\overleftrightarrow{AB}$; $P \in \overleftrightarrow{AB}$.
PROVE: There exists a line q, through P, such that $q \perp \overleftrightarrow{AB}$.

Proof: Two lines are perpendicular iff they intersect to form a right angle, that is, an angle of measure 90. The Angle Construction Axiom tells us that there exists a ray $(\overrightarrow{PC})$ such that $m\angle BPC = 90$. Therefore, the line q determined by $\overrightarrow{PC}$ is perpendicular to $\overleftrightarrow{AB}$.

Uniqueness Proof (*Theorem 6–1*)

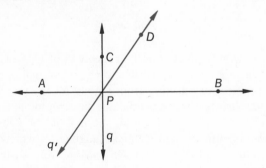

GIVEN: $q \perp \overleftrightarrow{AB}$ at P, where $P \in \overleftrightarrow{AB}$.
PROVE: q is the only line through P such that $q \perp \overleftrightarrow{AB}$.

Proof: The proof is indirect. Either there is only one line through P and perpendicular to $\overleftrightarrow{AB}$, or there is more than one. Assume that there is more than one; that is, assume that there exists another line through P (call it q'), also perpendicular to $\overleftrightarrow{AB}$. By the definition of perpendicular lines, $m\angle BPD = 90$, and $m\angle BPC = 90$. Now, $\overrightarrow{PC}$ and $\overrightarrow{PD}$ lie in the same half-plane, and both have the same endpoint. The Angle Construction Axiom states that there is exactly *one* ray in a half-plane corresponding to a given number between 0 and 180. Thus a contradiction of an axiom is reached; we cannot have "exactly one ray" as well as "two rays" from the same point P, corresponding to 90. The assumption that a second perpendicular line exists was false, and therefore q is the only line perpendicular to $\overleftrightarrow{AB}$ at the given point.

Definition 6–1: In a plane, a line is the **perpendicular bisector** of a segment iff it is perpendicular to the segment and contains the midpoint of the segment.

A line segment has one and only one midpoint, and, in a plane, there is one and only one perpendicular to a given line at a given point on the line. It is clear, then, that, in a plane, a line segment has one and only one perpendicular bisector; that is, the perpendicular bisector of a line segment in a plane exists and is unique.

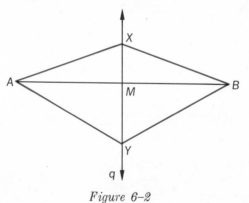

Figure 6–2

You will recall that a plane may be conceived of as a set of points. The geometric entities in a plane are subsets of the set of points of a plane. Consider now the problem of selecting from among all the points in a plane the subset of points that is the perpendicular bisector of a line segment. In Figure 6–2, $\overline{AB}$ has midpoint M, and line q is its perpendicular bisector. Since M is the midpoint, in nontechnical language it can be said that M is "just as far from A as it is from B." More rigorously stated: "M is **equidistant** from A and B"; that is, $AM = MB$. Consider now any two points, say X and Y, on line q. Examination suggests that X and Y are also equidistant from A and B; that is, $AX = BX$ and $AY = BY$. We are led to the surmise that perhaps every point on line q shares this "equidistant" property.

Theorem 6–2: **In a plane, a line is the perpendicular bisector of a segment iff it is the set of all points equidistant from the endpoints of the segment.**

DISCUSSION: The theorem refers to two sets of points:

(1) The set of points equidistant from the endpoints of a segment.
(2) The set of points that is the perpendicular bisector of a segment.

A proof of the theorem requires that we show that these two sets are equal, that is, that they are one and the same set. To prove two sets equal (see Definition 2–2) we must show that all the elements of set (1) are members of set (2), and conversely that all the elements of set (2) are members of set (1). Thus we must prove Theorem 6–2 as *two* assertions:

(1) If a point is contained in the perpendicular bisector of a segment, it is equidistant from the endpoints of the segment.

(2) If a point is equidistant from the endpoints of a segment, it is contained in the perpendicular bisector of the segment.

Proof of Assertion (1), Theorem 6–2

GIVEN: $q \perp \overline{AB}$; q bisects $\overline{AB}$ at M; X any point on q.
PROVE: $XA = XB$.

Case I: X is on $\overline{AB}$:

Proof: If X is on $\overline{AB}$, then it coincides with M, the midpoint, and $XA = XB$ at once, by definition of midpoint.

Case II: X is not on $\overline{AB}$:

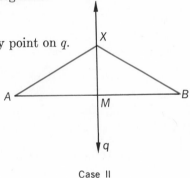

Case II

Proof

STATEMENTS	REASONS
1. $q \perp \overline{AB}$.	1. Given.
2. $\angle AMX$ and $\angle BMX$ are right angles.	2. Thm. 4–12.
3. $\angle AMX \cong \angle BMX$.	3. Thm. 4–2.
4. M the midpoint of $\overline{AB}$.	4. Given.
5. $AM = MB$.	5. Def. of midpoint of segment.
6. $\overline{AM} \cong \overline{MB}$.	6. Def. of congruent segments.
7. $\overline{XM} \cong \overline{XM}$.	7. Reflexive property of congruent segments (Thm. 5–1).
8. $\triangle AMX \cong \triangle BMX$.	8. SAS Ax. (5–2).
9. $\overline{XA} \cong \overline{XB}$.	9. Def. of congruence.
10. $XA = XB$.	10. Def. of congruent segments.

Proof of Assertion (2), Theorem 6-2

GIVEN: $q \perp \overline{AB}$; M the midpoint of $\overline{AB}$; X any point in the plane such that $XA = XB$.

PROVE: X is contained in q.

Case I: X is on $\overline{AB}$:

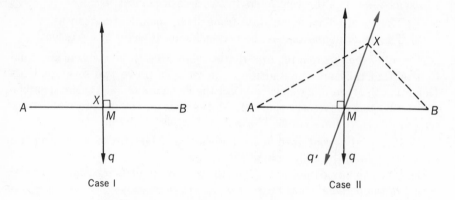

Case I   Case II

Proof: If X is contained in $\overline{AB}$ and is equidistant from A and B, then (by uniqueness of the midpoint of a segment) X coincides with M. Since M is contained in q, X is contained in q.

Case II: X is not on $\overline{AB}$.

Proof

STATEMENTS	REASONS
1. X any point in the plane ($XA = XB$), and M the midpoint of $\overline{AB}$.	1. Given.
2. Introduce $\overleftrightarrow{XM}$, name it q'.	2. Ax. 2–3.
3. $\overline{XA} \cong \overline{XB}$.	3. Def. of congruent segments.
4. $\overline{XM} \cong \overline{XM}$.	4. Reflexive property of congruent segments (Thm. 5–1).
5. $AM = MB$.	5. Def. of midpoint.
6. $\overline{AM} \cong \overline{MB}$.	6. Def. of congruent segments.
7. $\triangle AMX \cong \triangle BMX$.	7. SSS Ax. (5–4).
8. $\angle AMX \cong \angle BMX$.	8. Def. of congruence.
9. $q' \perp \overline{AB}$.	9. Def. of perpendicular lines.
10. q' coincides with q.	10. Uniqueness of perpendicular to a line (Thm. 6–1).

Corollary 6–2.1: In a plane, if two points are each equidistant from the endpoints of a segment, then the line determined by the two points is the perpendicular bisector of the segment.

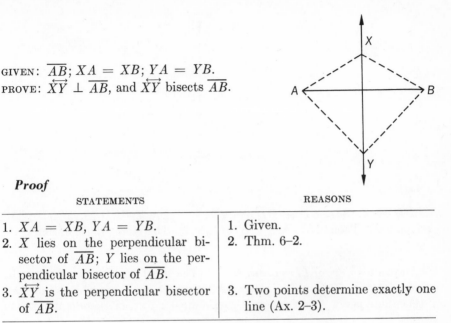

GIVEN: $\overline{AB}$; $XA = XB$; $YA = YB$.
PROVE: $\overleftrightarrow{XY} \perp \overline{AB}$, and $\overleftrightarrow{XY}$ bisects $\overline{AB}$.

Proof

STATEMENTS	REASONS
1. $XA = XB$, $YA = YB$.	1. Given.
2. X lies on the perpendicular bisector of $\overline{AB}$; Y lies on the perpendicular bisector of $\overline{AB}$.	2. Thm. 6-2.
3. $\overleftrightarrow{XY}$ is the perpendicular bisector of $\overline{AB}$.	3. Two points determine exactly one line (Ax. 2-3).

Corollary 6-2.1 is useful in that it enables us to prove that one line is the perpendicular bisector of another without having to prove two triangles congruent. Note that the conclusion of the corollary asserts two properties: **perpendicularity** to and **bisection** of a segment. The corollary may be used for either of these properties separately or for both at the same time. Thus, as in the figure for the proof, $\overleftrightarrow{XY} \perp \overline{AB}$ may sometimes be all that is required. On the other hand, proof that $\overleftrightarrow{XY}$ bisects $\overline{AB}$ may be all that is needed. This corollary should come to mind as a possible tool whenever perpendicularity, or bisection, or both, are required in a proof.

Theorem 6-1 establishes that, in a plane, a unique line exists perpendicular to a given line through a given point on the line. A similar assertion applies to the situation where the given point is *not* on the given line:

Theorem 6-3: In a plane, through a given point not on a given line, there is one and only one line perpendicular to the given line.

As in Theorem 6-1, Theorem 6-3 makes two assertions—the existence and the uniqueness of the perpendicular line.

Existence Proof (*Theorem 6-3*): Let q be the given line, and P a point not on q. Let A and B be any two points on q. Introduce $\overrightarrow{BP}$. Let r be the measure of $\angle ABP$. In the half-plane not including P (that is, on the side of q opposite P), introduce $\overrightarrow{BC}$ so that $m\angle ABC = r$ (by Angle Construction Axiom, 3-8). On $\overrightarrow{BC}$ choose S so that $BP = BS$, and hence $\overline{BP} \cong \overline{BS}$ (Axiom 2-4). Introduce $\overleftrightarrow{PS}$ intersecting q at D. Now, since $\overline{BP} \cong \overline{BS}$,

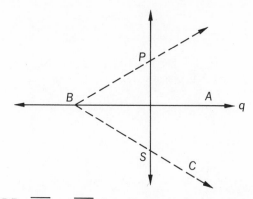

$\angle PBD \cong \angle SBD$; $\overline{BD} \cong \overline{BD}$ (why?); we have $\triangle PBD \cong \triangle SBD$ (SAS Axiom, 5–2). Then $\angle BDP \cong \angle BDS$ (why?). Therefore, by Definition 3–18, $\overleftrightarrow{PS} \perp q$.

Uniqueness Proof (*Theorem 6–3*): The proof is indirect. (Do not be misled by the drawing—it attempts to depict an impossible situation!) Either there is one line through P perpendicular to q, or there is more than one.

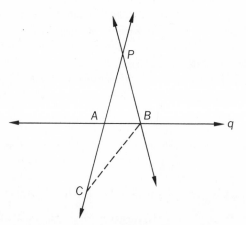

Assume that there is more than one line through P perpendicular to q—say $\overleftrightarrow{PA} \perp q$ and $\overleftrightarrow{PB} \perp q$ $(A \neq B)$. Choose C on the ray opposite to $\overrightarrow{AP}$ so that $AP = AC$, and hence $\overline{AP} \cong \overline{AC}$ (Axiom 2–4). Now, $\overline{AP} \cong \overline{AC}$; $\overline{AB} \cong \overline{AB}$; and $\angle PAB \cong \angle CAB$ (since they are both right angles). Therefore $\triangle CAB \cong \triangle PAB$ (SAS Axiom 5–2), and so $\angle CBA \cong \angle PBA$. But $\angle PBA$ is a right angle; thus $\angle CBA$ is a right angle, and so $\overleftrightarrow{CB} \perp q$ at B. But $\overleftrightarrow{PB} \perp q$ at B. This contradicts Theorem 6–1, which states that there is only one line perpendicular to a given line at a given point on the line. Hence our assumption that there is more than one line perpendicular to q through P is false; the theorem is proved.

As an immediate consequence of Theorem 6–3 we have:

Theorem 6–4: **No triangle has more than one right angle.**

Proof (Indirect): In $\triangle PAB$, assume $\angle PAB$ and $\angle PBA$ are both right angles. Then $\overline{PB} \perp \overline{AB}$ and $\overline{PA} \perp \overline{AB}$. There are now two lines through P perpendicular to the same line. This contradicts Theorem 6–3; hence the assumption of more than one right angle is false, and the theorem is proved.

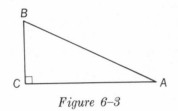

Definition 6–2: A triangle is a **right triangle** if one of its angles is a right angle. The sides which include the right angle are called the **legs,** and the side opposite the right angle is called the **hypotenuse.**

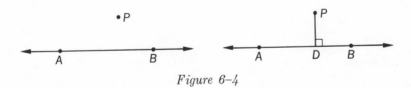

Figure 6–3

In Figure 6–3, $\angle ACB$ is the right angle (Theorem 6–4 assures that it is the only one), $\overline{BC}$ and $\overline{AC}$ are the legs, and $\overline{AB}$ is the hypotenuse.

A final note on language. For the situation pictured in Figure 6–4, it is customary to say: "Drop a perpendicular from P to AB." The point of intersection, D, is usually called the "foot" of the perpendicular.

Figure 6–4

EXAMPLES

1. If $\overline{AB} \perp \overline{BC}$, $\overline{BE} \perp \overline{AC}$, name three right triangles in the figure. Name the legs and hypotenuse of each.

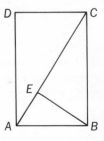

Solution

(a) $\triangle ABC$. Legs: $\overline{AB}$, $\overline{BC}$. Hypotenuse: $\overline{AC}$.

(b) $\triangle ABE$. Legs: $\overline{AE}$, $\overline{BE}$. Hypotenuse: $\overline{AB}$.

(c) $\triangle BEC$. Legs: $\overline{BE}$, $\overline{EC}$. Hypotenuse: $\overline{BC}$.

2. (a) From the figure, why can we say that $\overleftrightarrow{AB}$ is perpendicular to, and bisects, $\overline{CD}$?

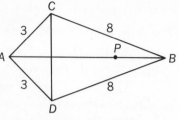

(b) Why can we say that P is just as far from C as it is from D?

Solution

(a) Since $AC = AD = 3$ and $CB = DB = 8$, A and B are equidistant from the endpoints of $\overline{CD}$. Hence, by Corollary 6–2.1, the line through A and B is the perpendicular bisector of $\overline{CD}$.

(b) Since $P \in AB$, P must be equidistant from C and D. Theorem 6–2 implies that any point on the perpendicular bisector of a segment is equidistant from the endpoints of the segment.

3. Prove, without using congruence of triangles: The median to a side of an equilateral triangle is also the altitude to the side.

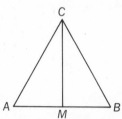

GIVEN: Equilateral $\triangle ABC$, median $\overline{CM}$.
PROVE: $\overline{CM}$ is the altitude to $\overline{AB}$.

Analysis: We could prove that $\overline{CM}$ is the altitude to $\overline{AB}$ if we could show that $\overline{CM} \perp \overline{AB}$. Since the desired altitude would also be a median, it would bisect $\overline{AB}$. In that case, $\overline{CM}$ would be the perpendicular bisector of $\overline{AB}$, which suggests Corollary 6–2.1. We must look for two points, each equidistant from A and B. Midpoint M is certainly one of them. But the sides of an equilateral triangle are congruent—in particular, $\overline{CA} \cong \overline{CB}$, so $CA = CB$. Hence C is a second point, and we are ready to write a proof.

Proof

STATEMENTS	REASONS
1. $\triangle ABC$ is equilateral.	1. Given.
2. $\overline{AC} \cong \overline{CB}$.	2. Def. of equilateral triangle.
3. $AC = CB$.	3. Def. of congruent segments.
4. $\overline{CM}$ the median to $\overline{AB}$.	4. Given.
5. M the midpoint of $\overline{AB}$.	5. Def. of median.
6. $AM = MB$.	6. Def. of midpoint.
7. $\overleftrightarrow{CM}$ is the perpendicular bisector of $\overline{AB}$.	7. Corollary 6–2.1 (steps 3 and 6).
8. $\overline{CM}$ is the altitude to $\overline{AB}$.	8. Def. of altitude.

Exercise 6–2

(**A**)

1. (a) If $\overleftrightarrow{CD} \perp \overline{AB}$, name two right triangles.

(b) Name the hypotenuse and legs of each of the right triangles of part (a).

2. If $\overline{CD} \perp \overline{AB}$ and $\overline{AC} \perp \overline{CB}$, name three right triangles. Name the legs and hypotenuse of each.

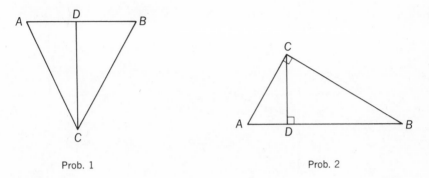

Prob. 1   Prob. 2

3. Consider the statement: "If George is President of the United States, then there can be no other President." Is this an *existence* or a *uniqueness* statement? On the basis of this statement alone, can you conclude that there is a President of the United States?

4. Consider the statement: "There is a citizen of France living in Outer Mongolia." Is this an *existence* or a *uniqueness* statement? On the basis of this statement alone, can you conclude that there are, or are not, any other citizens of France living in Outer Mongolia?

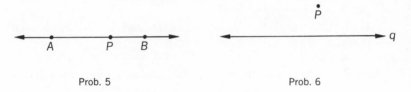

Prob. 5   Prob. 6

5. Given $\overleftrightarrow{AB}$ containing point P, use a protractor to draw q through P, so that $q \perp \overleftrightarrow{AB}$ (see Thm. 6–1).

6. Use the method suggested by the Existence Proof for Thm. 6–3 to construct a line through P perpendicular to q. (Use a ruler and protractor where needed.)

7. Given P the midpoint of $\overline{AC}$, P the midpoint of $\overline{BD}$, $\overline{AC} \perp \overline{BD}$, and $AB = 12$, find BC, CD, and DA.

8. In the figure, $\overline{AB} \cong \overline{BC} \cong \overline{CD} \cong \overline{DA}$; $AC = 16$; $DB = 9$. Find DP, PB, AP, and PC. (*Hint:* Use Corollary 6–2.1.)

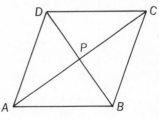

Probs. 7, 8

9. In the figure, q is the perpendicular bisector of $\overline{AB}$. Find the lengths x, y, and z.

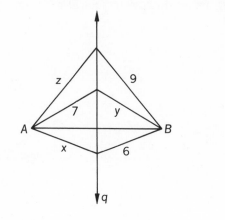

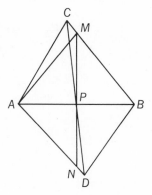

Prob. 9

Probs. 11 to 13

10. State a theorem to justify this assertion: "Each vertex of an equilateral triangle lies on the perpendicular bisector of the side opposite that vertex."

11. If $AM = MB$ and P is the midpoint of $\overline{AB}$, which segment is the perpendicular bisector of $\overline{AB}$?

12. Which distances would have to be equal if $\overline{CD}$ were to be the perpendicular bisector of $\overline{AB}$?

13. If A were equidistant from C and D, and B were equidistant from C and D, what relationship would exist between $\overline{AB}$ and $\overline{CD}$?

For problems 14 to 17 write formal proofs. Do not use congruence of triangles.

14. GIVEN: $\overleftrightarrow{CD}$ bisects $\overline{AB}$, $\overline{CD} \perp \overline{AB}$.
   PROVE: $\triangle ABC$ is isosceles.

15. GIVEN: $\triangle ADC$ is equilateral, $\triangle BCD$ is isosceles with base $\overline{CD}$.
   PROVE: $\overline{AB} \perp \overline{CD}$, $\overline{AB}$ bisects $\overline{CD}$.

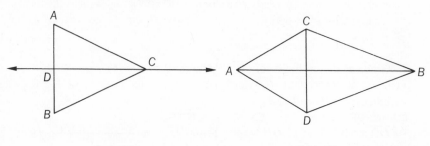

Prob. 14   Prob. 15

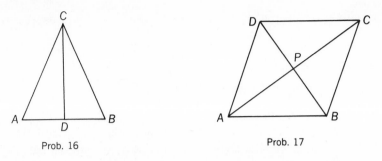

Prob. 16   Prob. 17

16. GIVEN: Isosceles $\triangle ABC$ with base $\overline{AB}$, median $\overline{CD}$ to $\overline{AB}$.
    PROVE: $\overline{CD} \perp \overline{AB}$.
17. GIVEN: $\overline{AB} \cong \overline{CD} \cong \overline{DA} \cong \overline{AB}$.
    PROVE: $\overline{DB}$ bisects $\overline{AC}$ and $\overline{AC}$ bisects $\overline{DB}$.

For problems 18 to 25 write formal proofs. Try not to use congruent triangles.

18. PROVE: The angles opposite the legs of a right triangle are not right
            angles.
19. PROVE: If the perpendicular bisector of a side of a triangle passes
            through the opposite vertex, the triangle is isosceles.
20. GIVEN: Median $\overline{CD}$, $\overline{CD} \perp \overline{AB}$.
    PROVE: $\triangle ABC$ is isosceles.

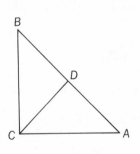

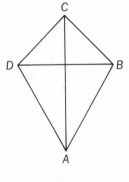

Prob. 20   Prob. 24

(B)

21. The perpendicular bisector of side $\overline{AB}$ of $\triangle ABC$ intersects $\overline{BC}$ at E.
    Prove that $\overline{AE} \cong \overline{BE}$.
22. PROVE: The point of intersection of the perpendicular bisectors of two
            sides of a triangle is equidistant from the three vertices.
23. PROVE: If three isosceles triangles have the same base, their vertices
            are collinear.
24. GIVEN: $\overline{AC}$ bisects $\angle DCB$ and $\angle DAB$.
    PROVE: $\overline{AC} \perp \overline{DB}$ and $\overline{AC}$ bisects $\overline{DB}$. (*Note:* Congruence of triangles
            needed.)

25. PROVE: The perpendicular bisector of the base of an isosceles triangle passes through the vertex.

6–3 AUXILIARY SETS

The alert reader will have noticed—for example, in the proof of Theorem 6–3 —such statements as: "Let A and B be any two points on q," and "Introduce $\overrightarrow{BP}$." These statements illustrate the technique of introducing auxiliary sets (sets that were not actually *given* in a problem at the start) into a proof, as an assistance in completing the proof. Mathematicians find this technique indispensable, but care must be taken to observe limitations on its use.

Any theorem, axiom, or definition that asserts the existence of a set of points suggests an auxiliary set that may be introduced into a proof. Below is a brief list of some of these sets. Others will come later as new theorems, axioms, and definitions are introduced.

(1) Given any line, we may name any two points on the line—say P and Q —and then name the line $\overleftrightarrow{PQ}$. Axiom 2–2 implies the existence of an infinite number of points on any line.

(2) Given any two points, say A and B, we may talk about $\overleftrightarrow{AB}$ (and draw a representation of $\overleftrightarrow{AB}$ into a diagram) at will (Axiom 2–3).

(3) Given a line q and any point P on the line, or not on the line q, a line perpendicular to q and passing through P may be introduced (Theorems 6–1 and 6–3).

(4) Given a segment, a line that is the perpendicular bisector of the segment may be introduced (Definition 6–1).

(5) Given any angle, a ray which is its bisector may be introduced (Axiom 5–1).

(6) Given any angle, say $\angle A$, another angle with the same measure as $\angle A$ may be introduced (Angle Construction Axiom).

(7) Given any segment $\overline{AB}$, another segment with the same measure as $\overline{AB}$ may be introduced (Point-Plotting Axiom, 2–4).

(8) Given a ray, another ray with the same endpoint, opposite to the given ray, may be introduced.

There are, as mentioned above, limitations on the use of auxiliary sets. Basically, one must be certain that the set to be introduced really does exist. Some help in clarifying this point may be had by a study of the following:

(1) Given $\overline{AB}$, midpoint M, and P not on $\overline{AB}$. Introduce the line through P that shall also be the perpendicular bisector of $\overline{AB}$. An examination of the figure suggests the impossibility of this. The perpendicular bisector of a segment exists;

a perpendicular through P to $\overline{AB}$ also exists, but these two sets are not necessarily the *same* set.

(2) Given $\triangle ABC$. Introduce the bisector of $\angle ACB$ that is also the altitude to $\overline{AB}$. Again, the bisector of $\angle ACB$ exists, and the altitude to $\overline{AB}$ exists, but they are not, in general, the same set.

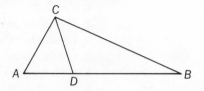

(3) The same remarks as in (2), but requiring a *median* to $\overline{AB}$ rather than an altitude. The median and the angle bisector from the same vertex of a triangle are not generally the same set.

(4) In the figure, introduce $\overline{CD}$ the perpendicular bisector of $\overline{AB}$. Again examination of the figure indicates the impossibility of this, although $\overline{CD}$ itself certainly exists.

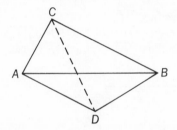

To sum up, any set known to exist may be introduced as an auxiliary set; combinations of two or more sets must be used with caution—only when such combinations are justifiable. In statement (2) above, if $\triangle ABC$ were isosceles, then the bisector of $\angle ACB$ would be the altitude to $\overline{AB}$ as well.

It is not hard to know which auxiliary sets may be introduced; the question of *when* to introduce them is much more difficult to answer. Experience gained by solving many problems is probably the most practical way to learn when to use auxiliary sets.

EXAMPLE

GIVEN: Figure $ADBC$; $\overline{BC} \cong \overline{AC}$; $\overline{DA} \cong \overline{DB}$.
PROVE: $\angle A \cong \angle B$.

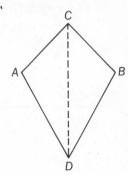

Analysis: How can we prove two angles congruent? One answer is to show that they are corresponding parts of congruent triangles. But this requires a *pair* of triangles—which we do not have at the start. We observe that if the auxiliary set $\overline{CD}$ were introduced, two triangles would be formed; we will then try to prove the two triangles congruent.

Proof

STATEMENTS	REASONS
1. Introduce $\overline{CD}$.	1. Ax. 2–3.
2. $\overline{CD} \cong \overline{CD}$.	2. Reflexive property of congruent segments (Thm. 5–1).
3. $\overline{BC} \cong \overline{AC}$, $\overline{DA} \cong \overline{DB}$.	3. Given.
4. $\triangle ACD \cong \triangle BCD$.	4. SSS Ax. (5–4).
5. $\angle CAD \cong \angle CBD$.	5. Def. of congruence.

Exercise 6–3

In the following (1 to 8), state whether the suggested auxiliary set may or may not be introduced, and state why.

(A)

1. In the figure, introduce $\overline{AC}$.
2. In the figure, introduce $\overline{DP}$ so that $\overline{DP} \perp \overline{AB}$.
3. In the figure, introduce $\overline{DB}$ so that $\overline{DB}$ bisects $\angle B$.

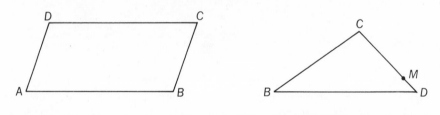

Probs. 1 to 3   Probs. 4, 5

4. In the figure, introduce $\overline{BM}$ so that $\overline{BM}$ bisects $\angle B$.
5. In the figure, introduce altitude $\overline{CH}$.
6. In the figure, introduce median $\overline{AC}$ so that $\overline{AC}$ bisects $\angle A$.

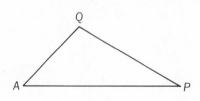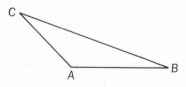

Prob. 6   Probs. 7, 8

7. In the figure, introduce altitude $\overline{CH}$.
8. In the figure, introduce $\overrightarrow{AD}$ to bisect $\angle A$ so that $\overrightarrow{AD}$ bisects $\overline{CB}$.

9. There are two particular auxiliary sets that may be introduced which will divide the figure into a pair of triangles.
   (a) Name the two auxiliary sets.
   (b) Which set would you choose if you wished to prove the two triangles congruent?
10. Using the information as given in the diagram, prove $\angle D \cong \angle B$.

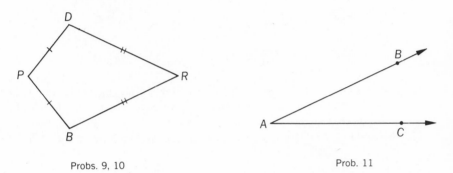

Probs. 9, 10   Prob. 11

11. Copy the diagram as closely as you can, using a ruler. With A as endpoint, introduce $\overrightarrow{AP}$ opposite to $\overrightarrow{AB}$. Introduce $\overrightarrow{AQ}$ opposite to $\overrightarrow{AC}$.
12. In the diagram resulting from problem 11, measure AB and AC. On $\overrightarrow{AP}$ locate D so that $AD = AB$. On $\overrightarrow{AQ}$, locate E so that $AE = AC$. Draw $\overline{DE}$. Prove $\triangle ABC \cong \triangle ADE$.

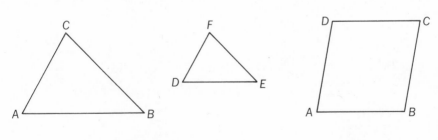

Prob. 13   Prob. 14

13. Copy the diagram as closely as you can. On $\overrightarrow{CA}$, locate D' so that $CD' = FD$. On $\overrightarrow{CB}$, locate E' so that $CE' = FE$. Draw $\overline{D'E'}$. If $\angle C \cong \angle F$, prove $\overline{D'E'} \cong \overline{DE}$.
14. GIVEN: $\overline{AB} \cong \overline{BC} \cong \overline{CD} \cong \overline{DA}$.
    PROVE: $\angle A \cong \angle C$.

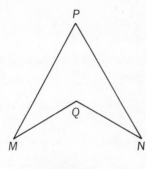

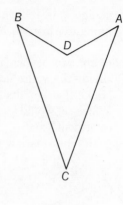

Prob. 15

15. GIVEN: $\overline{MP} \cong \overline{NP}$, $\overline{MQ} \cong \overline{NQ}$.   Prob. 18
PROVE: $\angle M \cong \angle N$.

16. Prove Thm. 5–12—If two sides of a triangle are congruent, the angles opposite these sides are congruent—by introducing the angle bisector of the vertex angle.

17. Prove Thm. 5–12 by introducing a median to the base.

(B)

18. GIVEN: $AD = DB$, $\angle A \cong \angle B$.
PROVE: $\overline{AC} \cong \overline{BC}$. (*Hint:* Use Thm. 5–12.)

Chapter 7

INEQUALITIES: ALGEBRAIC AND GEOMETRIC

7-1 ALGEBRA OF INEQUALITIES

In our study of triangles up to now, we have been concerned with situations involving congruent segments, or congruent angles. In this chapter we will consider certain relations that arise when two segments, or two angles, are not congruent.

If two segments are not congruent, then their measures (or lengths), are not equal, and, by the Trichotomy Axiom (see below), we conclude that one segment is longer than the other. Similarly, if two angles are not congruent, we conclude that the measure of one is greater than the measure of the other.

The Order Axioms of Section 2–5 are repeated here for convenience:

O–1 (Trichotomy Axiom): For every pair of real numbers, a and b, exactly one of the following is true:

$$a < b, \qquad a = b, \qquad a > b$$

O–2 (Addition Axiom): If $a < b$ and $c \leq d$, then $a + c < b + d$.

O–3 (Multiplication Axiom): If $a < b$, and $c > 0$, then $ac < bc$.

O–4 (Transitivity Axiom): If $a < b$, and $b < c$, then $a < c$.

In addition to these four axioms, we have this theorem:

Theorem 7–1: If $a = b + c$ and $c > 0$, then $a > b$.

Proof: Since $a = b + c$, we have $a - b = c$ (Subtraction Axiom, E–5). Since $c > 0$, it follows that $a - b > 0$ (Substitution Axiom, S–1). Hence, $a > b$ (Addition Axiom, O–2).

EXAMPLES

Justify each of the following by one of the Order Axioms (O–1 to O–4) or Theorem 7–1:

1. If $x - 4 < 7$, then $x < 11$.   *Answer:*   Axiom O–2.

2. If $\frac{y}{2} < 5$, then $y < 10$.   *Answer:*   Axiom O–3.

3. If $a - b = 4$, and $b < 2$, then $a < 6$.   *Answer:*   Axiom O–2.

4. If B is between A and C, then $AC > AB$.

Solution: If B is between A and C, then $AC = AB + BC$, where $BC > 0$. Then $AC > AB$ by Theorem 7–1.

5. If B is in the interior of $\angle ADC$, then $m\angle ADC > m\angle BDC$.

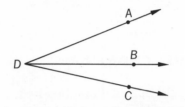

Solution: If B is in the interior of $\angle ADC$, then $m\angle ADC = m\angle ADB + m\angle BDC$, and $m\angle ADC > m\angle BDC$ by Theorem 7–1.

Exercise 7–1

Justify each of the following (1 to 8) by one of the Order Axioms, or Thm. 7–1:

1. If $x = 5$, then $x \not> 5$.
2. If $AB < BC$ and $BC < CD$, then $AB < CD$.
3. If $x + y = 6$ and $(-x) < -3$, then $y < 3$.
4. If $y < 2$, then $y \neq 2$.
5. If $a < 4$ and $b > 4$, then $a < b$.
6. If $x + y > 2$, then $3x + 3y > 6$.
7. If D is the midpoint of $\overline{AB}$, then $AB > AD$.
8. If $\overline{CD}$ is the bisector of $\angle ACB$, then $m\angle ACB > m\angle ACD$.

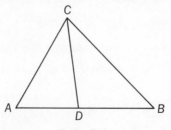

Probs. 7, 8

In 9 to 26 replace the question mark with the proper order symbol and identify the axiom or theorem on which your answer is based.

9. If $a > b$ and $k = k$, then $(a + k)$? $(b + k)$.

10. If $x < y$ and $a = b$, then $(x - a)$? $(y - b)$.

11. If $a > b$ and $x > y$, then $(a + x)$? $(b + y)$.

12. If $m \not> n$ and $m \neq n$, then m ? n.

13. If $p \not> q$ and $p \not< q$, then p ? q.

14. If $r > s$, then $4r$? $4s$.

15. If $x^2 - r^2 = y^2 - s^2$ and $r^2 < s^2$, then x^2 ? y^2.

16. If $\angle x$ and $\angle y$ are complementary and $m\angle y > 0$, then $m\angle x$? 90.

17. If $m\angle 1 > m\angle 3$ and $m\angle 2 = m\angle 4$, then $m\angle BCN$? $m\angle BMN$.

18. If $m\angle BCN = 2(m\angle 1)$, $m\angle BMN = 2(m\angle 3)$ and $m\angle 1 < m\angle 3$, then $m\angle BCN$? $m\angle BMN$.

19. If $m\angle BCN > m\angle BMN$ and $\angle 2 \cong \angle 4$, then $m\angle 1$? $m\angle 3$. (*Hint:* Try the different alternatives of Axiom O–1.)

20. If $\angle BCN \cong \angle BMN$ and $m\angle 1 > m\angle 3$, then $m\angle 2$? $m\angle 4$.

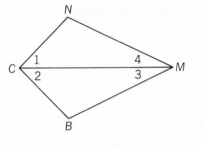

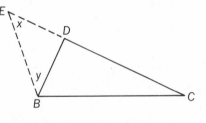

Probs. 17 to 20   Probs. 21, 22

21. $m\angle EBC$? $m\angle y$.

22. EC ? DC.

23. If $\angle 1 \cong \angle 3$ and $m\angle 2 > m\angle 4$, then $m\angle ABC$? $m\angle DEF$.

24. If $m\angle 1 < m\angle 3$ and $\angle 2 \cong \angle 4$, then $m\angle ABC$? $m\angle DEF$.

25. If $\angle ABC \cong \angle DEF$ and $m\angle 1 > m\angle 3$, then $m\angle 2$? $m\angle 4$.

26. If $\angle ABC \cong \angle DEF$ and $m\angle 2 < m\angle 4$, then $m\angle 1$? $m\angle 3$.

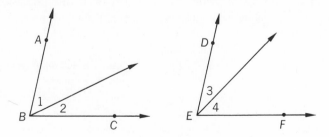

Probs. 23 to 26

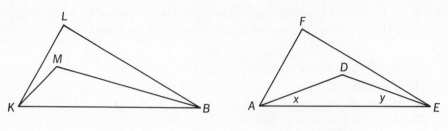

Prob. 27   Prob. 28

27. GIVEN: $m\angle MKL > m\angle MBL$; $m\angle MKB > m\angle MBK$.
      PROVE: $m\angle LKB > m\angle LBK$.
28. GIVEN: $\overline{DA} \cong \overline{DE}$.
      PROVE: $m\angle FAE > m\angle y$.

7–2 EXTERIOR ANGLES

Definition 7–1: $\angle DCE$ is an **exterior angle** of $\triangle BCD$ iff C is between B and E.

In Figure 7–1, $\angle 1$ through $\angle 6$ are exterior angles of $\triangle BCD$.

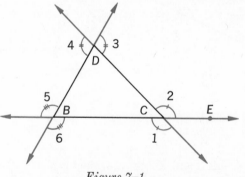

Figure 7–1

Every triangle has six exterior angles, which form three pairs of vertical angles (Figure 7–1). Further, each exterior angle is adjacent to, and a supplement of an interior angle of the triangle. Thus $\angle 1$ and $\angle 2$ are vertical angles, and $\angle 1$ and $\angle C$ are adjacent and supplementary (Theorem 4–6). We refer to $\angle B$ and $\angle D$ (of $\triangle BCD$) as the angles *nonadjacent* to $\angle 1$ and $\angle 2$.

Theorem 7–2 (The Exterior Angle Theorem): **The measure of an exterior angle of a triangle is greater than the measure of either of the nonadjacent interior angles of the triangle.**

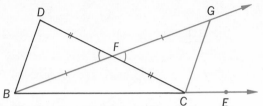

GIVEN: $\triangle BCD$.
PROVE: $m\angle DCE > m\angle D$; $m\angle DCE > m\angle DBC$.

Proof

STATEMENTS	REASONS
1. Let F be the midpoint of $\overline{DC}$.	1. Ax. 2–5.
2. Introduce G so that $\overrightarrow{FG}$ is opposite to $\overrightarrow{FB}$ and $FG = FB$.	2. Ax. 2–4.
3. $\overline{FG} \cong \overline{FB}$.	3. Why?
4. $\overline{FD} \cong \overline{FC}$.	4. Why?
5. $\angle DFB \cong \angle CFG$.	5. Why?
6. $\therefore \triangle DBF \cong \triangle CGF$.	6. Why?
7. $\angle D \cong \angle FCG$.	7. Why?
8. $m\angle D = m\angle FCG$.	8. Why?
9. $m\angle DCE = m\angle FCG + m\angle GCE$.	9. Angle Addition Ax. (3–9).
10. $m\angle DCE = m\angle D + m\angle GCE$.	10. Substitution Ax. (S–1).
11. $m\angle DCE > m\angle D$.	11. Thm. 7–1.
12. In like manner, $m\angle DCE > m\angle DBC$.	12. Steps 1 to 11.

Corollary 7–2.1: If a triangle has one right angle, then its other angles are acute.

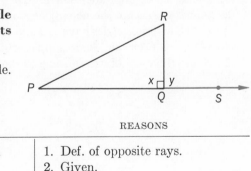

GIVEN: $\triangle PQR$; $\angle x$ a right angle.
PROVE: $\angle P$ and $\angle R$ are acute.

Proof

STATEMENTS	REASONS
1. Introduce $\overrightarrow{QS}$ opposite to $\overrightarrow{QP}$.	1. Def. of opposite rays.
2. $\angle x$ is a right angle.	2. Given.
3. $\overline{RQ} \perp \overline{PS}$.	3. Why?
4. $\angle y$ is a right angle.	4. Why?
5. $m\angle y = 90$.	5. Why?
6. $m\angle y > m\angle P,\ m\angle y > m\angle R$.	6. Thm. 7–2.
7. $90 > m\angle P,\ 90 > m\angle R$.	7. Substitution Ax. (S–1).
8. $\therefore \angle P$ and $\angle R$ are acute.	8. Def. of acute angle.

EXAMPLES

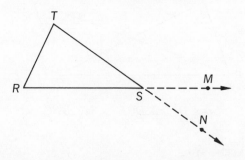

1. Name two exterior angles.   *Answer:* $\angle TSM$ and $\angle RSN$.
2. If $m\angle TSM = 145$, then $m\angle RST = $? and $m\angle RSN = $?
Solution: $\angle RST$ is supplementary to $\angle TSM$; therefore $m\angle RST = 35$. $\angle RSN$ and $\angle TSM$ form a pair of congruent vertical angles; therefore $m\angle RSN = 145$.
3. Name the interior angles nonadjacent to $\angle RSN$.   *Answer:* $\angle R$ and $\angle T$.
4. Complete in two ways: $m\angle RSN > m\angle$ _____.
Solution: By example 3 and Theorem 7–2 we have $m\angle RSN > m\angle R$ and $m\angle RSN > m\angle T$.

Exercise 7–2

(A)

1. Name the exterior angles of $\triangle BDF$.
2. Which angles are the nonadjacent interior angles of $\angle 8$?
3. Which exterior angles have $\angle 9$ and $\angle 5$ as nonadjacent interior angles?
4. Which exterior angles are supplementary to $\angle 4$?
5. Name the pairs of exterior angles that are vertical.

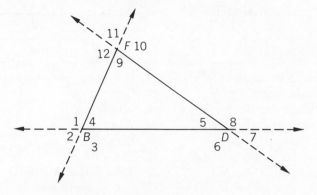

Probs. 1 to 5

6. Name an exterior angle of $\triangle FCD$.

7. Name an exterior angle of $\triangle CDE$.

Complete each statement in two ways:

8. $m\angle ECD > m\angle$ _____.   **9.** $m\angle FCD > m\angle$ _____.

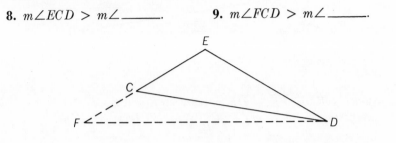

Probs. 6 to 9

10. Name an exterior angle of $\triangle BCD$.

11. Complete in two ways: $m\angle EDB > m\angle$ _____.

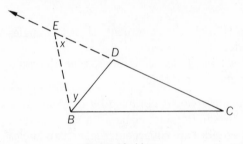

Probs. 10, 11

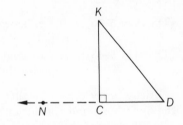

Probs. 12, 13

12. Complete in two ways: $\angle$ _____ is acute.

13. $m\angle KCN = $?

Using the figure complete each statement with an equality or inequality (assume R, S, and P are collinear):

14. If $m\angle R = 50$, and $m\angle T = 30$, then $m\angle 2$ _____.

15. If $m\angle T = 40$, and $m\angle 1 = 70$, then $m\angle 2$ _____.

16. If $m\angle R = 40$, and $m\angle 1 = 80$, then $m\angle 2$ _____.

17. If $m\angle T = 50$, and $m\angle R = 100$, then $m\angle 2$ _____.

18. If $m\angle R = 90$, and $m\angle T = 90$, then $m\angle 2$ _____.

19. If $m\angle R = 90$, then $m\angle 1$ _____.

20. If $m\angle 1 = 90$, then $m\angle T$ _____.

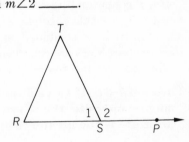

Probs. 14 to 20

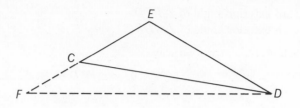

Prob. 21

(B)

21. GIVEN: $\triangle FDE$; $\overline{FE} \cong \overline{DE}$; C between F and E.
PROVE: (a) $m\angle F > m\angle EDC$; (b) $m\angle ECD > m\angle EDC$.

7-3 THEOREMS AND CONVERSES

If two theorems are related in a certain special way, each is said to be a **converse** of the other. For example, Theorems 5–12 and 5–13 are converses of each other:

(Theorem 5–12): If two sides of a triangle are congruent, then the angles opposite these sides are congruent.

(Theorem 5–13): If two angles of a triangle are congruent, then the sides opposite these angles are congruent.

Briefly, a converse of a theorem is a statement obtained by interchanging the hypothesis and conclusion (the "if" and "then" clauses) of the theorem. Thus Theorem 5–12 states that *if* "two sides are congruent," *then* "two angles are congruent," while Theorem 5–13 interchanges these clauses.

Frequently, a converse of a theorem is itself a theorem which can be proved —*but not always!* Consider, for example, Theorem 4–2: If each of two angles is a right angle, then the angles are congruent. A converse of this theorem is: "If two angles are congruent, then each of the two angles is a right angle." Plainly, this statement is not always true—the angles could be acute, and congruent.

If a theorem and its converse are both true, then the two may be combined into a single theorem using the iff notation. Thus Theorems 5–12 and 5–13 could be combined into: Two angles of a triangle are congruent iff their opposite sides are congruent.

The next two theorems are converses of each other.

Theorem 7–3: If two sides of a triangle are not congruent, then the angles opposite them are not congruent, and the angle whose measure is the greater is opposite the longer side.

GIVEN: $\triangle CDE$; $ED > EC$.
PROVE: $m\angle ECD > m\angle EDC$.

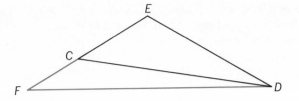

Proof

STATEMENTS	REASONS
1. Introduce $\overrightarrow{EC}$.	1. Def. of ray.
2. Introduce F so that $EF = ED$.	2. Point-Plotting Ax. (2–4).
3. $ED > EC$.	3. Given.
4. $\therefore EF > EC$.	4. Substitution Ax. (S–1).
5. Introduce $\overline{DF}$.	5. Ax. 2–3.
6. $m\angle EDF = m\angle EDC + m\angle CDF$.	6. Ax. 3–9.
7. $m\angle EDF > m\angle EDC$.	7. Thm. 7–1.
8. $\overline{EF} \cong \overline{ED}$.	8. Def. of congruent segments (step 2).
9. $\angle F \cong \angle EDF$.	9. Thm. 5–12.
10. $m\angle F = m\angle EDF$.	10. Def. of congruent angles.
11. $m\angle F > m\angle EDC$.	11. Substitution Ax. (S–1) (steps 6 and 9).
12. $\angle ECD$ is an exterior angle of $\triangle FDC$.	12. Def. of exterior angle.
13. $m\angle ECD > m\angle F$.	13. Thm. 7–2.
14. $m\angle ECD > m\angle EDC$.	14. Transitivity Ax. O–4.

Theorem 7–4: **If two angles of a triangle are not congruent, then the sides opposite them are not congruent, and the longer side is opposite the angle whose measure is the greater.**

GIVEN: $\triangle CDE$; $m\angle C > m\angle D$.
PROVE: $ED > EC$.

Proof (Indirect): There are three possibilities:

    (1) $ED = EC$
    (2) $ED < EC$
    (3) $ED > EC$

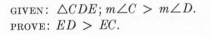

(1) Assume $ED = EC$. Then $\overline{ED} \cong \overline{EC}$, and by Theorem 5–12, $\angle C \cong \angle D$. But then $m\angle C = m\angle D$, which contradicts the hypothesis that $m\angle C > m\angle D$, therefore $ED \neq EC$.

(2) Assume $ED < EC$. Then, by Theorem 7–3, $m\angle C < m\angle D$. But this contradicts the hypothesis again, hence $ED \not< EC$.

(3) Since the first two possibilities lead to contradictions, we must conclude that $ED > EC$.

EXAMPLES

1. Write the converse of: If two angles are complementary, then they are each acute.

Solution: If each of two angles is acute, then they are complementary.

2. Write the converse of: Any two right angles are congruent.

Solution: It is usually easier to find the hypothesis and conclusion when a statement is written in the if–then form. The statement above then becomes: If each of two angles is a right angle, then the angles are congruent. (This is the form used as an example in the text, page 68.) The converse is: If two angles are congruent, then each is a right angle.

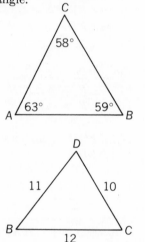

3. List the sides of $\triangle ABC$ in order, beginning with the shortest.

Solution: Since the longest side is opposite the angle with the greater measure (Theorem 7–4), we have $\overline{AB}, \overline{AC}, \overline{BC}$.

4. List the angles in order, beginning with the one whose measure is the greatest.

Solution: Since the angle of greatest measure is opposite the longest side (Theorem 7–3), we have: $\angle D, \angle C, \angle B$.

Exercise 7–3

(A)

Write the converse of each of the following propositions. In each case state whether you think the converse is true or false (1 to 8).

1. If a man lives in Los Angeles, he lives in California.
2. If it is raining, then it is cloudy.
3. If a triangle is equilateral, then it is equiangular.
4. If two triangles are congruent, then the angles of the two triangles are respectively congruent.
5. If two angles are supplementary, the sum of their measures is 180.
6. If two angles are complementary, the sum of their measures is 90.
7. The sum of the measures of the angles of a triangle is 180.
8. The acute angles of a right triangle are complementary.

9. Which is the longer side, $\overline{AB}$ or $\overline{BC}$?

10. List the sides in order of length, beginning with the shortest.

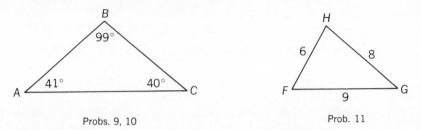

Probs. 9, 10   Prob. 11

11. List the angles in order of size, beginning with the one whose measure is the least.

12. If the angles have the indicated measures, which segment is the (a) shortest? (b) longest?

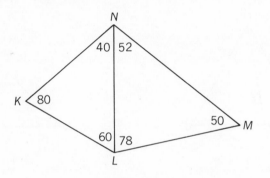

Prob. 12

13. In $\triangle PQR$, $PQ = 5$, $QR = 6$, and $RP = 7$. Name the angle whose measure is (a) least, and (b) greatest.

14. In $\triangle PQR$, $m\angle P = 37$, $m\angle Q = 73$, and $m\angle R = 70$. Name (a) the longest side, and (b) the shortest side.

15. GIVEN: Right $\triangle ABC$.
PROVE: $AC < BC$; $AB < BC$.

16. GIVEN: $CD > DF$; $BF < BC$.
PROVE: $m\angle DFB > m\angle DCB$.

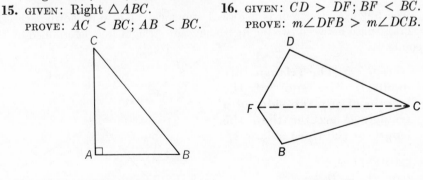

Prob. 15   Prob. 16

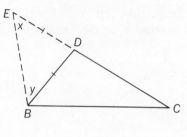

Prob. 17

(B)

17. GIVEN: $\triangle BCD$; E, D, and C collinear; $\overline{ED} \cong \overline{BD}$.
    PROVE: (a) $m\angle EBC > m\angle x$; (b) $EC > BC$; (c) $BD + DC > BC$.

18. GIVEN: $\triangle CDF$; $\overline{CD} \cong \overline{CF}$.
    PROVE: $CD > CE$.

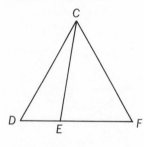

Prob. 18

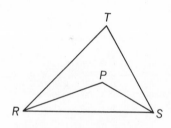

Prob. 19

19. GIVEN: $\triangle RST$; $RT > ST$; $\overrightarrow{RP}$ bisects $\angle TRS$; $\overrightarrow{SP}$ bisects $\angle TSR$.
    PROVE: $RP > SP$.

7–4   THE TRIANGLE INEQUALITY

The following theorem is a formal statement of a well-known fact—the shortest path between two points is along the straight line determined by the points.

Theorem 7–5 (The Triangle Inequality): The sum of the lengths of any two sides of a triangle is greater than the length of the third side.

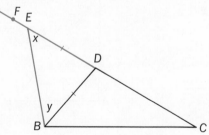

GIVEN: $\triangle BCD$.
PROVE: $DB + DC > BC$.

Proof

STATEMENTS	REASONS
1. Introduce $\overrightarrow{DF}$ opposite to $\overrightarrow{DC}$.	1. Def. of opposite rays.
2. Introduce E so that $DE = DB$.	2. Point-Plotting Ax. (2–4).
3. $\overline{DE} \cong \overline{DB}$.	3. Why?
4. $\angle x \cong \angle y$.	4. Why?
5. $m\angle EBC = m\angle y + m\angle DBC$.	5. Why?
6. $m\angle EBC > m\angle y$.	6. Thm. 7–1.
7. $m\angle x = m\angle y$.	7. Def. of angle congruence (step 4).
8. $m\angle EBC > m\angle x$.	8. Substitution Ax. (S–1).
9. $EC > BC$.	9. Thm. 7–4.
10. $EC = ED + DC$.	10. Def. of betweenness.
11. $EC = DB + DC$.	11. Why?
12. $DB + DC > BC$.	12. Why?

Theorem 7–6: The shortest segment joining a point to a line is the perpendicular segment.

GIVEN: Line q; $P \notin q$; $\overline{PR} \perp q$; $S \in q$; S distinct from R.
PROVE: $PR < PS$.

Proof (Indirect):

Since $\overline{PR} \perp q$, $\angle 1$ is a right angle
and $\triangle PRS$ is a right triangle. Now
there are three possibilities:

    (1) $PR = PS$
    (2) $PR > PS$
    (3) $PR < PS$

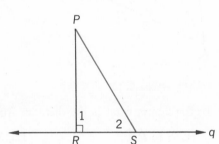

    (1) Assume $PR = PS$. Then $\overline{PR} \cong \overline{PS}$, hence $\angle 1 \cong \angle 2$ (Theorem 5–12), and thus $\angle 2$ is a right angle. This contradicts Corollary 7–2.1 (only *one* right angle in a triangle), hence $PR \neq PS$.

    (2) Assume $PR > PS$. Then $m\angle 2 > m\angle 1$ (Thm. 7–3), and thus $\angle 2$ is obtuse. This contradicts Corollary 7–2.1 (the other angles must be acute), hence $PR \not> PS$.

    (3) Since $PR \neq PS$ and $PR \not> PS$, we must conclude that $PR < PS$.

Definition 7–2: The **distance from a point to a line** (the point not in the line) is the length of the perpendicular segment from the point to the line. If the point is in the line, the distance is defined to be zero.

You are advised to learn this definition thoroughly. The concept of the distance from a point to a line is encountered in many theorems and problems. Frequently overlooked is the fact that the definition calls for a *perpendicular* segment.

Exercise 7–4

(A)

Which of the following sets of three numbers could be used as the lengths of the sides of a triangle? (*a* and *b* represent positive numbers.)

1. 3, 5, 7   **2.** 4, 2, 8
3. 5, 10, 15   **4.** 2, 3, 4
5. $a, b, a + b$ **6.** $a, b, a + 2b$
7. 121, 302, 200   **8.** 500, 296, 300

In the figure:

9. $AD <$? and $AD <$?   **10.** $EB <$? and $EB <$?

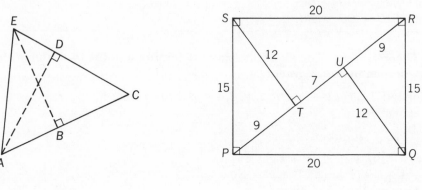

Probs. 9, 10   Probs. 11 to 19

In the figure, what is the distance from the indicated point to the line?

11. S to $\overleftrightarrow{PR}$ **12.** S to $\overleftrightarrow{PQ}$ **13.** P to $\overleftrightarrow{ST}$
14. R to $\overleftrightarrow{ST}$ **15.** U to $\overleftrightarrow{ST}$ **16.** P to $\overleftrightarrow{UQ}$
17. Q to $\overleftrightarrow{SP}$ **18.** Q to $\overleftrightarrow{TR}$ **19.** R to $\overleftrightarrow{PQ}$

20. GIVEN: Figure $ABCD$.
    PROVE: $AD + DC + CB > AB$.
21. GIVEN: $BC = CF$; B, C, and D are collinear.
    PROVE: $BD > DF$. (*Hint:* First consider $\triangle FCD$ and use Thm. 7–5.)

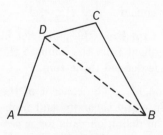

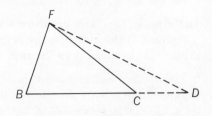

Prob. 20   Prob. 21

(B)

22. GIVEN: $\triangle CDE$; $\triangle CLE \cong \triangle CLK$.
    PROVE: $ED > KD$.

23. Prove Thm. 7-6 by first introducing point T on $\overrightarrow{PR}$ so that $RT = RP$, and then apply Thm. 7-5 to $\triangle PTS$.

24. GIVEN: Figure $ABCD$.
    PROVE: $AC < \frac{1}{2}(AB + BC + CD + DA)$.

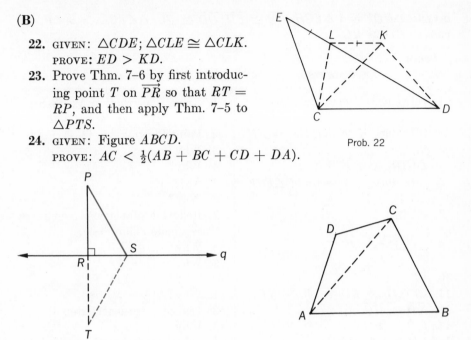

Prob. 22

Prob. 23   Prob. 24

25. PROVE: The sum of the altitudes of any triangle is less than the sum of the lengths of the sides.

7-5 INEQUALITIES FOR TWO TRIANGLES

These next theorems are somewhat like Theorems 7-3 and 7-4, except that they are concerned with *two* triangles rather than one.

Theorem 7-7: **If two sides of one triangle are congruent respectively to two sides of a second triangle, and the measure of the included angle of the first triangle is greater than the measure of the included angle of the second triangle, then the third side of the first triangle is longer than the third side of the second.**

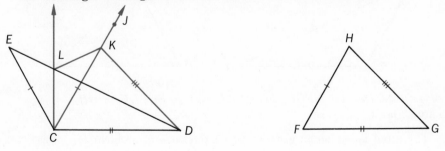

GIVEN: $\triangle CDE$ and $\triangle FGH$; $\overline{CE} \cong \overline{FH}$; $\overline{CD} \cong \overline{FG}$; $m\angle ECD > m\angle F$.
PROVE: $ED > HG$.

Proof

STATEMENTS	REASONS
1. Introduce $\overrightarrow{CJ}$ so that $m\angle JCD = m\angle F$.	1. Angle Construction Ax. (3–8).
2. Introduce K so that $CK = FH$.	2. Point-Plotting Ax. (2–4).
3. $\overline{CK} \cong \overline{FH}$.	3. Why?
4. $\triangle CDK \cong \triangle FGH$.	4. Why?
5. Introduce $\overrightarrow{CL}$, bisector of $\angle ECK$.	5. Ax. 5–1.
6. $\angle 1 \cong \angle 2$.	6. Why?
7. $\overline{CL} \cong \overline{CL}$.	7. Reflexive property of congruent segments (Thm. 5–1).
8. $\triangle CLE \cong \triangle CLK$.	8. Why?
9. $\overline{LE} \cong \overline{LK}$.	9. Why?
10. $LE = LK$.	10. Why?
11. In $\triangle DLK$, $LD + LK > KD$.	11. Why?
12. $\overline{KD} \cong \overline{HG}$.	12. Def. of congruence (step 4).
13. $KD = HG$.	13. Why?
14. $LD + LE > HG$.	14. Substitution Ax. (S–1) (steps 10, 11, 13).
15. $ED = LD + LE$.	15. Why?
16. $\therefore ED > HG$.	16. Why?

The next theorem is a converse of Theorem 7–7.

Theorem 7–8: **If two sides of one triangle are congruent respectively to two sides of a second triangle, and the third side of the first triangle is longer than the third side of the second, then the measure of the angle opposite the third side of the first triangle is greater than the measure of the angle opposite the third side of the second triangle.**

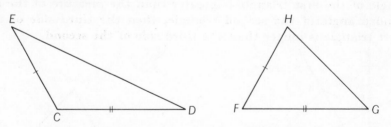

GIVEN: $\triangle CDE$ and $\triangle FGH$; $EC \cong HF$; $CD \cong FG$; $DE > GH$.
PROVE: $m\angle C > m\angle F$.

The proof is left as an exercise (see Exercise 7–5, problem 1).

Exercise 7–5

(B)

1. Prove Theorem 7–8. Use the indirect method as follows:
   I. Show that the assumption $m\angle C = m\angle F$ contradicts part of the hypothesis.
   II. Show that the assumption $m\angle C < m\angle F$ contradicts part of the hypothesis (using Theorem 7–7).
   III. Make the conclusion $m\angle C > m\angle F$.

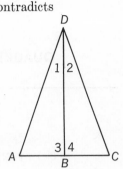

2. If $\overline{AD} \cong \overline{DC}$ and $m\angle 1 > m\angle 2$, is $AB > BC$?
3. If $AD < CD$ and $\overline{AB} \cong \overline{BC}$, is $m\angle 3 > m\angle 4$?

Probs. 2, 3

4. PROVE: If $\overline{RS}$ is a median of $\triangle PQR$, and if $m\angle PSR > m\angle QSP$, then $PR > QR$.
5. PROVE: If P is a point on $\overline{AB}$, the base of isosceles $\triangle ABC$, and $AP < PB$, then $m\angle ACP < m\angle PCB$.

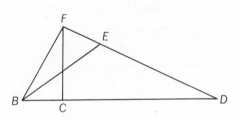

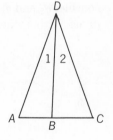

Prob. 6

Prob. 7

6. GIVEN: $\triangle BDF$; $C \in \overline{BD}$; $E \in \overline{FD}$; $FE = BC$; $BE > FC$.
   PROVE: $BD > FD$.
7. GIVEN: $\triangle ACD$; $AD = CD$; $m\angle 1 < m\angle 2$.
   PROVE: $BC > AB$.
8. GIVEN: $\triangle ABC$; $FC = DB$; $AB > AC$.
   PROVE: $FB > CD$.

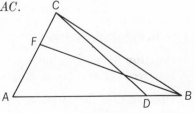

Prob. 8

Chapter 8

QUADRILATERALS AND PARALLELOGRAMS

8–1 PARALLEL LINES

Heretofore our geometry has emphasized the study of relationships that occur when lines intersect. Interesting and useful relationships occur when two lines do not intersect.

Figure 8–1 may be interpreted as a diagram of a room, with lines q_1, q_2, and q_3 drawn in for special consideration. Consider first q_1 and q_2. These lines intersect, and Axiom 3–5 tells us that q_1 and q_2 are coplanar. Next, consider q_2 and q_3. They do not seem to intersect, nor do they lie in the same plane. It is evident that two lines in space need not be coplanar.

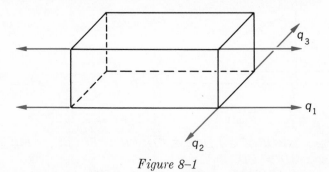

Figure 8–1

Definition 8–1: Two lines are **skew** iff they are not coplanar.

Finally, lines q_1 and q_3 illustrate the possibility of two lines that *are* coplanar, but do not intersect.

Definition 8–2: Two lines are **parallel** iff they are coplanar and do not intersect. (Notation: $q_1 \parallel q_2$; read "q_1 is parallel to q_2.")

Observe that Definition 8–2 requires that two lines lie in a plane if they are to be parallel. It is not difficult to show that they lie in only one plane.

162

Theorem 8–1: If two lines are parallel, they lie in exactly one plane.

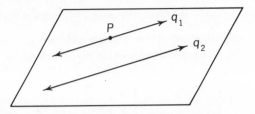

Proof: Suppose $q_1 \parallel q_2$. Then by definition, q_1 and q_2 lie in a plane. Choose any point P on q_1. Exactly one plane is determined by a line and a point not on the line (Axiom 3–4). Hence there is exactly one plane containing two parallel lines.

Theorem 8–1 is sometimes stated: **Two parallel lines determine a plane.**

We are now faced with a rather unusual situation. The definition of parallel lines, while quite explicit, is not "usable" in the same sense that the definition for perpendicular lines was. If two lines in a plane appear to be parallel, we are unable to see *all* of the two lines and determine with certainty that they never intersect, since every line extends infinitely far in two directions. Thus it becomes necessary to develop tests for parallelism of two lines other than the definition. As a first such test we have:

Theorem 8–2: If two coplanar lines are perpendicular to the same line, they are parallel.

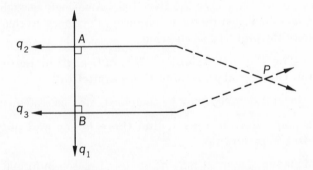

Proof (Indirect): Suppose $q_2 \perp q_1$ at A, and $q_3 \perp q_1$ at B. Now, either $q_2 \parallel q_3$, or q_2 and q_3 intersect in a point (name it P). Assume q_3 intersects q_2 at P. If the point P were on q_1, then there would be two lines (q_2 and q_3) both perpendicular to the same line at the same point. This contradicts Theorem 6–1. If P were not on q_1, then there would be two lines both perpendicular to the same given line through a point not on the given line. This contradicts Theorem 6–3. Hence the assumption that the two lines intersect is false, and we conclude that $q_2 \parallel q_3$.

As a matter of convenience, we point out that if two lines are parallel, any two segments (one on each of the two lines) are also parallel, as well as any two rays, or a segment and a ray, a line and a ray, and a line and a segment.

Theorem 8–3: **Through a given point not on a given line, there exists at least one line parallel to the given line.**

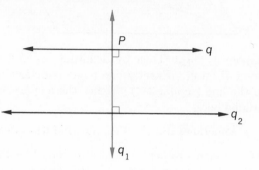

Proof: Let q_2 be the given line with P not on q_2. Introduce q_1 through P such that $q_1 \perp q_2$ (Theorem 6–3). Now introduce q such that $q \perp q_1$ at P (Theorem 6–1). But q and q_2 are both perpendicular to the same line (q_1), hence by Theorem 8–2, $q \parallel q_2$.

Observing that Theorem 8–3 is an *existence* theorem, it would seem natural, as in the development of perpendicular lines in Chapter 6, to establish *uniqueness*, that is, to show that through a given point not on a given line there is *only one* line parallel to the given line. Amazingly enough, this property cannot be established by using the theory developed to this point. We must introduce the property as an axiom.

Axiom 8–1 (The Parallel Axiom): **Through a given point not on a given line, there is at most one line parallel to the given line.**

Theorem 8–3 and Axiom 8–1 may be combined into one statement:

Through a point not on a given line there is one and only one line parallel to the given line.

This combination statement may be used as a reason in formal proofs.

A glance at the diagrams for Theorems 8–2 and 8–3 shows the presence of a *third* line—one that intersects both parallel lines. This third line is an example of an auxiliary set that is of great importance in the study of parallel lines. It is called a transversal.

Definition 8–3: A line is a **transversal** of two coplanar lines iff it intersects them in two different points.

This is often stated: A transversal "cuts" the two lines. A ray or a segment may also serve as a transversal.

The definition of transversal does not require that the two coplanar lines be parallel. However, in the case that the two lines intersect (are not parallel), the word "different" in the definition rules out the possibility that the transversal intersects the two lines at their common point. Thus (Figure 8–2) if q_1 and q_2 intersect at P, t is *not* a transversal, but r *is* a transversal. If the two lines are parallel, among the many transversals that may be introduced are the very useful transversals perpendicular to both of the parallel lines (see Theorem 8–11).

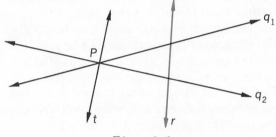

Figure 8–2

We may also use the word transversal to describe a line that intersects segments and rays, as well as other lines.

EXAMPLE

In the figure:

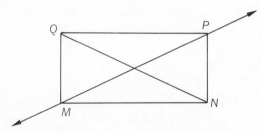

(a) Name four transversals of $\overline{QM}$ and $\overline{PN}$.
(b) Name two transversals of $\overline{PM}$ and $\overline{MN}$.
(c) Is $\overleftrightarrow{MP}$ a transversal of $\overline{QM}$ and $\overline{MN}$? Why?

Solution: By inspection and Definition 8–3:
(a) $\overline{QP}$, $\overline{MN}$, $\overleftrightarrow{MP}$, and $\overline{QN}$.   (b) $\overline{QN}$ and $\overline{QM}$.
(c) No, because $\overleftrightarrow{MP}$ intersects both segments at the *same* point, M.

Exercise 8–1

Note: In the exercises of this chapter, all figures are assumed to be in a plane.

(A)

1. What two conditions must be satisfied if two lines are to be parallel?
2. State the definition of parallel lines in two parts, without using iff.
3. Is this a satisfactory definition for parallel lines? $q_1 \parallel q_2$ iff $q_1 \cap q_2 = \emptyset$. Explain.
4. Is this a satisfactory definition for skew lines?
   q_1 and q_2 are skew iff $q_1 \cap q_2 = \emptyset$. Explain.
5. (a) If two lines are coplanar, must they be parallel?
      If two lines are coplanar, can they be skew?
   (b) If two lines are not coplanar, must they be parallel?
      If two lines are not coplanar, can they be parallel?
   (c) If two lines are in space, must they be parallel?
      If two lines are in space, must they be skew?
6. Draw a line (name it q), and locate a point P not on q, about 1 inch away from q. Study the proof of Theorem 8–3 and, using a protractor, draw a line through P parallel to q.

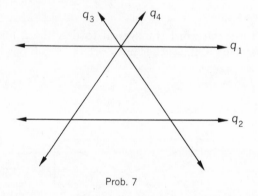

Prob. 7

7. In the figure, q_1, q_2, q_3, and q_4 are straight lines. Name all transversals of q_1 and q_2; q_1 and q_3; q_1 and q_4; q_2 and q_3; q_2 and q_4; q_3 and q_4.
8. In the figure:
   (a) Name four segments that are transversals of $\overline{AB}$ and $\overline{CD}$.
   (b) Name four segments that are transversals of $\overline{AD}$ and $\overline{BC}$.

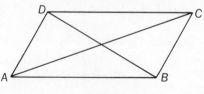

Prob. 8

9. Furnish the reason for each step of the
following proof:

GIVEN: Isosceles $\triangle ABC$ (base $\overline{AB}$);
median $\overline{CM}$; $\overline{CM} \perp \overline{DE}$.
PROVE: $\overline{DE} \parallel \overline{AB}$.

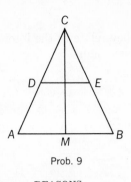

Prob. 9

Proof

STATEMENTS	REASONS
1. Isosceles $\triangle ABC$, base $\overline{AB}$.	1.
2. $\overline{CA} \cong \overline{CB}$.	2.
3. $CA = CB$.	3.
4. Median $\overline{CM}$.	4.
5. M the midpoint of $\overline{AB}$.	5.
6. $AM = MB$.	6.
7. $\overline{CM} \perp \overline{AB}$.	7.
8. $\overline{DE} \perp \overline{CM}$.	8.
9. $\overline{DE} \parallel \overline{AB}$.	9.

(B)

10. GIVEN: $\overline{CD} \perp \overline{DA}$; isosceles $\triangle ACB$ (base $\overline{AB}$); $\angle 1$ and $\angle 2$ are
complementary.
PROVE: $\overline{CD} \parallel \overline{AB}$.

11. GIVEN: $\triangle ABC$; $m\angle CAB = 90$; $\triangle ADB$ is isosceles (base $\overline{AB}$), with
median $\overline{DM}$.
PROVE: $\overline{DM} \parallel \overline{CA}$.

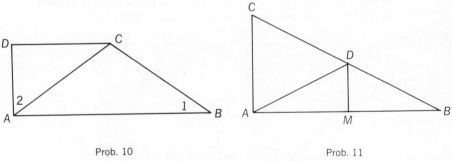

Prob. 10   Prob. 11

8–2 ANGLES RELATED TO PARALLEL LINES

When two lines are cut by a transversal, eight angles are formed, four at
each point of intersection. In order to discuss the properties of these angles

as they relate to the intersected lines, it is necessary to classify these angles in some manner.

Definition 8–4: Let t be a transversal of q_1 and q_2, intersecting them at A and B respectively. Let X be a point of q_1 and Y a point of q_2 such that X and Y are on opposite sides of t. Then $\angle XAB$ and $\angle YBA$ are **alternate interior angles.** (Figure 8–3.)

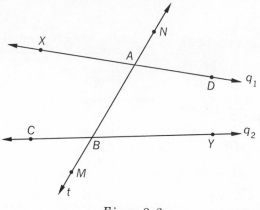

Figure 8–3

Note that by the same definition (using C and D rather than X and Y), $\angle CBA$ and $\angle DAB$ are also alternate interior angles.

Pairs of angles such as $\angle XAN$ and $\angle YBM$ (also $\angle DAN$ and $\angle CBM$) in Figure 8–3 are often referred to as alternate **exterior** angles.

A third pair is readily classified in terms of previous definitions:

Definition 8–5: If two lines are cut by a transversal so that $\angle 5$ and $\angle 3$ are alternate interior angles, and if $\angle 5$ and $\angle 7$ are vertical angles, then $\angle 3$ and $\angle 7$ are **corresponding angles.** (Figure 8–4).

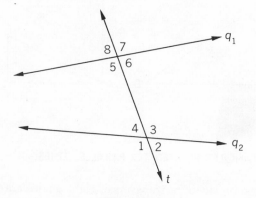

Figure 8–4

To sum up the above discussion, we list here the pairs of angles under their classifications (Figure 8–4):

(1) Alternate interior angles: $\angle 3$ and $\angle 5$; $\angle 4$ and $\angle 6$.
(2) Alternate exterior angles: $\angle 1$ and $\angle 7$; $\angle 2$ and $\angle 8$.
(3) Corresponding angles: $\angle 1$ and $\angle 5$; $\angle 4$ and $\angle 8$; $\angle 2$ and $\angle 6$; $\angle 3$ and $\angle 7$.

In the case where the two lines intersected by a transversal are parallel, an astonishing number of theorems follow. You are advised to learn to distinguish carefully between those theorems that enable you to prove that lines are parallel (What will the *conclusions* of such theorems be?), and theorems which specify certain results when the lines are *given* as being parallel.

There are times in mathematics when we need a theorem to be used chiefly in the proof of another theorem. Usually such preliminary theorems, called *lemmas*, have limited application elsewhere.

Lemma 8–1: **If two lines are cut by a transversal so that one pair of alternate interior angles are congruent, then the other pair of alternate interior angles are congruent.**

GIVEN: q_1 and q_2; transversal t;
      $\angle 1 \cong \angle 2$.
PROVE: $\angle 3 \cong \angle 4$.

The proof of this lemma is left as an exercise.

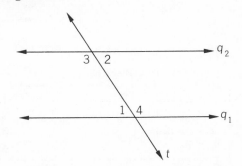

Theorem 8–4: **If two lines are cut by a transversal so that a pair of alternate interior angles are congruent, then the lines are parallel.**

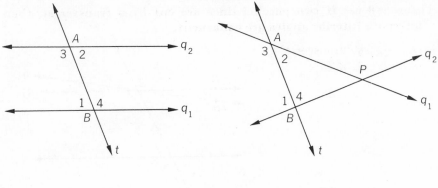

(a)   (b)

GIVEN: q_1 and q_2; transversal t; $\angle 1 \cong \angle 2$.
PROVE: $q_1 \parallel q_2$.

Proof (**Indirect**): Either q_1 is parallel to q_2, or q_1 intersects q_2 at a point, say P. Assume the lines intersect [figure (b)]. Then $\angle 1$ is an exterior angle of $\triangle ABP$, and $\angle 2$ is interior and nonadjacent to $\angle 1$. Hence $m\angle 1 > m\angle 2$ (Thm. 7–2). Now the hypothesis states that $\angle 1 \cong \angle 2$. We have reached a contradiction: $\angle 1$ cannot be *both* congruent to $\angle 2$, and have a measure greater than $m\angle 2$. The assumption that the lines intersect is false. Hence we conclude the lines are parallel; $q_1 \parallel q_2$.

Theorem 8–5: **If two lines are cut by a transversal so that a pair of corresponding angles are congruent, the lines are parallel.**

GIVEN: q_1; q_2; transversal t;
$\qquad \angle 1 \cong \angle 2$.
PROVE: $q_1 \parallel q_2$.

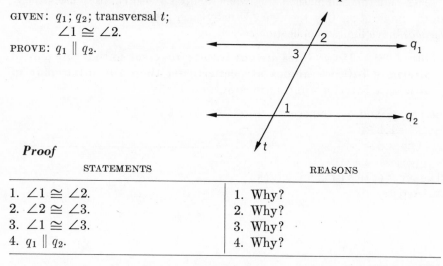

Proof

STATEMENTS	REASONS
1. $\angle 1 \cong \angle 2$.	1. Why?
2. $\angle 2 \cong \angle 3$.	2. Why?
3. $\angle 1 \cong \angle 3$.	3. Why?
4. $q_1 \parallel q_2$.	4. Why?

The next two theorems are converses of Theorems 8–4 and 8–5. Both these theorems require that lines be *parallel* before the conclusions apply.

Theorem 8–6: **If two parallel lines are cut by a transversal, then alternate interior angles are congruent.**

GIVEN: $q_1 \parallel q_2$; transversal t.
PROVE: $\angle 1 \cong \angle 2$.

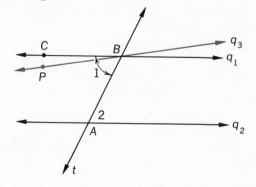

Proof (Indirect): Either $\angle 1 \cong \angle 2$, or $\angle 1 \not\cong \angle 2$. Assume the angles are not congruent. Introduce q_3 containing $\overrightarrow{BP}$ so that $\angle ABP \cong \angle 2$. Then $m\angle ABP = m\angle 2$. Since $\angle 1 \not\cong \angle 2$, $m\angle 1 \neq m\angle 2$, hence $m\angle 1 \neq m\angle ABP$. Then, by the Angle Construction Axiom (Axiom 3–8), $\overrightarrow{BP}$ and $\overrightarrow{BC}$ must be distinct rays, and so q_3 and q_1 are distinct lines. Now, $\angle ABP$ and $\angle 2$ are alternate interior angles, and since $\angle ABP \cong \angle 2$, $q_3 \parallel q_2$ (Theorem 8–4). Since we are given $q_1 \parallel q_2$, there are now *two* distinct lines through B, both parallel to the same line q_2. This contradicts The Parallel Axiom (Axiom 8–1). Therefore $\angle 1 \not\cong \angle 2$ is false. We conclude that $\angle 1 \cong \angle 2$, and by Lemma 8–1, the other pair of alternate interior angles are also congruent.

Theorem 8–7: If two parallel lines are cut by a transversal, each pair of corresponding angles are congruent.

The proof is left as an exercise.

Theorem 8–8: If two parallel lines are cut by a transversal, interior angles on the same side of the transversal are supplementary.

GIVEN: $q_1 \parallel q_2$; transversal t.
PROVE:

  $\angle 1$ and $\angle 2$ are supplementary;
  $\angle 3$ and $\angle 4$ are supplementary.

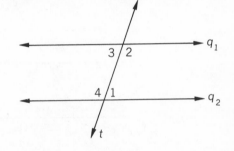

Proof

STATEMENTS	REASONS
1. $q_1 \parallel q_2$	1. Why?
2. $\angle 1 \cong \angle 3$, $\angle 2 \cong \angle 4$.	2. Why?
3. $\angle 2$ and $\angle 3$ are supplementary, $\angle 1$ and $\angle 4$ are supplementary.	3. Why?
4. $\angle 2$ and $\angle 1$ are supplementary, $\angle 3$ and $\angle 4$ are supplementary.	4. Why?

The proofs of the following three theorems are quite straightforward, and are left as exercises.

Theorem 8–9: If two lines are cut by a transversal so that interior angles on the same side of the transversal are supplementary, the lines are parallel.

Theorem 8–10: In a plane, two lines parallel to a third line are parallel to each other.

Theorem 8–11: **In a plane, if a line is perpendicular to one of two parallel lines, it is perpendicular to the other.**

EXAMPLES

1. Given $m\angle B = 30$, $\overrightarrow{BP} \parallel \overrightarrow{AC}$, and $\overrightarrow{BQ} \parallel \overrightarrow{AP}$, find $m\angle 1$, $m\angle 2$, $m\angle 3$, $m\angle 4$, and $m\angle 5$.

Solution

(1) Since $\overrightarrow{BQ} \parallel \overrightarrow{AP}$, $m\angle 1 = 150$ (Thm. 8–8).
(2) $m\angle 2 = 30$ (Thm. 8–7).
(3) $m\angle 5 = 30$ (Thm. 8–7).
(4) $m\angle 4 = 30$ (Thm. 8–6).
(5) $m\angle 3 = 150$ (Thm. 8–8).

2. GIVEN: $\angle 1 \cong \angle 2$; $\overline{AB} \perp q_2$; $\overline{AB} \perp q_3$; transversal t.
   PROVE: $q_1 \parallel q_3$.

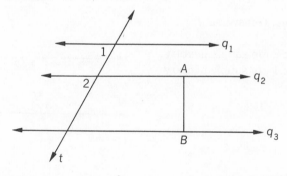

Proof

STATEMENTS	REASONS
1. $\angle 1 \cong \angle 2$.	1. Given.
2. $q_1 \parallel q_2$.	2. Thm. 8–5.
3. $\overline{AB} \perp q_2$, $\overline{AB} \perp q_3$.	3. Given.
4. $q_3 \parallel q_2$.	4. Thm. 8–2.
5. $q_1 \parallel q_3$.	5. Thm. 8–10.

Exercise 8–2

(A)

1. Name all pairs of alternate interior angles.
2. Name all pairs of alternate exterior angles.
3. Name all pairs of corresponding angles.
4. Name all pairs of angles that are interior and on the same side of the transversal.

Classify the following pairs of angles
using problems 1 to 4 as a guide:

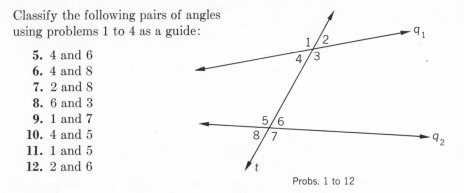

   5. 4 and 6
   6. 4 and 8
   7. 2 and 8
   8. 6 and 3
   9. 1 and 7
 10. 4 and 5
 11. 1 and 5
 12. 2 and 6

Probs. 1 to 12

13. For transversal $\overleftrightarrow{DB}$, classify angles 1 and 4.
14. For transversal $\overline{BC}$, classify angles 2 and 3.

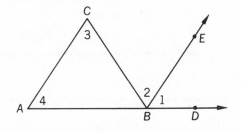

Probs. 13, 14

Consider $\overline{AC}$, $\overline{BD}$, $\overline{DA}$, and $\overline{BC}$ as transversals. Judging only on the basis
of what is given, decide whether statements 15 to 21 are *true* or *false*.

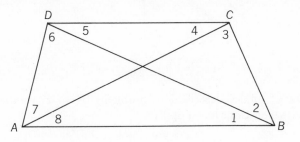

Probs. 15 to 21

15. $\angle 4$ and $\angle 8$ are alternate interior angles.
16. $\angle 6$ and $\angle 2$ are alternate interior angles.
17. $\angle 4 \cong \angle 8$.
18. $\angle 4$ and $\angle 2$ are corresponding angles.
19. If $\angle 3 \cong \angle 7$, then $\overline{DC} \parallel \overline{AB}$.   **20.** If $\overline{DC} \parallel \overline{AB}$, then $\angle 5 \cong \angle 1$.
21. If $\overline{AB} \parallel \overline{DC}$, then $m\angle BAD + m\angle ADC = 180$.

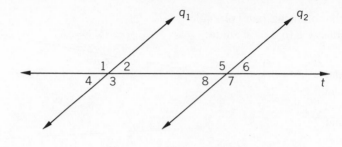

Prob. 22

22. In the figure: $q_1 \parallel q_2$, transversal t, $m\angle 1 = 140$. Find the measure of each of angles 2, 3, 4, 5, 6, 7 and 8.

23. In the figure, $q_1 \parallel q_3$, $q_2 \parallel q_3$, $t_1 \perp q_1$, $m\angle 1 = 40$. Find the measure of each of angles 2, 3, 4, 5, 6, 7, 8.

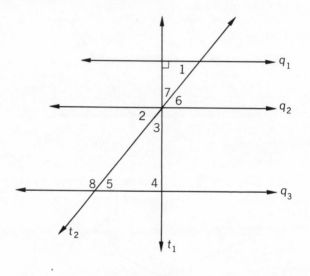

Prob. 23

For each pair of angles described in problems 24 to 27, state which two segments and which transversal apply:

EXAMPLE

    $\angle 1$ and $\angle 5$ are alternate interior angles.

    Answer: $\overline{DC}$ and $\overline{AB}$; transversal $\overline{AC}$.

24. $\angle 8$ and $\angle 4$ are alternate interior angles.

25. $\angle CDA$ and $\angle DCB$ are interior and on the same side of the transversal.

26. $\angle 3$ and $\angle 8$ are interior and on the same side of the transversal.

27. $\angle 6$ and $\angle 2$ are alternate interior angles.

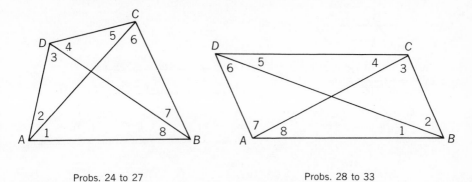

Probs. 24 to 27   Probs. 28 to 33

Which segments (if any) may be proved parallel by each of the statements below (28 to 33)?

28. $\angle 1 \cong \angle 5$.
29. $(m\angle 7 + m\angle 8) + (m\angle 1 + m\angle 2) = 180$.
30. $\angle 5 \cong \angle 2$.   **31.** $\angle 4 \cong \angle 7$.
32. $m\angle CDA + m\angle BAD = 180$.   **33.** $\angle 3 \cong \angle 7$.

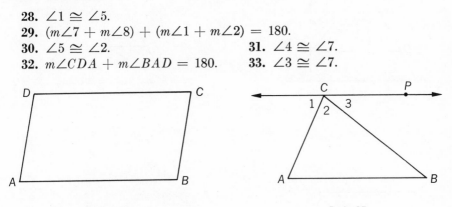

Prob. 34   Prob. 35

34. In the figure, $\overline{AB} \parallel \overline{CD}$, $\overline{AD} \parallel \overline{BC}$, and $m\angle A = 80$. Find the measure of each of angles B, C, and D.

35. In the figure, $\overleftrightarrow{CP} \parallel \overline{AB}$, $m\angle 1 = 45$, $m\angle 2 = 95$. Find $m\angle A + m\angle B + m\angle 2$.

36. In the figure, $\angle 2 \cong \angle 3$, $m\angle 1 = 110$, $\overline{AP} \parallel \overline{CB}$. Find the measures of angles 2, 3, B, and C.

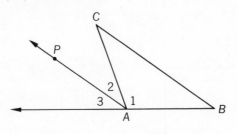

Prob. 36

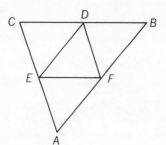

Prob. 37

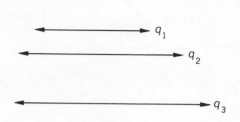

Prob. 42

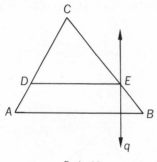

Prob. 46

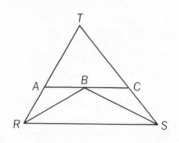

Prob. 47

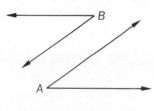

(a)

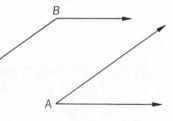

(b)

Prob. 48

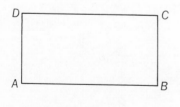

Prob. 49

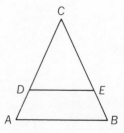

Prob. 50

37. In the figure, $\overline{CB} \parallel \overline{EF}$, $\overline{CA} \parallel \overline{DF}$, $\overline{AB} \parallel \overline{ED}$, $m\angle EDF = 60$, $m\angle DEF = 50$, $m\angle DFE = 70$. Find the measures of $\angle A$, $\angle B$, and $\angle C$.

38. Write a formal proof for Lemma 8–1.

39. Write a formal proof for Thm. 8–7. (*Hint:* Prove the theorem for *one* pair of corresponding angles.)

40. PROVE: If two parallel lines are cut by a transversal, and if any pair of corresponding angles are congruent, the other three pairs are congruent.

41. PROVE: Thm. 8–9.

42. GIVEN: $q_1 \parallel q_3$; $q_2 \parallel q_3$
    PROVE: $q_1 \parallel q_2$. (*Hint:* Introduce an auxiliary set.)
    (*Note:* This is Thm. 8–10.)

43. PROVE: Thm. 8–11.

44. PROVE: If two parallel lines are cut by a transversal, then alternate exterior angles are congruent.

45. PROVE: If two lines are cut by a transversal so that the alternate exterior angles are congruent, the lines are parallel.

46. GIVEN: $\triangle ABC$; $\angle CDE \cong \angle CAB$; $q \perp \overline{AB}$.
    PROVE: $q \perp \overline{DE}$.

47. GIVEN: $\overline{RB}$ bisects $\angle TRS$; $\overline{SB}$ bisects $\angle TSR$; $\overline{AC} \parallel \overline{RS}$.
    PROVE: (a) $\triangle ARB$ is isosceles; (b) $\triangle BCS$ is isosceles.

48. PROVE: In a plane, if the sides of an angle are parallel to the sides of a second angle, the angles are either (a) congruent or (b) supplementary. (*Hint:* Introduce opposite rays, or consider "extending" an existing ray.)

49. GIVEN: $\overline{DC} \perp \overline{CB}$; $\overline{AB} \perp \overline{BC}$; $m\angle a = 90$.
    PROVE: $m\angle D = 90$.

50. GIVEN: Isosceles $\triangle ABC$ (base $\overline{AB}$); $\overline{DE} \parallel \overline{AB}$.
    PROVE: $\triangle CDE$ is isosceles.

51. GIVEN: Isosceles $\triangle ABC$ (base $\overline{AB}$); $\overline{DE} \parallel \overline{CB}$. PROVE: $\overline{AD} \cong \overline{DE}$.

52. GIVEN: $q_1 \parallel q_2$; angle bisectors $\overrightarrow{AR}$ and $\overrightarrow{BP}$; transversal t.
    PROVE: $\overrightarrow{AR} \parallel \overrightarrow{BP}$.

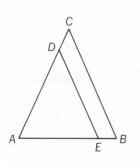

Prob. 51

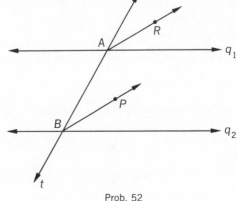

Prob. 52

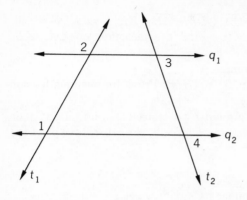

Prob. 53

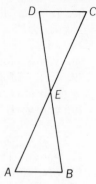

Probs. 54, 55

53. GIVEN: $\angle 1 \cong \angle 2$.
PROVE: $\angle 3 \cong \angle 4$.
54. GIVEN: $\overline{DC} \parallel \overline{AB}$; $\overline{DC} \cong \overline{AB}$.
PROVE: $\overline{DB}$ bisects $\overline{AC}$; $\overline{AC}$ bisects $\overline{DB}$.
55. GIVEN: E midpoint of $\overline{AC}$; E midpoint of $\overline{BD}$.
PROVE: $\overline{DC} \parallel \overline{AB}$.

(B)

56. GIVEN: $AC = BC$; $\overrightarrow{CE} \parallel \overline{AB}$.
PROVE: $\overrightarrow{CE}$ bisects $\angle DCB$.
57. GIVEN: $\overrightarrow{CE}$ bisects $\angle DCB$; $\overrightarrow{CE} \parallel \overline{AB}$.
PROVE: $\angle A \cong \angle B$.

58. Given two parallel lines. If a third coplanar line intersects one of the parallel
lines, it must intersect the other.

59. GIVEN: $\triangle ABC$; $\overrightarrow{PM} \parallel \overline{BC}$; $\overrightarrow{PM} \perp \overline{AB}$;
$\overline{BC} \perp \overline{AB}$; $\overrightarrow{PN} \perp \overline{AC}$.
PROVE: $\angle A \cong \angle MPN$.

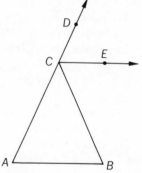

Probs. 56, 57

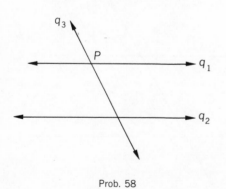

Prob. 58

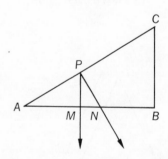

Prob. 59

60. GIVEN: $\triangle ABC$; $\overline{BE}$ bisects $\angle ABC$; $\overline{DQ}$ the perpendicular bisector of $\overline{BE}$.

PROVE: $\overline{DE} \parallel \overline{BC}$.

61. GIVEN: $q_1 \parallel q_2$; $\overline{AD} \perp q_1$; $\overline{BC} \perp q_2$.

PROVE: $AD = BC$.

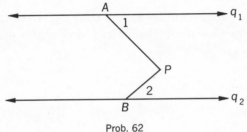

Prob. 60   Prob. 61

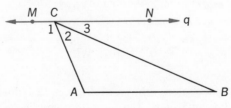

Prob. 62

62. GIVEN: $q_1 \parallel q_2$.

PROVE: $m\angle APB = m\angle 1 + m\angle 2$.

8-3 FURTHER PROPERTIES OF TRIANGLES

The theory of parallels developed thus far enables us to prove a key theorem of our geometry.

Theorem 8-12: **The sum of the measures of the angles of a triangle is 180.**

GIVEN: $\triangle ABC$.

PROVE: $m\angle A + m\angle 2 + m\angle B = 180$.

180 QUADRILATERALS AND PARALLELOGRAMS

Proof

STATEMENTS	REASONS
1. Introduce q through C so that $q \parallel \overline{AB}$.	1. Through a point not on a given line, there is exactly one line parallel to the given line (Thm. 8–3, Ax. 8–1).
2. $\angle MCN$ is a straight angle.	2. Def. of straight angle (alternate).
3. $m\angle MCN = 180$.	3. Def. of straight angle.
4. $m\angle 1 + m\angle 2 + m\angle 3 = m\angle MCN$.	4. Angle Addition Ax. (3–9).
5. $m\angle 1 + m\angle 2 + m\angle 3 = 180$.	5. Transitivity Ax. (O–4).
6. $\angle 1 \cong \angle A, \angle 3 \cong \angle B$.	6. Thm. 8–6.
7. $m\angle 1 = m\angle A, m\angle 3 = m\angle B$.	7. Def. of congruent angles.
8. $m\angle A + m\angle 2 + m\angle B = 180$.	8. Substitution Ax. (S–1).

Corollary 8–12.1: **If two angles of one triangle are congruent, respectively, to two angles of another, the third angles are congruent.**

GIVEN: $\angle A \cong \angle R$; $\angle C \cong \angle T$.
PROVE: $\angle B \cong \angle S$.

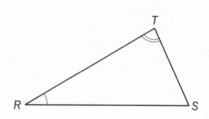

Proof

STATEMENTS	REASONS
1. $m\angle A + m\angle B + m\angle C = 180$. $m\angle R + m\angle S + m\angle T = 180$.	1. Thm. 8–12.
2. $m\angle A + m\angle B + m\angle C = m\angle R + m\angle S + m\angle T$.	2. Why?
3. $\angle A \cong \angle R, \angle C \cong \angle T$.	3. Why?
4. $m\angle A = m\angle R, m\angle C = m\angle T$.	4. Why?
5. $m\angle A + m\angle C = m\angle R + m\angle T$.	5. Why?
6. $\therefore m\angle B = m\angle S$.	6. Why?
7. $\angle B \cong \angle S$.	7. Why?

You should note particularly that Corollary 8–12.1 does not *require* that the two triangles be congruent, but certainly applies when the triangles *are* congruent.

Corollary 8–12.2: **The acute angles of a right triangle are complementary.**

The proof of Corollary 8–12.2 is left as an exercise.

Corollary 8–12.3: **The measure of an exterior angle of a triangle is equal to the sum of the measures of the two nonadjacent interior angles.**

GIVEN: $\triangle ABC$; exterior $\angle CBD$.
PROVE: $m\angle CBD = m\angle A + m\angle C$.

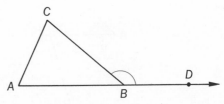

Proof

STATEMENTS	REASONS
1. $m\angle A + m\angle B + m\angle CBA = 180$.	1. Thm. 8–12.
2. $\angle ABC$ and $\angle CBD$ are supplementary.	2. Thm. 4–6.
3. $m\angle ABC + m\angle CBD = 180$.	3. Def. of supplementary angles.
4. $m\angle A + m\angle B + m\angle CBA = m\angle CBA + m\angle CBD$.	4. Substitution Ax. (S–1).
5. $m\angle A + m\angle B = m\angle CBD$.	5. Subtraction Ax. (E–5).

Corollary 8–12.4: **The measure of each of the angles of an equilateral triangle is 60.**

GIVEN: Equilateral $\triangle ABC$.
PROVE: $m\angle A = m\angle B = m\angle C = 60$.

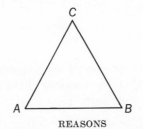

Proof

STATEMENTS	REASONS
1. $\triangle ABC$ is equilateral.	1. Given.
2. $\angle A \cong \angle B \cong \angle C$.	2. Equilateral triangles are equiangular (Thm. 5–12.1).
3. $m\angle A = m\angle B = m\angle C$.	3. Def. of congruent angles.
4. $m\angle A + m\angle B + m\angle C = 180$.	4. Thm. 8–12.
5. $3(m\angle A) = 180$.	5. Substitution Ax. (S–1).
6. $m\angle A = 60$.	6. Division Ax. (E–7).
7. $m\angle B = m\angle C = 60$.	7. Substitution Ax. (S–1).

EXAMPLES

1. In the figure, find $m\angle 1$, $m\angle 2$, $m\angle 3$, $m\angle 4$, $m\angle 5$.

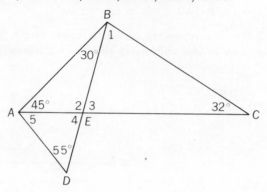

Solution:

(a) In $\triangle ABE$, $m\angle 2 + 30 + 45 = 180$

$$\therefore \underline{m\angle 2 = 105}$$

(b) $\angle 2$ and $\angle 3$ are supplementary, so $\underline{m\angle 3 = 180 - 105 = 75}$.

(c) $\angle 2$ is exterior to $\triangle BEC$. Hence, by Corollary 8–12.3,

$$m\angle 2 = m\angle 1 + 32$$
$$105 = m\angle 1 + 32$$
$$\underline{73 = m\angle 1}$$

(d) $\angle 3$ and $\angle 4$ are vertical angles and are congruent. $m\angle 4 = m\angle 3$ or $\underline{m\angle 4 = 75}$.

(e) In $\triangle ADE$, $m\angle 5 + m\angle 4 + 55 = 180$

$$m\angle 5 + 75 + 55 = 180$$
$$\underline{m\angle 5 = 50}$$

2. The measure of one angle of a triangle is twice the measure of a second angle. The measure of the third angle is three times the measure of the second angle. Find each measure.

Solution: Let $\angle A$ represent the first angle, $\angle B$ the second, and $\angle C$ the third angle. Then if $x = m\angle B$, $2x = m\angle A$, and $3x = m\angle C$, by Theorem 8–12,

$$m\angle A + m\angle B + m\angle C = 180$$
$$x + 2x + 3x = 180$$
$$6x = 180$$
$$\underline{x = 30}, \quad \underline{2x = 60}, \quad \underline{3x = 90}$$

Exercise 8-3

(A)

1. If the measures of two angles of a triangle are as follows, what is the measure of the third angle?
   (a) 10 and 40   (b) r and r (c) $(45 + x)$ and $(45 - x)$
   (d) 100 and 49   (e) 60 and 60   (f) 30 and 60

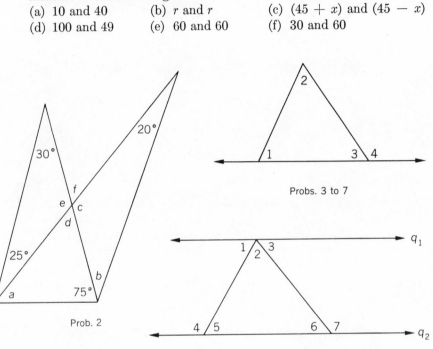

Probs. 3 to 7

Prob. 2

Probs. 8 to 10

2. Find the measure of each of the named angles in the diagram.
3. If $m\angle 1 = 70$ and $m\angle 2 = 40$, find $m\angle 4$.
4. If $m\angle 1 = 35$ and $m\angle 2 = 50$, find $m\angle 3$.
5. If $m\angle 2 = 45$ and $m\angle 4 = 115$, find $m\angle 1$.
6. If $m\angle 1 = r$ and $m\angle 2 = s$, find $m\angle 4$.
7. If $m\angle 1 = m\angle 3 = 60$, find $m\angle 2$.

In problems 8 to 10, $q_1 \parallel q_2$:

8. $m\angle 7 = 120$, $m\angle 5 = 40$. Find the measure of all other numbered angles.
9. $m\angle 6 = 65$, $m\angle 5 = 70$. Find the measure of all other numbered angles.
10. $m\angle 4 = 140$, $\angle 2 \cong \angle 6$. Find the measure of all other numbered angles.

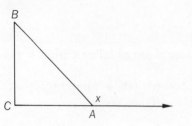

Prob. 11

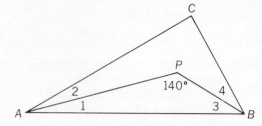

Prob. 12

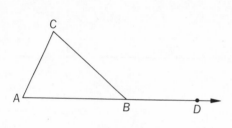

Prob. 17

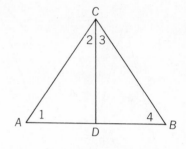

Prob. 18

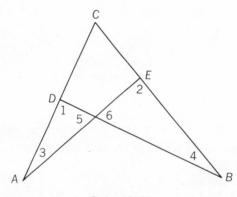

Probs. 19, 20

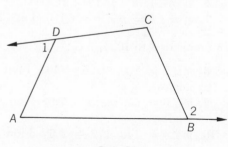

Probs. 21, 22

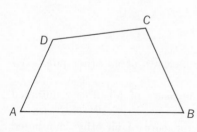

Prob. 23

Prob. 24

11. Given $\overline{AC} \cong \overline{BC}$ and $\overline{AC} \perp \overline{BC}$, find $m\angle B$, $m\angle x$, and $m\angle CAB$.

12. Given $\overrightarrow{AP}$ bisects $\angle CAB$ and $\overrightarrow{BP}$ bisects $\angle CBA$, find $m\angle C$.

13. The measure of a base angle of an isosceles triangle is equal to twice them easure of a second angle. Find the measure of each of the three angles of the triangle.

14. The measure of one of the angles of a triangle is three times the measure of a second angle. The measure of an exterior angle at the third vertex is 136. Find the measure of each angle of the triangle.

15. Show that a triangle is equilateral if the measures of its angles can be represented by $(x + 15)$, $(3x - 75)$, and $(2x - 30)$.

16. PROVE: Corollary 8–12.2.

17. PROVE: Corollary 8–12.3 using the given figure.   (*Hint:* Introduce $\overrightarrow{BP} \parallel \overline{AC}$.)

18. GIVEN: $\overline{CD} \perp \overline{AB}$; $\angle 2 \cong \angle 3$.
    PROVE: $\angle 1 \cong \angle 4$.

19. GIVEN: $\angle 1 \cong \angle 2$.
    PROVE: $\angle 3 \cong \angle 4$.

20. GIVEN: $\overline{BD} \perp \overline{AC}$; $\overline{AE} \perp \overline{BC}$.
    PROVE: $\angle 3 \cong \angle 4$.

21. GIVEN: $\overrightarrow{CD} \parallel \overline{AB}$; $\overrightarrow{CD}$ bisects $\angle ECB$.
    PROVE: $\overline{AC} \cong \overline{BC}$.

22. GIVEN: $\overrightarrow{CD}$ bisects $\angle ECB$; $\overline{AC} \cong \overline{BC}$.
    PROVE: $\overrightarrow{CD} \parallel \overline{AB}$.

23. GIVEN: Figure $ABCD$.
    PROVE: $m\angle A + m\angle B + m\angle C + m\angle D = 360$.   (*Hint:* Introduce one diagonal.)

24. GIVEN: Figure $ABCD$; $\overrightarrow{CD}$; $\overrightarrow{AB}$.
    PROVE: $m\angle 1 + m\angle 2 = m\angle A + m\angle C$.

25. PROVE: Thm. 8–12 using the given diagram, with $\overrightarrow{BP} \parallel \overline{AC}$. (*Note:* You must *not* use Thm. 8–12 in this proof.)

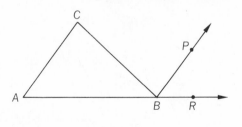

Prob. 25

(B)

26. GIVEN: $\overline{AC} \cong \overline{BC}$; $\overline{EB} \cong \overline{BD}$.
    PROVE: $m\angle CFE = 3(m\angle BDE)$.

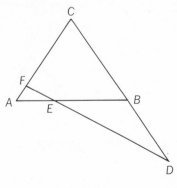

Prob. 26

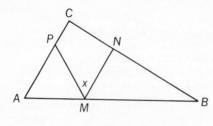

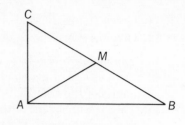

Prob. 27

Prob. 28

27. GIVEN: $\angle C$ a right angle; $\overline{AP} \cong \overline{AM}$; $\overline{MB} \cong \overline{BN}$.
   PROVE: $m\angle x = 45$.
28. GIVEN: $\triangle ABC$; $\overline{CA} \perp \overline{AB}$; $AM = MB$.
   PROVE: $AM = CM$.

8–4 POLYGONS

Given three noncollinear points, each pair determines a segment. The resulting figure is, as you know, a triangle. Suppose we are given five coplanar points, no three of which are collinear. Figure 8–5 shows some of the ways in which five coplanar points determine segments. Parts (a) and (b) are illustrations of *polygons*, (c) and (d) are not.

In order to develop an accurate definition of polygon, let us examine more closely the situation for five points. Since there is more than one way to join

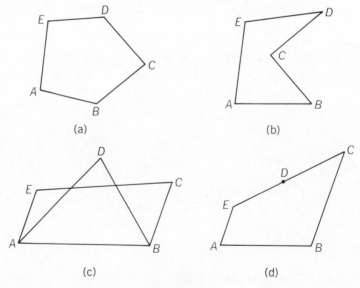

(a)   (b)

(c)   (d)

Figure 8–5

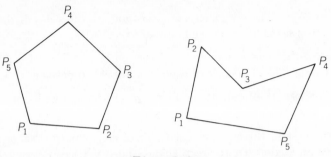

Figure 8-6

five points by segments, our goal is to make clear which resulting figures we shall call polygons, and which figures we shall rule out. Suppose we join five points by segments—that is, starting with a first point, join it to a second, the second to a third, the third to a fourth, and then join the fourth point to the first. To indicate the *order* in which the points were chosen to be joined, during this process, we shall use subscripts on the letter P. That is, P_1 is the first point chosen, P_2 the second, and more generally, P_n signifies the nth point.

Now consider five distinct coplanar points, no three of which are collinear. Join them with segments so that any two segments which intersect do so only at their endpoints. Label the points $P_1, P_2, \ldots, P_5$ so that the resulting segments are $\overline{P_1P_2}, \overline{P_2P_3}, \ldots, \overline{P_5P_1}$. The union of these segments is a polygon (Figure 8-6).

More generally, consider n distinct coplanar points, $(n \geq 3)$, no three of which are collinear: $P_1, P_2, \ldots, P_{n-1}, P_n$. Let the segments $\overline{P_1P_2}$, $\overline{P_2P_3}, \ldots, \overline{P_{n-1}P_n}, \overline{P_nP_1}$ be formed so that, as above, the only points in common to any two of these segments are endpoints. The union of these segments is a polygon of n sides (Figure 8-7). (The three dots in Figure 8-7 indicate other possible points and segments, depending upon the actual number, n.)

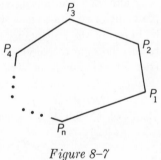

Figure 8-7

Definition 8-6: Let $P_1, P_2, P_3, \ldots, P_n$ be n distinct coplanar points $(n \geq 3)$. Let the n segments $\overline{P_1P_2}, \overline{P_2P_3}, \ldots, \overline{P_{n-1}P_n}, \overline{P_nP_1}$, be such that:

(1) No two segments intersect except at their endpoints.

(2) No two segments with a common endpoint are collinear.

The union of these n segments is a **polygon.**

The words *equilateral* and *equiangular* as applied to triangles are also applied to polygons of more than three sides, and have the same meaning: equilateral—all sides congruent; equiangular—all angles congruent.

Definition 8–7:   The n segments of a polygon are the **sides** of the polygon. Intersecting segments are called **consecutive sides.**

Definition 8–8:   The n points of intersection of the sides of a polygon are its **vertices.** The endpoints of each side are called **consecutive vertices.**

Definition 8–9:   A **diagonal** of a polygon is a segment with nonconsecutive vertices as endpoints.

As in the case of the triangle, each pair of consecutive sides of a polygon determines an angle. There are n angles and n vertices associated with an n-sided polygon. Just as we did for the triangle, we refer to the n angles associated with a polygon as "the angles of the polygon," whether or not the sides of the angles actually appear as rays.

Definition 8–10:   An angle of a polygon is an angle determined by a pair of consecutive sides. Angles of a polygon whose vertices are consecutive vertices of the polygon are **consecutive angles.**

A customary notation for polygons is to name consecutive vertices with consecutive letters of the alphabet, placing them either in clockwise or counterclockwise order. A study of the notation of Figure 8–5(a) and (b), as well as future illustrations, should help to clarify this.

A particular subset of the set of all polygons is the set of **convex** polygons. Each side of a polygon is contained in a line which separates the plane into two half-planes. Figure 8–8(a) shows polygon $ABCDE$, with two of the lines ($\overleftrightarrow{CD}$ and $\overleftrightarrow{BC}$) containing sides $\overline{CD}$ and $\overline{BC}$. Observe that $\overleftrightarrow{CD}$ divides the plane into two half-planes such that all the points of the polygon, except $\overline{CD}$, lie in *one* of the half-planes. (A similar situation exists for $\overleftrightarrow{BC}$.) You should readily be able to convince yourself that, in fact, the situation described is true for every side of $ABCDE$. On the other hand, for polygon $PQRST$ [Figure 8–8(b)], the same remarks do not apply. Considering the line that contains $\overline{QR}$, observe that there are points of the polygon lying in *both* half-planes of which $\overleftrightarrow{QR}$ is the edge.

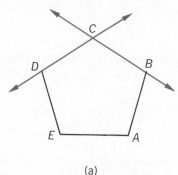

(a)

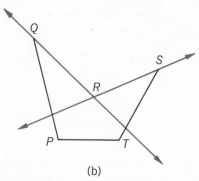

(b)

Figure 8–8

Definition 8–11: A polygon is a **convex polygon** iff no two of its vertices lie on opposite sides of a line containing any side of the polygon.

We shall have occasion to refer to polygons often, but the remainder of this chapter will be devoted almost entirely to convex polygons of four sides ($n = 4$).

Definition 8–12: A set of points is a **quadrilateral** iff it is a polygon and the number of its sides is four.

Exercise 8–4

From the figure:

1. Name the sides of the polygon.
2. Name at least three pairs of consecutive sides.
3. Name at least three pairs of consecutive angles.
4. Name at least three pairs of nonconsecutive angles.
5. Draw and name all diagonals having A as one endpoint.

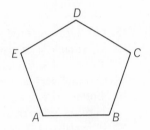

Probs. 1 to 5

From the figure:

6. How many sides in the figure?
7. Draw line $\overleftrightarrow{AB}$. Is the polygon convex?
8. Is the figure a quadrilateral?

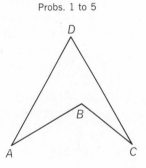

Probs. 6 to 8

From the figure:

9. Is the figure a quadrilateral?
10. Is the figure a convex polygon?
11. Draw *all* possible diagonals.

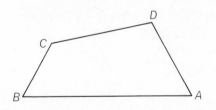

Probs. 9 to 11

Prob. 12

12. Draw three collinear points A, B, and C as shown. Place a fourth point D as shown. Introduce $\overline{AB}$, $\overline{BC}$, $\overline{CD}$, and $\overline{DA}$. Is the resulting figure a quadrilateral? Why or why not?

13. How many sides does a polygon with 43 vertices have? How many angles?

14. Test the figure against the requirements of Definition 8–6 (polygon).

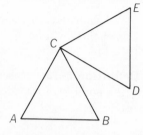

(a) Do any two segments intercept except at endpoints?

(b) Are any two segments with a common endpoint collinear?

(c) Why is this figure *not* a polygon?

Prob. 14

15. (a) Draw a convex quadrilateral and a diagonal from one vertex. How many triangles result?

(b) Draw a five-sided convex polygon, and all possible diagonals from one vertex. How many triangles result?

16. Follow the instructions of problem 15 for a six-, a seven-, and an eight-sided convex polygon.

17. Generalizing from problems 15 and 16:

(a) State a relationship between the number of sides of a convex polygon and the number of triangles resulting when all possible diagonals are drawn from one vertex.

(b) Let n ($n \geq 3$) represent the number of sides of a convex polygon. Write an algebraic expression for your answer to part (a).

18. (a) What is the sum of the measures of the angles of a triangle?

(b) What is the sum of the measures of the angles of four triangles?

(c) Represent algebraically the sum of the measures of $(n - 2)$ triangles.

Problems 15 to 18 lead to the following generalization: The sum of the measures of the angles of a convex polygon of n sides is $(n - 2)180$.

EXAMPLES

1. Find the sum of the measures of the angles of a seven-sided polygon.

Solution: Since $n = 7$, $(n - 2)180 = (7 - 2)180$

$$= (5)180$$

$$= 900$$

2. The sum of the measures of the angles of a convex polygon of n sides is 2700. Find the number of sides of the polygon.

Solution: We write

$$(n - 2)180 = 2700$$

$$(n - 2) = 15$$

$$n = 17 \quad \text{(The polygon has 17 sides.)}$$

19. Find the sum of the measures of the angles of a convex polygon of: six sides; eight sides; ten sides; twenty sides.

Find the number of sides of a convex polygon if the sum of the measures of its angles is:

20. 1260   **21.** 1980   **22.** 4140

23. Could the sum of the measures of the angles of a convex polygon of n sides be 920? Why?

24. How many sides has a convex polygon if the sum of the measures of its angles is equal to the sum of the measures of 16 right angles?

25. How many sides has a convex polygon if the sum of the measures of its angles is equal to the sum of the measures of 24 right angles?

26. Find the measure of each angle of a convex equiangular polygon of six sides.

27. Find the measure of each angle of a convex equiangular polygon of 15 sides.

28. (a) Draw an equilateral convex polygon with all of its angles right angles.

(b) Can you draw an equilateral polygon (with all right angles) different from your answer to part (a)? (See Exercise 8–5, problem 27.)

29. How many sides does a convex polygon have if each of its angles has a measure of 150?

30. How many sides does a convex polygon have if each of its angles has a measure of 108?

8–5 QUADRILATERALS

Some quadrilaterals with certain special properties are referred to by particular names. A list describing these special quadrilaterals follows.

Definition 8–13: A set of points is a **trapezoid** iff it is a quadrilateral with one and only one pair of parallel sides. The parallel sides are called **bases.**

Definition 8–14: A trapezoid is an **isosceles** trapezoid iff the nonparallel sides are congruent.

Definition 8–15: A set of points is a **parallelogram** iff it is a quadrilateral with both pairs of nonconsecutive sides parallel. (Notation: $\square ABCD$.)

Definition 8–16: A set of points is a **rhombus** iff it is a parallelogram all of whose sides are congruent.

Definition 8–17: A set of points is a **rectangle** iff it is a parallelogram all of whose angles are right angles.

Definition 8–18: A set of points is a **square** iff it is a rectangle all of whose sides are congruent.

The following five theorems (and a corollary) indicate some of the basic properties of parallelograms. Each of the theorems can be proved in a very straightforward manner; hence all proofs are left as exercises.

Theorem 8–13: Either diagonal separates a parallelogram into two congruent triangles.

Theorem 8–14: Any two nonconsecutive sides of a parallelogram are congruent.

Definition 8–19: The **distance between two parallel lines** is the distance from any point on one line to the other line.

(Recall Definition 7–2, the distance from a point to a line.)

Corollary 8–14.1: If $q_1 \parallel q_2$, and P and R are any two points on q_1, then the distances of P and R from q_2 are equal.

(This theorem is sometimes stated: **Parallel lines are everywhere equidistant.**)

Theorem 8–15: In a parallelogram, any two consecutive angles are supplementary.

Theorem 8–16: In a parallelogram, any two nonconsecutive angles are congruent.

Theorem 8–17: The diagonals of a parallelogram bisect each other.

The next three theorems furnish some methods, other than the definition, for determining when a quadrilateral is a parallelogram. Again proofs are very straightforward, and are left as exercises.

Theorem 8–18: If both pairs of nonconsecutive sides of a quadrilateral are congruent, the quadrilateral is a parallelogram.

Theorem 8–19: If two nonconsecutive sides of a quadrilateral are both congruent and parallel, the quadrilateral is a parallelogram.

Theorem 8–20: If the diagonals of a quadrilateral bisect each other, the quadrilateral is a parallelogram.

The proof of the following theorem provides an example of how the properties of a parallelogram help to develop new theorems.

Theorem 8–21: The segment joining the midpoints of two sides of a triangle is parallel to the third side, and is half as long as the third side.

GIVEN: $\triangle ABC$; M the midpoint of $\overline{AB}$; N the midpoint of $\overline{BC}$.
PROVE: $\overline{MN} \parallel \overline{AC}$; $MN = \frac{1}{2}AC$.

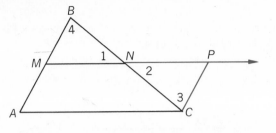

Proof

STATEMENTS	REASONS
1. Introduce P on the ray opposite to $\overrightarrow{NM}$ so that $NP = NM$.	1. Ax. 2–4.
2. $\overline{NP} \cong \overline{NM}$.	2. Why?
3. N the midpoint of $\overline{BC}$.	3. Given.
4. $BN = NC$.	4. Why?
5. $\overline{BN} \cong \overline{NC}$.	5. Why?
6. $\angle 1 \cong \angle 2$.	6. Vertical angles are congruent.
7. $\triangle MBN \cong \triangle NCP$.	7. SAS Ax. (5–2).
8. $\angle 3 \cong \angle 4$.	8. Def. of congruence.
9. $\overleftrightarrow{AB} \parallel \overleftrightarrow{CP}$.	9. Thm. 8–4.
10. M the midpoint of $\overline{AB}$.	10. Given.
11. $AM = MB$.	11. Why?
12. $\overline{AM} \cong \overline{MB}$.	12. Why?
13. $\overline{MB} \cong \overline{CP}$.	13. Def. of congruence.
14. $\overline{AM} \cong \overline{CP}$.	14. Transitive property of congruent segments (Thm. 5–3).
15. $ACPM$ is a parallelogram.	15. Thm. 8–19 (steps 9 and 14).
16. $\overline{MN} \parallel \overline{AC}$.	16. Def. of parallelogram.
17. $MN = \frac{1}{2}MP$.	17. Step 1.
18. $\overline{MP} \cong \overline{AC}$.	18. Thm. 8–14.
19. $MP = AC$.	19. Def. of congruent segments.
20. $MN = \frac{1}{2}AC$.	20. Substitution Ax. (S–1) (step 17).

Here are three more theorems and a definition to complete this section. Proofs of the theorems are left as exercises.

Theorem 8–22: **If a parallelogram has one right angle, then it has four right angles and the parallelogram is a rectangle.**

Theorem 8–23: **The diagonals of a rhombus are perpendicular to each other.**

Theorem 8–24: **If the diagonals of a quadrilateral bisect each other, and are perpendicular, then the quadrilateral is a rhombus.**

Definition 8–20: The **perimeter** of a polygon is the sum of the lengths of its sides.

EXAMPLES

1. The measure of one angle of a parallelogram is 40. Find the measure of each of the remaining angles.

Solution: Since consecutive angles are supplementary (Theorem 8–15), the measure of a second angle must be 140. Since any two nonconsecutive angles of a parallelogram are congruent (Theorem 8–14), a third angle must have measure 40, and the fourth angle measure 140.

2. If P is the midpoint of $\overline{AC}$, Q the midpoint of $\overline{AB}$, $m\angle A = 25$, $m\angle B = 42$, and $BC = 18$, find $\overline{PQ}$ and $m\angle 1$.

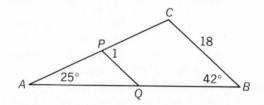

Solution: Since $\overline{PQ}$ is a segment connecting midpoints of two sides of a triangle, it is parallel to the third side, and PQ is half the length of the third side, hence $PQ = 9$ (Theorem 8–21). Since $\overline{PQ} \parallel \overline{CB}$, $\angle AQP \cong \angle B$, so $m\angle AQP = 42$. As an exterior angle of $\triangle AQP$, $m\angle 1 = m\angle A + m\angle AQP$, therefore

$$m\angle A = 25 + 42, \quad \text{or} \quad m\angle A = 67.$$

3. GIVEN: $\overline{TR} \cong \overline{RS}$; $\square ARST$; $\square RBST$.
   PROVE: $\triangle ABC$ is isosceles.

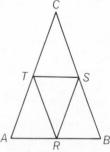

Proof

STATEMENTS	REASONS
1. $\square ARST$, $\square RBST$.	1. Given.
2. $\angle A \cong \angle RST$, $\angle B \cong \angle STR$.	2. Thm. 8–16.
3. $\overline{TR} \cong \overline{RS}$.	3. Given.
4. $\angle STR \cong \angle RST$.	4. Thm. 5–12.
5. $\angle A \cong \angle B$.	5. Substitution Ax. (S–1) (steps 2, 4).
6. $\overline{CA} \cong \overline{CB}$.	6. Thm. 5–13.
7. $\triangle ABC$ is isosceles.	7. Def. of isosceles triangle.

Exercise 8–5

(A)

State *always* if the statement is always true, *sometimes* if sometimes true, and *never* if never true (statements 1 to 18).

1. A parallelogram is a quadrilateral.
2. A quadrilateral is a parallelogram.
3. A rhombus is a trapezoid.
4. A square is a rectangle.
5. A rhombus is a square.
6. A square is a rhombus.
7. A quadrilateral with no sides parallel is a rhombus.
8. A quadrilateral with exactly one pair of nonconsecutive sides congruent is a parallelogram.
9. The bases of a trapezoid are congruent.
10. The set of all squares is a subset of the set of all rhombuses.
11. The set of all rhombuses is a subset of the set of all squares.
12. The set of all rhombuses is a subset of the set of all trapezoids.
13. The set of all trapezoids is a subset of the set of all rhombuses.
14. The set of all parallelograms is a subset of the set of all quadrilaterals.
15. The set of all quadrilaterals is a subset of the set of all parallelograms.
16. The diagonals of a quadrilateral bisect each other.
17. If a polygon has three distinct diagonals, it is a quadrilateral.
18. Nonconsecutive angles of a trapezoid are supplementary.

19. If the measure of one angle of a rhombus is 50, find the measures of the angles of the triangles formed by drawing the (a) longer diagonal, (b) shorter diagonal.
20. If the measure of one angle of a parallelogram is 70, find the measure of each of the remaining angles.
21. Find the length of each side of a parallelogram if one of its sides has length 6, and its perimeter is 28.
22. The length of one side of a parallelogram is two more than twice the length of another. The perimeter is 108. Find the length of each side.
23. If A, B, and C are midpoints, and $AB = 5$, $BC = 3$, and $AC = 6$, find RS, ST, and TR.

Prob. 23

24. The perimeter of a rhombus is 212. Find the length of each side.
25. The measure of one angle of a parallelogram is twice that of a consecutive angle. Find the measure of each angle of the parallelogram.

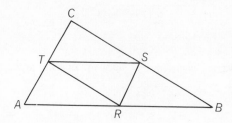

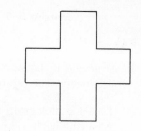

Prob. 26   Prob. 27

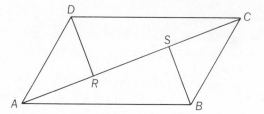

Prob. 38

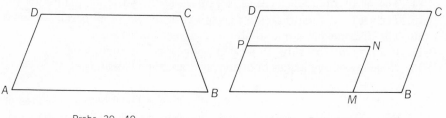

Probs. 39, 40   Prob. 41

26. If T, R, and S, are midpoints, and the perimeter of $\triangle ABC$ is 84, find the perimeter of $\triangle RST$.

27. Is an equilateral polygon with all of its angles right angles necessarily a square? What additional property is needed so that the statement will be true?

28. PROVE: Thm. 8–13 for just one diagonal. Is the proof for the second diagonal different?

29. PROVE: Thm. 8–14.

30. PROVE: Corollary 8–14.1.

31. PROVE: Thm. 8–15.   **32.** PROVE: Thm. 8–16.

33. PROVE: Thm. 8–17.   **34.** PROVE: Thm. 8–18.

35. PROVE: Thm. 8–19.   **36.** PROVE: Thm. 8–20.

37. PROVE: The diagonals of a rhombus are perpendicular to each other.

38. GIVEN: $\square ABCD$; $\overline{DR} \perp \overline{AC}$; $\overline{BS} \perp \overline{AC}$.
     PROVE: $\overline{DR} \parallel \overline{BS}$; $\overline{DR} \cong \overline{BS}$.

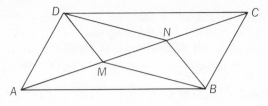

Prob. 42

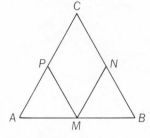

Prob. 43

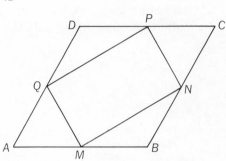

Prob. 44

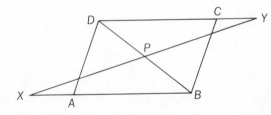

Prob. 45

39. GIVEN: Isosceles trapezoid $ABCD$; $\overline{AB} \parallel \overline{CD}$.
    PROVE: $\angle A \cong \angle B$. (*Hint:* Consider the distances from C and D to $\overline{AB}$.)
40. GIVEN: Trapezoid $ABCD$; bases $\overline{AB}$ and $\overline{CD}$; $\angle A \cong \angle B$.
    PROVE: $ABCD$ is an isosceles trapezoid.
41. GIVEN: $ABCD$ and $AMNP$ are parallelograms.
    PROVE: (a) $m\angle D + m\angle N = 180$; (b) $\angle N \cong \angle C$.
42. GIVEN: $\square ABCD$; $\overline{AD} \cong \overline{AM}$; $\overline{CN} \cong \overline{CB}$.
    PROVE: $MBND$ is a parallelogram.
43. GIVEN: $\overline{AC} \cong \overline{BC}$; M, N, P are midpoints.
    PROVE: $MNCP$ is a rhombus.
44. GIVEN: Rhombus $ABCD$; M, N, P, Q midpoints.
    PROVE: $MNPQ$ is a rectangle.
45. GIVEN: $\square ABCD$; $AX = CY$; D, C, Y, collinear; B, A, X, collinear.
    PROVE: $\overline{XY}$ bisects $\overline{DB}$.

46. PROVE: Either diagonal of a rhombus bisects the angles whose vertices
are the endpoints of the diagonal.

47. Let P be the midpoint of a diagonal of parallelogram $ABCD$. Let $\overline{XY}$
be any segment through P with endpoints on $\overline{BC}$ and $\overline{AD}$ respectively.
Prove that P bisects $\overline{XY}$.

48. PROVE: The diagonals of a rectangle are congruent.

49. Examine the diagrams. If P, Q, R, and S are midpoints, make a
conjecture about $PQRS$. State your conjecture and prove it. (*Hint:*
Introduce a diagonal of $ABCD$.)

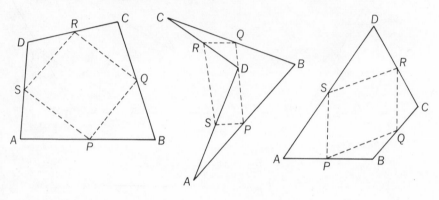

Prob. 49

50. PROVE: The segments joining the midpoints of opposite sides of a quadrilateral bisect each other. (*Hint:* See problem 49.)

(B)

51. GIVEN: $\overline{DE} \parallel \overline{AB}$; $\overline{DF} \parallel \overline{CB}$; $\overline{EF} \parallel \overline{AC}$.
PROVE: D, E, and F are midpoints.

52. Write an indirect proof: Two medians of a triangle cannot bisect each
other.

53. GIVEN: $\square ABCD$; angle bisectors $\overrightarrow{AP}$, $\overrightarrow{CM}$, $\overrightarrow{DM}$, $\overrightarrow{BP}$.
PROVE: $QMNP$ is a rectangle.

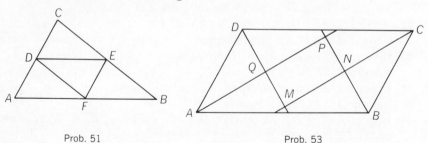

Prob. 51   Prob. 53

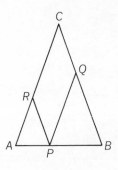

54. GIVEN: Isosceles $\triangle ABC$ (base $\overline{AB}$);

$\overline{PQ} \parallel \overline{AC}$;

$\overline{RP} \parallel \overline{CQ}$.

PROVE: (a) $RPQC$ is a parallelogram;

(b) $\triangle APR$ and $\triangle PBQ$ are isosceles.

Prob. 54

55. GIVEN: $\angle A \cong \angle C$; $\angle B \cong \angle D$.

PROVE: $ABCD$ is a parallelogram. (*Hint:* Draw a diagonal. Use your knowledge of the sum of the angles of a triangle.)

56. GIVEN: Square $ABCD$; R, S, P, Q divide the sides into segments of measure m and n as shown.

PROVE: $PQRS$ is a square.

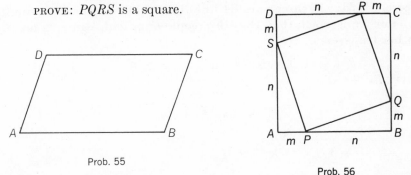

Prob. 55

Prob. 56

57. PROVE: A parallelogram is a rectangle if its diagonals are congruent.

58. PROVE: Thm. 8–22.

59. PROVE: Thm. 8–23.

60. PROVE: Thm. 8–24.

8–6 MANY PARALLEL LINES

Definition 8–21: If a transversal t intersects two lines, q_1 and q_2, in points A and B, respectively, then we say that q_1 and q_2 **intercept** $\overline{AB}$ on t. (Figure 8–9.)

If a transversal intersects three or more lines, more than one segment is intercepted. Thus in Figure 8–10, $\overline{AB}$, $\overline{BC}$, and $\overline{CD}$ are intercepted segments. These intercepted segments may or may not be congruent. Of particular interest is the case where the intercepting lines are parallel.

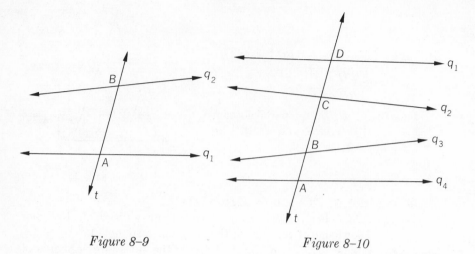

Figure 8-9   Figure 8-10

Theorem 8-25: **If three parallel lines intercept congruent segments on one transversal, then they intercept congruent segments on any other transversal.**

GIVEN: $q_1 \parallel q_2 \parallel q_3$; transversals t_1 and t_2; $\overline{AB} \cong \overline{BC}$.
PROVE: $\overline{RS} \cong \overline{ST}$.

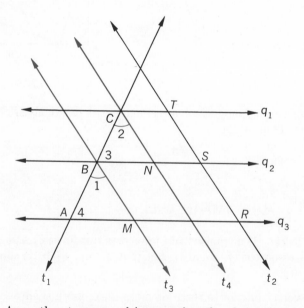

REMARK: Any other transversal intersecting the three given parallel lines must either intersect transversal t, or be parallel to transversal t. The case where the transversals intersect will be considered here; the case where they are parallel is left as an exercise.

Proof

STATEMENTS	REASONS
1. Through C introduce $t_4 \parallel t_2$, through B introduce $t_3 \parallel t_2$.	1. Parallel Ax. (8–1).
2. $t_3 \parallel t_4$.	2. Thm. 8–10.
3. $q_1 \parallel q_2 \parallel q_3$.	3. Given.
4. $\angle 1 \cong \angle 2$, $\angle 3 \cong \angle 4$.	4. Why?
5. $\overline{AB} \cong \overline{BC}$.	5. Given.
6. $\triangle AMB \cong \triangle BNC$.	6. ASA Ax. (5–3).
7. $\overline{BM} \cong \overline{CN}$.	7. Def. of congruence.
8. $NSTC$, $MRSB$ are parallelograms.	8. Def. of parallelogram.
9. $\overline{BM} \cong \overline{SR}$, $\overline{CN} \cong \overline{TS}$.	9. Thm. 8–14.
10. $\overline{SR} \cong \overline{TS}$.	10. Substitution Ax. (S–1) (steps 7, 9).

Corollary 8–25.1: If three or more parallel lines intercept congruent segments on one transversal, then they intercept congruent segments on any other transversal.

The proof of this corollary follows by repeated applications of Theorem 8–25, along with the transitive property of congruence of segments.

EXAMPLE

1. If $\overline{NQ} \parallel \overline{MP} \parallel \overline{AB}$, $CR = RS = SH$, $AC = 9$, $BC = 12$; find AM, MN, NC, BP, PQ, QC.

Solution: Through C introduce $q \parallel \overline{NQ}$. Then we have $q \parallel \overline{NQ} \parallel \overline{MP} \parallel \overline{AB}$, four parallel lines. Since $CR = RS = SH$, the four parallel lines intercept congruent segments on transversal $\overline{CH}$. Therefore they intercept congruent segments on any other transversal.

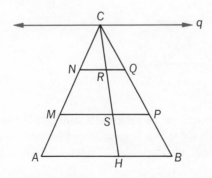

(1) On $\overline{CA}$: $\overline{CN} \cong \overline{NM} \cong \overline{MA}$ so $CN = NM = MA$. But $CA = 9$. Hence $CN = NM = MA = 3$.

(2) On $\overline{CB}$: $\overline{CQ} \cong \overline{QP} \cong \overline{PB}$ so $CQ = QP = PB$. But $CB = 12$. Hence $CQ = QP = PB = 4$.

Exercise 8–6

(A)

In the figure, $\overleftrightarrow{AM} \parallel \overleftrightarrow{BN} \parallel \overleftrightarrow{CP} \parallel \overleftrightarrow{DQ}$.

1. If $AB = BC = CD$, and $MQ = 30$, how long is $\overline{MN}$?

2. If $MN = NP = PQ$, and $CD = 5$, find AB and AD.

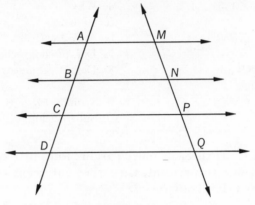

Probs. 1, 2

3. GIVEN: D the midpoint of $\overline{AC}$; $\overleftrightarrow{DE} \parallel \overline{AB}$.

PROVE: $\overleftrightarrow{DE}$ bisects $\overline{CB}$. (*Hint:* How can you introduce Thm. 8–22 into the problem?)

4. GIVEN: $\overleftrightarrow{PM} \parallel \overline{AB}$; $\overleftrightarrow{PN} \parallel \overline{CB}$; P the midpoint of $\overline{AC}$.

PROVE: $\triangle ANP \cong \triangle PMC$.

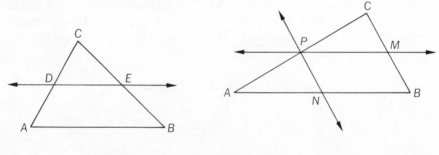

Prob. 3   Prob. 4

5. PROVE: The length of the segment joining the midpoints of the nonparallel sides of a trapezoid and parallel to the bases is one-half the sum of the bases. (*Hint:* Introduce a diagonal, use Thm. 8–21.)

EXAMPLES

Given trapezoid $ABCD$, M and N midpoints, $\overline{AB} \parallel \overline{CD} \parallel \overline{MN}$.

(a) If $AB = 20$ and $CD = 10$, find MN.

Solution: Using the result of problem 5:

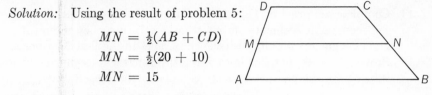

$$MN = \tfrac{1}{2}(AB + CD)$$
$$MN = \tfrac{1}{2}(20 + 10)$$
$$MN = 15$$

(b) If $CD = 10$ and $MN = 12$, find AB.

Solution: Again using problem 5:

$$MN = \tfrac{1}{2}(AB + CD)$$
$$12 = \tfrac{1}{2}(AB + 10)$$
$$24 = AB + 10$$
$$14 = AB$$

If $ABCD$ is a trapezoid, $\overline{AB} \parallel \overline{CD}$, M and N are midpoints, use the result of problem 5 to solve the following problems (6 to 8):

6. If $AB = 10$ and $DC = 8$, find MN.
7. If $AB = 12$ and $MN = 11$, find DC.
8. If $DC = 9$ and $MN = 11$, find AB.

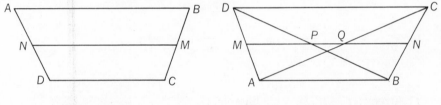

Probs. 6 to 8   Probs. 9 to 11

For problems 9 to 11, given trapezoid $ABCD$, midpoints M and N:

9. If $AB = 18$ and $CD = 24$, find MP, QN, PQ.
10. If $CD = 16$ and $AB = 8$, find MN, MP, QN, and PQ.
11. If $MN = 11$ and $CD = 14$, find AB, MP, QN, and PQ.

For problems 12 and 13, given trapezoid $ABCD$, $m\angle A = m\angle B = 45$, $\overline{DP} \perp \overline{AB}, \overline{CQ} \perp \overline{AB}, \overline{AB} \parallel \overline{CD}$:

12. If $CQ = 10$ and $AB = 30$, find AP, QB, and DC.
13. If $AB = 25$ and $DP = 5$, how long is the segment connecting the midpoints of $\overline{AD}$ and $\overline{BC}$?

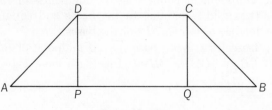

Probs. 12, 13

14. Complete the proof of Thm. 8–25. Prove: If three parallel lines intercept congruent segments on one transversal, then they intercept congruent segments on any transversal parallel to the first transversal.

15. Prove: If three parallel lines intercept congruent segments on one transversal, the parallel lines are equidistant from each other.

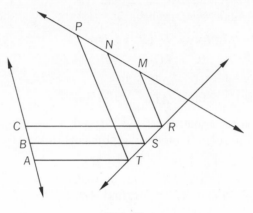

Prob. 16

16. GIVEN: $\overline{CR} \parallel \overline{BS} \parallel \overline{AT}$; $\overline{MR} \parallel \overline{NS} \parallel \overline{PT}$; $\overline{AB} \cong \overline{BC}$.
PROVE: $MN = NP$.

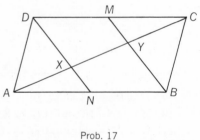

17. GIVEN: $\square ABCD$; midpoints M, N.
PROVE: $NBMD$ is a parallelogram.

18. Use the figure and result of problem **17**:
GIVEN: $\square ABCD$; midpoints M, N.
PROVE: $AX = XY = YC$.

Prob. 17

19. PROVE: A line through the midpoint of one side of a trapezoid parallel to the bases bisects the other side.

(B)

20. PROVE: The segment connecting the midpoints of the diagonals of a trapezoid is parallel to the bases and equal to half the difference of the lengths of the bases.

21. GIVEN: Isosceles $\triangle ABC$, base $\overline{AB}$, M midpoint of $\overline{BC}$, $\overline{MP} \perp \overline{AB}$.
PROVE: $PB = \frac{1}{4}(AB)$. (*Hint:* Introduce *more than one* line parallel to $\overline{MP}$.)

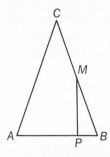

Prob. 21

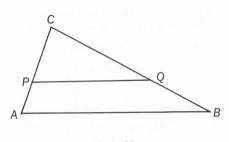

Prob. 22

22. GIVEN: $AP = \frac{1}{3}(AC)$, $\overline{PQ} \parallel \overline{AB}$.
PROVE: $BQ = \frac{1}{3}(BC)$.

8–7 RIGHT TRIANGLE THEOREMS

We have now developed sufficient material so that several theorems concerning right triangles can be established.

Theorem 8–26: If the hypotenuse and an acute angle of one right triangle are congruent to the corresponding parts of a second right triangle, then the triangles are congruent.

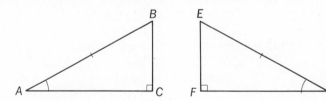

GIVEN: $\triangle ABC$; $\triangle DEF$; $\angle C$ and $\angle F$ are right angles; $\overline{AB} \cong \overline{DE}$; $\angle A \cong \angle D$.
PROVE: $\triangle ABC \cong \triangle DEF$.

Proof

STATEMENTS	REASONS
1. $\angle C$ and $\angle F$ are right angles.	1. Given.
2. $\angle C \cong \angle F$.	2. Any two right angles are congruent (Thm. 4–2).
3. $\angle A \cong \angle D$.	3. Given.
4. $\therefore \angle B \cong \angle E$.	4. Corollary 8–12.1.
5. $\overline{AB} \cong \overline{DE}$.	5. Given.
6. $\triangle ABC \cong \triangle DEF$.	6. ASA Ax. (5–3).

Theorem 8–27: **If the hypotenuse and one leg of one right triangle are congruent to the corresponding parts of a second right triangle, then the triangles are congruent.**

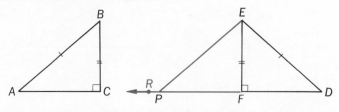

GIVEN: $\triangle ABC$; $\triangle DEF$; $\overline{AB} \cong \overline{DE}$; $\overline{BC} \cong \overline{EF}$; $\angle C$ and $\angle F$ are right angles.

PROVE: $\triangle ABC \cong \triangle DEF$.

Proof

STATEMENTS	REASONS
1. On $\overrightarrow{FR}$ opposite to $\overrightarrow{FD}$ introduce P so that $FP = AC$.	1. Ax. 2–4.
2. $\overline{FP} \cong \overline{AC}$.	2. Def. of congruent segments.
3. $\angle EFD$ is a right angle.	3. Given.
4. $\therefore \overline{EF} \perp \overline{PD}$.	4. Def. of perpendicular lines.
5. $\angle EFP$ is a right angle.	5. Thm. 4–12.
6. $\angle C$ is a right angle.	6. Given.
7. $\angle EFP \cong \angle C$.	7. Thm. 4–2.
8. $\overline{BC} \cong \overline{EF}$.	8. Given.
9. $\triangle ACB \cong \triangle PFE$.	9. SAS Ax. (5–2).
10. $\overline{AB} \cong \overline{PE}$.	10. Def. of congruence.
11. $\overline{AB} \cong \overline{DE}$.	11. Given.
12. $\therefore \overline{PE} \cong \overline{DE}$.	12. Transitive property, congruent segments (Thm. 5–3).
13. $\angle EPF \cong \angle D$.	13. Thm. 5–12 ($\triangle PDE$).
14. But $\angle EPF \cong \angle A$.	14. Def. of congruence.
15. $\angle D \cong \angle A$.	15. Transitive property, congruent angles (Thm. 5–7).
16. $\triangle ACB \cong \triangle DFE$.	16. Thm. 8–26 (steps 11, 15).

Theorem 8–28: **The length of the median to the hypotenuse of a right triangle is one half the length of the hypotenuse.**

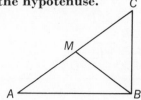

GIVEN: $\triangle ABC$;
$\qquad$ $\angle ABC$ is a right angle;
$\qquad$ median $\overline{BM}$.

PROVE: $BM = \frac{1}{2}AC$.

DISCUSSION: The proof consists essentially of two parts. *First*, auxiliary sets are introduced so that rectangle $ABCD$ is formed. (This part is left as an exercise.) *Second*, use is made of properties of a rectangle to arrive at the desired conclusion.

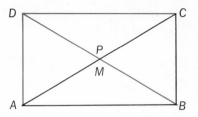

Proof (Second part): Consider rectangle $ABCD$ with diagonals $\overline{AC}$ and $\overline{BD}$. The diagonals of a rectangle bisect each other, so P is the midpoint of $\overline{AC}$. But M is the midpoint of $\overline{AC}$; by the uniqueness of the midpoint of a segment it follows that M and P coincide. Hence $\overline{BP}$ and median $\overline{BM}$ are the same segment. Next, the diagonals of a rectangle are equal in length ($AC = BD$). Since $BM = \frac{1}{2}BD$, $BM = \frac{1}{2}AC$ by substitution.

Theorem 8–29: **If an acute angle of a right triangle has measure 30, then the side opposite it is half as long as the hypotenuse.**

GIVEN: $\triangle ABC$; $m\angle C = 30$; $\angle CAB$ a right angle.
PROVE: $AB = \frac{1}{2}BC$.

Proof: Into $\triangle ABC$ introduce median $\overline{AM}$. Then $AM = \frac{1}{2}BC$ by Theorem 8–28, and $BM = \frac{1}{2}BC$ by the definitions of median and midpoint of a segment. Therefore $AM = MB$, and so $\overline{AM} \cong \overline{MB}$. Since two sides of $\triangle ABM$ are congruent, the angles opposite are congruent and have equal measures: $m\angle MAB = m\angle ABM$. Since $m\angle C = 30$ and $m\angle CAB = 90$, it follows that $m\angle B = 60$, and so $m\angle MAB = 60$. But then $m\angle AMB = 60$, and $\triangle ABM$ is equiangular, hence equilateral. Thus $\overline{AB} \cong \overline{BM}$ and $AB = BM$. Hence, by transitivity of equality, $AB = \frac{1}{2}BC$.

EXAMPLES

Given $\triangle ABC$, $\overline{BC} \perp \overline{CA}$, median $\overline{CN}$.
1. If $m\angle NCA = 30$ and $BC = 7$, find BA and CN.
2. If $m\angle B = 60$ and $CN = 3\frac{1}{4}$, find AB and BC.

Solutions
1. Since $\overline{CN}$ is a median, N is the midpoint of $\overline{BA}$. $CN = \frac{1}{2}BA$ (Thm. 8–25), or $CN = NA$. Then $\overline{CN} \cong \overline{NA}$, $\angle NCA \cong \angle A$ and $m\angle NCA = m\angle A = 30$. Hence $\triangle ABC$ is a 30°–60°–90° triangle, and $AB = 2BC$ (Thm. 8–29). Therefore $AB = 14$, and $CN = \frac{1}{2} \cdot 14 = 7$.

2. If $CN = 3\frac{1}{4}$, then $AB = 2CN = 6\frac{1}{2}$. Since $m\angle B = 60$, $\triangle ABC$ is 30°–60°–90°. Hence $BC = \frac{1}{2}AB$, or $BC = \frac{1}{2} \cdot 6\frac{1}{2} = 3\frac{1}{4}$.

3. Given $\square MNPQ$, $\overline{NR} \perp \overline{QR}$, $m\angle M = 135$. If $MN = 12$ and $NR = 6$, find QR.

Solution: Since $MNPQ$ is a parallelogram, $\angle QPN \cong \angle M$, hence $m\angle QPN = 135$. Then $m\angle RPN = 45$. Since $\overline{NR} \perp \overline{QR}$, $m\angle R = 90$ and so $m\angle PNR = 45$. Then $\triangle PRN$ is isosceles; $PN = PR = 6$. Now $MN = QP = 12$. Therefore $QR = QP + PR = 12 + 6 = 18$.

Exercise 8–7

(A)

In the figure: $\overline{AB} \perp \overline{BC}$, median $\overline{MB}$ (1 to 9):

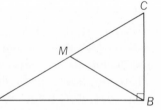

1. If $BC = 8$ and $m\angle A = 30$, find AC.
2. If $m\angle C = 60$ and $BC = 4\frac{1}{2}$, find AC.
3. If $m\angle C = 60$ and $AC = 11$, find BC.
4. If $MB = 11$, find AC.
5. If $CM = 21$, find BM.
6. If $m\angle C = 60$ and $AC = 12$, find BM.
7. If $AM = 9$ and $m\angle A = 30$, find BC.
8. If $AC = 30$, find BM.
9. If $MC = 14$, and $m\angle C = 60$, find BC.

Probs. 1 to 9

In the figure: $\square ABCD$, $\overline{CE} \perp \overline{AE}$ (10 to 15):

10. If $AD = 9$ and $m\angle A = 30$, find CE.
11. If $AD = 12$ and $m\angle ABC = 150$, find CE.
12. If $CE = 20$ and $m\angle DCB = 45$, find BE.
13. If $AD = 21$ and $m\angle A = 60$, find BE.
14. If $m\angle ADC = 135$ and $BE = 4$, find CE.
15. If $\overline{CE} \cong \overline{BE}$, find $m\angle A$ and $m\angle DCB$.

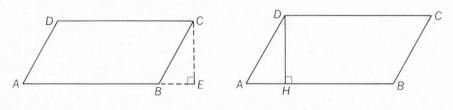

Probs. 10 to 15   Probs. 16 to 19

In the figure: $\Box ABCD$, $\overline{DH} \perp \overline{AB}$ (16 to 19):

16. If $m\angle A = 30$ and $DH = 9$, find AD.
17. If $m\angle ADH = 60$ and $DH = 11$, find BC.
18. If $DH = AH$, find $m\angle C$.
19. If $m\angle C = 45$ and $AH = 24$, find DH.

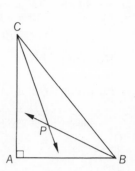

In the figure: $\overrightarrow{CA} \perp \overline{AB}$, $\overrightarrow{CP}$ bisects $\angle ACB$, $\overrightarrow{BP}$ bisects $\angle ABC$ (20 and 21):

20. If $m\angle ACB = 30$, find $m\angle CPB$.
21. If $\overline{CA} \cong \overline{AB}$, find $m\angle CPB$.

In the figure: $\overline{CD} \perp \overline{AB}$ (22 and 23):

Probs. 20, 21

22. If $m\angle A = 30$, $m\angle B = 45$, $AC = 12$, find DB.
23. If $m\angle ACD = 60$, $m\angle DCB = 45$, $DB = 9$, find AC.
24. GIVEN: $m\angle x = 135$; $\overline{AC} \cong \overline{BC}$.
      PROVE: $\triangle ABC$ is a right triangle.

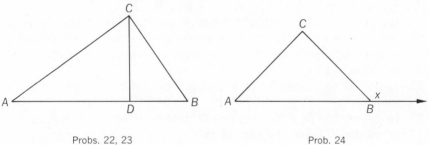

Probs. 22, 23   Prob. 24

25. GIVEN: $\overline{MR} \perp \overline{AC}$; $\overline{MS} \perp \overline{BC}$; M the midpoint of $\overline{AB}$; $MR = MS$.
      PROVE: $\triangle ABC$ is isosceles.
26. GIVEN: $\overline{CA} \perp \overline{AB}$; $\overline{DE} \perp \overline{BC}$; $\overline{AC} \cong \overline{CE}$.
      PROVE: $\overrightarrow{CD}$ bisects $\angle ACE$.

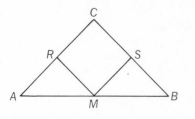
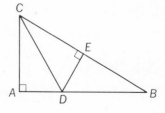

Prob. 25   Prob. 26

In the figure (27 and 28):

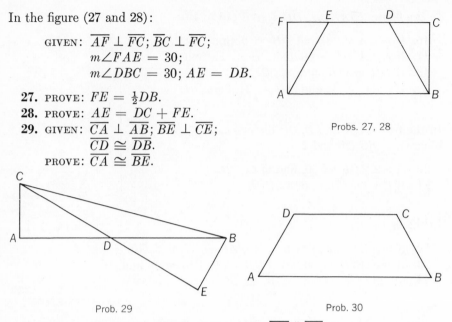

GIVEN: $\overline{AF} \perp \overline{FC}$; $\overline{BC} \perp \overline{FC}$;
$m\angle FAE = 30$;
$m\angle DBC = 30$; $AE = DB$.

27. PROVE: $FE = \frac{1}{2}DB$.
28. PROVE: $AE = DC + FE$.
29. GIVEN: $\overline{CA} \perp \overline{AB}$; $\overline{BE} \perp \overline{CE}$;
$\overline{CD} \cong \overline{DB}$.
PROVE: $\overline{CA} \cong \overline{BE}$.

Probs. 27, 28

Prob. 29

Prob. 30

30. GIVEN: Trapezoid $ABCD$; $AD = CB$; $\overline{AB} \parallel \overline{DC}$.
PROVE: $\angle A \cong \angle B$. (*Hint:* Drop perpendiculars from D and C to $\overline{AB}$.)
31. PROVE: In a right triangle, if a side opposite one acute angle is half as long as the hypotenuse, then that acute angle has measure 30. (*Hint:* See Thm. 8–28.)
32. PROVE: If two altitudes of a triangle are congruent, the triangle is isosceles.
33. In square $ABCD$, E is a point on $\overline{BC}$ between B and C. If $\overline{ED} \cong \overline{EA}$, prove that E is the midpoint of $\overline{BC}$.
34. PROVE: A right triangle is "cut" into two isosceles triangles by the median to the hypotenuse.

(B)

35. GIVEN: $\triangle ABC$; $\triangle DEF$; altitudes $\overline{CH}$ and $\overline{FJ}$; medians $\overline{CM}$ and $\overline{FN}$;
$\overline{CH} \cong \overline{FJ}$; $\overline{CM} \cong \overline{FN}$, $\angle B \cong \angle E$.
PROVE: $\triangle ABC \cong \triangle DEF$.

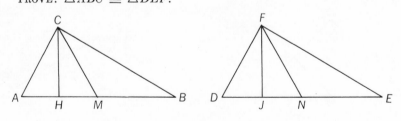

Prob. 35

36. PROVE: Two acute triangles are congruent if two sides and the altitude on the third side of one triangle are congruent respectively to the corresponding sides and altitude of the second triangle.

37. PROVE: If the diagonals of a trapezoid are congruent, the trapezoid is isosceles.

38. GIVEN: Trapezoid $ABCD$; $\overline{DA} \perp \overline{AB}$; E the midpoint of $\overline{CB}$.
PROVE: $AE = DE$.

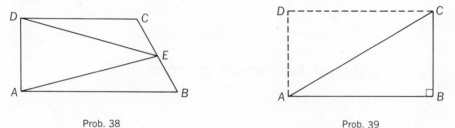

Prob. 38   Prob. 39

39. The first part of the proof of Thm. 8–28 was left as an exercise. Prove, starting with right $\triangle ABC$, that auxiliary sets may be introduced to form rectangle $ABCD$. (*Note:* Somewhere in your proof you must show that $\overrightarrow{AD}$ intersects $\overrightarrow{CD}$.)

Chapter 9

AREA OF POLYGONAL REGIONS

9–1 POLYGONAL REGIONS

In this chapter we will study the areas of polygons, or, more precisely, the areas of polygonal regions.

Before presenting a definition of "polygonal region," we shall discuss "triangular region." A triangular region is a geometric figure consisting of a triangle and its interior as indicated by the shading in Figure 9–1.

Definition 9–1: A **triangular region** is the union of a triangle and its interior.

Figure 9–1

A polygonal region is a plane figure that can, with one restriction, be divided into triangular regions as in Figure 9–2. The "one restriction" on the division into triangular regions is that the resulting triangles must not overlap. Thus the situation illustrated in Figure 9–3 is not acceptable, because $\triangle AGE$ and $\triangle FBC$ overlap, forming $\triangle FGD$. An acceptable division of the same polygon is shown in Figure 9–4.

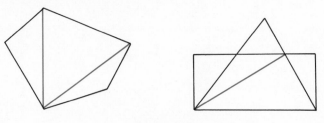

Figure 9–2

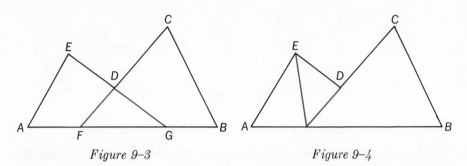

Figure 9-3   Figure 9-4

Definition 9-2: A **polygonal region** is the union of a finite number of coplanar triangular regions such that if any two triangular regions intersect, the intersection is either a segment or a point.

Here are some more examples of polygonal regions divided into triangular regions.

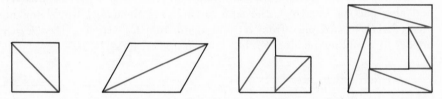

You know from past experience that each polygon has an "area" which is related in some fashion to the size and shape of the polygon. We recognize this concept in the next axiom and the definition following.

Axiom 9-1: **To every polygonal region there corresponds a unique positive real number.**

Definition 9-3: The **area** of a polygonal region is the unique number associated with it by Axiom 9-1. (Notation: area(R).)

Henceforth in this text, "region R" should be understood to mean "polygonal region R."

The word *unique* as used in Axiom 9-1 must be carefully interpreted. It does *not* mean that there is one and only one number associated with a given region. It *does* mean that for a *given choice of unit* there is one and only one such number.

The intuitive idea that two triangles having the same size and shape should also have the same area is stated formally as:

Axiom 9-2: **If two triangles are congruent, then the triangular regions determined by them have equal areas.**

Figure 9-5 illustrates some polygonal regions divided—not into triangular regions—but into other polygonal regions. From a consideration of sketches

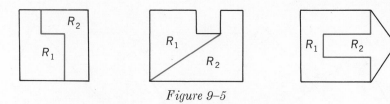

Figure 9–5

such as those in Figure 9–5, we are led to the following axiom:

Axiom 9–3: If R is the union of regions R_1 and R_2 and if R_1 and R_2 intersect in at most a finite number of segments and points, then:

$$\textbf{area}(R) = \textbf{area}(R_1) + \textbf{area}(R_2)$$

Restricting $R_1 \cap R_2$ to at most a finite number of segments and points simply eliminates the overlapping of R_1 and R_2. Note that, if overlapping occurred, we would have the condition illustrated by Figure 9–6, in which R_1 and R_2 overlap, forming $\triangle ABC$. Since area($\triangle ABC$) is part of area(R_1) and also part of area(R_2), the sum [area(R_1) + area(R_2)] would include area ($\triangle ABC$) *twice*, once from R_1 and again from R_2. Hence, [area(R_1) + area(R_2)] would *not* be area(R), but [area(R) + area($\triangle ABC$)].

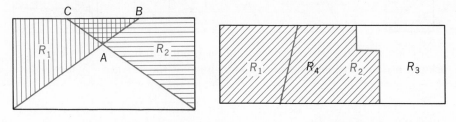

Figure 9–6   *Figure 9–7*

Although Axiom 9–3 does specify the division of R into *two* regions, this can easily be extended to three (Figure 9–7), for if R_1 and R_2 are considered as one region, R_4, we have:

$$\text{area}(R) = \text{area}(R_4) + \text{area}(R_3)$$
$$\text{area}(R_4) = \text{area}(R_1) + \text{area}(R_2)$$

and $\qquad\qquad$ area(R) = area(R_1) + area(R_2) + area(R_3)

It can be shown that if a region R is divided into n regions, $R_1, R_2, \ldots, R_n$, with the restriction of Axiom 9–3, then:

$$\text{area}(R) = \text{area}(R_1) + \text{area}(R_2) + \cdots + \text{area}(R_n)$$

Henceforth, when we refer to the "area of a polygon," we will mean the area of the corresponding polygonal region. For example, "area of a rectangle" means the area of the region that is determined by the rectangle.

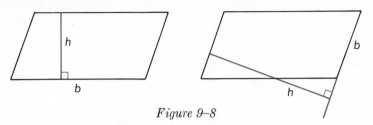

Figure 9–8

Several of the formulas we will introduce make reference to the "base" and "altitude" of various polygons, particularly of rectangles, triangles, parallelograms, and trapezoids.

Any side of a parallelogram may be considered as a base, and the corresponding altitude is a segment from any point in the opposite side, perpendicular to the base. Figure 9–8 indicates two possibilities. In each case *b* represents the length of the base, and *h* represents the length of the altitude.

Since a rectangle is a parallelogram, the discussion in the preceding paragraph applies to rectangles. However, since consecutive sides of a rectangle are perpendicular, a side of the rectangle consecutive to the base is an altitude (Figure 9–9).

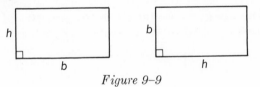

Figure 9–9

If a triangle is being considered, any side may be used as a base, and the altitude is the segment from the opposite vertex, perpendicular to the base (see "altitude," Definition 5–14). Figure 9–10 shows the three possibilities for one triangle.

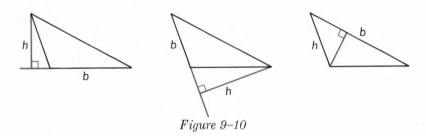

Figure 9–10

A trapezoid has two bases—the parallel sides. The altitude is a segment perpendicular to the bases, with its endpoints on the lines containing the bases (Figure 9–11).

In practice, it is convenient to have some unit to use when working with the area of a region. Actually, although we are free to choose any unit we

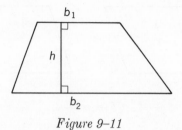

Figure 9-11

wish, we will use a *square unit* corresponding to the unit we are using for distance. Thus, if we are measuring distance in feet, we will measure area in square feet; if distance is in inches, area will be in square inches; if yards, area will be in square yards.

To develop some formulas for the areas of the regions we have been discussing, we will need to make an assumption as to how to compute the area of one particular region. It might seem logical to start with a square, say of side s, and assume the area to be s^2. This is certainly a simple formula, but it is surprisingly difficult to develop other formulas from this. Instead we choose the following axiom.

Axiom 9-4: **The area of a rectangle is the product of the length of its base and the length of its altitude.** (Formula: $A = bh$.)

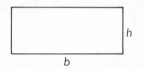

From Axiom 9-4 we have a theorem regarding the area of a square.

Theorem 9-1: **The area of a square is the square of the length of a side.** (Formula: $A = s^2$.)

Proof: Since a square is a rectangle with four sides of equal length, we have $b = h = s$, and the formula from Axiom 9-4 gives us:

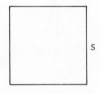

$$A = bh$$
$$A = s \cdot s$$
$$A = s^2$$

Note that in Axiom 9-4 and Theorem 9-1 we used the phrases "length of its base," "length of its altitude," and "length of a side." The words *base*, *altitude*, and *side* are also used to indicate the *lengths* of these segments. As this usage has been discussed earlier in Chapter 5, we merely mention that we will continue to use the words in this manner. With this use of the words, Axiom 9-4 and Theorem 9-1 may be restated as follows:

Axiom 9-4: **The area of a rectangle is the product of its base and altitude.**

Theorem 9-1: **The area of a square is the square of a side.**

Exercise 9-1

(A)

Show that each of the figures of problems 1 to 6 is a polygonal region by indicating a division into triangular regions. In each case try to choose the minimum number of triangular regions.

1.   **2.**   **3.**

4.   **5.**   **6.**

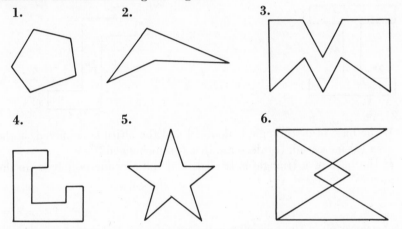

Problems 7 to 12 refer to the regions above. In each case, indicate a division of the given region that contains only triangles and quadrilaterals, with at least one quadrilateral.

7. Problem 1   **8.** Problem 2   **9.** Problem 3
10. Problem 4   **11.** Problem 5   **12.** Problem 6

Find the area of a rectangle with the given dimensions:

13. 6 ft. long by 3 ft. wide.   **14.** 8 ft. long by 5 ft. wide.
15. 5 in. by $2\frac{1}{2}$ in.   **16.** 7 in. by $3\frac{1}{2}$ in.
17. 4.5 cm. by 2.7 cm.   **18.** 3.4 cm. by 2.9 cm.

Find the area of a square with a side having the given length (19 to 22):

19. $5\frac{1}{2}$ in.   **20.** $4\frac{1}{3}$ in.
21. 12.3 mi.   **22.** 13.2 mi.

23. Find the altitude of a rectangle whose base is 12 ft. and whose area is 132 sq. ft.
24. Find the base of a rectangle whose altitude is 15 ft. and whose area is 315 sq. ft.

Compute the area of each of the following regions (25 to 28):

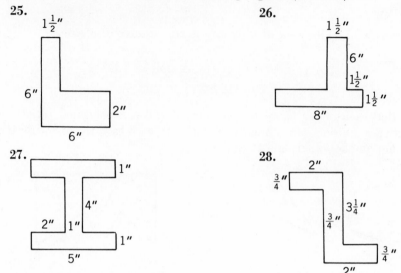

25.

26.

27.

28.

29. If the base of a rectangle is doubled and the altitude is halved, is the area (a) increased, (b) decreased, or (c) unchanged?

30. If the base of a triangle is tripled, and the altitude is halved, is the area (a) increased, (b) decreased, or (c) unchanged?

(B)

State whether each of the following is *true* or *false*.

31. A triangle is a polygonal region.

32. Every polygonal region has a unique area.

33. The union of two polygonal regions has an area equal to the sum of the areas of each region.

34. A triangular region is a polygonal region.

35. If two triangles do not have the same area they are not congruent.

36. Every plane figure with an area is a polygon.

In the proofs for problems 37 and 38, do not use formulas other than those introduced in this section.

37. GIVEN: Rectangle $ABDF$; $\overline{AE} \parallel \overline{BC}$.
   PROVE: area($ABDF$) = area($ABCE$).

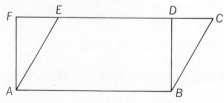

Prob. 37

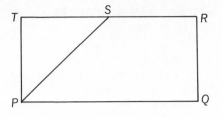

Prob. 38

38. GIVEN: Rectangle $PQRT$; S the midpoint of $\overline{RT}$.
PROVE: area$(PQRS) = 3[\text{area}(\triangle PST)]$.

9–2 AREAS OF TRIANGLES AND SOME QUADRILATERALS

Theorem 9–2: **The area of a right triangle is half the product of the lengths of its legs.** (Formula: $A = \frac{1}{2}ba$.)

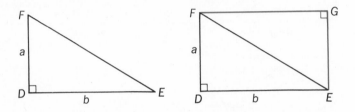

Proof: Given right $\triangle DEF$ with right angle at D. Let $DE = b$ and $DF = a$. Introduce lines through F and E parallel to $\overline{DE}$ and $\overline{DF}$, respectively. These lines will intersect, forming rectangle $DEGF$. Since $DEGF$ is also a parallelogram, the diagonal $\overline{FE}$ gives us $\triangle DEF \cong \triangle GFE$ (Thm. 8–13). Then by Axiom 9–2, area$(\triangle DEF) = $ area$(\triangle GFE)$, and by Axiom 9–3 we have:

$$\text{area}(DEFG) = \text{area}(\triangle DEF) + \text{area}(\triangle GFE)$$
$$= \text{area}(\triangle DEF) + \text{area}(\triangle DEF)$$
$$= 2[\text{area}(\triangle DEF)]$$

Thus $\qquad$ area$(\triangle DEF) = \frac{1}{2}[\text{area}(DEGF)]$

or $\qquad\qquad A = \frac{1}{2}ba$

Using Theorem 9–2, we can obtain a formula for the area of *any* triangle.

Theorem 9–3: **The area of a triangle is half the product of any base and the corresponding altitude.** (Formula: $A = \frac{1}{2}bh$.)

Proof: There are three cases to consider. In each case, let b represent the chosen base, h the corresponding altitude and A the area of $\triangle RST$.

Case I: A Right Triangle. This is covered by Theorem 9–2, since the altitude is one of the legs. Therefore:

$$A = \tfrac{1}{2}bh$$

Case II: The Altitude Exterior to the Triangle. Let $UR = b'$. Since $\triangle UST$ and $\triangle URT$ are right triangles, area($\triangle UST$) $= \frac{1}{2}(b' + b)h$ and area($\triangle URT$) $= \frac{1}{2}b'h$. Then we have:

area($\triangle UST$) $=$ area($\triangle URT$) $+ A$ (Ax. 9–3)

$\tfrac{1}{2}(b' + b)h = \tfrac{1}{2}b'h + A$ (Substitution Ax., S–1)

$\tfrac{1}{2}b'h + \tfrac{1}{2}bh = \tfrac{1}{2}b'h + A$ (Distributive Property, Ax. F–11)

$\tfrac{1}{2}bh = A$ (Subtraction Ax., E–5).

or $A = \tfrac{1}{2}bh$

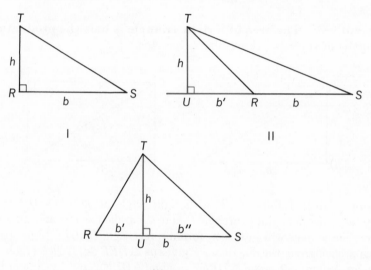

Case III: The Altitude in the Interior of the Triangle. Let $RU = b'$ and $US = b''$. Since $\triangle RUT$ and $\triangle UST$ are right triangles, area($\triangle RUT$) $= \frac{1}{2}b'h$ and area($\triangle UST$) $= \frac{1}{2}b''h$. Then we have:

area($\triangle RST$) $=$ area($\triangle RUT$) $+$ area($\triangle UST$)   (Ax. 9–3)

$A = \tfrac{1}{2}b'h + \tfrac{1}{2}b''h$ (Substitution Ax., S–1)

$A = \tfrac{1}{2}(b' + b'')h$ (Distributive Property, Ax. F–11)

$A = \tfrac{1}{2}bh$ (Substitution Ax., $b = (b' + b'')$, S–1)

This concludes the proof, since we have shown that in each case, $A = \tfrac{1}{2}bh$.

Notice that, as stated before, any side of a triangle may be considered the base when computing its area. Figure 9–12 shows the three possibilities for an acute triangle. Since Axiom 9–1 tells us that the area of a triangle is a *unique* number, we know that the area of a given triangle is the same, regardless of which side is considered as the base. Hence, from Figure 9–12 we can write:

$$\tfrac{1}{2}b_1h_1 = \tfrac{1}{2}b_2h_2 = \tfrac{1}{2}b_3h_3$$

This property will be investigated further in some of the exercises.

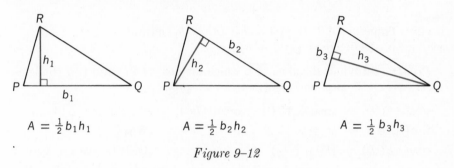

$$A = \tfrac{1}{2}b_1h_1 \qquad\qquad A = \tfrac{1}{2}b_2h_2 \qquad\qquad A = \tfrac{1}{2}b_3h_3$$

Figure 9–12

The method for computing the area of a triangle gives us a basis for computing the area of any polygonal region, since we need only divide the region into its component triangular regions. The area of the region is then found by applying the extension of Axiom 9–3 discussed earlier, and summing the areas of the triangles. We limit ourselves, however, to finding formulas for the areas of parallelograms and trapezoids.

Theorem 9–4: **The area of a parallelogram is the product of a base and the corresponding altitude.**

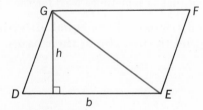

GIVEN: $\square DEFG$; $DE = b$; altitude h.
PROVE: area$(DEFG) = bh$.

Proof: Introduce diagonal $\overline{GE}$. By Theorem 8–13 we know that GE divides $DEFG$ into two congruent triangles. Axiom 9–2 then tells us that area$(\triangle DEG) = $ area$(\triangle FGE)$, hence:

$$\text{area}(DEFG) = 2[\text{area}(\triangle DEG)] = 2 \cdot \tfrac{1}{2}bh = bh$$

and the theorem is proved.

Theorem 9–5: The area of a trapezoid is half the product of its altitude and the sum of its bases.

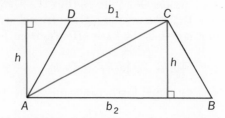

GIVEN: Trapezoid $ABCD$; $AB = b_2$; $DC = b_1$; altitude h.

PROVE: area$(ABCD) = \frac{1}{2}h(b_1 + b_2)$.

Proof: Introduce diagonal $\overline{AC}$, which divides $ABCD$ into two triangles. area$(\triangle ABC) = \frac{1}{2}b_2h$ and area$(\triangle ACD) = \frac{1}{2}b_1h$.

area$(ABCD)$ = area$(\triangle ACD)$ + area(ABC) (Why?)

area$(ABCD) = \frac{1}{2}b_1h + \frac{1}{2}b_2h$ (Why?)

area$(ABCD) = \frac{1}{2}h(b_1 + b_2)$ (Distributive Property, Ax. F–11)

The next two theorems are essentially algebraic in nature, as they refer to the *ratio* of two numbers. In your work in algebra you were introduced to the concept of ratio. We review it here briefly.

The ratio of one number to a second is the quotient of the first number divided by the second. For example, the ratio of 3 to 2 is written $\frac{3}{2}$, and $\frac{4}{7}$ would be read "the ratio of 4 to 7." In general, $\frac{p}{q}$ $(q \neq 0)$ is the ratio of p to q. Another symbol that is sometimes used for the ratio of p to q is $p:q$.

Theorem 9–6: If two triangles have equal altitudes, then the ratio of their areas is equal to the ratio of their bases.

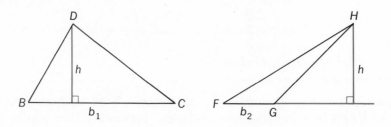

GIVEN: $\triangle BCD$ and $\triangle FGH$, with altitude from D equal to the altitude from H; $BC = b_1$; $FG = b_2$.

PROVE: $\dfrac{\text{area}(\triangle BCD)}{\text{area}(\triangle FGH)} = \dfrac{b_1}{b_2}$.

Proof

$$\text{area}(\triangle BCD) = \tfrac{1}{2}b_1h$$

$$\text{area}(\triangle FGH) = \tfrac{1}{2}b_2h$$

$$\therefore \quad \frac{\text{area}(\triangle BCD)}{\text{area}(\triangle FGH)} = \frac{\tfrac{1}{2}b_1h}{\tfrac{1}{2}b_2h} = \frac{b_1}{b_2}$$

Theorem 9–7: **If two triangles have equal bases, then the ratio of their areas is equal to the ratio of their altitudes.**

The proof of Theorem 9–7 is left as an exercise.

Theorem 9–8: **If two triangles have equal altitudes and equal bases, then they have equal areas.**

The proof of Theorem 9–8 is almost trivial, and is left as an exercise.

To illustrate the implications of the last theorem, each of the following triangles has an area equal to that of each of the others.

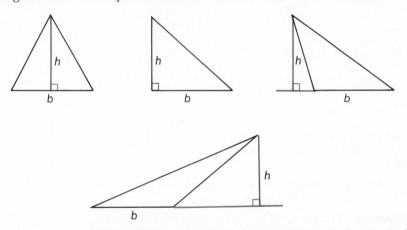

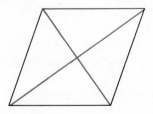

Theorem 9–9: **The area of a rhombus is half the product of the lengths of the diagonals.**

The proof of Theorem 9–9 is left as an exercise.

EXAMPLES

1. Consider right $\triangle ABC$ with $AC = 6$, $AB = 8$, $BC = 10$. Find

   (a) area($\triangle ABC$);
   (b) the altitude to the hypotenuse.

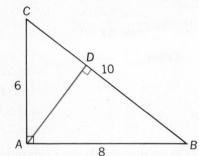

Solution

(a) By Theorem 9–2, area($\triangle ABC$) is one half the product of the legs. Therefore area($\triangle ABC$) $= \frac{1}{2} \cdot 6 \cdot 8 = 24$.

(b) By Theorem 9–3, area($\triangle ABC$) is one-half the product of any base and the corresponding altitude. Therefore:

$$\text{area}(ABC) = \tfrac{1}{2}BC \cdot AD$$

and since we know area($\triangle ABC$) $= 24$, we have:

$$\tfrac{1}{2} \cdot 10 \cdot AD = 24$$

$$5AD = 24$$

$$AD = \frac{24}{5}$$

2. If $AB = DE$ and area($\triangle ABC$) $= 50$, find area($\triangle DEF$).

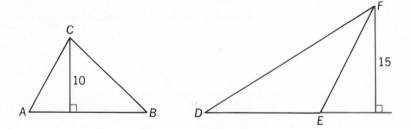

Solution: By Theorem 9–7, since the triangles have equal bases, the ratio of the areas is equal to the ratio of the altitudes. Thus:

$$\frac{\text{area}(\triangle DEF)}{50} = \frac{15}{10} \qquad \text{area}(\triangle DEF) = 50 \cdot \frac{15}{10} = 75$$

3. Find the area of a parallelogram if two consecutive sides have lengths 10 and 20, and the included angle has measure 30.

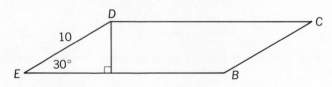

Solution: The formula for the area, $A = bh$, requires the lengths of a base and altitude. We know $b = EB = 20$, but we do not know the value for h. However, $\triangle DFD$ is a right triangle, and $m\angle E = 30$, so that by Theorem 8–26, $h = \frac{1}{2}(ED) = 5$. Therefore area$(\square BCDE) = bh = 100$.

4. Find the area of trapezoid $BCDE$ if $h = 10$, $ED = 20$ and $m\angle B = m\angle C = 45$.

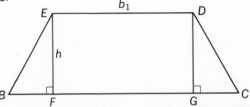

Solution: The formula, $A = \frac{1}{2}h(b_1 + b_2)$ requires values for h and b_1, both of which we have, and a value for b_2, which we do not have. But since we are given $m\angle B = m\angle C = 45$, we know that $\triangle BEF$ and $\triangle CDG$ are isosceles right triangles. Therefore, $BF = EF = 10$, and $CG = DG = 10$. Also, since $\overline{ED} \parallel \overline{BC}$, and $\overline{EF} \parallel \overline{DG}$, we have $FG = ED = 20$. Thus $BC = BF + FG + GC = 40$, and:

$$A = \tfrac{1}{2}h(b_1 + b_2) = \tfrac{1}{2} \cdot 10(20 + 40) = 300$$

5. Given rhombus $ABCD$, $AF = 10$, and $DF = 4$, find area$(ABCD)$.

Solution: $AF = 10$ and $DF = 4$. Since a rhombus is a parallelogram, we know that $AC = 2(AF) = 20$, and $DB = 2(DF) = 8$ (Thm. 8–17). Then, by Thm. 9–9,

area$(ABCD) = \frac{1}{2}(20)(8) = 80$.

Exercise 9–2

(A)

Find area$(\triangle BCD)$ using the information given in each problem (1 to 10).

1. $BC = 16$, $DE = 7$
2. $BC = 25$, $DE = 12$
3. $BC = 10.4$, $DE = 3.2$
4. $BC = 8.6$, $DE = 4.4$
5. $BC = 12$, $DC = 12$, $m\angle C = 30$
6. $BE = 5$, $EC = 9$, $m\angle B = 45$
7. $BE = 7$, $EC = 11$, $m\angle C = 45$
8. $BD = 10$, $BC = 20$, $m\angle B = 30$
9. $BD = 5$, $DC = 12$, $\overline{BD} \perp \overline{DC}$
10. $DC = 15$, $BD = 8$, $\overline{BD} \perp \overline{DC}$

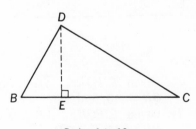

Probs. 1 to 10

Find area($\square DEFG$) using the information given in each problem (11 to 16).

11. $GF = 12$, $GH = 3\frac{1}{3}$ **12.** $GH = 4$, $GF = 8\frac{1}{2}$
13. $DE = 15$, $FE = 10$, $m\angle E = 150$
14. $m\angle F = 30$, $GF = 14$, $EF = 12$
15. $GF = 16$, $HE = 12$, $m\angle F = 45$
16. $HE = 10$, $GH = 6$, $m\angle E = 135$

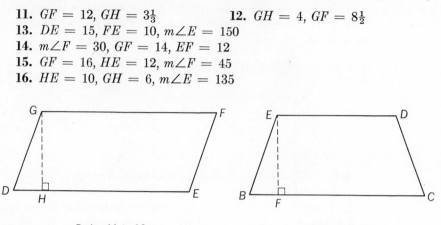

Probs. 11 to 16   Probs. 17 to 22

Find the area of trapezoid $BCDE$ using the information given in each problem (17 to 22).

17. $ED = 4$, $BC = 8$, $EF = 3$ **18.** $EF = 5$, $ED = 6$, $BC = 10$
19. $EB = 12$, $m\angle B = 30$, $ED = 6$, $BC = 16$
20. $DC = 8$, $m\angle C = 30$, $BC = 9$, $ED = 7$
21. $\overline{EB} \cong \overline{DC}$, $ED = EF = 6$, $BF = 5$
22. $\angle B \cong \angle C$, $EF = 5$, $BF = ED = 6$

23. Given right $\triangle CDE$, area($\triangle CDE$) $= 240$, $CD = 30$, and $DE = 34$, find (a) CE, (b) CF.
24. Given right $\triangle CDE$, area($\triangle CDE$) $= 150$, $CE = 15$, and $CF = 12$; find (a) DE, (b) CD.

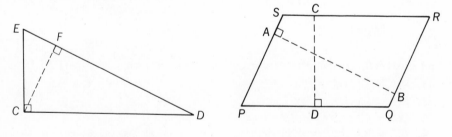

Probs. 23, 24   Probs. 25, 26

25. Given $\square PQRS$, $\overline{AB} \perp \overline{PS}$, $\overline{CD} \perp \overline{PQ}$, $PQ = 12$, $CD = 5$, and $QR = 10$; find AB.
26. Given $\square PQRS$, $\overline{AB} \perp \overline{QR}$, $\overline{CD} \perp \overline{RS}$, $PS = 8$, $AB = 10$, and $SR = 16$; find CD.

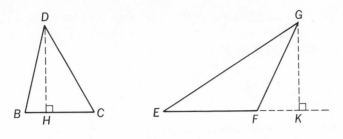

Probs. 27, 28

27. Given $\triangle BCD$, $\triangle EFG$, $\overline{DH} \perp \overline{BC}$, $\overleftrightarrow{GK} \perp \overleftrightarrow{EF}$, $DH = GK$, $\dfrac{BC}{EF} = \frac{3}{4}$, and area($\triangle BCD$) = 45; find area($\triangle EFG$).

28. Given $\triangle BCD$, $\triangle EFG$, $\overline{DH} \perp \overline{BC}$, $\overleftrightarrow{GK} \perp \overleftrightarrow{EF}$, $BC = EF$, $\dfrac{DH}{GK} = \frac{2}{3}$, and area($\triangle EFG$) = 36; find area($\triangle BCD$).

29. PROVE: A median of a triangle divides it into two triangles of equal area.

30. PROVE: The triangle formed by the segment joining any vertex of a parallelogram to the midpoint of a nonconsecutive side has an area one-fourth the area of the parallelogram.

(B)

31. A triangle and a parallelogram have equal areas and equal bases. How are their altitudes related?

For problems 32 to 35, given $\square BCDE$ and G the midpoint of $\overline{BE}$, find the ratio of the areas of:

32. $\square BCDE$ and $\triangle CDF$ **33.** $\triangle CDG$ and $\triangle CDF$
34. $\triangle BCG$ and $\triangle GDE$ **35.** $\triangle DGE$ and $\triangle CDF$

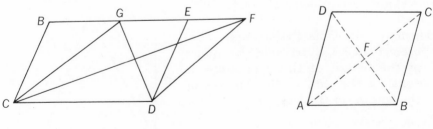

Probs. 32 to 35   Probs. 36 to 39

Find the area of rhombus $ABCD$ for each of the sets of dimensions in problems 36 to 39.

36. $AB = 10$, $m\angle DAB = 60$, $AC = 10\sqrt{3}$.
37. $BC = 8$, $m\angle ABC = 120$, $AC = 8\sqrt{3}$.
38. $m\angle DAB = 90$, $AC = 12$.   **39.** $m\angle ADC = 90$, $BD = 10$.

40. PROVE: If quadrilateral $PQRS$ has perpendicular diagonals, its area equals one-half the product of the lengths of the diagonals.

41. PROVE: A line through the point of intersection of the diagonals of a parallelogram divides the parallelogram into two regions of equal area.

42. PROVE: The diagonals of a parallelogram divide it into four triangles which are equal in area.

43. PROVE: Thm. 9–7.

44. PROVE: Thm. 9–8.

45. PROVE: Thm. 9–9. (*Hint:* Use Thms. 8–17, 8–23, and 9–8.)

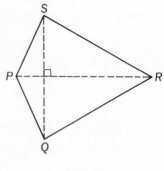

Prob. 40

9–3 THE PYTHAGOREAN THEOREM

Pythagoras was a brilliant Greek mathematician who lived about 540 B.C. This theorem bears his name because many historians have given him credit for being the first to write a proof of it; however, the theorem was apparently known long before Pythagoras. There is evidence that the Chinese knew of this relationship before 1100 B.C., and the Egyptians (at least for numerical cases) about 2000 B.C. This is probably one of the best-known theorems in mathematics—as well as one of the most used, having innumerable applications in engineering design and surveying, to mention just two areas.

There are hundreds of proofs for the Pythagorean Theorem. The one we give is of fairly recent origin, having been discovered by General James A. Garfield several years before he became President of the United States. (A second proof is considered in Chapter 10.)

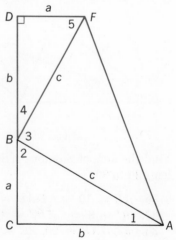

Theorem 9–10 (The Pythagorean Theorem): **In a right triangle, the square of the length of the hypotenuse is equal to the sum of the squares of the lengths of the legs.**

GIVEN: $\triangle ABC$; $\angle C$ a right angle.
PROVE: $c^2 = a^2 + b^2$.

Proof: Introduce the ray opposite to $\overrightarrow{BC}$ and locate D on that ray so that $BD = b$. At D introduce $\overline{DF} \perp \overline{BD}$ with F on the same side of $\overleftrightarrow{BC}$ as A, so that $DF = a$. Then $\triangle ABC \cong \triangle BFD$ (SAS Axiom, Axiom 5–2), and it follows that $\angle 4 \cong \angle 1$. Since $\angle 1$ and $\angle 2$ are complementary, it follows that $\angle 4$ and $\angle 2$ are complementary, and therefore $\angle 3$ is a right angle. Therefore, $\triangle ABF$ is a right triangle with each leg of length c. Also, area($ACDF$) = area($\triangle ABF$) + area($\triangle ABC$) + area($\triangle BFD$). Since B is between D and C, $CD = a + b$, and since $ACDF$ is a trapezoid, the equation above becomes:

$$\tfrac{1}{2}(a + b)(a + b) = \tfrac{1}{2}c^2 + \tfrac{1}{2}ab + \tfrac{1}{2}ab$$
$$\tfrac{1}{2}(a^2 + 2ab + b^2) = \tfrac{1}{2}c^2 + ab$$
$$\tfrac{1}{2}a^2 + ab + \tfrac{1}{2}b^2 = \tfrac{1}{2}c^2 + ab$$
$$\tfrac{1}{2}a^2 + \tfrac{1}{2}b^2 = \tfrac{1}{2}c^2$$
$$a^2 + b^2 = c^2$$

or
$$c^2 = a^2 + b^2$$

and the theorem is proved.

Theorem 9–11 is the converse of the Pythagorean Theorem.

Theorem 9–11: **If the square of the length of one side of a triangle is equal to the sum of the squares of the lengths of the other two sides, then the triangle is a right triangle, with the right angle opposite the first side.**

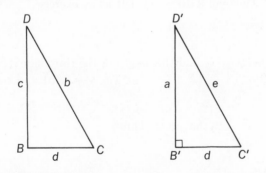

GIVEN: $\triangle ACD$; $b^2 = c^2 + d^2$.
PROVE: $\angle B$ is a right angle.

Analysis: We wish to show that $\angle B$ is a right angle. To do so, we will introduce a right triangle, $\triangle B'C'D'$, with legs of length c and d, and $\angle B'$ a right angle. Then by proving the two triangles congruent, we will have $\angle B \cong \angle B'$, and $\angle B$, therefore, a right angle.

Proof: Introduce right $\triangle B'C'D'$, with $\angle B'$ a right angle. By the Pythagorean Theorem we know $e^2 = c^2 + d^2$. But since we are given that $b^2 = c^2 + d^2$, we have $e^2 = c^2$, or by Axiom E–8, $e = c$. Hence, $\triangle BCD \cong \triangle B'C'D'$ (SSS Axiom, Axiom 5–4) and $\angle B = \angle B'$. Thus $\angle B$ is a right angle, which was to be proved.

There are two theorems concerning certain special right triangles that will be of interest to us. The first is a converse of Theorem 8–29.

Theorem 9–12: If one leg of a right triangle is half as long as the hypotenuse, the angle opposite that leg has measure 30.

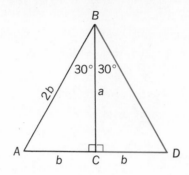

The proof of Theorem 9–12 is suggested by the drawing and is left as an exercise.

Theorem 9–13: The hypotenuse of an isosceles right triangle is $\sqrt{2}$ times as long as a leg.

The proof of Theorem 9–13 is also left as an exercise.

EXAMPLES

1. Given right $\triangle RST$, find the length of the third side if:
   (a) $r = 9$ and $t = 12$.   (b) $s = \sqrt{61}$ and $r = 5$.

Solution

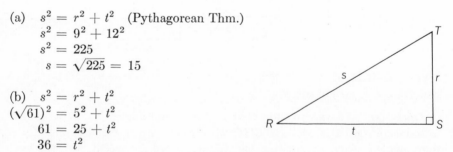

(a) $s^2 = r^2 + t^2$ (Pythagorean Thm.)
$$s^2 = 9^2 + 12^2$$
$$s^2 = 225$$
$$s = \sqrt{225} = 15$$

(b) $s^2 = r^2 + t^2$
$$(\sqrt{61})^2 = 5^2 + t^2$$
$$61 = 25 + t^2$$
$$36 = t^2$$
$$6 = t \quad \text{or} \quad t = 6$$

2. Can the following sets of numbers be the lengths of the sides of a right triangle?
   (a) 16, 30, 34.   (b) 4, 5, 6.
   Solution: (a) $34^2 = 1156$, $30^2 = 900$, $16^2 = 256$. Thus $34^2 = 30^2 + 16^2$, and by Theorem 9–11, such a triangle would be a right triangle.

(b) $6^2 = 36$, $5^2 = 25$, $4^2 = 16$. Since none of the resulting numbers is equal to the sum of the other two, such a triangle could not be a right triangle.

3. If $\triangle ABC$ is a right triangle and $m\angle A = 30$, find the length of the other sides, given:

(a) $a = 5$.   (b) $b = 14$.

Solution: (a) By Theorem 8–29, $b = 2a = 10$. By the Pythagorean Theorem, $b^2 = a^2 + c^2$ or $c^2 = b^2 - a^2$:

$$c^2 = b^2 - a^2$$
$$c^2 = 100 - 25$$
$$c^2 = 75$$
$$c = \sqrt{75} = \sqrt{25 \cdot 3}$$
$$c = 5\sqrt{3}$$

(b) By Theorem 8–29, $a = \frac{1}{2}b = 7$. By the Pythagorean Theorem,

$$c^2 = b^2 - a^2$$
$$c^2 = 196 - 49$$
$$c^2 = 147$$
$$c = \sqrt{147} = \sqrt{49 \cdot 3}$$
$$c = 7\sqrt{3}$$

4. If $\triangle DEF$ is an isosceles right triangle, find the lengths of the other sides, given:

(a) $d = 6$.   (b) $f = 8\sqrt{2}$.

Solution: (a) $d = 6$, therefore, because the triangle is isosceles, $e = 6$, and by Theorem 9–13, $f = 6\sqrt{2}$.

(b) By Theorem 9–13

$$d\sqrt{2} = f \qquad d = \frac{f}{\sqrt{2}} \qquad d = \frac{8\sqrt{2}}{\sqrt{2}} = 8$$

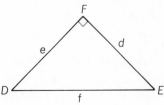

Exercise 9–3

(A)

In each of problems 1 to 10, find the length of the third side of right $\triangle BCD$:

1. $b = 3, c = 4$ **2.** $b = 5, c = 12$
3. $d = 25, b = 24$ **4.** $d = 17, c = 15$
5. $d = \frac{13}{2}, c = \frac{5}{2}$ **6.** $d = \frac{25}{2}, b = \frac{7}{2}$
7. $b = 3, c = 3$
8. $d = 10, b = 5$
9. $d = \sqrt{13}, b = 3$
10. $d = \sqrt{34}, c = 5$

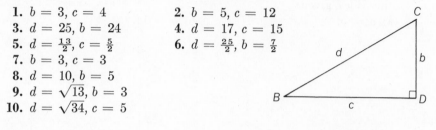

Probs. 1 to 10

Which of the following sets of numbers could be the lengths of the sides of a right triangle (11 to 20)?

11. 10, 24, 26   **12.** 6, 8, 10   **13.** 5, 7, 9
14. 9, 23, 24   **15.** 1, $1\frac{1}{3}$, $1\frac{2}{3}$ **16.** $1\frac{2}{3}$, 4, $4\frac{1}{3}$
17. 9, 40, 41   **18.** 11, 60, 61   **19.** 2, 4, $2\sqrt{3}$
20. 5, 5, $5\sqrt{2}$

If $\triangle RST$ is a right triangle and $m\angle R = 30$, find the lengths of the other sides (21 to 26). Given:

21. $r = 4$ **22.** $s = 12$ **23.** $s = 5$
24. $r = \frac{3}{2}$ **25.** $t = 2\sqrt{3}$ **26.** $t = 3\sqrt{3}$

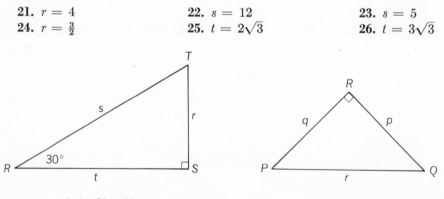

Probs. 21 to 26   Probs. 27 to 30

If $\triangle PQR$ is an isosceles right triangle, find the lengths of the other sides (27 to 30). Given:

27. $p = 4$ **28.** $q = 5$ **29.** $r = 7\sqrt{2}$ **30.** $r = 9\sqrt{2}$

31. Find the altitude of an equilateral triangle with side of length 8.
32. Find the length of the diagonal of a square with side of length 7.
33. In trapezoid $ABCD$, find AB if $m\angle A = 30$.
34. In trapezoid $ABCD$, find AB if $m\angle A = 60$.

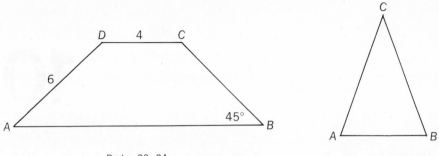

Probs. 33, 34

Probs. 35 to 40

(B)

For problems 35 to 40, given isosceles $\triangle ABC$ and $\overline{AC} \cong \overline{BC}$, find area($\triangle ABC$) if:

35. $AC = 20, m\angle A = 30$ **36.** $AB = 24, m\angle A = 30$

37. $AB = 24, m\angle A = 45$ **38.** $BC = 20, m\angle B = 45$

39. $AB = 24, m\angle B = 60$ **40.** $AC = 20, m\angle B = 60$

Find the length of a side of an equilateral triangle (41 to 44) whose altitude is:

41. $10\sqrt{3}$ **42.** $8\sqrt{3}$ **43.** 10 **44.** 8

Find the length of the side of a square (45 to 48) whose diagonal is:

45. $10\sqrt{2}$ **46.** $8\sqrt{2}$ **47.** 10 **48.** 8

49. Find the area of an isosceles triangle given the base is 20 and the congruent sides are each 26.

50. PROVE: If equilateral $\triangle ABC$ has side of length s, then

$$\text{area}(\triangle ABC) = \frac{s^2\sqrt{3}}{4}.$$

Use the formula of problem 50 to find the areas of the equilateral triangles with (51 to 54):

51. $s = 3$ **52.** $s = 5$ **53.** $s = \sqrt{7}$ **54.** $s = \sqrt{11}$

Problems 55 to 60 refer to rhombus $PQRS$.

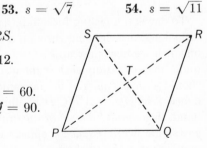

55. Find PQ if $PR = 16$, and $SQ = 12$.

56. Find RS if $PR = QS = 20$.

57. Find QS if $PQ = 12$ and $m\angle SPQ = 60$.

58. Find PR if $QR = 20$ and $m\angle SPQ = 90$.

59. Find area($PQRS$) if $SQ = 10$ and $m\angle PQR = 120$.

60. Find area($PQRS$) if $QR = 10$, and $m\angle PQR = 135$.

Probs. 55 to 60

61. Prove Thm. 9–12.   **62.** Prove Thm. 9–13.

Chapter 10

PROPORTION AND SIMILARITY

10–1 INTUITIVE SIMILARITY

You have seen that a correspondence that defines a congruence requires that corresponding parts be congruent. In this chapter we shall study a more general relationship (which includes congruence as a special case); that of **similarity.** Congruent figures may be informally described as "having the same size and shape"; similar figures may be informally described as "having the same shape, but not necessarily the same size." Thus, any two equilateral triangles are similar, any two squares are similar, and any two segments are similar (Figure 10–1). (A definition of a similarity is given in Section 10–2.)

Figure 10–1

To develop a feeling for similarity on an intuitive basis, imagine the effect of looking at a drawing through a magnifying glass. Under magnification, a one inch segment may appear to be two inches in length. It would seem that, under magnification, *each* segment of a drawing composed of many segments should appear enlarged in the same manner (Figure 10–2). The correspondence $ABCDE \leftrightarrow A'B'C'D'E'$ illustrates such a possibility. On the other hand, the overall "shape" of the drawing does not appear changed, which suggests that while *segments* appear enlarged, the measures of corresponding *angles* seem to be unchanged.

We do not need to restrict our imagination to the effect of a magnification only. Consider looking at Figure 10–2(b) through the wrong end of a telescope. The emerging polygon at (a) appears smaller—all the segments

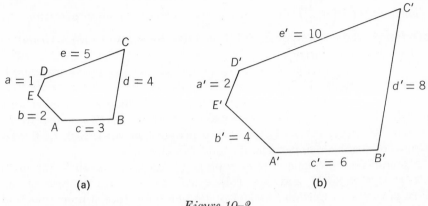

Figure 10–2

"shrinking" in the same way—but the overall polygon still appears to have the same "shape."

Clearly, $ABCDE \leftrightarrow A'B'C'D'E'$ is not a congruence, since corresponding sides are not congruent. Some special relationship seems to exist however, since each side of $A'B'C'D'E'$ is twice as long as the corresponding side of $ABCDE$, and corresponding angles seem congruent. In the remainder of this section we investigate this relationship between corresponding sides of polygons; along with the algebra needed to develop its details.

Let the symbols a, b, c, ... and a', b', c', ... represent the lengths of sides (Figure 10–2), and observe that a, b, c, ... and a', b', c', ... form two sequences of positive numbers. Each number of the first sequence is exactly half the corresponding number of the second sequence. Alternatively, each number of the second sequence is twice the corresponding number of the first. Algebraically:

$$a = \tfrac{1}{2}a' \qquad \text{or} \qquad a' = 2a$$
$$b = \tfrac{1}{2}b' \qquad\qquad\quad b' = 2b$$
$$c = \tfrac{1}{2}c' \qquad\qquad\quad c' = 2c$$
$$\vdots \qquad\qquad\qquad\qquad \vdots$$

By use of the Division Axiom (E–7) and Transitivity Axiom of Equality (E–3), we may also write:

$$\frac{a}{a'} = \frac{b}{b'} = \frac{c}{c'} = \cdots = \frac{1}{2} \qquad \text{or} \qquad \frac{a'}{a} = \frac{b'}{b} = \frac{c'}{c} = \cdots = 2$$

Sequences of positive numbers related in this way are called *proportional*.

Definition 10–1: Two sequences of positive numbers a, b, c, ... and p, q, r, ... are **proportional** iff:

$$\frac{a}{p} = \frac{b}{q} = \frac{c}{r} = \cdots = k \qquad \text{or} \qquad \frac{p}{a} = \frac{q}{b} = \frac{r}{c} = \cdots = \frac{1}{k} \quad (k \neq 0)$$

The number $k \left(\text{or } \dfrac{1}{k} \right)$ is the constant to which the number represented by each ratio of the series is equal. It is called the **constant of proportionality** or the **ratio of similitude.**

You will recall from algebra that a statement that two ratios are equal is called a proportion. Definition 10–1 describes equalities between more than two ratios. Such "chains" of equalities are called **continued proportions.** Most frequently our work will use equalities between just two ratios. In the language of Definition 10–1, we have a **proportion** when each of the sequences of positive numbers contains just *two* members.

Algebraically, of course, a proportion is an equation. As such, the usual rules of algebra apply, and these rules enable us to change the form of any given proportion. Certain forms of proportions offer special properties that are used frequently enough to be worthy of note. We list some of these algebraic properties below, and identify them so that we shall be able to conveniently refer to them when they are used in the construction of proofs.

ALGEBRAIC PROPERTIES OF PROPORTIONS

IF: $a > 0,\, b > 0,\, c > 0,\, d > 0,$ and $\dfrac{a}{b} = \dfrac{c}{d}.$

THEN: (1) $ad = bc$

(2) $\dfrac{a}{c} = \dfrac{b}{d}$

(3) $\dfrac{b}{a} = \dfrac{d}{c}$ (Proportion by Inversion)

(4) $\dfrac{a + b}{b} = \dfrac{c + d}{d}$ (Proportion by Addition)

(5) $\dfrac{a - b}{b} = \dfrac{c - d}{d}$ (Proportion by Subtraction)

When using these properties as reasons in a proof, we shall refer to the first two as "Proportion Property (1), or (2)"; the others will be called by their listed names. The five properties listed are certainly not all the possible ones, but they suffice for our needs. Algebraic derivations of these are left as exercises.

EXAMPLES

1. Show that the following pair of sequences is proportional, and find the constant of proportionality:

$$2,\, 7,\, 9,\, 11 \qquad \text{and} \qquad 6,\, 21,\, 27,\, 33.$$

Solution: Examine the ratios: $\frac{2}{6}, \frac{7}{21}, \frac{9}{27},$ and $\frac{11}{33}.$ Since each simplifies to $\frac{1}{3},$ we may write: $\frac{2}{6} = \frac{7}{21} = \frac{9}{27} = \frac{11}{33}.$ Hence, by Definition 10–1, the sequences are proportional, with constant of proportionality $\frac{1}{3}.$

Alternatively, $\frac{6}{2} = \frac{21}{7} = \frac{27}{9} = \frac{33}{11} = \frac{3}{1}$; so that the constant of proportionality is 3.

2. Complete the following statements:

(a) If $\dfrac{a}{3} = \dfrac{4}{5}$, then $5a =$ _____.

(b) If $\dfrac{x}{4} = \dfrac{3}{y}$, then $\dfrac{x}{3} =$ _____.

(c) If $\dfrac{m}{5} = \dfrac{x}{y}$, then $m = \dfrac{x}{y}$ (?).

(d) If $\dfrac{a}{3} = \dfrac{b}{4}$, then $\dfrac{a+3}{3} =$ _____.

(e) If $\dfrac{12+3}{3} = \dfrac{x+5}{5}$, then $\dfrac{12}{3} =$ _____.

Solutions

(a) If $\dfrac{a}{3} = \dfrac{4}{5}$, then $5a = 3 \cdot 4$ (Proportion Prop. 1).

(b) If $\dfrac{x}{4} = \dfrac{3}{y}$, then $\dfrac{x}{3} = \dfrac{4}{y}$ (Proportion Prop. 2).

(c) If $\dfrac{m}{5} = \dfrac{x}{y}$, then $m = \dfrac{x}{y}$ (5)   (Multiplication Ax., O–3).

(d) If $\dfrac{a}{3} = \dfrac{b}{4}$, then $\dfrac{a+3}{3} = \dfrac{b+4}{4}$ (Proportion by Addition).

(e) If $\dfrac{12+3}{3} = \dfrac{x+5}{5}$, then $\dfrac{12}{3} = \dfrac{x}{5}$ (Proportion by Subtraction).

$$\left(Note: \quad \frac{12+3-3}{3} = \frac{12}{3} \text{ and } \frac{x+5-5}{5} = \frac{x}{5}. \right)$$

Exercise 10–1

(A)

Show that the following pairs of sequences are proportional. Find the constant of proportionality. Assume all letters denote positive numbers (1 to 10):

1. 1, 2, 3   and   3, 6, 9
2. 1, 3, 5   and   2, 6, 10
3. 2, 5, 7, 9, 15   and   8, 20, 28, 36, 60
4. 1, 7, 10, 11   and   3, 21, 30, 33
5. 10, 4, 6, 12, 14   and   5, 2, 3, 6, 7
6. 15, 9, 6, 21, 12   and   5, 3, 2, 7, 4
7. $\frac{1}{2}, \frac{1}{3}, \frac{1}{4}, \frac{1}{5}$ and $\frac{1}{3}, \frac{2}{9}, \frac{1}{6}, \frac{2}{15}$
8. $\frac{2}{5}, \frac{1}{4}, \frac{3}{7}, \frac{2}{3}$ and $\frac{3}{10}, \frac{3}{16}, \frac{9}{28}, \frac{1}{2}$
9. $2x, 3x, 4x$ and $6y, 9y, 12y$
10. $a, 6a, 7a$ and $2b, 12b, 14b$

11. In the following list of sequences of numbers, find all pairs of sequences that are proportional.

    (a) 1, 2, 3   (b) 9, 7, 17   (c) 5, 7, 9   (d) 18, 14, 34
    (e) 27, 21, 51   (f) 15, 30, 45   (g) 10, 14, 18   (h) $2\frac{1}{2}, 3\frac{1}{2}, 4\frac{1}{2}$
    (i) $\frac{1}{3}, \frac{2}{3}, 1$

12. If $\dfrac{4}{1} = \dfrac{x}{2} = \dfrac{12}{y} = \dfrac{z}{10}$, find x, y, and z.

13. If $\dfrac{3}{x} = \dfrac{5}{y} = \dfrac{13}{z} = \dfrac{3}{1}$, find x, y, and z.

14. Complete each statement:

    (a) If $\dfrac{x}{y} = \dfrac{4}{5}$, then $5x = $ _____.

    (b) If $\dfrac{a}{4} = \dfrac{1}{3}$, then $3a = $ _____.

    (c) If $\dfrac{7}{3} = \dfrac{2}{z}$, then $7z = $ _____.

Find x in each of the following proportions (15 to 18):

15. $\dfrac{x}{3} = \dfrac{5}{6}$ **16.** $\dfrac{4}{5} = \dfrac{7}{x}$ **17.** $\dfrac{2}{11} = \dfrac{3}{x}$ **18.** $\dfrac{13}{4} = \dfrac{x}{5}$

19. Complete each statement:

    (a) If $\dfrac{x}{3} = \dfrac{5}{9}$, then $x = \dfrac{5}{9}$ (?).   (b) If $\dfrac{a}{b} = \dfrac{2}{3}$, then $a = \dfrac{2}{3}$ (?).

    (c) If $\dfrac{m}{n} = \dfrac{a}{b}$, then $m = \dfrac{a}{b}$ (?).

Using the Algebraic Properties of Proportions, complete the following statements (20 to 27):

20. If $\dfrac{x}{2} = \dfrac{y}{3}$, then $\dfrac{x+2}{2} = $ _____.

21. If $\dfrac{3}{a} = \dfrac{b}{5}$, then $\dfrac{3+a}{a} = $ _____.

22. If $\dfrac{x}{y} = \dfrac{a}{b}$, then ———— $= \dfrac{a+b}{b}$.

23. If $\dfrac{5}{4} = \dfrac{15}{12}$, then $\dfrac{5-4}{4} = $ _____.

24. If $\dfrac{a+3}{3} = \dfrac{c+4}{4}$, then $\dfrac{a}{3} = $ _____.

25. If $\dfrac{x+y}{y} = \dfrac{a+b}{b}$, then $\dfrac{x}{y} = $ _____.

26. If $\dfrac{2}{3} = \dfrac{4}{6}$, then $\dfrac{2}{4} = $ _____.

27. If $\dfrac{x}{9} = \dfrac{y}{18}$, then $\dfrac{x}{y} = $ _____.

Which of the following are correct? Assume all letters represent positive numbers (28 to 33):

28. $\dfrac{4x}{14} = \dfrac{3x}{13}$

29. $\dfrac{a}{10a} = \dfrac{b}{10b}$

30. $\dfrac{a}{a^2} = \dfrac{b}{ab} = \dfrac{x}{bx}$

31. $\dfrac{x+y}{x^2+y^2} = \dfrac{1}{x+y}$

32. $\dfrac{x+y}{x^2-y^2} = \dfrac{1}{x-y}$

33. $\dfrac{a}{a^2} = \dfrac{b}{b^2} = \dfrac{c}{c^2} = \dfrac{d}{d^2}$

34. PROVE: If $\dfrac{a}{b} = \dfrac{c}{d}$, then $ad = bc$.

35. PROVE: If $\dfrac{a}{b} = \dfrac{c}{d}$, then $\dfrac{a}{c} = \dfrac{b}{d}$.

36. PROVE: If $\dfrac{a}{b} = \dfrac{c}{d}$, then $\dfrac{b}{a} = \dfrac{d}{c}$.

37. PROVE: If $\dfrac{a}{b} = \dfrac{c}{d}$, then $\dfrac{a+b}{b} = \dfrac{c+d}{d}$.
   (*Hint:* Add 1 to both sides.)

38. PROVE: If $\dfrac{a}{b} = \dfrac{c}{d}$, then $\dfrac{a-b}{b} = \dfrac{c-d}{d}$.

(B)

GIVEN: $\dfrac{a}{b} = \dfrac{c}{d}$ (a, b, c, d, denote positive numbers).

PROVE (39 to 42):

39. $\dfrac{a-1}{b} = \dfrac{bc-d}{bd}$

40. $\dfrac{a}{b} = \dfrac{c-a}{d-b}$

41. $\dfrac{a+1}{1} = \dfrac{bc+d}{d}$

42. $\dfrac{a+b}{a-b} = \dfrac{c+d}{c-d}$

10–2 SIMILAR POLYGONS

We are now prepared to define more precisely what is meant by the statement: Two polygons are similar.

Definition 10–2: A one-to-one correspondence between the vertices of two polygons is a **similarity between the polygons** iff:
(1) Corresponding sides are proportional.
(2) Corresponding angles are congruent.
(Notation: $ABCD\ldots \sim A'B'C'D'\ldots$. In words: "$ABCD\ldots$ is similar to $A'B'C'D'\ldots$.")

The phrase "corresponding sides are proportional" must be clearly understood. A side of a polygon is a segment, and to each segment there corresponds a unique positive number, its length. The ratio of two sides means the ratio of the length of the first segment to the length of the second segment, say $\dfrac{AB}{A'B'}$. By definition, a proportion is an equality between two ratios: e.g., $\dfrac{AB}{A'B'} = \dfrac{CD}{C'D'}$. In Definition 10–2 then, "corresponding sides are proportional" means that it is possible to obtain a continued proportion, in which each ratio is the ratio of the lengths of a pair of corresponding sides. As an example (Figure 10–3), under $ABCDE \leftrightarrow A'B'C'D'E'$, if:

(1) $\dfrac{AB}{A'B'} = \dfrac{BC}{B'C'} = \dfrac{CD}{C'D'} = \dfrac{DE}{D'E'} = \dfrac{EA}{E'A'}$

and

(2) $\angle A \cong \angle A'$, $\angle B \cong \angle B'$, $\angle C \cong \angle C'$, $\angle D \cong \angle D'$, and $\angle E \cong \angle E'$,

then $ABCDE \sim A'B'C'D'E'$.

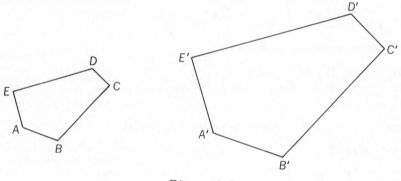

Figure 10–3

Note most particularly that Definition 10–2 requires *two* conditions: (1) corresponding sides must be proportional, and (2) corresponding angles must be congruent. Let us examine some situations that arise when one or the other of the two conditions is not satisfied.

1. Given $ABCD \leftrightarrow A'B'C'D'$ (Figure 10–4), where $ABCD$ is a rectangle and $A'B'C'D'$ is a parallelogram, but not a rectangle. Corresponding sides are proportional (ratio 1 to 2, or 2 to 1), but corresponding angles are not congruent. Clearly the "shapes" are quite different.

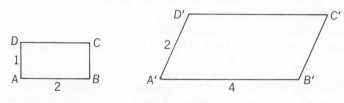

Figure 10–4

2. Given $ABCD \leftrightarrow A'B'C'D'$ (Figure 10–5), where $ABCD$ is a square and $A'B'C'D'$ is a rectangle, but not a square. Since all the angles of a square, as well as of a rectangle, are right angles, the corresponding angles are congruent. However, corresponding sides are not proportional, and the two quadrilaterals certainly do not have the same "shape."

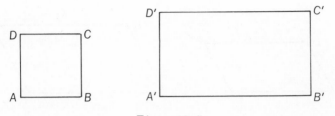

Figure 10–5

In this chapter our major emphasis will be on similarity of triangles. Since a triangle is a polygon, Definition 10–2 applies. It happens however that in the case of triangles, and *only* in the case of triangles, whenever one of the conditions of the definition holds, the other condition holds as well. That is, for two triangles, if corresponding angles are congruent, the corresponding sides will be proportional; conversely, if the corresponding sides are proportional, corresponding angles will be congruent. This situation will be more readily understood as we develop theorems to enable us to prove that two triangles are similar.

EXAMPLES

1. Given $ABCD \sim RSTP$ with ratio of similitude $\frac{3}{2}$ and sides of $ABCD$ as shown, find all the sides of $RSTP$.

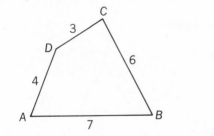 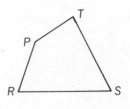

Solution: Since $ABCD \sim RSTP$, it follows that $\dfrac{AB}{RS} = \dfrac{BC}{ST} = \dfrac{CD}{TP} = \dfrac{DA}{PR} = \dfrac{3}{2}$ or $\dfrac{7}{RS} = \dfrac{6}{ST} = \dfrac{3}{TP} = \dfrac{4}{PR} = \dfrac{3}{2}$. From $\dfrac{4}{PR} = \dfrac{3}{2}$, we have $PR = \dfrac{8}{3}$; from $\dfrac{3}{TP} = \dfrac{3}{2}$, we have $TP = 2$; from $\dfrac{6}{ST} = \dfrac{3}{2}$, we have $ST = 4$; from $\dfrac{7}{RS} = \dfrac{3}{2}$, we have $RS = \dfrac{14}{3}$.

2. If $ABCD \sim EFGH$:

    (a) Write the continued proportion between corresponding sides.

    (b) List the pairs of congruent angles.

For (c) and (d) use the result of part (a).

    (c) Solve for AB in terms of EF, DA, and EH.

    (d) Solve for GH in terms of CD, DA, and HE.

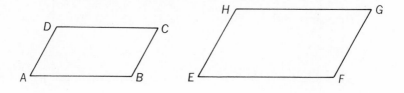

Solutions

    (a) If $ABCD \sim EFGH$, then $ABCD \leftrightarrow EFGH$, so:

$$\frac{AB}{EF} = \frac{BC}{FG} = \frac{CD}{GH} = \frac{DA}{HE}$$

    (b) $\angle A \cong \angle E$, $\angle B \cong \angle F$, $\angle C \cong \angle G$, $\angle D \cong \angle H$.

    (c) Select $\dfrac{AB}{EF} = \dfrac{DA}{HE}$, since these two ratios contain the measures asked for in the problem. Then: $AB = \left(\dfrac{DA}{HE}\right) EF$ by the Multiplication Axiom (E–6).

    (d) Select $\dfrac{CD}{GH} = \dfrac{DA}{HE}$. Then $\dfrac{GH}{CD} = \dfrac{HE}{DA}$ (Proportion by Inversion) and $GH = \left(\dfrac{HE}{DA}\right) CD$ by the Multiplication Axiom (E–6).

3. PROVE: Two equiangular triangles are similar.

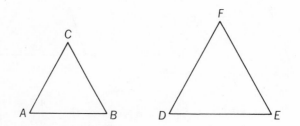

GIVEN: $\triangle ABC$ and $\triangle DEF$ are equiangular.

PROVE: $\triangle ABC \sim \triangle DEF$.

Analysis: To prove polygons similar, we have only Definition 10–2. This requires that corresponding angles be congruent, and corresponding sides proportional.

Proof

STATEMENTS	REASONS
1. $\triangle ABC$ and $\triangle DEF$ are equiangular.	1. Given.
2. $\triangle ABC$ and $\triangle DEF$ are equilateral.	2. Corollary 5–13.1.
3. $m\angle A = m\angle B = m\angle C = 60$, $m\angle D = m\angle E = m\angle F = 60$.	3. Corollary 8–12.4.
4. $m\angle A = m\angle D$, $m\angle B = m\angle E$, $m\angle C = m\angle F$.	4. Substitution Ax. (S–1).
5. $\angle A \cong \angle D$, $\angle B \cong \angle E$, $\angle C \cong \angle F$.	5. Def. of congruent angles.
6. $AB = BC = CA$, $DE = EF = FD$.	6. Def. of equilateral triangle.
7. $\dfrac{AB}{DE} = \dfrac{BC}{EF}, \dfrac{BC}{EF} = \dfrac{CA}{FD}$.	7. Division Ax. (E–7).
8. $\dfrac{AB}{DE} = \dfrac{BC}{EF} = \dfrac{CA}{FD}$.	8. Transitivity Ax. (E–3).
9. $\triangle ABC \sim \triangle DEF$.	9. Definition 10–2 (steps 5, 8).

Exercise 10–2

(A)

Given $ABCDEF \sim RSTUVW$ and the sides of $ABCDEF$ are longer than the corresponding sides of $RSTUVW$ (1 to 9):

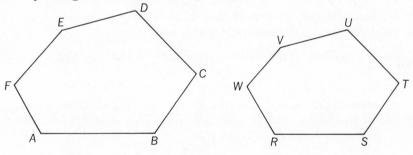

Probs. 1 to 9

1. Write the continued proportion between corresponding sides.
2. List the pairs of congruent angles.
3. If $AB = 3$ and $RS = 1$, what is the ratio of similitude for these two similar polygons?
4. If $DE = \frac{2}{3}$ and $UV = \frac{1}{2}$, what is the ratio of similitude for these two similar polygons?
5. If the ratio of similitude for the two polygons is $\frac{3}{1}$ and $AB = 2$, $BC = 2$, $CD = 3$, $DE = 3$, $EF = 2$, $FA = 1$; find all the sides of $RSTUVW$.

6. If the ratio of similitude is $\frac{3}{2}$ and $AB = 2$, $BC = 3$, $CD = 4$, $DE = 3$, $EF = 2$, and $FA = 1$; find all the sides of $RSTUVW$.
7. If the ratio of similitude is $\frac{4}{3}$ and $RS = 2$, $ST = 2$, $TU = 1$, $UV = \frac{3}{4}$, $VW = \frac{1}{2}$ and $WR = \frac{1}{2}$; find all the sides of $ABCDEF$.
8. If the ratio of similitude is $\frac{3}{5}$ and $m\angle A = 150$, find $m\angle R$.
9. If the ratio of similitude is $\frac{2}{3}$ and $m\angle T = 87$, find $m\angle C$.

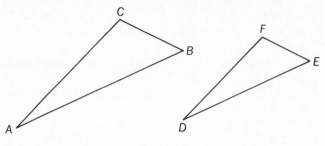

Probs. 10 to 15

Given $\triangle ABC \sim \triangle DEF$ (10 to 15):

10. Write the continued proportion between corresponding sides, and list the congruent angles.

Use the results of problem 10 for problems 11 to 15.

11. Solve for AB in terms of BC, DE, and EF.
12. Solve for EF in terms of BC, FD, and CA.
13. Solve for CA in terms of FD, AB, and DE.
14. Solve for FD in terms of BC, EF, and CA.
15. Solve for DE in terms of AB, CA, and FD.

16. If $\triangle ABC \sim \triangle DEF$, does it necessarily follow that $\triangle DEF \sim \triangle ABC$? Explain.
17. The sides of a triangle are 3, 5, and 8 inches respectively. If the shortest side of a similar triangle is 5, find the other two sides.
18. In the figure, $ABCD \sim EFGH$, with sides of lengths as shown. If $GF = 3$, find EF, GH, and HE.

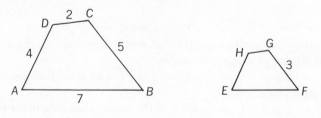

Prob. 18

19. Are two congruent polygons similar? Are two similar polygons congruent? What is the ratio of similitude of two congruent polygons?

20. Can a square be similar to a triangle? Explain.
21. Can a rectangle be similar to a rhombus? Explain.
22. Can a parallelogram be similar to a trapezoid? Explain.
23. Given $\overline{CD} \perp \overline{AB}$, and $\triangle ADC \sim \triangle CDB$, write the continued proportion between corresponding sides, and list the pairs of congruent angles.

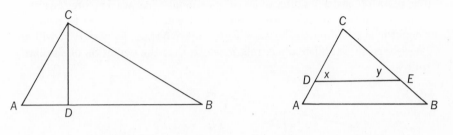

Prob. 23   Probs. 24 to 26

Given $\triangle CDE \sim \triangle CAB$ (24 to 26):

24. Write the continued proportion between corresponding sides, and list the pairs of congruent angles.
25. If $AD = 9$, $DC = 15$, $CE = 18$, $DE = 21$, $m\angle x = r$ and $m\angle y = s$, find AB, CB, EB, $m\angle A$ and $m\angle B$.
26. If $AC = 28$, $AB = 35$, $BC = 21$, and $EC = 6$, find DC, DE, AD.

(B)

27. PROVE: An equilateral triangle with sides of measure n is similar to an equilateral triangle with sides of measure m.
28. PROVE: If two triangles are congruent, they are similar.
29. GIVEN: Square $ABCD$; midpoints R, S; $\overline{ST} \perp \overline{BC}$; $\overline{RT} \perp \overline{AB}$.
     PROVE: $RBST \sim ABCD$.
30. GIVEN: $\triangle ABC \sim \triangle DEF$; $\triangle DEF \sim \triangle RST$.
     PROVE: $\triangle ABC \sim \triangle RST$.

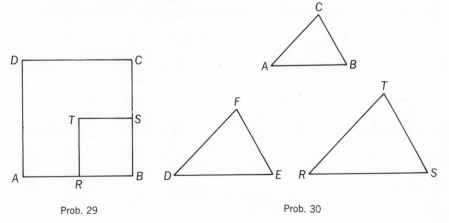

Prob. 29   Prob. 30

10-3 **PROPORTIONAL DIVISION OF SEGMENTS**

The definition of congruence of triangles required six pairs of congruent parts; three pairs of sides and three pairs of angles. The definition of similar polygons, applied to triangles, calls for three pairs of congruent angles, and three pairs of corresponding sides proportional. As we explored ways of proving triangles *congruent*, we found that it was not necessary to prove all six congruences. In much the same way, to prove triangles *similar* it will not be necessary to establish all six relationships that the definition of similarity requires.

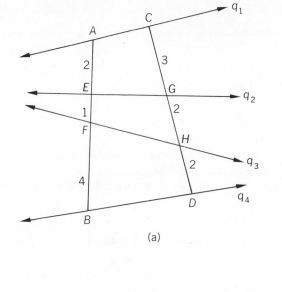

(a)

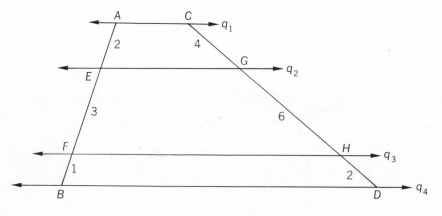

(b)

Figure 10-6

Certain preliminary concepts are needed before we can proceed to the task of deriving triangle similarity theorems. We first examine **proportional division** of segments.

Consider two segments, $\overline{AB}$ and $\overline{CD}$, intersecting q_1, q_2, q_3, q_4, as shown in Figure 10–6. In Figure 10–6(a), $\overline{AB}$ is divided into three segments, $\overline{AE}$, $\overline{EF}$, and $\overline{FB}$, whose measures form the sequence 2, 1, 4. $\overline{CD}$ is divided into $\overline{CG}$, $\overline{GH}$, and $\overline{HD}$, whose measures form the sequence 3, 2, 2. Clearly the two sequences are not proportional. On the other hand, Figure 10–6(b) shows $\overline{AB}$ and $\overline{CD}$ divided into three segments each, such that the sequences of measures formed are 2, 3, 1 and 4, 6, 2, sequences that *are* proportional. We describe this situation by saying: "$\overline{AB}$ and $\overline{CD}$ are *divided proportionally*."

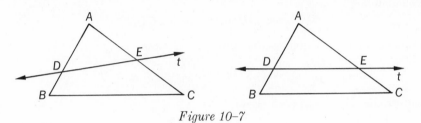

Figure 10–7

Consider next, $\triangle ABC$ and transversal t (Figure 10–7). Each of sides $\overline{AB}$ and $\overline{AC}$ is divided into a pair of segments by the transversal t. We should not expect that t will automatically divide the two sides proportionally. Our next theorem states the conditions under which this proportional division of the sides of a triangle will occur.

Theorem 10–1:   If a line parallel to one side of a triangle intersects the other two sides in distinct points, it divides the other two sides proportionally.

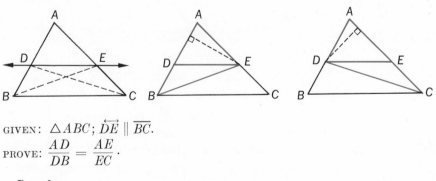

GIVEN: $\triangle ABC$; $\overleftrightarrow{DE} \parallel \overline{BC}$.

PROVE: $\dfrac{AD}{DB} = \dfrac{AE}{EC}$.

Proof

(1) Introduce $\overline{BE}$, and consider $\triangle ADE$ and $\triangle BDE$. Think of $\overline{AD}$ and $\overline{BD}$ as bases of the two triangles respectively. Then the altitude from E

to $\overline{AD}$ is a common altitude for both triangles. By Theorem 9–6,

$$\frac{\text{area } \triangle BDE}{\text{area } \triangle ADE} = \frac{BD}{AD} \quad \text{or} \quad \text{area } \triangle BDE = \frac{BD}{AD} (\text{area } \triangle ADE)$$

(2) Introduce $\overline{CD}$, and consider $\triangle ADE$ and $\triangle CDE$. Using a common altitude from D to $\overleftrightarrow{AC}$, we obtain, as in part (1):

$$\frac{\text{area } \triangle CDE}{\text{area } \triangle ADE} = \frac{CE}{AE} \quad \text{or} \quad \text{area } \triangle CDE = \frac{CE}{AE} (\text{area } \triangle ADE)$$

(3) Next consider $\triangle BDE$ and $\triangle CDE$, with common base $\overline{DE}$. Since $\overleftrightarrow{DE} \parallel \overline{BC}$, and since parallel lines are everywhere equidistant, an altitude from B to $\overleftrightarrow{DE}$ is congruent to an altitude from C to $\overleftrightarrow{DE}$. Hence, by Theorem 9–8,

$$\text{area } \triangle BDE = \text{area } \triangle CDE$$

From (1) and (2), it follows, by substitution, that:

$$\frac{BD}{AD} (\text{area } \triangle ADE) = \frac{CE}{AE} (\text{area } \triangle ADE)$$

and by the Division Axiom (E–7),

$$\frac{BD}{AD} = \frac{CE}{AE}$$

Using Proportion by Inversion, we write:

$$\frac{AD}{BD} = \frac{AE}{CE}$$

as was to be proved.

Theorem 10–2: **If a line intersects two sides of a triangle, and divides those two sides proportionally, then the line is parallel to the third side.**

GIVEN: $\triangle ABC$; $\dfrac{AD}{DB} = \dfrac{AE}{EC}$.

PROVE: $\overleftrightarrow{DE} \parallel \overline{BC}$.

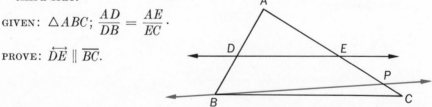

Proof (*Indirect*): Either $\overleftrightarrow{DE} \parallel \overline{BC}$ or $\overleftrightarrow{DE} \nparallel \overline{BC}$. Suppose $\overleftrightarrow{DE} \nparallel \overline{BC}$. Then through B, by the Parallel Axiom (Axiom 8–1), we may introduce $\overleftrightarrow{BP} \parallel \overleftrightarrow{DE}$, where $\overleftrightarrow{BP}$ and $\overline{BC}$ are distinct. Consider now $\triangle ABP$. $\overleftrightarrow{DE} \parallel \overleftrightarrow{BP}$ therefore, by Theorem 10–1, $\overleftrightarrow{DE}$ must divide $\overline{AB}$ and $\overline{AP}$ proportionally. Thus $\dfrac{AD}{DB} = \dfrac{AE}{EP}$, or $EP = \dfrac{AE \cdot DB}{AD}$. But we are given $\dfrac{AD}{DB} = \dfrac{AE}{EC}$, from which $\dfrac{AE \cdot DB}{AD} = EC$. By the Transitivity Axiom (Axiom E–3),

$EP = EC$. This implies that P and C are the same points (by the Point-Plotting Axiom, Axiom 2–4), which would imply that $\overleftrightarrow{BP}$ and $\overleftrightarrow{BC}$ are the same line. This is a contradiction—hence $\overleftrightarrow{DE} \parallel \overline{BC}$.

EXAMPLES

Which of the following sets of data lead to the conclusion that $\overline{PQ} \parallel \overline{AB}$?

1. $CP = 9, PA = 3, CQ = 12, QB = 4$.
2. $CP = 7, PA = 4, CQ = 10, QB = 6$.
3. $CA = 20, PA = 4, CB = 30, QB = 7$.

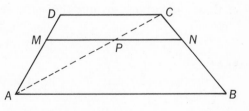

Solutions

1. If $\dfrac{CP}{PA} = \dfrac{CQ}{QB}$, then $\overline{PQ} \parallel \overline{AB}$ (Theorem 10–2). Consider $\dfrac{9}{3} \overset{?}{=} \dfrac{12}{4}$.

$$9 \cdot 4 \overset{?}{=} 3 \cdot 12 \qquad \text{(Proportion Prop. 1)}$$
$$36 = 36 \qquad \text{True.}$$

Hence $\overline{PQ} \parallel \overline{AB}$.

2. Consider $\frac{7}{4} \overset{?}{=} \frac{10}{6}$.

$$42 \neq 40$$

Hence $\overline{PQ} \not\parallel \overline{AB}$.

3. We are not told directly the lengths of the segments required by Theorem 10–2. Consider then:

$$\frac{CP}{PA} = \frac{CQ}{QB}$$
$$\frac{CP + PA}{PA} = \frac{CQ + QB}{QB} \qquad \text{(Proportion by Addition)}$$

or

$$\frac{CA}{PA} = \frac{CB}{QB}$$
$$\frac{20}{4} \overset{?}{=} \frac{30}{7}$$
$$140 \neq 120$$

Hence $\overline{PQ} \not\parallel \overline{AB}$.

4. GIVEN: Trapezoid $ABCD$;
bases $\overline{AB}, \overline{DC}$;
$\overline{MN} \parallel \overline{AB}$.

PROVE: $\dfrac{MD}{AM} = \dfrac{CN}{NB}$.

Analysis: The only theorems we have to now that lead to writing proportions, require triangles. We would have triangles if we introduced a diagonal, say $\overline{AC}$. Following this we investigate resulting proportions.

Proof

STATEMENTS	REASONS
1. Trapezoid $ABCD$, bases $\overline{AB}$, $\overline{DC}$.	1. Given.
2. $\overline{AB} \parallel \overline{DC}$.	2. Def. of bases of trapezoid (8–13).
3. $\overline{MN} \parallel \overline{AB}$.	3. Given.
4. $\overline{MN} \parallel \overline{DC}$.	4. Thm. 8–10.
5. Introduce $\overline{AC}$.	5. Ax. 2–3.
6. (a) In $\triangle ACD$, $\dfrac{AM}{MD} = \dfrac{PA}{CP}$.	6. Thm. 10–1.
(b) In $\triangle ACB$, $\dfrac{CP}{PA} = \dfrac{CN}{NB}$.	
7. $\dfrac{MD}{AM} = \dfrac{CP}{PA}$.	7. Proportion by Inversion (step 6a).
8. $\dfrac{MD}{AM} = \dfrac{CN}{NB}$.	8. Transitivity Ax. (E–3) (steps 6b, 7).

Exercise 10–3

(A)

In the figure for problems 1 to 10, $\overline{DE} \parallel \overline{AB}$.

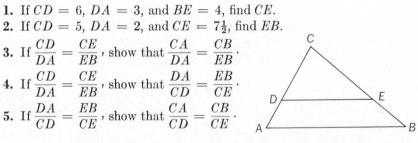

Probs. 1 to 10

1. If $CD = 6$, $DA = 3$, and $BE = 4$, find CE.

2. If $CD = 5$, $DA = 2$, and $CE = 7\frac{1}{2}$, find EB.

3. If $\dfrac{CD}{DA} = \dfrac{CE}{EB}$, show that $\dfrac{CA}{DA} = \dfrac{CB}{EB}$.

4. If $\dfrac{CD}{DA} = \dfrac{CE}{EB}$, show that $\dfrac{DA}{CD} = \dfrac{EB}{CE}$.

5. If $\dfrac{DA}{CD} = \dfrac{EB}{CE}$, show that $\dfrac{CA}{CD} = \dfrac{CB}{CE}$.

Note that the results of problems 3 and 5 enable us to write two further proportions that result when two segments are divided proportionally. Both of these proportions involve the *entire* segment, as well as the intercepted segments. These results are useful enough to be worth remembering.

EXAMPLE

In the figure above, if $AC = 12$, $AD = 3$, and $EB = 4$, find BC.

Solution: We have:

$$\frac{AC}{AD} = \frac{BC}{EB} \quad \text{(see prob. 3)}$$

$$\frac{12}{3} = \frac{BC}{4} \quad \text{or} \quad BC = 16$$

6. If $AC = 12$, $CD = 4$, and $CE = 8$, find BC.
7. If $BC = 22$, $EB = 6$, and $CD = 8$, find AC.
8. If $AD = 5$, $CD = 7$, and $BC = 18$, find BE.
9. If $AC = 15$, $CE = 6$, and $BC = 18$, find AD.
10. If $CD = 4$, $DA = 3$, and $CE = 7$, find BC.

In the figure for problems 11 to 15, $\angle 1 \cong \angle 2$.

11. $\dfrac{MR}{RN} = $ _____   **12.** $\dfrac{QP}{QM} = $ _____

13. $\dfrac{MN}{MR} = $ _____   **14.** $\dfrac{QP}{MP} = $ _____

15. $\dfrac{MN}{RN} = $ _____

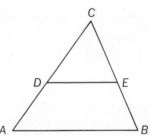

Probs. 11 to 15

In the problems below (16 to 20), which sets of data lead to the conclusion that $\overline{DE} \parallel \overline{AB}$?

16. $CA = 14$, $CD = 6$, $CB = 7$, $CE = 3$.
17. $AC = 12$, $DA = 3$, $CB = 8$, $CE = 6$.
18. $CD = 6$, $DA = 5$, $CE = 9$, $EB = 8$.
19. $CB = 21$, $EB = 9$, $CA = 14$, $CD = 5$.
20. $CA = 24$, $CB = 6$, $CD = 8$, $EB = 4$.

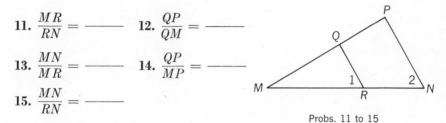

Probs. 16 to 20

From the figure for problems 21 to 26, complete the following:

21. $\dfrac{m}{n} = $ _____   **22.** $\dfrac{m+n}{m} = $ _____

23. $\dfrac{n}{b} = $ _____   **24.** $\dfrac{a-b}{b} = \dfrac{m-}{}$

25. $\dfrac{m-n}{a-b} = \dfrac{}{b}$ **26.** $\dfrac{m+n}{a+b} = \dfrac{n}{}$

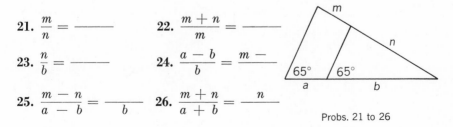

Probs. 21 to 26

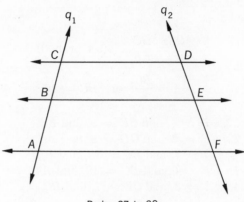

Probs. 27 to 29

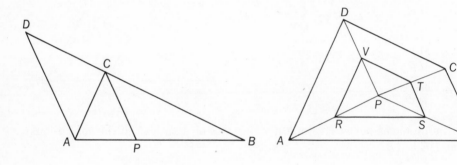

Prob. 30   Prob. 31

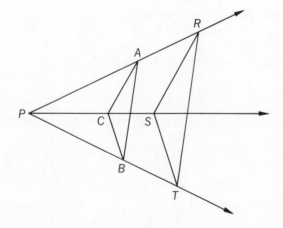

Prob. 32

(B)

27. GIVEN: $\overline{CD} \parallel \overline{BE} \parallel \overline{AF}$; transversals q_1, q_2.

   PROVE: $\dfrac{CB}{BA} = \dfrac{DE}{EF}$.

This problem illustrates the theorem: If three or more parallels are cut by two transversals, the intercepted segments on the transversals are proportional.

EXAMPLE

In the figure for problems 27 to 29, if $CB = 4$, $BA = 8$, and $DF = 9$, find EF.

Solution: Using the theorem of problem 27, we have:

$$\frac{CB}{BA} = \frac{DE}{EF} \qquad \text{or} \qquad \frac{CB + BA}{BA} = \frac{DE + EF}{EF} \qquad \text{or} \qquad \frac{CA}{BA} = \frac{DF}{EF}$$

Hence:

$$\frac{12}{8} = \frac{9}{EF} \qquad \text{or} \qquad EF = 6$$

Use the results of problem 27 for problems 28 and 29.

28. If $BA = 12$, $CA = 15$, and $DE = 2$, find DF.
29. If $AC = 21$, $DF = 18$, and $CB = 7$, find EF.

30. GIVEN: $\overline{CP} \parallel \overline{AD}$; $\overline{CP}$ bisects $\angle ACB$.

   PROVE: $\dfrac{AP}{PB} = \dfrac{AC}{CB}$.

31. GIVEN: $\overline{RS} \parallel \overline{AB}$; $\overline{ST} \parallel \overline{BC}$; $\overline{VT} \parallel \overline{DC}$.
   PROVE: $\overline{VR} \parallel \overline{DA}$.
32. GIVEN: $\overline{AC} \parallel \overline{RS}$; $\overline{CB} \parallel \overline{ST}$.
   PROVE: $\overline{AB} \parallel \overline{RT}$.
33. The nonparallel sides of a trapezoid are of lengths 10 in. and 15 in., respectively. A line parallel to the bases divides the 10 in. side in the ratio 1 to 4. Find the lengths of the segments of the 15 in. side.
34. The nonparallel sides of a trapezoid are of lengths 6 in. and 9 in., respectively. A line parallel to the bases divides the longer diagonal in the ratio 3 to 4. Find the lengths of the segments cut off of the nonparallel sides.

10–4   TRIANGLE SIMILARITY THEOREMS I

Theorem 10–3:   If corresponding angles of two triangles are congruent, the triangles are similar.

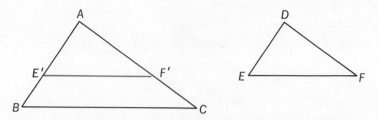

GIVEN: $\triangle ABC$; $\triangle DEF$; $\angle A \cong \angle D$; $\angle B \cong \angle E$; $\angle C \cong \angle F$.
PROVE: $\triangle ABC \sim \triangle DEF$.

Analysis: Since, by hypothesis, we know that the corresponding angles are congruent, it remains to prove that the corresponding sides are proportional. That is, if we can show that $\dfrac{AB}{DE} = \dfrac{AC}{DF} = \dfrac{BC}{EF}$, then by Definition 10–2, the triangles will be similar.

Proof: On $\overrightarrow{AB}$ and $\overrightarrow{AC}$ locate points E' and F', respectively, such that $AE' = DE$ and $AF' = DF$. Then, since $\overline{AE'} \cong \overline{DE}$, $\overline{AF'} \cong \overline{DF}$, and $\angle A \cong \angle D$, $\triangle E'AF' \cong \triangle EDF$ (why?). Since $\angle AE'F' \cong \angle E$ and $\angle E \cong \angle B$, then $\angle AE'F' \cong \angle B$.
We consider two possibilities:

(1) E' and B may coincide. If so, $\triangle AE'F'$ and $\triangle ABC$ are the same triangle, hence $\triangle ABC \cong \triangle DEF$. Then $\overline{AB} \cong \overline{DE}$, $\overline{AC} \cong \overline{DF}$, $\overline{BC} \cong \overline{EF}$, and $AB = DE$, $AC = DF$, $BC = EF$. From the last three equations we may write:

$$\frac{AB}{DE} = 1 \quad \frac{AC}{DF} = 1 \quad \text{and} \quad \frac{BC}{EF} = 1$$

Hence $\dfrac{AB}{DE} = \dfrac{AC}{DF} = \dfrac{BC}{EF}$.

(2) If E' and B are distinct points, then $\overleftrightarrow{E'F'} \parallel \overline{BC}$. (Why?) By Theorem 10–1, $\dfrac{AE'}{E'B} = \dfrac{AF'}{F'C}$. Using the Proportion by Inversion property, $\dfrac{E'B}{AE'} = \dfrac{F'C}{AF'}$. Using the Proportion by Addition property,

$$\frac{AE' + E'B}{AE'} = \frac{AF' + F'C}{AF'} \quad \text{or} \quad \frac{AB}{AE'} = \frac{AC}{AF'}$$

But, $AE' = DE$ and $AF' = DF$. Hence, by substitution, $\dfrac{AB}{DE} = \dfrac{AC}{DF}$.

To finish the proof, it remains to show that $\dfrac{AC}{DF} = \dfrac{BC}{EF}$. By an identical chain of reasoning, beginning with $\overrightarrow{CA}$ and $\overrightarrow{CB}$, this can be proven. (The details are left as an exercise.) Hence we have: $\dfrac{AB}{DE} = \dfrac{AC}{DF} = \dfrac{BC}{EF}$, and so $\triangle ABC \sim \triangle DEF$.

In actual practice it turns out that we use a corollary of Theorem 10–3 more than the theorem itself. Recall that if two angles of one triangle are congruent respectively to two angles of a second triangle, the third angles are congruent (Corollary 8–12.1). Thus only *two* angles of each triangle need be considered for a proof of similarity.

Corollary 10–3.1 (AA Similarity Corollary): If two pairs of corresponding angles of two triangles are congruent, the triangles are similar.

The proof of this corollary is left as an exercise.

Corollary 10–3.2: If a line parallel to one side of a triangle intersects the other two sides in distinct points, then it determines a triangle similar to the given triangle.

GIVEN: $\triangle ABC$; $\overleftrightarrow{DE} \parallel \overleftrightarrow{AB}$.
PROVE: $\triangle CDE \sim \triangle ABC$.

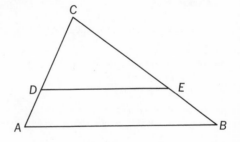

Proof

STATEMENTS	REASONS
1. $\triangle ABC$, $\overleftrightarrow{DE} \parallel \overleftrightarrow{AB}$.	1. Given.
2. $\angle CDE \cong \angle CAB$.	2. Why?
3. $\angle C \cong \angle C$.	3. Why?
4. $\triangle ABC \sim \triangle CDE$	4. AA Similarity Corollary (10–3.1).

EXAMPLES

1. Can two triangles be similar if the first contains a 95° angle and the second contains an 85° angle? Explain.

Solution: If the first contains a 95° angle, then the second must contain an angle of the same measure. But then the second triangle would have the sum of the measures of two of its angles equal to $85 + 95 = 180$, and there would be *no* third angle, hence no triangle. Thus the two triangles cannot be similar.

2. GIVEN: $\square ABCD$; diagonal $\overline{DB}$;
       transversal q.
   PROVE: $\triangle DXE \sim \triangle BYE$.

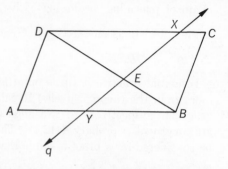

Analysis: To prove triangles similar, we have a definition, and theorems. Since the theorems require less than the definition, it seems desirable to try to use a theorem. Corollary 10–3.1 calls for two pairs of congruent angles. Since $ABCD$ is a parallelogram, and the diagonal is a transversal of two parallel sides, we will try to find one pair of congruent angles in the parallelogram. Since the line q and the diagonal $\overline{DB}$ are intersecting straight lines, perhaps congruent vertical angles will help.

Proof

STATEMENTS	REASONS
1. $\square ABCD$.	1. Given.
2. $\overline{DC} \parallel \overline{AB}$.	2. Def. of parallelogram.
3. $\angle ABD \cong \angle CDB$.	3. Thm. 8–6.
4. $\angle DEX \cong \angle YEB$.	4. Thm. 4–11.
5. $\triangle DXE \sim \triangle BYE$	5. AA Similarity Corollary (10–3.1).

Exercise 10–4

(A)

1. Are triangles ABC and DEF similar if $m\angle A = 67$, $m\angle B = 54$, $m\angle D = 54$, $m\angle E = 59$? If so, write the correspondence.

2. Are triangles ABC and DEF similar if $m\angle A = 41$, $m\angle B = 73$, $m\angle D = 73$ and $m\angle E = 86$? If so, write the correspondence.

3. Is it possible for two triangles to be similar if one triangle contains an $87°$ angle, and the second contains a $94°$ angle? Explain.

4. Is it possible for two triangles to be similar if the first contains a $52°$ and a $71°$ angle, and the second contains a $71°$ and an $85°$ angle? Explain.

5. Draw any $\triangle ABC$. (Draw the sides longer than 2 in.) Draw a 4 in. segment $\overline{MN}$. How can you draw $\triangle MNP$ so that $\triangle MNP \sim \triangle ABC$?

6. The vertex angle of isosceles $\triangle ABC$ is a $50°$ angle. Find the measures of the base angles of a triangle similar to $\triangle ABC$.

7. One base angle of isosceles $\triangle ABC$ is a 40° angle. Find the measures of both base angles of a triangle similar to $\triangle ABC$.

8. If an angle of one isosceles triangle is congruent to an angle of a second isosceles triangle, are the two triangles necessarily similar? Explain.

9. In the figure, if $\angle A \cong \angle EDC$, name two similar triangles. (Your notation must show the correct correspondence.)

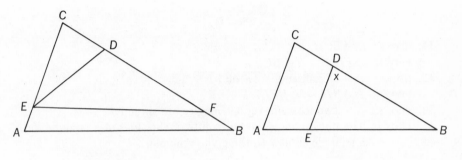

Prob. 9   Prob. 11

10. PROVE: If a pair of corresponding acute angles of two right triangles are congruent, the triangles are similar.

11. GIVEN: $m\angle x = m\angle C$.
    PROVE: $\triangle ABC \sim \triangle EBD$.

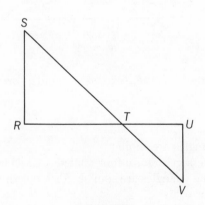

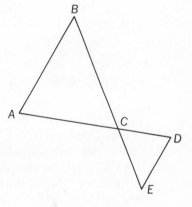

Prob. 12   Prob. 13

12. GIVEN: $\overline{SR} \perp \overline{RU}$; $\overline{UV} \perp \overline{RU}$.
    PROVE: (a) $\triangle RST \sim \triangle UVT$;   (b) $\dfrac{RS}{ST} = \dfrac{UV}{VT}$.

13. GIVEN: $\overline{AB} \parallel \overline{DE}$.
    PROVE: $\triangle ABC \sim \triangle DEC$.

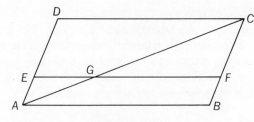

Prob. 14

14. GIVEN: $\square ABCD$, $\overline{EF} \parallel \overline{AB}$.
      PROVE: $\triangle EGA \sim \triangle FGC$.
15. GIVEN: $\triangle ABC$; altitudes $\overline{AE}$ and $\overline{BD}$.
      PROVE: $\triangle APD \sim \triangle BPE$.
16. PROVE: Any two isosceles right triangles are similar.
17. PROVE: The lines joining the midpoints of the sides of a triangle form
      a triangle similar to the given triangle.

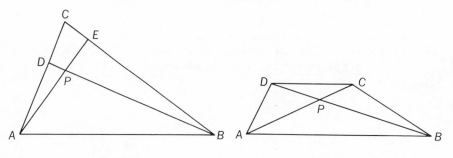

Prob. 15   Prob. 21

18. For Thm. 10–3, using the proof in the text as a guide, prove
$\dfrac{AC}{DF} = \dfrac{BC}{EF}$.
19. PROVE: Corollary 10–3.1.
20. PROVE: Any two equilateral triangles are similar.
21. In a trapezoid, the diagonals intersect to form four triangles, as shown
in the figure. Two of the resulting triangles are similar. Pick out those
two, and prove your choice is correct.
22. PROVE: Two isosceles triangles are similar if a base angle of one is
                congruent to a base angle of the other.
23. PROVE: Two isosceles triangles are similar if the vertex angle of one is
                congruent to the vertex angle of the other.

(B)

24. PROVE: The bisectors of two corresponding angles of two similar tri-
                angles have the same ratio as a pair of corresponding sides.

10–5 TRIANGLE SIMILARITY THEOREMS II

In this section we complete the groundwork for, and then derive, two basic theorems on the similarity of triangles. Two preparatory theorems pave the way. The first establishes the Transitive Property of similarity of triangles.

Theorem 10–4: **If one triangle is similar to a second, and the second triangle is similar to a third, then the first triangle is similar to the third.**

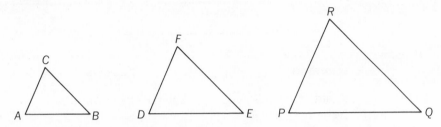

GIVEN: $\triangle ABC \sim \triangle DEF$, $\triangle DEF \sim \triangle PQR$.
PROVE: $\triangle ABC \sim \triangle PQR$.

Proof: $\triangle ABC \sim \triangle DEF$ implies that $\angle A \cong \angle D$ and $\angle B \cong \angle E$ (why?). $\triangle DEF \sim \triangle PQR$ implies that $\angle D \cong \angle P$ and $\angle E \cong \angle Q$. By the Transitivity Theorem of Congruence of Angles (Theorem 5–7), it follows that $\angle A \cong \angle P$ and $\angle B \cong \angle Q$. Hence, by the AA Similarity Corollary (10–3.1), $\triangle ABC \sim \triangle PQR$.

The second such "paving" theorem is also quite simple to prove, and the proof is left as an exercise.

Theorem 10–5: **If two triangles are congruent, they are similar.**

At the start of this chapter mention was made that congruence is a special case of similarity; Theorem 10–5 helps to explain this. Suppose $\triangle ABC \sim \triangle DEF$, and consider the ratios of corresponding sides:

$$\frac{AB}{DE} = \frac{BC}{EF} = \frac{CA}{FD} = k$$

Now, if the triangles are also congruent, corresponding sides are congruent, and their measures are equal. For example, $AB = DE$. Then each of the above ratios consists of a nonzero number divided by itself, and is therefore equal to 1. That is, the constant of proportionality (k) in the case of congruent triangles is always the same—namely 1 (see also the proof of Theorem 10–3).

With the above discussion in mind, it will come as no surprise that the next two theorems resemble strongly the SAS and SSS Axioms (Axioms 5–2, 5–4) for congruence of triangles.

260 PROPORTION AND SIMILARITY

Theorem 10–6 (SAS Similarity Theorem): If two pairs of corresponding sides of two triangles are proportional, and the included angles are congruent, the triangles are similar.

GIVEN: $\triangle ABC$; $\triangle DEF$;
$\angle A \cong \angle D$;
$\dfrac{AB}{DE} = \dfrac{AC}{DF}$.

PROVE: $\triangle ABC \sim \triangle DEF$.

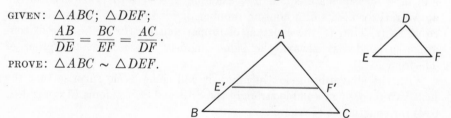

Proof

STATEMENTS	REASONS
1. Introduce E' and F' on $\overrightarrow{AB}$ and $\overrightarrow{AC}$, respectively, so that $AE' = DE$ and $AF' = DF$.	1. Point-Plotting Ax. (2–4).
2. $\dfrac{AB}{DE} = \dfrac{AC}{DF}$.	2. Given.
3. $\dfrac{AB}{AE'} = \dfrac{AC}{AF'}$.	3. Substitution Ax. (S–1).
4. $\dfrac{AB - AE'}{AE'} = \dfrac{AC - AF'}{AF'}$ or $\dfrac{E'B}{AE'} = \dfrac{F'C}{AF'}$.	4. Proportion by subtraction.
5. $\overline{E'F'} \parallel \overline{BC}$.	5. Thm. 10–2.
6. $\triangle ABC \sim \triangle AE'F'$.	6. Corollary 10–3.2.
7. $\overline{AE'} \cong \overline{DE}$, $\overline{AF'} \cong \overline{DF}$.	7. Def. of congruence (step 1).
8. $\angle A \cong \angle D$.	8. Given.
9. $\triangle AE'F' \cong \triangle DEF$.	9. SAS Ax. (5–3).
10. $\triangle AE'F' \sim \triangle DEF$.	10. Thm. 10–5.
11. $\triangle ABC \sim \triangle DEF$.	11. Transitivity of similarity (Thm. 10–4) (steps 6, 10).

Theorem 10–7 (SSS Similarity Theorem): If corresponding sides of two triangles are proportional, the triangles are similar.

GIVEN: $\triangle ABC$; $\triangle DEF$;
$\dfrac{AB}{DE} = \dfrac{BC}{EF} = \dfrac{AC}{DF}$.

PROVE: $\triangle ABC \sim \triangle DEF$.

Proof

STATEMENTS	REASONS
1. Introduce E' on $\overrightarrow{AB}$, and F' on $\overrightarrow{AC}$, so that $AE' = DE$ and $AF' = DF$.	1. Point-Plotting Ax. (2–4).
2. $\dfrac{AB}{DE} = \dfrac{BC}{EF} = \dfrac{AC}{DF}$.	2. Given.
3. $\dfrac{AB}{AE'} = \dfrac{AC}{AF'}$.	3. Substitution Ax. (S–1).
4. $\angle A \cong \angle A$.	4. Reflexive Thm. of congruent angles (4–1).
5. $\triangle ABC \sim \triangle AE'F'$	5. SAS Similarity Thm. (10–6).
6. $\dfrac{E'F'}{BC} = \dfrac{AE'}{AB}$.	6. Def. of similar polygons (10–2).
7. $E'F' = BC\left(\dfrac{AE'}{AB}\right)$.	7. Multiplication Ax. (E–6).
8. $E'F' = BC\left(\dfrac{DE}{AB}\right)$.	8. Substitution Ax. (S–1) (step 1).
9. $\dfrac{BC}{EF} = \dfrac{AC}{DF}$.	9. Proportion by Inversion.
10. $EF = BC\left(\dfrac{DF}{AC}\right)$.	10. Multiplication Ax. (E–6).
11. $\dfrac{DE}{AB} = \dfrac{DF}{AC}$.	11. Proportion by Inversion.
12. $EF = BC\left(\dfrac{DE}{AB}\right)$.	12. Substitution Ax. (S–1) (steps 10, 11).
13. $EF = E'F'$.	13. Substitution Ax. (S–1) (steps 8, 12).
14. $\overline{EF} \cong \overline{E'F'}$, $\overline{AE'} \cong \overline{DE}$, $\overline{AF'} \cong \overline{DF}$.	14. Def. of congruent segments (steps 13, 1).
15. $\triangle AE'F' \cong \triangle DEF$.	15. SSS Ax. (5–4).
16. $\triangle AE'F' \sim \triangle DEF$.	16. Thm. 10–5.
17. $\triangle ABC \sim \triangle DEF$.	17. Transitivity of similarity (Thm. 10–4) (steps 5, 16).

Our list of theorems is now quite extensive, and still growing. There are other theorems, which are also of interest, that do not appear in the text. We choose to include three of these among the exercises that follow this section. While these theorems *may* be used in other problems, we shall be able to further our development of geometry without their use. The decision to introduce them as exercises is influenced by the desire to keep the final list of theorems to a reasonable size. (See Exercise 10–5, problems 19, 24, and 29.)

EXAMPLES

1. The lengths of the sides of a triangle are 2, 3, and 4, respectively. Find the lengths of the sides of a similar triangle of perimeter 360.

Solution: Since the triangles are similar, corresponding sides must be proportional. Let a, b, and c represent the lengths of the sides of the second triangle. Then:

$$\frac{a}{2} = \frac{b}{3} = \frac{c}{4} = k$$

or

$$a = 2k \qquad b = 3k \qquad c = 4k$$

Since the perimeter is the sum of the sides, we want:

$$a + b + c = 360$$

or

$$2k + 3k + 4k = 360$$
$$9k = 360$$
$$k = 40$$

Therefore $a = 2(40) = 80$, $b = 3(40) = 120$, $c = 4(40) = 160$. We point out that the importance of this example lies in the *method* illustrated.

2. GIVEN: $\overline{DE} \parallel \overline{AB}; \overline{EF} \parallel \overline{BC}$.

   PROVE: $\dfrac{DE}{AB} = \dfrac{EF}{BC}$.

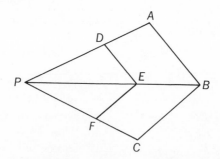

Analysis: The problem requires that we establish a proportion. A typical method for establishing a proportion is to demonstrate a pair, or pairs, of similar triangles. To proceed with this, we first pick out "hopeful" pairs of triangles, and try to prove them similar. An examination of the terms of the required proportion shows that no one pair of triangles contains the desired segments. However, we could obtain ratios involving DE and AB if we consider $\triangle PED$ and $\triangle PBA$; in like manner we could obtain ratios involving EF and BC from $\triangle PFE$ and $\triangle PCB$. So we consider these two pairs of triangles.

Proof

STATEMENTS	REASONS
1. $\overline{DE} \parallel \overline{AB}$.	1. Given.
2. $\triangle PDE \sim \triangle PAB$.	2. Corollary 10–3.2.
3. $\dfrac{DE}{AB} = \dfrac{PE}{PB}$.	3. Def. of similar polygons (corresponding sides are proportional) (10–3).
4. $\overline{FE} \parallel \overline{BC}$.	4. Given.
5. $\triangle PFE \sim \triangle PCB$.	5. Corollary 10–3.2.
6. $\dfrac{PE}{PB} = \dfrac{EF}{BC}$.	6. Def. of similar polygons (10–2).
7. $\dfrac{DE}{AB} = \dfrac{EF}{BC}$.	7. Transitivity Ax. (E–3) (steps 3, 6).

3. For the hypothesis and diagram of example 2 above, suppose we are asked to prove: $DE \cdot BC = EF \cdot AB$. In words, prove that the product of the lengths of two segments is equal to the product of the lengths of two other segments. Realizing that Proportion Property 1 transforms a proportion into exactly the type of product we seek, we see that the approach is the same as that of example 2, but with one additional step. That is, try to find pairs of similar triangles, establish proportions involving the lengths of the desired segments, and use properties of proportions to obtain the desired results. Thus, in example 2, a final step might be $DE \cdot BC = EF \cdot AB$, with Proportion Property 1 as the reason.

Examples 2 and 3 are illustrations of what may be established by proving polygons similar. Properties of similar polygons are of use in many kinds of problems. Below is a brief list of such problems; other uses will become evident as we progress further.

(1) To prove angles congruent.

(2) To establish proportions.

(3) To prove that the product of the measures of two segments is equal to the product of the measures of two other segments.

(4) To prove lines parallel (by use of Thm. 10–2).

Exercise 10–5

(A)

Given a correspondence $ABC \leftrightarrow DEF$ between two triangles, which of the following statements (1 to 6) are sufficient to show that $\triangle ABC \sim \triangle DEF$?

1. $\angle A \cong \angle D$ and $\angle B \cong \angle E$.   2. $\dfrac{AB}{AC} = \dfrac{DE}{DF}$.

3. Corresponding sides are proportional.

4. Both triangles are equilateral.

5. Both triangles are isosceles, and $\angle A \cong \angle D$.

6. $m\angle C = m\angle F = 90$, and $AB = DE$.

Below is a list of the lengths of sides of pairs of triangles. For each pair, determine whether they are or are not similar. If they are, write: $\triangle$_____ is similar to $\triangle$_____, making certain that the order of the letters shows the correct correspondence. State a theorem to justify your conclusion (7 to 10):

EXAMPLES

1. $AB = 5$, $AF = 3$, $FB = 7$; $QS = 9$, $QR = 15$, $RS = 21$.
2. $RS = 2$, $ST = 4\frac{1}{2}$, $TR = 3$; $PM = 4\frac{1}{2}$, $MN = 3$, $NP = 6$.

Solutions

1. If the triangles are similar, shortest sides should correspond as well as intermediate and longest sides. Let us arrange the two sequences in order of size: 3, 5, 7; and 9, 15, 21. Next examine:

$$\frac{3}{9} = \frac{1}{3} \qquad \frac{5}{15} = \frac{1}{3} \qquad \frac{7}{21} = \frac{1}{3}$$

Thus we have:

$$\frac{3}{9} = \frac{5}{15} = \frac{7}{21}$$

the corresponding sides are proportional, and the triangles are similar (SSS Similarity Thm., 10–7). To determine the correct correspondence, sketch $\triangle AFB$, and "build" a sketch of $\triangle QRS$ by matching the corresponding lengths:

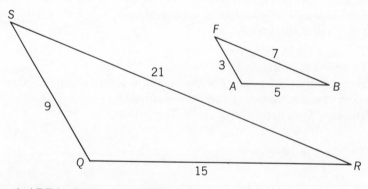

Hence $\triangle ABF$ is similar to $\triangle QRS$.

2. Arranging the lengths in order, we obtain: 2, 3, $\frac{9}{2}$; and 3, $\frac{9}{2}$, 6. Three ratios are formed:

$$\frac{2}{3}, \quad \frac{3}{\frac{9}{2}}\left(=\frac{2}{3}\right), \quad \text{and} \quad \frac{\frac{9}{2}}{6}\left(=\frac{3}{4}\right)$$

Since the ratios are not all equal, corresponding sides are not proportional, and the triangles are not similar.

7. $RS = 2$, $ST = 5$, $TR = 6$; $AB = \frac{15}{2}$, $BC = 9$, $CA = 3$
8. $DE = 5$, $EF = 2$, $FD = 4$; $MN = \frac{5}{2}$, $NP = 2$, $PM = 3$
9. $XY = 6$, $YZ = 7$, $ZX = 8$; $AB = 40$, $BC = 35$, $CA = 30$
10. $DE = 1.8$, $EF = 2.4$, $DF = 3$; $MN = .4$, $MP = .5$, $NP = .3$

11. Examine each of the following figures, and decide whether or not the triangles are similar. If they are, state a theorem to support your conclusion.

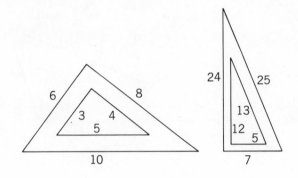

(a)

(b)

(c)

(d)

(e)

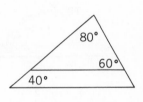

(f)

12. In the figure, $FD = 20$, $FH = 15$, $FE = 24$, $FK = 18$, $HK = 27$. Show why $\triangle FHK \sim \triangle FDE$. How long is $\overline{DE}$?

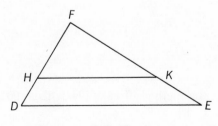

Prob. 12

13. In the figure, given $\overleftrightarrow{BE}$ and $\overleftrightarrow{DC}$, show why $\triangle ABC \sim \triangle ADE$.

14. In the figure, if $BD = \frac{1}{4}(BC)$, $BE = \frac{1}{4}(BA)$, and $DE = 9$:

    (a) Complete: $\triangle$_____ $\sim$ $\triangle$_____.

    (b) How long is $\overline{AC}$?

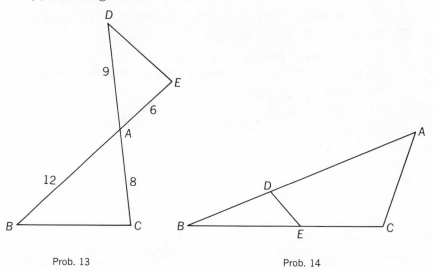

Prob. 13   Prob. 14

15. If $\triangle ABC \sim \triangle RST$, $AB = 3$, $BC = 5$, $CA = 7$, and the perimeter of $\triangle RST$ is 60, find RS, ST, and TR.

16. If $ABCDE \sim A'B'C'D'E'$, $AB = 1$, $BC = 2$, $CD = 3$, $DE = 4$, $EA = 5$, and the perimeter of $A'B'C'D'E'$ is 330, find the sides of $A'B'C'D'E'$.

17. The sides of $\triangle ABC$ are of lengths 5, 6, and 7, respectively, and those of $\triangle DEF$ are 20, 24, and 28.

    (a) Why is $\triangle ABC \sim \triangle DEF$?

    (b) Compute the ratio of similitude.

    (c) Find the perimeter of each triangle.

    (d) Compute the ratio of the perimeters. Is this ratio related to any other ratio associated with the two triangles?

18. The following is a property of continued proportions. Write an algebraic proof.

    (Lemma)   IF: $\dfrac{a}{a'} = \dfrac{b}{b'} = \dfrac{c}{c'} = \cdots = k$

                THEN: $\dfrac{a + b + c + \cdots}{a' + b' + c' + \cdots} = k$

    (*Hint:* Apply the method of example 1, page 262, and then use the Addition Ax., E–4.)

19. Theorem: If two polygons are similar, the ratio of their perimeters equals the ratio of any pair of corresponding sides.
(*Hint:* Use the Lemma of problem 18.)

EXAMPLE

The sides of a polygon are of length 1, 2, 3, 4, and 5 respectively. Find the perimeter of a similar polygon if its longest side is of length 20.

Solution: The two longest sides must correspond, hence the ratio of similitude is $\frac{5}{20}$, or $\frac{1}{4}$, and the ratio of the perimeters is also $\frac{1}{4}$. The perimeter of the first polygon is: $P = 1 + 2 + 3 + 4 + 5 = 15$. Let P' represent the perimeter of the second polygon. By the theorem of problem 19:

$$\frac{P}{P'} = \frac{1}{4} \quad \text{or} \quad \frac{15}{P'} = \frac{1}{4} \quad \text{or} \quad \underline{60 = P'}$$

20. The perimeters of two similar polygons are 10 in. and 14 in., respectively. One side of the smaller polygon is 4 in. long. Find the length of the corresponding side of the larger polygon.

21. One pair of corresponding sides of two similar polygons have lengths of 16 in. and 20 in., respectively. The perimeter of the smaller polygon is 40 in. Find the perimeter of the larger polygon.

22. The lengths of the sides of a polygon are 2, 5, 6, 9, and 10, respectively. The perimeter of a similar polygon is 24. Find the lengths of the sides of the second polygon.

23. A quadrilateral figure on a map has sides of length $\frac{1}{2}$, $1\frac{1}{2}$, 2, and 3 in., respectively. If the actual piece of land represented by the quadrilateral on the map has a perimeter of 770 miles, find the dimensions of the piece of land.

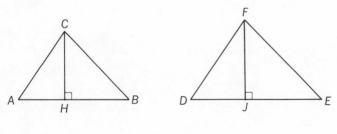

Prob. 24

24. Theorem: If two triangles are similar, corresponding altitudes have the same ratio as any pair of corresponding sides.
GIVEN: $\triangle ABC \sim \triangle DEF$; altitudes $\overline{CH}$, $\overline{FJ}$.

PROVE: $\dfrac{CH}{FJ} = \dfrac{CA}{FD} = \dfrac{CB}{FE} = \dfrac{AB}{DE}.$

25. Rays of light from the sun form shadows of upright objects on the ground. $\overline{RM}$ represents a tower, $\overline{MP}$ represents its 160 ft. shadow; $\overline{QN}$ represents a 12 ft. pole and $\overline{NP}$ its 8 ft. shadow. Find the height (RM) of the tower.

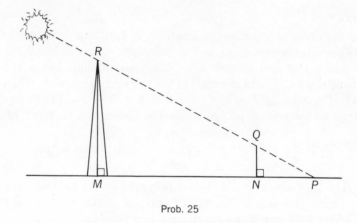

Prob. 25

26. $\overline{LP}$ represents a lamppost and $\overline{MN}$ represents a man 6 ft. tall standing 15 ft. from the base of the lamppost. If the shadow ($\overline{NS}$) of the man is 5 ft. long, how high is the lamppost?

27. The sides of a triangle are of length 8, 10, and 12 in., respectively. A 9 in. segment, parallel to the longest side, terminates on the other two sides. Find the lengths of the segments into which the other two sides are divided.

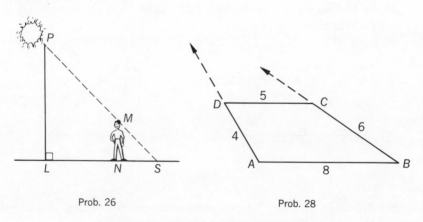

Prob. 26   Prob. 28

28. In the figure, $AB = 8$, $BC = 6$, $CD = 5$, $DA.= 4$, and $ABCD$ is a trapezoid. How far from D (on $\overrightarrow{AD}$) and from C (on $\overrightarrow{BC}$) is P, if P is the point of intersection of $\overrightarrow{AD}$ and $\overrightarrow{BC}$?

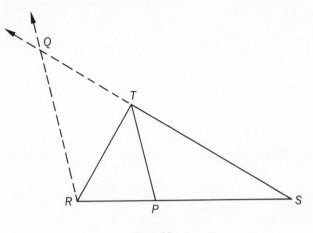

Prob. 29

29. Theorem: An angle bisector of one angle of a triangle divides the opposite side into segments which are proportional to the adjacent sides.

GIVEN: $\triangle RST$; $\overline{TP}$ bisects $\angle RTS$.

PROVE: $\dfrac{RP}{PS} = \dfrac{RT}{TS}$.

(*Hint:* Introduce $\overleftrightarrow{ST}$. Introduce $\overrightarrow{RQ}$ so that $\overrightarrow{RQ} \parallel \overline{PT}$. Show that $QT = TR$.) Write a formal proof.

In the figure for problems 30 and 31, $\overline{CD}$ bisects $\angle ACB$.

EXAMPLE

$AC = 5$, $BC = 7$, $AB = 10$. Find AD and DB.

Solution: Let $AD = x$. Then $DB = 10 - x$. By the theorem of problem 29:

$$\frac{CA}{CB} = \frac{AD}{DB}$$

Hence

$$\frac{5}{7} = \frac{x}{10 - x}$$

$$50 - 5x = 7x$$

$$50 = 12x$$

$$\frac{50}{12} = x$$

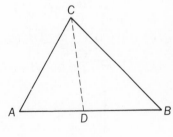

Probs. 30, 31

Then

$$AD = \tfrac{50}{12} = \tfrac{25}{6}, \qquad DB = 10 - \tfrac{25}{6} = \tfrac{35}{6}$$

30. If $AC = 3$, $BC = 5$, and $AB = 7$, find AD and DB.

31. If $AC = 6$, $BC = 8$, and $AB = 12$, find AD and DB.

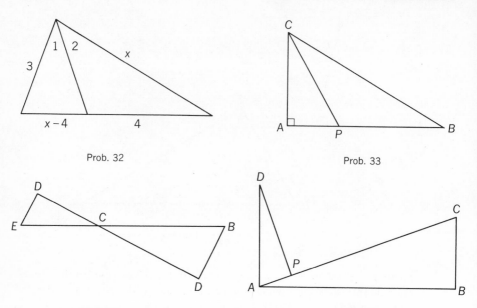

Prob. 32

Prob. 33

Prob. 34

Prob. 35

32. In the figure, $\angle 1 \cong \angle 2$. Find x.

33. In $\triangle ABC, \overline{CA} \perp \overline{AB}, m\angle B = 30, \overline{CP}$ bisects $\angle ACB$.

Find k, if $k = \dfrac{AP}{PB}$.

34. GIVEN: $\overline{EB}$ intersects $\overline{DA}$ at C; $CA = 4(DC)$; $CB = 4(CE)$.

PROVE: $\triangle DEC \sim \triangle ABC$.

35. GIVEN: $\overline{DA} \perp \overline{AB}$; $\overline{CB} \perp \overline{AB}$; $\overline{DP} \perp \overline{AC}$.

PROVE: (a) $\triangle ABC \sim \triangle DPA$; (b) $\dfrac{AB}{DP} = \dfrac{BC}{AP}$;

(c) $AB \cdot DA = AC \cdot DP$.

36. PROVE: Thm. 10–5.

37. GIVEN: $\overline{CA} \perp \overline{AB}$; $\overline{CD} \perp \overline{BD}$.

PROVE: $\dfrac{CP}{PB} = \dfrac{CA}{BD}$.

Prob. 37

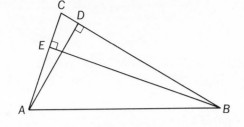

Prob. 38

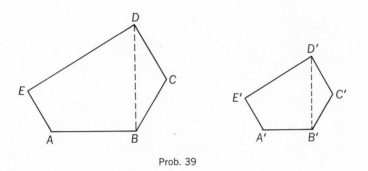

Prob. 39

38. GIVEN: $\triangle ABC$; altitudes $\overline{AD}$, $\overline{BE}$.
PROVE: $AD \cdot BC = BE \cdot CA$.
Can you relate this result to concepts of Chapter 9?

39. GIVEN: $ABCDE \sim A'B'C'D'E'$.
PROVE: $\triangle BCD \sim \triangle B'C'D'$.

40. PROVE: If one of two similar triangles is isosceles, the other is also isosceles.

41. GIVEN: $\triangle ABC$; M the midpoint of $\overline{AD}$; P the midpoint of $\overline{DB}$; N the midpoint of $\overline{CD}$; D between A and B.
PROVE: $\triangle MNP \sim \triangle ACB$.

42. GIVEN: $\angle A \cong \angle B$; $AC = BD$.
PROVE: $\overline{CD} \parallel \overline{AB}$.

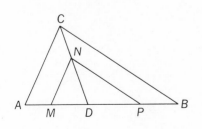

Prob. 41

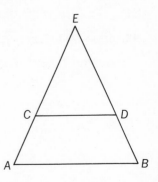

Prob. 42

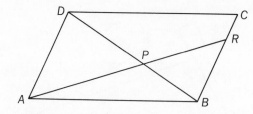

Prob. 43

43. GIVEN: $\square ABCD$; $\overline{AR}$ intersects $\overline{DB}$ at P.

    PROVE: $DP \cdot PR = AP \cdot PB$.

44. GIVEN: $\overline{A'B'} \parallel \overline{AB}$.

    PROVE: $\dfrac{A'B'}{AB} = \dfrac{B'C'}{BC}$.

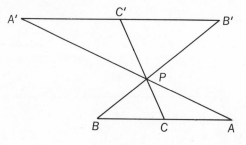

Prob. 44

45. PROVE: In similar triangles, corresponding angle bisectors have the same ratio as any pair of corresponding sides.

46. PROVE: In similar triangles, corresponding medians have the same ratio as any pair of corresponding sides.

47. PROVE: If two triangles are similar, and the ratio of similitude is 1, then the triangles are congruent.

48. GIVEN: Medians $\overline{CM}, \overline{FN}$; $\dfrac{CA}{FD} = \dfrac{CM}{FN} = \dfrac{AB}{DE}$; $\triangle ABC$; $\triangle DEF$.

    PROVE: $\triangle ABC \sim \triangle DEF$.

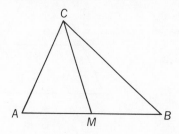
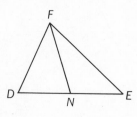

Prob. 48

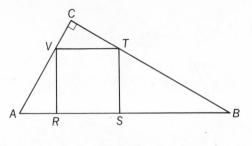

Prob. 49

49. GIVEN: $\overline{AC} \perp \overline{CB}$; $\triangle ABC$; square $RSTV$.
   PROVE: (a) $\triangle ARV \sim \triangle VCT \sim \triangle TSB$; (b) $AR \cdot CT = VR \cdot VC$.

50. GIVEN: $\overline{GH} \parallel \overline{XY}$; $\overline{HK} \parallel \overline{ZY}$.

   PROVE: (a) $\dfrac{PG}{PX} = \dfrac{PK}{PZ}$; (b) $\overline{GK} \parallel \overline{XZ}$; (c) $\triangle GHK \sim \triangle XYZ$.

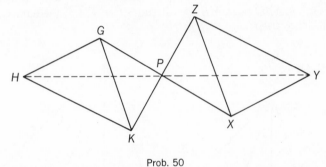

Prob. 50

(B)

51. $\angle A$ of $\triangle ABC$ is a right angle. From E, $(E \in \overline{AC})$, $\overline{ED} \perp \overline{BC}$ is introduced such that D is the foot of the perpendicular. Prove that two similar triangles result. Write three equal ratios determined by the similarity.

52. GIVEN: $\triangle ABC$; $\overline{HR} \perp \overline{AC}$; $\overline{KT} \perp \overline{CB}$; $\overline{JS} \perp \overline{AB}$.
   PROVE: $\triangle RST \sim \triangle ABC$.

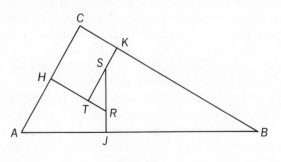

Prob. 52

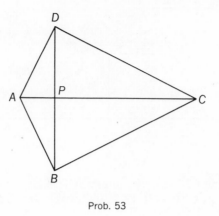

Prob. 53

53. GIVEN: $\overline{DB} \perp \overline{AC}$; $DP = BP = 2(AP) = \frac{1}{2}(PC)$.
    PROVE: (a) $\triangle APD \sim \triangle DPC$; (b) $\triangle BPC \sim \triangle APD$; (c) $\overline{AD} \perp \overline{DC}$.
54. GIVEN: $\triangle ABC \sim \triangle A'B'C'$; altitudes $\overline{CH}$, $\overline{C'H'}$; medians $\overline{CM}$, $\overline{C'M'}$.
    PROVE: $\triangle CHM \sim \triangle C'H'M'$.

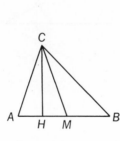
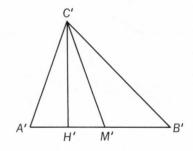

Prob. 54

10–6 RIGHT-TRIANGLE SIMILARITIES

The simple act of dropping an altitude to the hypotenuse of a right triangle leads to some surprising relationships, as well as an algebraic proof of a key theorem in mathematics, the Pythagorean Theorem (Chapter 9, Thm. 9–10).

It is easy to see that, with altitude $\overline{CD}$, three triangles are formed: $\triangle ACD$, $\triangle ABC$, and $\triangle CBD$ (Figure 10–8). What may not be so easy to see is that the three triangles are similar: $\triangle ACD \sim \triangle ABC \sim \triangle CBD$. Before looking at a proof, we suggest a way in which to remember the correspondences involved: $ACD \leftrightarrow ABC \leftrightarrow CBD$. First note that vertices of right angles must correspond. Next note that each of the smaller triangles has an angle (and a vertex) in common with the large triangle, $\triangle ABC$, hence those vertices correspond to themselves. Last, the remaining vertices must correspond.

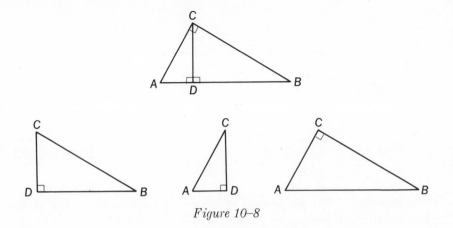

Figure 10–8

Theorem 10–8: **In any right triangle, the altitude to the hypotenuse separates the triangle into two triangles which are similar to each other and to the original triangle.**

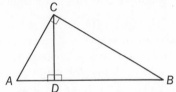

GIVEN: $\triangle ABC$; $\angle ACB$ a right angle; altitude $\overline{CD}$.

PROVE: $\triangle ACD \sim \triangle ABC \sim \triangle CBD$.

DISCUSSION (See also Figure 10–8): If we can prove $\triangle ACD \sim \triangle ABC$, and $\triangle ABC \sim \triangle CBD$, by the Transitivity of Similarity Theorem (Thm. 10–4) $\triangle ACD \sim \triangle CBD$ as well, and we will have our conclusion proved.

Proof: In $\triangle ACD$ and $\triangle ABC$, $\angle ADC$ and $\angle ACB$ are right angles, so $\angle ADC \cong \angle ACB$. $\angle A$ is common to both triangles, and $\angle A \cong \angle A$. By the AA Similarity Corollary (10–3.1), $\triangle ACD \sim \triangle ABC$. (Proof that $\triangle ABC \sim \triangle CBD$ is left as an exercise.) Hence $\triangle ACD \sim \triangle ABC \sim \triangle CBD$.

Definition 10–3: If a, b, and c are positive numbers, b is the **geometric mean** of a and c iff $\dfrac{a}{b} = \dfrac{b}{c}$.

The geometric mean may also be referred to as the **mean proportional.**
Before considering the main theorem of this section, we introduce a concept which has many applications in higher mathematics—the concept of **projection.** We shall not study it deeply; for our purposes this concept serves to clarify the meaning of a theorem.

Consider a point P and a line q, with $P \notin q$ [Figure 10–9(a) and (b)]. Drop a perpendicular from P to q, and label the foot of this perpendicular Q. Q is the *projection* of P on q. In the case that $P \in q$ [Figure 10–9(c)], we say that P is its own projection on q.

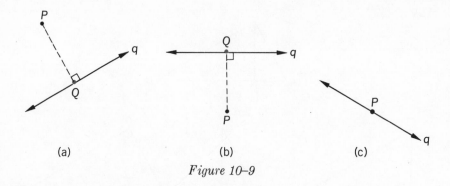

(a)   (b)   (c)

Figure 10–9

Definition 10–4: The **projection of a point on a line** is the foot of the perpendicular from the point to the line.

Definition 10–5: The **projection of a given segment on a line,** in the same plane, is the segment whose endpoints are the projections of the endpoints of the given segment.

In Figure 10–10, $\overline{PQ}$ is the projection of $\overline{AB}$ on line q. In the case that the given segment intersects the line q [Figure 10–10(c)] the segment and its projection have a point in common (point A). Imaginatively speaking, one might say that the projection of a segment on a line is the "shadow" of the segment thrown on the line.

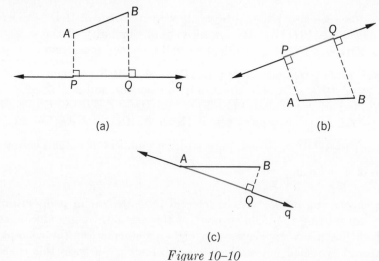

(a)   (b)

(c)

Figure 10–10

Theorem 10–9: **Given a right triangle and an altitude to the hypotenuse:**
(1) The altitude is the geometric mean of the lengths of the projections of the legs on the hypotenuse.

(2) **The length of either leg is the geometric mean of the length of the hypotenuse and the length of the projection of that leg on the hypotenuse.**

GIVEN: $\triangle ABC$; $\angle ACB$ a right angle; altitude $\overline{CD}$.

PROVE: (1) $\dfrac{AD}{CD} = \dfrac{CD}{DB}$;

(2) $\dfrac{AD}{AC} = \dfrac{AC}{AB}$ and $\dfrac{BD}{BC} = \dfrac{BC}{BA}$.

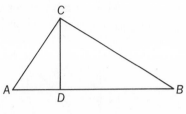

Proof

(1) By Theorem 10–8, $\triangle ADC \sim \triangle CDB$. Hence $\dfrac{AD}{CD} = \dfrac{CD}{DB}$.

(2) By Theorem 10–8, $\triangle ADC \sim \triangle ACB$. Hence $\dfrac{AD}{AC} = \dfrac{AC}{AB}$. By Theorem 10–8, $\triangle BDC \sim \triangle BCA$. Hence $\dfrac{BD}{BC} = \dfrac{BC}{BA}$.

Theorem 10–9 leads to a completely algebraic proof of the Pythagorean Theorem, which we restate here:

Theorem 9–10: **The square of the length of the hypotenuse of a right triangle is equal to the sum of the squares of the lengths of the legs.**

GIVEN: $\triangle ABC$; $\angle ABC$ a right angle.
PROVE: $b^2 = a^2 + c^2$.

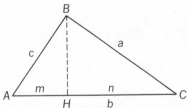

DISCUSSION: Introduce altitude $\overline{BH}$ to hypotenuse $\overline{AC}$. For convenience, let $AB = c$, $BC = a$, and $AC = b$. Further, let $b = m + n$, where m and n are the lengths of $\overline{AH}$ and $\overline{HC}$ respectively. Note that $\overline{AH}$ is the projection of $\overline{AB}$ on $\overline{AC}$, and $\overline{HC}$ is the projection of $\overline{BC}$ on $\overline{AC}$.

Proof: By Theorem 10–9, $\dfrac{b}{c} = \dfrac{c}{m}$ or $bm = c^2$. Also, $\dfrac{b}{a} = \dfrac{a}{n}$ or $a^2 = bn$.

By addition,

$$a^2 + c^2 = bm + bn$$
$$a^2 + c^2 = b(m + n)$$

and so $\qquad a^2 + c^2 = b^2 \qquad$ by substitution, b for $(m + n)$.

EXAMPLES

1. Draw the projections of $\overline{AB}$ on q_1 and on q_2.

Solution: Sketch perpendiculars from A and B to q_1 and q_2, respectively. Label the points of intersection M, N, P, and Q. Then $\overline{MN}$ is the projection of $\overline{AB}$ on q_1, and $\overline{PQ}$ is the projection of $\overline{AB}$ on q_2.

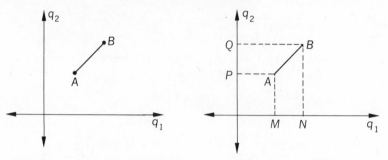

2. In the figure, given $\triangle PQR$ with right $\angle RPQ$, altitude $\overline{PH}$, $RH = 4$, and $HQ = 5$, find x, y, z.

Solution: By Theorem 10–9(2),

$$\frac{QR}{RP} = \frac{RP}{RH}$$

Then $\dfrac{9}{z} = \dfrac{z}{4}$, $z^2 = 36$, $\underline{z = 6}$.

Again:

$$\frac{QR}{y} = \frac{y}{5}$$

Then $\dfrac{9}{y} = \dfrac{y}{5}$, $45 = y^2$, $y = \sqrt{45}$ or $\underline{y = 3\sqrt{5}}$.

By Theorem 10–9(1), $\dfrac{RH}{PH} = \dfrac{PH}{HQ} \cdot \dfrac{4}{x} = \dfrac{x}{5}$, $20 = x^2$, $x = \sqrt{20}$, or $\underline{x = 2\sqrt{5}}$.

Exercise 10–6

(**A**)

1. Copy the drawing as closely as you can. Use a ruler to help sketch the projection of each of the given line segments on the line q. Label and state the results in the form: _____ is the projection of _____ on q.

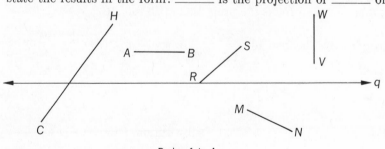

Probs. 1 to 4

Use the results of problem 1 as a "source of inspiration" to answer questions 2, 3, and 4. (Each question refers to a figure in a plane.)

2. Is the projection of a segment on a line always a segment? Explain.
3. Can the length of the projection of a segment on a line be equal to the length of the segment? Explain.
4. Can the length of the projection of a segment on a line be greater than the length of the segment?

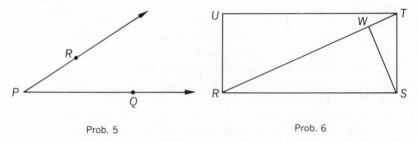

Prob. 5   Prob. 6

5. In the diagram, sketch and name the projection of $\overline{PQ}$ on $\overrightarrow{PR}$. $\overline{PR}$ on $\overrightarrow{PQ}$.
6. In the figure, if $\overline{SW} \perp \overline{RT}$, name the projection of $\overline{RS}$ on $\overline{RT}$. Of $\overline{ST}$ on $\overline{RT}$.

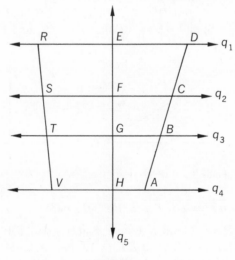

Prob. 7

7. In the figure, $q_1 \parallel q_2 \parallel q_3 \parallel q_4$, $q_5 \perp q_1$, transversals $\overline{RV}$ and $\overline{AD}$. Name the projections of $\overline{AB}$, $\overline{BC}$, $\overline{CD}$, $\overline{RS}$, $\overline{ST}$, and $\overline{TV}$ on line q_5. State a condition that would justify the statement that the projections of these six segments are all congruent.
8. Find the geometric mean of the numbers 4 and 9.
9. Find the geometric mean of the numbers 3 and 12.

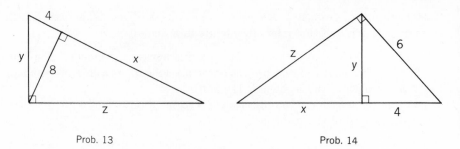

Prob. 13   Prob. 14

10. Find the geometric mean of the numbers 5 and 10.
11. Find the geometric mean of the numbers 3 and 25.
12. Find the mean proportional of 3 and 26.
13. In the figure as shown, find x, y, and z.
14. In the figure as shown, find x, y, and z.
15. If the altitude to the hypotenuse of a right triangle is of length 12, and the hypotenuse is of length 25, find the lengths of the legs, and of the projections of the legs on the hypotenuse.

Given right $\triangle DEF$, altitude $\overline{FG}$ to hypotenuse $\overline{DE}$ (16 to 19):

16. If $DG = 2$, and $GE = 8$, find FG, DF, and FE.
17. If $FG = 9$, and $DG = 3$, find DF, FE, and DE.
18. If $FE = 12$, and $DG = 10$, find DF, FG, and GE.
19. If $FD = 8$, and $GE = 12$, find DG, FG, and FE.

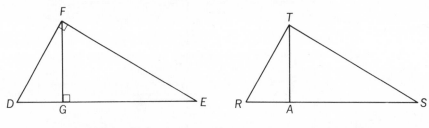

Probs. 16 to 19   Probs. 20 to 23

In the figure, $\overline{RT} \perp \overline{TS}$, $\overline{TA} \perp \overline{RS}$ (20 to 23):

20. If $m\angle R = 60$ and $RA = 5$, find RS and TA.
21. If $m\angle RTA = 30$ and $RT = 12$, find AS and TA.
22. If $m\angle ATS = 60$ and $TR = 16$, find RS.
23. If $m\angle R = 60$ and $RA = b$, find RS.
24. If the legs of a right triangle have lengths 9 and 12, respectively, find the length of the hypotenuse. Find the length of the altitude to the hypotenuse.
25. If the legs of a right triangle have lengths 5 and 12, respectively, find the length of the hypotenuse. Find the length of the altitude to the hypotenuse.

26. If one leg of an isosceles right triangle is of length 4, find the length of the altitude to the hypotenuse.

(B)

27. GIVEN: $RS = RT$; $ST = SV$.

PROVE: $\dfrac{RT}{ST} = \dfrac{ST}{TV}$.

For problems 28 and 29:

GIVEN: Right $\triangle GJK$; altitude $\overline{KH}$;
hypotenuse $\overline{GJ}$.

28. PROVE: $\dfrac{GH}{HJ} = \dfrac{(GK)^2}{(JK)^2}$.

29. PROVE: $(GK) \cdot (KJ) = (KH) \cdot (GJ)$.

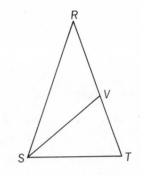

Prob. 27

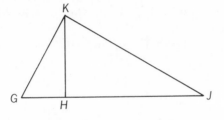

Probs. 28, 29

10–7 AREAS OF SIMILAR TRIANGLES

At the start of this chapter we discussed the idea that straight line segments appear "magnified" or "reduced" under the relationship of similarity between polygons. We examine next *areas* of similar triangles.

Intuitively, it is a bit easier to compare areas of squares, so let us begin by comparing the area of a square, side of length s, with the area of a square whose side is twice as long—$2s$. Since the two squares are similar, and the ratio of similitude is $\frac{2}{1}$, one might perhaps guess that the area of the larger square is twice the area of the smaller. A look at Figure 10–11, however, suggests that this is not the case at all! The area of the smaller square is s^2, that of the larger is $(2s)^2 = 4s^2$. If we compare the two areas by a ratio, $\dfrac{4s^2}{s^2} = \dfrac{4}{1}$, we find that the larger square has an area four times that of the

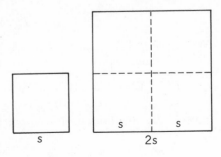

Figure 10–11

smaller. This approach can readily be generalized for any two squares. Let the corresponding sides be (ks) and s, where $k > 0$. Then the ratio of the areas is:

$$\frac{(ks)^2}{s^2} = \frac{k^2 s^2}{s^2} = k^2$$

As another example, suppose $k = 3$. That is, we have two squares such that a side of one is three times a side of the other. Then the ratio of the areas is $\frac{(3)^2}{1}$ or $\frac{9}{1}$; the area of one square is 9 times that of the other. Note that the number k is just the ratio of the two sides: $\frac{ks}{s} = k$. The ratio of the two areas is k^2.

While the same result is applicable to all similar polygons, our particular interest is with similar triangles. We state this formally as the next theorem.

Theorem 10–10: **If two triangles are similar, then the ratio of their areas is the square of the ratio of the lengths of any two corresponding sides.**

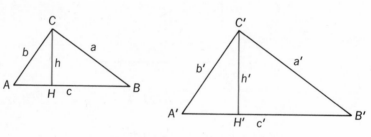

GIVEN: $\triangle ABC \sim \triangle A'B'C'$; $\dfrac{a}{a'} = \dfrac{b}{b'} = \dfrac{c}{c'} = k.$

PROVE: $\dfrac{\text{area}(\triangle ABC)}{\text{area}(\triangle A'B'C')} = k^2.$

Proof: Introduce altitudes $\overline{CH}$ and $\overline{C'H'}$ so that we can consider the areas of the triangles. Then, area$(\triangle ABC) = \frac{1}{2}ch$ and area$(\triangle A'B'C') = \frac{1}{2}c'h'$. From this we obtain:

$$\frac{\text{area}(\triangle ABC)}{\text{area}(\triangle A'B'C')} = \frac{\frac{1}{2}ch}{\frac{1}{2}c'h'} = \frac{ch}{c'h'}$$

Now, since $\triangle ABC \sim \triangle A'B'C'$, $\angle A \cong \angle A'$. Further, $\angle AHC$ and $\angle A'H'C'$ are both right angles (why?); hence $\angle AHC \cong \angle A'H'C'$. Then $\triangle AHC \sim \triangle A'H'C'$ (AA Similarity Corollary, 10-3.1), and $\dfrac{h}{h'} = \dfrac{b}{b'}$. But $\dfrac{b}{b'} = \dfrac{c}{c'}$ (given). By the Transitivity Axiom (E-3), $\dfrac{h}{h'} = \dfrac{c}{c'}$. Then:

$$\frac{ch}{c'h'} = \frac{c}{c'} \cdot \frac{h}{h'} = \frac{c}{c'} \cdot \frac{c}{c'} = \left(\frac{c}{c'}\right)^2 \qquad \frac{\text{area}(\triangle ABC)}{\text{area}(\triangle A'B'C')} = \left(\frac{c}{c'}\right)^2$$

Now $\dfrac{c}{c'} = k$, so that $\left(\dfrac{c}{c'}\right)^2 = k^2$, and we can conclude:

$$\frac{\text{area}(\triangle ABC)}{\text{area}(\triangle A'B'C')} = k^2$$

As mentioned earlier, areas of similar polygons are related in the same way as areas of similar triangles. We state without proof:

Theorem 10–11: Areas of similar polygons have the same ratio as the squares of the lengths of any pair of corresponding sides.

Although this theorem is not proved in this text, it is not a difficult concept, and is useful enough to be remembered.

EXAMPLES

1. Corresponding sides of two similar triangles are of length 2 and 5 in., respectively. Find the ratio of the altitudes, perimeters, and areas of the triangles (see Exercise 10–5, problems 19, 24).

Solution: The ratio of the *altitudes* and the *perimeters* is equal to the ratio of the lengths of any two corresponding sides, and is $\frac{2}{5}$.

The ratio of the *areas* is equal to the ratio of the squares of the lengths of any two corresponding sides, and is $\dfrac{2^2}{5^2}$ or $\dfrac{4}{25}$.

2. The ratio of the areas of two similar triangles is $\frac{81}{64}$. If a side of the smaller triangle has length 10, find the length of the corresponding side of the larger triangle.

Solution: Let x represent the length wanted. Then

$$\frac{x^2}{(10)^2} = \frac{81}{64}$$

$$\frac{x}{10} = \frac{9}{8}$$

$$8x = 90$$

$$x = \frac{90}{8} \quad \text{or} \quad 11\tfrac{1}{4}$$

3. Given $\triangle ABE$ with $\overline{CD} \parallel \overline{AB}$. If $DB = \frac{1}{6}(DE)$, and area$(\triangle ABC) = 147$ sq. in., find area$(\triangle CDE)$.

Solution: Since $\overline{CD} \parallel \overline{AB}$, we know that $\triangle CDE \sim \triangle ABE$. Therefore their areas have a ratio equal to the ratio of the squares of the lengths of a pair of corresponding sides. This implies that we should find the ratio of the lengths of two

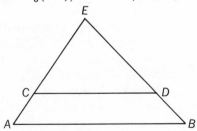

corresponding sides. Now:

$$DB = \frac{1}{6}\,(DE)$$

$$\frac{DB}{DE} = \frac{1}{6}$$

But $\overline{DB}$ is *not* a side, while $\overline{DE}$ is. We want the ratio $\dfrac{DE}{BE}$ in order to complete the problem. Observing that $EB = DE + DB$, Proportion by Addition comes to mind. Thus:

$$\frac{DB}{DE} = \frac{1}{6}$$

$$\frac{DB + DE}{DE} = \frac{1 + 6}{6} \qquad \text{or} \qquad \frac{EB}{DE} = \frac{7}{6}$$

Then

$$\frac{\text{area}(\triangle ABE)}{\text{area}(\triangle CDE)} = \frac{7^2}{6^2} = \frac{49}{36}$$

$$\frac{147}{\text{area}(\triangle CDE)} = \frac{49}{36}$$

$$36 \cdot 147 = 49\,(\text{area}(\triangle CDE))$$

$$\frac{36 \cdot 147}{49} = \text{area}(\triangle CDE)$$

$$108 = \text{area}(\triangle CDE)$$

Exercise 10–7

(A)

What is the ratio of the altitudes, perimeters, and areas of two similar triangles if a pair of corresponding sides are of the following lengths (see Exercise 10–5, problems 19 and 24)?

1. 3 and 4   2. 5 and 7   3. $2\frac{1}{2}$ and $3\frac{1}{3}$
4. $\frac{1}{4}$ and $\frac{1}{16}$ 5. x and y 6. a^2 and b^2

7. A side of one of two similar triangles is 4 times as long as the corresponding side of the second. If the area of the first is 5, find the area of the second.
8. A side of one of two similar triangles is $3\frac{1}{2}$ times as long as the corresponding side of the second. If the area of the first is 4, find the area of the second.
9. A side of one of two similar triangles is 10 times as long as the corresponding side of the second. The area of the second is how many times the area of the first?

10. A side of one of two similar triangles is 10 times as long as the corresponding side of the second. The area of the first is how many times the area of the second?

11. The area of the larger of two similar triangles is 16 times the area of the smaller. If a side of the larger has length 32, find the length of the corresponding side of the smaller triangle.

12. The area of the larger of two similar triangles is 9 times the area of the smaller. The length of a side of the larger is how many times the length of the corresponding side of the smaller?

13. The areas of two similar triangles are 36 sq. in. and 25 sq. in. Find the length of the base of the smaller if the base of the larger has length 30 in.

14. The areas of two similar triangles form the ratio $\frac{81}{49}$. If a side of the first has length 18, find the length of the corresponding side of the second.

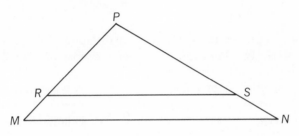

Probs. 15 to 18

Given $\triangle MNP$ with $\overline{RS} \parallel \overline{MN}$ (15 to 18):

15. If $RM = 1$ and $PR = 3$, find $\dfrac{\text{area}(\triangle PRS)}{\text{area}(\triangle PMN)}$.

16. If $PS = 3(SN)$, find the ratio of the areas of $\triangle PRS$ and $\triangle PMN$.

17. If $RM = \frac{1}{4}(RP)$, find the ratio of the areas of $\triangle PRS$ and $\triangle PMN$.

18. If RS is $\frac{5}{9}$ of MN, find the ratio of the areas of $\triangle PRS$ and $\triangle PMN$.

19. What must be the length of a side of an equilateral triangle so that its area shall be four times that of an equilateral triangle of side 16?

20. What must be the length of a side of a square so that its area shall be $\frac{1}{9}$ that of a square of side 27?

21. The ratio of the lengths of the sides of two squares is $\frac{2}{3}$. If the area of the larger is 405 more than the area of the smaller, find the area of each square.

22. Two similar polygons have areas of 200 sq. in. and 1152 sq. in. respectively. If a side of the first has length 20, find the length of the corresponding side of the second.

23. The ratio of the areas of two similar 72-sided polygons is $\frac{25}{16}$. What is the ratio of their perimeters?

24. Two corresponding sides of two similar polygons have lengths of 15 and 18 ft., respectively. Find the ratio of their perimeters and the ratio of their areas.

25. In the figure, $\triangle RST$, $\overline{AB} \parallel \overline{RS}$, $RS = 36$. Find the length of $\overline{AB}$ so that area($\triangle ATB$) = $\frac{1}{9}$ area($\triangle RST$).

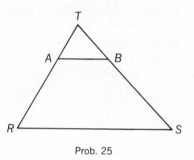

Prob. 25

26. The lengths of the sides of a quadrilateral are 4, 6, 10, and 12 in., respectively. Find the lengths of the sides of a similar quadrilateral whose area is 25 times as large.

27. The lengths of the adjacent sides of a parallelogram are 8 and 12 ft., respectively. Find the lengths of the corresponding sides of a similar parallelogram whose area is one-fourth as large.

28. The diagonals of trapezoid $ABCD$ intersect at Q. The midpoints of segments $\overline{QA}$, $\overline{QB}$, $\overline{QC}$, and $\overline{QD}$ are connected to form another trapezoid. Find the ratio of the area of the smaller trapezoid to the given trapezoid.

29. By what number must the length of the side of a square be multiplied so that its area will be nine times as great?

30. By what number must the length of the side of an equilateral triangle be multiplied so that its area will be three times as great?

31. PROVE: The areas of two similar triangles have the same ratio as the squares of two corresponding altitudes.

32. PROVE: The areas of two similar triangles have the same ratio as the squares of the perimeters.

33. The perimeter of a square is equal to the perimeter of an equilateral triangle. Find the ratio of the areas of the two figures.

(B)

34. If similar triangles are drawn on the side and on the altitude of an equilateral triangle, so that the side and altitude are corresponding sides of the triangles, prove that the ratio of their areas is $\frac{4}{3}$.

35. The altitude of one equilateral triangle is equal to the length of the side of a second equilateral triangle. What is the ratio of their areas?

36. A triangular lot has dimensions $RS = 140$, $RT = 150$, $ST = 130$, and altitude $\overline{TP}$ with $TP = 120$. A fence $(\overline{XY})$ is to be erected x feet from R, so that $\overline{XY} \parallel \overline{TP}$, and area$(\triangle RXY) = \frac{1}{2}$ area$(\triangle RST)$. Find x $(x = RX)$.

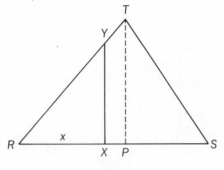

Prob. 36

37. The area of a triangle is 256 sq. in. Lines parallel to a base divide one side into four segments of equal length. Find the areas of the four parts into which the triangle is divided.

10–8 TRIGONOMETRIC RATIOS

The word *trigonometry* derives from two Greek words combining to mean the measurement of triangles. Today the study of trigonometry goes far beyond such elementary considerations. In this and the next section we offer a brief introduction to trigonometry. The following theorem affords a start.

Theorem 10–12: **If an acute angle of one right triangle is congruent to an acute angle of a second right triangle, the triangles are similar.**

Proof: Since the triangles are *right* triangles, each contains a right angle, and we have one pair of corresponding angles congruent immediately. Since a second pair of angles are congruent by hypothesis, the triangles are similar (AA Similarity Corollary 10–3.1).

Consider now two right triangles (Figure 10–12), $\triangle ABC$ and $\triangle A'B'C'$. Let $m\angle A = m\angle A' = r$ $(0 < r < 90)$. By Theorem 10–9, $\triangle ABC \sim \triangle A'B'C'$. Let $AC = b$, $BC = a$, $AB = c$, $A'C' = b'$, $B'C' = a'$, and $A'B' = c'$. Then, by the definition of similar polygons:

$$\frac{a}{a'} = \frac{b}{b'} = \frac{c}{c'} = k$$

from which we may write:

$$a = ka', \quad b = kb', \quad \text{and} \quad c = kc'$$

By the Division Axiom (E-7), we have:

(1) $\dfrac{a}{c} = \dfrac{ka'}{kc'}$ or $\dfrac{a}{c} = \dfrac{a'}{c'}$.

(2) $\dfrac{b}{c} = \dfrac{kb'}{kc'}$ or $\dfrac{b}{c} = \dfrac{b'}{c'}$.

(3) $\dfrac{a}{b} = \dfrac{ka'}{kb'}$ or $\dfrac{a}{b} = \dfrac{a'}{b'}$.

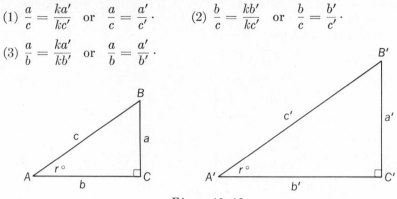

Figure 10–12

Every right triangle with an angle of measure r is similar to $\triangle ABC$, and thus while the sides corresponding to $\overline{AB}$, $\overline{BC}$, and $\overline{AC}$ may have greater or smaller lengths, the corresponding *ratios* of these sides would be equal to the three ratios $\dfrac{a}{c}$, $\dfrac{b}{c}$, and $\dfrac{a}{b}$.   In short, the values of these three ratios depend entirely upon the measure of the acute angle of the given right triangle, and not on the lengths of the sides.

The three ratios listed above (there are others which we do not discuss) are called **trigonometric ratios** and are named:

$$\text{sine } r^\circ = \frac{a}{c}, \quad \text{cosine } r^\circ = \frac{b}{c}, \quad \text{and} \quad \text{tangent } r^\circ = \frac{a}{b}$$

and are usually abbreviated as $\sin r^\circ$, $\cos r^\circ$, and $\tan r^\circ$. We include the degree symbol to emphasize that our unit of measure is the degree, since angle measures other than degrees are also used in trigonometry.

For some angles these ratios can be computed exactly, using only information already available to us.   In particular, we shall compute the ratios associated with the 30° and 45° angles, and leave those associated with the 60° angle as an exercise.

Let $\triangle ACB$ be a right triangle, as shown. Since all 30°–60°–90° triangles are similar, and since the length of the side opposite the 30° angle must be half the length of the hypotenuse, choose $c = 2$ and $a = 1$ or any pair of numbers such that $c = 2a$. By the Pythagorean Theorem:

$$a^2 + b^2 = c^2$$
$$1 + b^2 = 4$$
$$b^2 = 3$$
$$b = \sqrt{3}$$

Hence

$$\sin 30° = \frac{a}{c} = \tfrac{1}{2} \qquad \cos 30° = \frac{b}{c} = \frac{\sqrt{3}}{2} \qquad \tan 30° = \frac{a}{b} = \frac{1}{\sqrt{3}} = \frac{\sqrt{3}}{3}$$

Let $\triangle RST$ be a right triangle as shown. A 45°–45°–90° triangle must be isosceles. Let $r = t = 1$. Then, by the Pythagorean Theorem:

$$s^2 = r^2 + t^2$$
$$s^2 = 1 + 1 = 2$$
$$s = \sqrt{2}$$

Hence

$$\sin 45° = \frac{r}{s} = \frac{1}{\sqrt{2}} = \frac{\sqrt{2}}{2}$$

$$\cos 45° = \frac{t}{s} = \frac{1}{\sqrt{2}} = \frac{\sqrt{2}}{2}$$

$$\tan 45° = \frac{r}{t} = \frac{\sqrt{2}}{\sqrt{2}} = 1$$

Note the change of notation. You should be able to pick out the sides required to compute the trigonometric ratios regardless of how the sides may be named. As a guide for selecting the correct sides of a triangle in a given problem, you may think as follows:

(1) For $\sin r°$, the ratio consists of the length of the *leg opposite* the angle divided by the length of the *hypotenuse*.

(2) For $\cos r°$, the ratio consists of the length of the *leg adjacent* to the angle, divided by the length of the *hypotenuse*.

(3) For $\tan r°$, the ratio consists of the length of the *leg opposite* divided by the length of the *leg adjacent* to the angle.

We shall use a concise notation that is traditional in trigonometry, but requires some explanation. The symbol "sin A" shall be taken to mean $\sin (m\angle A)$, where A is the vertex of the angle. Similar notation is used for the cosine and tangent of any angle.

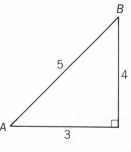

EXAMPLES

From the diagram, find:

1. $\sin A$, $\cos A$, and $\tan A$.
2. $\sin B$, $\cos B$, and $\tan B$.

Exs. 1, 2

Solutions

1. The length of the leg opposite $\angle A$ is 4, the length of the leg adjacent to $\angle A$ is 3. Hence: $\sin A = \frac{4}{5}$, $\cos A = \frac{3}{5}$, and $\tan A = \frac{4}{3}$.

2. The length of the leg opposite $\angle B$ is 3, the length of the leg adjacent to $\angle B$ is 4. Hence: $\sin B = \frac{3}{5}$, $\cos B = \frac{4}{5}$, and $\tan B = \frac{3}{4}$.

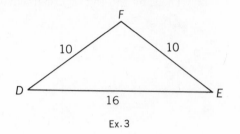

Ex. 3

3. In the figure, find $\sin D$ and $\tan E$.

Solution: To compute $\sin D$ we have only a definition—a definition that requires the length of a hypotenuse, which in turn calls for the existence of a right triangle. To obtain a right triangle, introduce altitude $\overline{FK}$ ($\overline{FK} \perp \overline{DE}$):

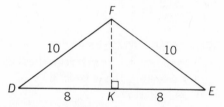

In right $\triangle DKF$, $\overline{DF}$ is a hypotenuse of length 10.

The length of the opposite leg ($\overline{FK}$) is needed next. Noting that $\triangle DFE$ is isosceles with base $\overline{DE}$, we recall that the altitude to the base of an isosceles triangle also bisects the base. Hence $DK = 8$. By the Pythagorean Theorem:

$$(DK)^2 + (FK)^2 = (DF)^2$$
$$64 + (FK)^2 = 100$$
$$(FK)^2 = 36$$
$$FK = 6$$

Now

$$\sin D = \tfrac{6}{10} = \tfrac{3}{5} \quad \text{and} \quad \tan E = \tfrac{6}{8} = \tfrac{3}{4}$$

Exercise 10–8

(A)

1. From the figure, find $\sin r°$, $\cos r°$, $\tan r°$.
2. From the figure, find $\sin S$, $\cos S$, $\tan S$.
3. From the figure for problem 2, find $\sin T$, $\cos T$, $\tan T$.

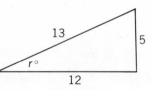

Prob. 1

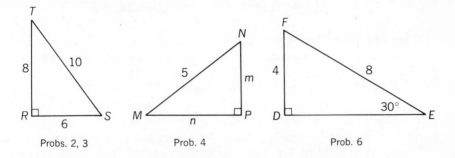

Probs. 2, 3   Prob. 4   Prob. 6

4. From the figure, write an expression for sin N, cos N, tan N.

5. Find exact values for sin 60°, cos 60°, tan 60°.

6. Use the information shown in the figure to find sin 30° and cos 30°.

7. In computing the ratios associated with 30°, we chose the hypotenuse to be of length 2, and the opposite leg to be of length 1. The thought often occurs that this seems to be a "special" choice—wouldn't the ratios be different for another choice of numbers? In the figure, let a represent the length of the opposite leg, and $2a$ the length of the hypotenuse. Compute the length of the leg adjacent to the 30° angle, and then find sin 30°, cos 30°, and tan 30°.

Using the information given by the figure, find x (8 to 13):

8. If $x =$ cos R.

9. If $x =$ cos P.

10. If $x =$ tan R.

11. If $x =$ sin R.

12. If $x =$ sin P.

13. If $x =$ tan P.

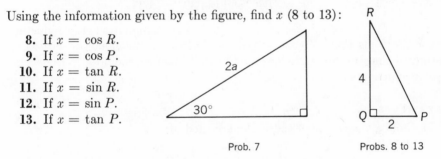

Prob. 7   Probs. 8 to 13

Using the information as shown in the figure, find (14 to 19):

14. sin C **15.** cos C **16.** tan C **17.** sin B **18.** cos B **19.** tan B

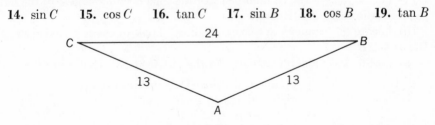

Probs. 14 to 19

20. Make a careful drawing of a right triangle (use a ruler and protractor) with a 50° angle. By measuring, determine approximately: sin 50°, cos 50°, and tan 50°.

10-9 NUMERICAL TRIGONOMETRY AND TABLES

While the preceding section makes it evident that certain trigonometric ratios can be computed exactly—e.g., for 30°, 45°, and 60°—for most angles we have only approximations. These approximations are computed by methods much too advanced for our purposes, but we can use the data derived by these methods. These data are conveniently arranged in the form of a table, a portion of which is reproduced on the next page for immediate use, while the more complete table is printed on page 417 of the Appendix.

With a little practice, you can readily learn to use the table of values of the trigonometric ratios. Note first the left-hand column under the heading "Angle." Reading straight down the page, angles from 0° to 45° are listed in order. This listing continues at the top center of the page, with 46°, continuing to 90°. Second, observe that following the Angle heading immediately to the right and across the top are the names of the three trigonometric ratios: Sine, Cosine, and Tangent. To find the ratio associated with a given angle, locate the angle under the Angle heading, and read the number in the table to the right under the appropriate ratio heading.

EXAMPLES

sin 25° = .423, cos 19° = .946, and tan 32° = .625.

The remainder of this section is devoted to an examination of introductory type problems that may be solved by the use of trigonometric ratios. A study of these examples, followed by further practice, should help to develop some appreciation for their use.

EXAMPLES

1. Find the measure of the angle indicated, if:

    (a) sin A = .559   (b) cos B = .891   (c) tan C = .287

Solution

(a) Locate .559 in the column beneath the Sine heading. Look to the left, and read the entry 34. Hence $m\angle A = 34$.

(b) Locate .891 under the Cosine heading. Look to the left, and read 27. Hence $m\angle B = 27$.

(c) Locate .287 under Tangent. To the left read 16. Hence $m\angle C = 16$.

2. If tan $A = \frac{2}{3}$, find numerical values for sin A and cos A.

Solution: Sketch a right triangle, $\triangle ABC$.

Since tan $A = \dfrac{CB}{BA}$, then $\dfrac{CB}{BA} = \dfrac{2}{3}$. Let $CB = 2$ and $AB = 3$. To compute the other two ratios, we shall require the length of the hypotenuse. By the Pythagorean Theorem,

$$(AC)^2 = 3^2 + 2^2 = 13$$
$$AC = \sqrt{13}$$

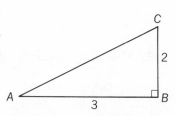

Angle (deg)	Sine	Cosine	Tangent
16	.276	.961	.287
17	.292	.956	.306
18	.309	.951	.325
19	.326	.946	.344
20	.342	.940	.364
21	.358	.934	.384
22	.375	.927	.404
23	.391	.921	.424
24	.407	.914	.445
25	.423	.906	.466
26	.438	.899	.488
27	.454	.891	.510
28	.469	.883	.532
29	.485	.875	.554
30	.500	.866	.577
31	.515	.857	.601
32	.530	.848	.625
33	.545	.839	.649
34	.559	.829	.675
35	.574	.819	.700

Hence

$$\sin A = \frac{2}{\sqrt{13}} = \frac{2\sqrt{13}}{13} \quad \text{and} \quad \cos A = \frac{3}{\sqrt{13}} = \frac{3\sqrt{13}}{13}$$

3. An isosceles triangle has a base of length 6 and a vertex angle of 30°.
   (a) Find the length of the altitude to the base.
   (b) Find the lengths of the congruent sides.
   (c) Find the length of the altitude to a side.

Solution: Let $\triangle ABC$ represent the given isosceles triangle, with $\overline{AB} \cong \overline{BC}$, and altitude $\overline{CH}$. Since $m\angle ACB = 30$, $m\angle A + m\angle B = 150$. Since $\angle A \cong \angle B$, $m\angle A = m\angle B = 75$.

(a) To find CH, select a right triangle, making use of the given information. In $\triangle AHC$, we note that $\overline{CH}$ is opposite the 75° angle, while $\overline{AH}$ is adjacent to it. This suggests the tangent ratio: $\tan 75° = \dfrac{h}{AH}$. Now, the altitude to the base of an isosceles triangle bisects the base, so $AH = 3$. And, from the table, $\tan 75° = 3.732$. Therefore

$$3.732 = \frac{h}{3}$$

$$11.196 = h \quad \text{or} \quad h \approx 11.2$$

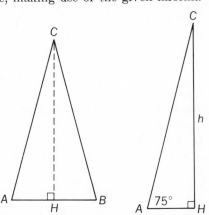

(b) The same triangle ($\triangle AHC$) may be used to compute AC. Since $\overline{AH}$ is an adjacent side, and $\overline{AC}$ is the hypotenuse, the cosine ratio is suggested.

$$\cos 75° = \frac{AH}{AC}$$

$$.259 = \frac{3}{AC}$$

$$AC = \frac{3}{.259}$$

$$AC = 11.58$$

or

$$AC \approx 11.6 \quad \text{and} \quad BC \approx 11.6$$

(c) To find $\overline{BJ}$, we may use $\triangle BJC$. $\overline{BJ}$ is opposite the 30° angle, while $\overline{BC}$ is the hypotenuse, so the sine ratio is suggested.

$$\sin 30° = \frac{JB}{BC}$$

$$BC(\sin 30°) = JB$$

Using $BC \approx 11.6$ from part (b), and $\sin 30° = \frac{1}{2}$, we have:

$$\tfrac{1}{2}(11.6) \approx JB$$

$$5.8 \approx JB$$

Two physical situations occur frequently enough to warrant the naming of certain angles. Imagine a person standing at D (Figure 10–13), looking down

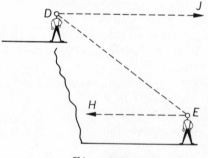

Figure 10–13

toward E. The angle formed by the horizontal ray $\overrightarrow{DJ}$ and $\overrightarrow{DE}$ is called the "angle of depression." Picture next a person standing at E looking up toward D. The angle formed by the horizontal ray $\overrightarrow{EH}$ and $\overrightarrow{ED}$ is called the "angle of elevation." In both cases it is essential to take the horizontal ray into account.

4. In the diagram, A, B, and C represent observers standing in two

buildings. Using the notation shown, name two angles of elevation, and two angles of depression.

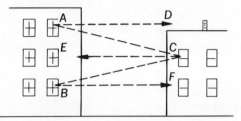

Solution: At A, $\overrightarrow{AD}$ represents the horizontal, and $\overrightarrow{AC}$ the direction toward C. Then $\angle CAD$ is an angle of depression.

At B, $\overrightarrow{BF}$ represents the horizontal, and $\overrightarrow{BC}$ the direction toward C. Then $\angle FBC$ is an angle of elevation.

At C, $\overrightarrow{CE}$ represents the horizontal. Then $\angle ECA$ is an angle of elevation, and $\angle CBF$ is an angle of depression.

5. The angle of elevation of the sun is 70°. A flagpole casts a shadow 15 ft. long. Find the height of the flagpole.

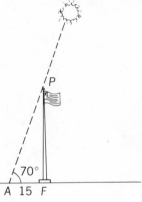

Solution: Rays of light may be considered as straight lines. The angle of elevation of the sun is the angle between the horizontal and the line of sight to the sun $(\overrightarrow{AP})$.

Now, in the figure, $\overline{AF}$ is adjacent to $\angle A$, and $\overline{PF}$ (representing the flagpole) is opposite to $\angle A$. Hence we choose the tangent ratio:

$$\frac{PF}{FA} = \tan 70°$$

$$PF = (FA) \tan 70°$$

$$PF = (15)(2.747)$$

$$PF \approx 41.2$$

The height of the flagpole is approximately 41.2 ft.

Exercise 10-9

(A)

Use the table on page 417 to find values of the three trigonometric ratios of the following angles (1 to 6):

1. 15°   **2.** 34°   **3.** 51°   **4.** 70°   **5.** 80°   **6.** 89°

In each case, find $m\angle A$ (7 to 11):

7. $\sin A = .052$ **8.** $\cos A = .052$ **9.** $\tan A = .052$
10. $\tan A = 0.000$ **11.** $\sin A = 0.000$

12. If a tower casts a shadow 40 ft. long when the angle of elevation of the sun is 50°, find the height of the tower.

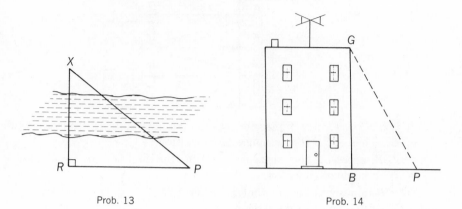

Prob. 13   Prob. 14

13. *R* and *X* represent points on opposite sides of a river. A surveyor measures a right angle at *R* ($\angle XRP$), and then measures a length of 100 ft. from *R* to *P*. Next, $m\angle RPX = 40$. Find the distance from *R* to *X*.

14. To find the height of a building $(\overline{GB})$, a surveyor measures $\overline{BP}$ so that $BP = 120$ ft. The angle of elevation at *P* is 62°. Find *GB*.

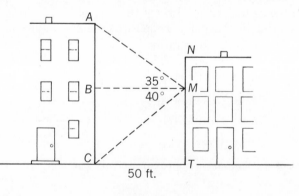

Prob. 15

15. A man at the window *M* of building $\overline{NT}$ looks across at an opposite building, $\overline{AC}$. He measures the angles (as shown), and knows that the buildings are 50 ft. apart. Find the height of building $\overline{AC}$.

16. An antenna pole $(\overline{AT})$ is to be braced with a guy wire from *T* to a post in the ground at *G*, 23 ft. from *A*. At *G*, the angle measures 41°. Find the length of the wire.

17. Find the altitude $\overline{DE}$ of $\square ABCD$ if $DA = 50$, $AB = 80$, and $m\angle A = 52$. Find the area of $\square ABCD$.

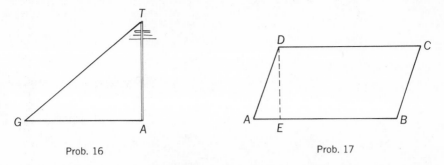

Prob. 16   Prob. 17

18. A tower on the bank of a river is known to rise 163 ft. above the water. If the angle of elevation of the top of the tower from a point on the opposite side of the river is 15°, find the width of the river.

19. Find the altitude of an equilateral triangle with side of length 328.

20. Find the length of the side of an equilateral triangle whose altitude is of length 62.

21. In an isosceles $\triangle ABC$, $AB = 12$ and $m\angle B = 70$. Find the length of base $\overline{BC}$ and the length of the altitude to the base.

22. Find, to the nearest degree, the angle of elevation of the sun when a tree 96 ft. high casts a 116 ft. shadow.

23. Find, to the nearest degree, the angles of an isosceles triangle if the length of its base is 18 and each side has length 12.

(B)

24. Find the area of an isosceles triangle if the vertex angle is a 40° angle, and the altitude is of length 6.

25. To find the distance from each shore to an island B, an engineer measures $\overline{AD}$ ($\overline{AD} \perp \overline{AC}$), $\angle ADC$ and $\angle ADB$. He finds $AD = 100$ ft., $m\angle ADB = 57$ and $m\angle ADC = 74$. Find the distances AB and BC.

26. Two observers, one at P, and one at Q, are 1000 yds. apart. Each measures the angle of depression to a point B at the bottom of a canyon. The angle of depression at P is 28°, at Q, 62°. How deep is the canyon?

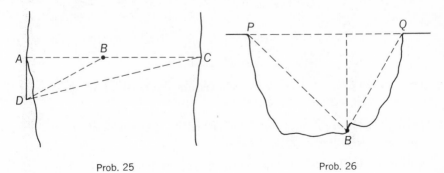

Prob. 25   Prob. 26

Chapter 11

CIRCLES AND RELATED SETS

11-1 DEFINITIONS

Circles are among the most frequently encountered geometric shapes (wheels, gears, clock faces, and telescope lenses to name just a few), and yet it is interesting to see how few people can describe a circle without using their hands. (Can you?)

Definition 11-1: A **circle** is the set of all points in a plane which are a given distance from a given point in the plane. The given point is called the **center**, and the given distance is the **radius** of the circle. (Figure 11-1.)

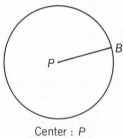

Center : P
Radius : PB
Figure 11-1

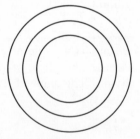

Three concentric circles
Figure 11-2

Definition 11-2: Two. or more circles are **concentric** iff they have the same center. (Figure 11-2)..

Definition 11-3: A segment is a **chord** of a circle iff its endpoints are points of the circle. (Figure 11-3.)

Definition 11-4: A line is a **secant** iff it contains a chord. (Figure 11-3.)

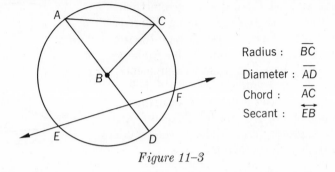

Figure 11–3

Radius : $\overline{BC}$

Diameter : $\overline{AD}$

Chord : $\overline{AC}$

Secant : $\overleftrightarrow{EB}$

Definition 11–5: A chord is a **diameter** iff it includes the center of the circle. (Figure 11–3.)

Definition 11–6: A segment is a **radius** iff one of its endpoints is the center and the other a point of the circle. The endpoint on the circle is the **outer end** of the radius.

Note that in Definitions 11–1 and 11–6 we are using the word *radius* to mean a number (distance) as well as a segment. This should create no misunderstanding, since the context will make clear which meaning is intended.

We will follow the practice of identifying a circle by means of the letter naming its center. For example, in Figure 11–3, the circle would be named *circle B*.

Exercise 11–1

(A)

Use a compass and ruler to make sketches illustrating each of the following as closely as you can (1 to 8):

1. Circle C, radius $\overline{AC}$, chord $\overline{AB}$, diameter $\overline{BD}$.
2. Circle O, chords $\overline{AB}$, $\overline{BC}$, and $\overleftrightarrow{CA}$.
3. Circle P, secants $\overleftrightarrow{AB}$ and $\overleftrightarrow{AC}$, B and C on the circle. (Make at least two different sketches.)
4. Circle P, secants $\overleftrightarrow{AB}$ and $\overleftrightarrow{AC}$ (A on the circle), chord $\overline{BC}$.
5. Circle C, P at a distance from the center greater than the radius, $\overleftrightarrow{PT}$ intersecting circle C in T only, and secant $\overrightarrow{PA}$ with A on circle C.
6. Chords $\overline{AB}$, $\overline{BC}$, $\overline{CD}$, and $\overline{DA}$, in the same circle.
7. Chords $\overline{AB}$, $\overline{BC}$, $\overline{CD}$, and $\overline{DA}$, in the same circle so that $ABCD$ is a parallelogram. (Do you think this is possible?)
8. Same as problem 7, except that $ABCD$ is to be a trapezoid. (Do you think this is possible?)

9. Make at least three drawings something
like the one at the right, using different
length radii. In each case use a protractor
to find $m\angle1$, $m\angle2$, and $m\angle3$. Make a
conjecture based on your measurements.

10. Draw at least four circles with different
length radii. In each circle draw diameter
$\overline{AB}$ and chords $\overline{AC}$ and $\overline{BC}$. Measure $\angle C$
with a protractor. Make a conjecture
based on your measurements.

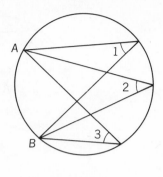

Prob. 9

11–2 TANGENT LINES

In this section we shall talk about points being "inside" or "outside" a
circle, or, synonymously, points being in the "interior" or "exterior" of a
circle.

Definition 11–7: The **interior** of a circle is the union of its center and the
set of all points in the plane of the circle whose distances from the center
are less than the radius. The **exterior** of a circle is the set of all points in
the plane of the circle whose distances from the center are greater than
the radius.

In Figure 11–4, line q is "tangent" to the circle at A.

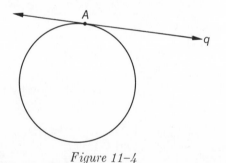

Figure 11–4

Definition 11–8: A line is **tangent** to a circle iff it is in the plane of the
circle and intersects the circle in only one point. The point of intersection
is the **point of tangency,** or **point of contact.** The line and the circle
are **tangent** to each other.

Note that Definition 11–8 refers to a *line* and *not* a ray or a segment.
Rays and segments can certainly be tangent to a circle, but only under
certain special conditions. First, the ray or segment must be a subset of a
line that is tangent to the circle. Second, the ray or segment must contain

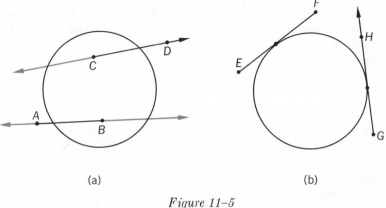

(a)   (b)

Figure 11-5

the point of tangency. Figure 11-5(a) illustrates the situation in which a segment ($\overline{AB}$) and a ray ($\overrightarrow{CD}$) each intersect a circle in only one point, but each is a subset of a *secant* line rather than of a tangent line. Figure 11-5(b) shows a ray and a segment each of which *is* tangent to the circle.

Our next concern is with relations that may occur between a line and a circle in the same plane. Examination of Figure 11-6 indicates that there appear to be three possibilities. The line might not intersect the circle at all; the line might be tangent to the circle; or the line might intersect the circle in two points.

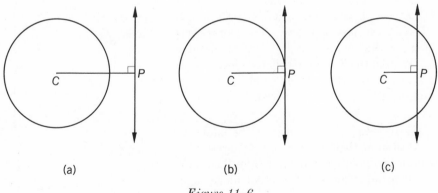

(a)   (b)   (c)

Figure 11-6

It is convenient to discuss these three possibilities in terms of P, the foot of the perpendicular from the center, C, of the circle, to the line. That is, if P is in the exterior of circle C, the line lies entirely in the exterior of the circle (Figure 11-6). If P is on circle C, the line is tangent to the circle. If P is in the interior of circle C, the line is a secant, and intersects the circle in two points. We summarize this in (a rather lengthy) Theorem 11-1.

Theorem 11–1: **If a line and a circle are in the same plane, and if P is the foot of the perpendicular from the center of the circle to the line, then:**

(1) **Every point of the line is outside the circle or,**

(2) **P is on the circle and the line is tangent to the circle at P, or**

(3) **P is inside the circle, and the line intersects the circle in two points which are equidistant from P.**

Analysis: If C is the center of the circle and the radius is r, then by the Trichotomy Property (Axiom O–1) either $CP < r$, $CP = r$, or $CP > r$, which simply means that P is either inside, on, or outside circle C. We will show that if P is outside, then (1) holds; if P is on the circle, then (2) holds; and if P is inside, then (3) holds.

Proof

(1) If *P is in the exterior* of the circle, then $CP > r$. Choose any point, A, on the line, such that $A \neq P$. Since $\overline{CP} \perp \overleftrightarrow{PA}$, Theorem 7–6 tells us that $\overline{CP}$ is the shortest segment joining C to the line, hence $CA > CP$. Since $CP > r$, it follows that $CA > r$. That is, any point on the line other than P must be in the exterior of the circle, and (1) is proved.

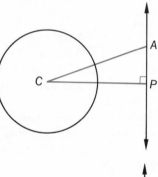

(2) If *P is on the circle*, then $CP = r$. As in (1), choose $A \neq P$ and then $CA > CP$. Since $CP = r$, we have $CA > r$. Therefore, every point on the line, except P, is outside of circle C. That is, the line intersects the circle in only one point. But then the line and the circle are tangent at P, and (2) is proved.

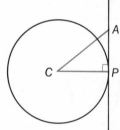

(3) If *P is in the interior* of the circle, we need to show that the line and the circle intersect in two points equidistant from the foot of the perpendicular, P. The proof hinges upon showing three parts:

    I. If a point lies on the line *and* on the circle, then that point must be a certain distance, call it k, from P.

    II. Conversely, if a point lies on the line and is also at the distance k from P, then that point also lies on the circle.

    III. There are exactly two such points.

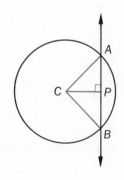

Part I: Let A be a point on the line *and* on the circle. Then, since $\triangle CPA$ is a right triangle, we have:

$$(CP)^2 + (PA)^2 = r^2$$

or
$$(PA)^2 = r^2 - (CP)^2$$

Now, since $r > CP$, and CP is positive, it follows that $r^2 > (CP)^2$ and so $[r^2 - (CP)^2]$ is a positive number. Therefore

$$\sqrt{(PA)^2} = \sqrt{r^2 - (CP)^2} \qquad \text{(Ax. E–8)}$$

or
$$PA = \sqrt{r^2 - (CP)^2}$$

Thus, any point lying on the line and on the circle must be at distance $\sqrt{r^2 - (CP)^2}$ from P. (This is the distance k referred to in the discussion prior to this proof.)

Part II: Consider next any point A on the line and at a distance $\sqrt{r^2 - (CP)^2}$ from P. We have

$$PA = \sqrt{r^2 - (CP)^2}$$
$$(PA)^2 = r^2 - (CP)^2$$

or
$$(PA)^2 + (CP)^2 = r^2$$

This last equation says that (by the converse of the Pythagorean Theorem (Thm. 9–11)), $\triangle CPA$ is a right triangle. Then:

$$(PA)^2 + (CP)^2 = (CA)^2$$

and by substitution: $(CA)^2 = r^2$, hence $\underline{CA = r}$. But then, by definition of radius, A must lie on the circle. We have now completed parts I and II, with $k = \sqrt{r^2 - (CP)^2}$.

Part III: Consider the opposite rays: $\overrightarrow{PA}$ and $\overrightarrow{PB}$. The Point-Plotting Axiom (Axiom 2–4) tells us that there is exactly one point on $\overrightarrow{PA}$ at distance $\sqrt{r^2 - (CP)^2}$ from P, and exactly one point on $\overrightarrow{PB}$ that same distance from P. By the proof above, these points must lie on the circle. Since there are exactly two rays, there are exactly two such points, and we have completed the major part of the proof.

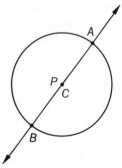

It remains only to consider the special case in which the line passes through C. Here, C and P coincide, and $\overline{AB}$ is a diameter. Thus $PA = PB = r$, and there are two points equidistant from P. We have now completed the proof for case (3), and Theorem 11–1 is proved.

Many of the basic theorems on tangents and chords are corollaries of Theorem 11–1. In each case, the proof consists of pointing out which case of Theorem 11–1 applies. (In all cases it is to be understood that the line and the circle are coplanar.)

Corollary 11–1.1: Every line tangent to a circle is perpendicular to the radius drawn to the point of contact.

Proof: This is case (2), in which the point of contact is the foot of the perpendicular, $\overline{CP}$; hence the tangent and radius are perpendicular.

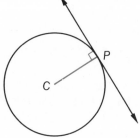

Corollary 11–1.2: Any line perpendicular to a radius at its outer end is tangent to the circle.

Proof: Again case (2) applies, since the outer end of the radius must be the foot of the perpendicular from C; and we have tangency.

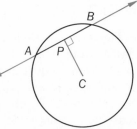

Corollary 11–1.3: Any perpendicular from the center of a circle to a chord bisects the chord.

Proof: This is case (3), since P is inside the circle. Hence $PA = PB$, and so $\overline{CP}$ bisects $\overline{AB}$.

Corollary 11–1.4: The segment joining the center of the circle to the midpoint of a chord is perpendicular to the chord.

Proof: (See the figure for Corollary 11–1.3.) By case (3), the foot of the perpendicular from C is equidistant from A and B. Since the midpoint of a segment is unique, we have shown that the midpoint and the foot of the perpendicular are the same point. Hence the bisecting segment is perpendicular to the chord.

Corollary 11–1.5: **The perpendicular bisector of a chord passes through the center of the circle.**

The proof is left as an exercise.

Corollary 11–1.6: **If a line intersects the interior of a circle, then it intersects the circle in exactly two points.**

The proof is left as an exercise.

Before establishing the next theorem, we shall clarify our language. The distance from the center of a circle to a chord is the same as the distance from the center of the circle to the line containing the chord. This concept is needed for the theorem that follows this next definition.

Definition 11–9: Two **circles** are **congruent** iff they have congruent radii.

Theorem 11–2: **In the same circle, or in congruent circles, chords equidistant from the center are congruent.**

Theorem 11–3: **In the same circle, or in congruent circles, any two congruent chords are equidistant from the center.**

The proofs of Theorems 11–2 and 11–3 are left as exercises.
The next definitions describe certain relations between coplanar circles.

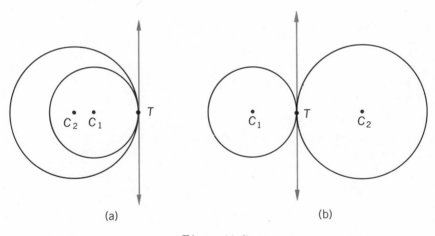

Figure 11–7

Definition 11–10: Two **circles** are **tangent** iff they are each tangent to the same line at the same point. Two circles are **internally tangent** iff their centers are on the same side of the common tangent line [Figure 11–7(a)] and **externally tangent** iff their centers lie on opposite sides of the common tangent line [Figure 11–7(b)].

EXAMPLES

1. If $\overline{BC}$ is tangent to circle A at C, $AB = 10$, and $BC = 8$, find AC.

Solution: By Corollary 11–1.1, $\overline{AC} \perp$
$\overline{BC}$, and therefore $\triangle ABC$ is a right triangle. By the Pythagorean Theorem, we
have:

$$(AC)^2 = (AB)^2 - (BC)^2$$
$$(AC)^2 = 100 - 64$$
$$(AC)^2 = 36$$
$$\underline{AC = 6}$$

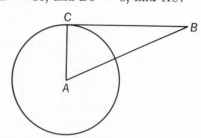

2. Given circle O, $OA = 25$, $CA = 48$, and $\overline{OB} \perp \overline{AC}$, find OB.

Solution: Since $\overline{OB} \perp \overline{AC}$, we have,
by Corollary 11–1.3, that $BC = BA$.
Hence $BA = 24$. Applying the Pythagorean Theorem:

$$(OB)^2 = (OA)^2 - (AB)^2$$
$$(OB)^2 = 625 - 576$$
$$(OB)^2 = 49$$
$$\underline{OB = 7}$$

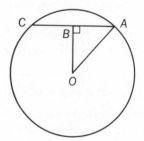

Exercise 11–2

(A)

1. Is $\overline{AB}$ tangent to circle D? Why?
2. Is $\overline{BC}$ tangent to circle D? Why?
3. GIVEN: Circle D; radius $\overline{DB} \perp$ radius $\overline{DE}$; $\overleftrightarrow{AB} \parallel \overline{DE}$.
   PROVE: $\overleftrightarrow{AC}$ is tangent to circle D.
4. GIVEN: $\overleftrightarrow{AC}$ is tangent to circle D at B; $\overline{DE} \parallel \overleftrightarrow{AC}$.
   PROVE: $\overline{DE} \perp \overline{DB}$.

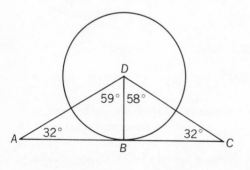

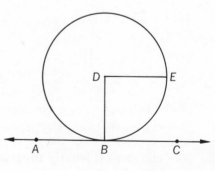

Probs. 1, 2   Probs. 3, 4

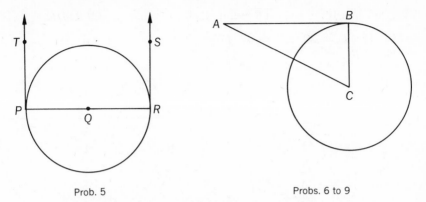

Prob. 5   Probs. 6 to 9

5. GIVEN: $\overrightarrow{PT}$ and $\overrightarrow{RS}$ tangent to circle Q; diameter $\overline{PR}$.
PROVE: $\overrightarrow{PT} \parallel \overrightarrow{PS}$.

In problems 6 to 9, $\overline{AB}$ is tangent to circle C; radius $\overline{CB}$.

  6. If $AB = 12$ and $BC = 5$, $AC = $?
  7. If $AC = 17$ and $AB = 15$, $BC = $?
  8. If $AC = 20$ and $m\angle A = 30$, $BC = $?
  9. If $AC = 16$ and $m\angle C = 45$, $AB = $?

10. GIVEN: $\overline{PA}$ and $\overline{PB}$ tangent to circle C; radii $\overline{CA}$ and $\overline{CB}$.
     PROVE: (a) $PB = PA$; (b) $\angle x \cong \angle y$.

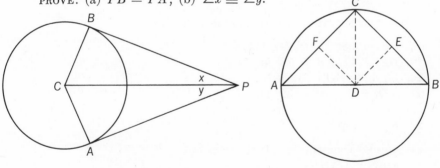

Prob. 10   Probs. 11 to 15

For problems 11 to 15:

    GIVEN: $\overline{AB}$ a diameter of circle D; chord $\overline{AC} \cong$ chord $\overline{BC}$; $\overline{DF} \perp \overline{AC}$;
             $\overline{DE} \perp \overline{BC}$.

11. PROVE: $\overline{CD} \perp \overline{AB}$.
12. PROVE: (a) $\triangle DBE \cong \triangle DCE$; (b) $\overline{DE}$ bisects $\angle CDB$.
13. PROVE: (a) $\overline{DE} \cong \overline{BE}$ (*Hint:* Use problems 11 and 12b);
         (b) $m\angle B = 45$.
14. PROVE: $\triangle DCE \cong \triangle DCF$.
15. PROVE: $\angle ACB$ is a right angle. (*Hint:* Use problems 12a, 13b, and 14.)

In problems 16 and 17, $\overline{AB}$ is a diameter of circle C, $\overline{AB} \perp \overline{DE}$.

16. If $AB = 20$, $DE = 16$, $FC = ?$
17. If $FC = 5$, $DE = 24$, $AB = ?$

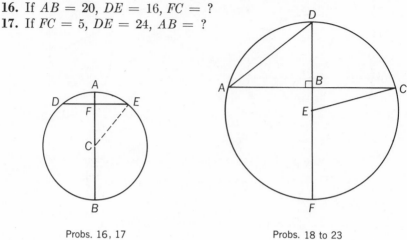

Probs. 16, 17   Probs. 18 to 23

For problems 18 to 23, given circle E, diameter $\overline{DF}$, $\overline{AC} \perp \overline{DF}$. Answer each problem as follows: (You need not solve the problems.)

   Write "M" if more numerical information is given than is needed to solve the problem.
   Write "I" if there is insufficient information.
   Write "S" if the information is sufficient.
   Write "C" if the information is contradictory.

18. $BE = 3.5$, $AC = 24$, $AD = ?$
19. $DF = 40$, $AB = 16$, $EC = ?$
20. $EC = 8$, $FD = 16$, $BE = ?$
21. $AD = 20$, $AC = 32$, $DB = 13$, $DF = ?$
22. $AC = 6$, $DE = 5$, $BF = ?$
23. $BF = 5$, $EC = 6$, $AC = ?$

24. GIVEN: Diameter $\overline{AC} \perp$ diameter $\overline{BD}$.
   PROVE: $ABCD$ is a square.

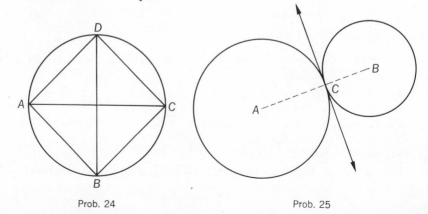

Prob. 24   Prob. 25

25. GIVEN: Circles A and B externally tangent at C.
PROVE: A, C, and B are collinear.
26. GIVEN: $ABCD$ is a rectangle; circle E.
PROVE: $\overline{AB}$ and $\overline{CD}$ are equidistant from E.

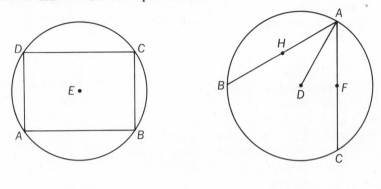

Prob. 26   Prob. 29

27. PROVE: If a diameter bisects one of two parallel chords which are not diameters, it bisects the other.
28. PROVE: If a diameter bisects each of two chords which are not diameters, the chords are parallel to each other.
29. GIVEN: A, B, and C on circle D; $\overline{AB} \cong \overline{AC}$; F the midpoint of $\overline{AC}$; H the midpoint of $\overline{AB}$.
PROVE: $\angle DAB \cong \angle DAC$.

(B)

30. PROVE: If two chords of a circle form congruent angles with the radius to the point of intersection of the two chords, the chords are congruent.
31. PROVE: If two congruent chords of a circle intersect, the segments of one are respectively congruent to the segments of the other.
32. GIVEN: Circles E and F; $\overleftrightarrow{AB}$ and $\overleftrightarrow{CD}$ tangent to both circles at A, B, C, and D.
PROVE: $\overline{AB} \cong \overline{CD}$.

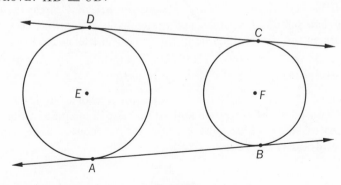

Prob. 32

33. PROVE: If three circles are tangent to the same line at the same point, the three centers are collinear with the point of tangency.

34. GIVEN: Two concentric circles with center O; chord $\overline{BC}$ a subset of chord $\overline{AD}$.

PROVE: $\overline{AB} \cong \overline{CD}$. (*Hint:* Introduce a perpendicular from O to $\overline{BC}$.)

35. PROVE: Corollary 11–1.5. (*Hint:* Use Corollaries 11–1.3, 11–1.4, or Thm. 6–2.)

36. PROVE: Corollary 11–1.6.

37. PROVE: Thm. 11–2.

38. PROVE: Thm. 11–3.

39. PROVE: The line joining the centers of two intersecting circles is the perpendicular bisector of their common chord.

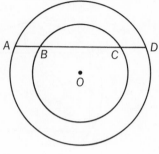

Prob. 34

11–3 ARCS AND CENTRAL ANGLES

In this section we investigate certain relations between the measures of arcs and angles. First, some definitions.

Definition 11–11: An angle is a **central angle** of a circle iff its vertex is the center of the circle. (Figure 11–8.)

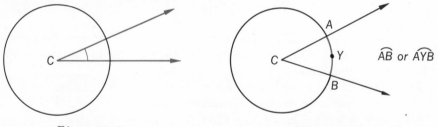

Figure 11–8   *Figure 11–9*

Definition 11–12: A set of points is a **minor arc** of a circle iff it is the union of two points of a circle, not the endpoints of a diameter, and all the points on the circle which lie in the interior of the central angle whose sides contain the two points. (Notation: $\overset{\frown}{AB}$ or $\overset{\frown}{AYB}$.) The two points are the **endpoints** of the arc. (Figure 11–9.)

Definition 11–13: A set of points is a **major arc** of a circle iff it is the union of two points of the circle and all points of the circle in the exterior of the central angle whose sides contain the two points. The two points are the **endpoints** of the arc. (Figure 11–10.)

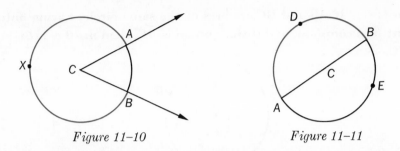

Figure 11–10   Figure 11–11

Definition 11–14: A set of points is a **semicircle** iff it is the union of the endpoints of a diameter and all points of the circle that lie on the same side of the diameter. (Figure 11–11.)

In Figure 11–11, $\widehat{ADB}$ and $\widehat{AEB}$ are both semicircles.

As indicated in the preceding definitions, an arc may be named using the endpoint letters alone, or using the endpoint letters plus the letter for some third point on the arc. For example, $\widehat{AB}$ and $\widehat{AXB}$ represent the same arc (Figure 11–10). The reason for sometimes using a third letter is that $\widehat{AB}$ actually has two interpretations: minor arc $\widehat{AB}$ and major arc $\widehat{AB}$. The use of a third letter rules out possible misinterpretations.

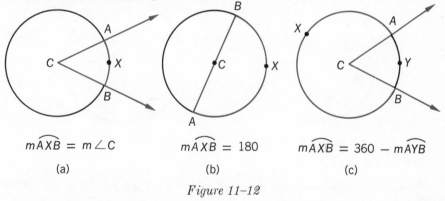

$m\widehat{AXB} = m\angle C$	$m\widehat{AXB} = 180$	$m\widehat{AXB} = 360 - m\widehat{AYB}$
(a)	(b)	(c)

Figure 11–12

Definition 11–15: The **degree measure of an arc** is
(1) the measure of the central angle iff the arc is a minor arc [Figure 11–12(a)],
(2) 180 if the arc is a semicircle [Figure 11–12(b)],
(3) 360 minus the measure of the corresponding minor arc iff the arc is a major arc [Figure 11–12(c)]. (Notation: $m\widehat{AB}$.)

As a matter of convenience, we will use the phrase "measure of an arc" to mean "degree measure of an arc."

The following axiom formalizes a kind of "betweenness" property for points on the same arc.

Axiom 11–1: **If $\widehat{AB}$ and $\widehat{BC}$ are arcs of the same circle, having only point B in common, and if their union is $\widehat{AC}$, then $m\widehat{AB} + m\widehat{BC} = m\widehat{AC}$.**

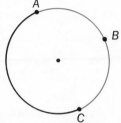

Definition 11–16: Two **arcs** are **congruent** iff they are arcs of the same, or congruent, circles, and have equal measures.

As in the corresponding definitions for congruent figures, the intuitive concept for the congruence of arcs is that arcs can (somehow) be made to coincide.

Theorem 11–4: **In the same circle or in congruent circles, if two chords are congruent, the corresponding minor arcs are congruent.**

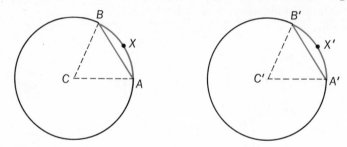

GIVEN: Circle $C \cong$ circle C'; chord $\overline{AB} \cong$ chord $\overline{A'B'}$.
PROVE: $\widehat{AXB} \cong \widehat{A'X'B'}$.

Proof: Introduce radii $\overline{CB}, \overline{CA}, \overline{C'B'}$, and $\overline{C'A'}$. Then $\triangle CAB \cong \triangle C'A'B'$, SSS Axiom (Axiom 5–4). Hence $\angle C \cong \angle C'$. Therefore $\widehat{AXB} \cong \widehat{A'X'B'}$, and the proof is complete.

Although the theorem above specifies the congruence of the *minor* arcs, it is a simple matter to show that the major arcs are also congruent. Apply Definition 11–15(3) to convince yourself of this.

The next theorem is a converse of Theorem 11–4. Its proof is similar to that for Theorem 11–4, and is left as an exercise.

Theorem 11–5: **In the same circle, or in congruent circles, if two arcs are congruent, then so are the corresponding chords.**

Observe that Theorem 11–5 does not specify that the congruent arcs must be minor arcs; they may be either minor or major arcs.

EXAMPLES

1. Given circle O with A, B, and C such that $\overarc{AB} \cong \overarc{BC} \cong \overarc{CA}$, find $m\angle AOB$.

Solution: In problems such as this it is convenient to think of a circle as an arc whose measure is 360. Since $\overarc{AB}$, $\overarc{BC}$, and $\overarc{CA}$ are congruent, their measures must be equal, and sum to 360. Hence each arc has measure 120. Therefore $m\angle AOB = 120$ (Definition 11–15(1)).

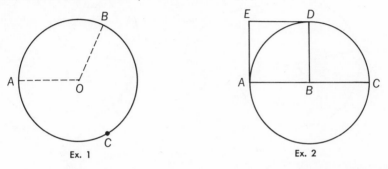

Ex. 1   Ex. 2

2. GIVEN: Circle B; diameter $\overline{AC}$; $\overline{ED} \cong \overline{AB}$; $\overline{AE} \cong \overline{DB}$; $\overarc{AD} \cong \overarc{DC}$.
   PROVE: $ABDE$ is a square.

Proof: Since $\overline{AC}$ is a diameter, $\overarc{ADC}$ is a semicircle (Definition 11–14) and has measure 180 (Definition 11–15). Because $\overarc{AD} \cong \overarc{DC}$, we also know that $m\overarc{AD} = m\overarc{DC}$ (Definition 11–16). Therefore $m\overarc{AD} = 90$, hence $m\angle ABD = 90$ (Definition 11–15), and $\angle ABD$ is a right angle. Thus we have that $ABCD$ is a parallelogram ($\overline{ED} \cong \overline{AB}$, $\overline{AE} \cong \overline{DB}$, Theorem 8–18) and a rectangle because it contains a right angle (Theorem 8–22). It remains to show that all sides of $ABCD$ are congruent. But $\overline{AB} \cong \overline{BD}$ since they are radii of a circle. Hence it is readily seen that $\overline{AB} \cong \overline{BC} \cong \overline{CD} \cong \overline{DA}$, and the rectangle is a square (Definition 8–18).

Exercise 11–3

(**A**)

1. If the measure of an arc is doubled, is the length of its chord doubled? The measure of its central angle?

2. If a circle is divided into six congruent arcs, what is the measure of each of the six central angles corresponding to the arcs?

3. Given circle B and diameter $\overline{AC}$, find:

   (a) $m\overarc{CD}$ (b) $m\overarc{AD}$ (c) $m\overarc{AEC}$

   (d) $m\overarc{AED}$ (e) $m\overarc{DCE}$

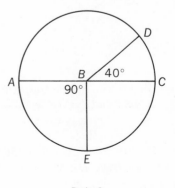

Prob. 3

4. If $\overline{AC}$ is a diameter, $\overline{DE}$ is tangent at B, and $\overleftrightarrow{DE} \parallel \overline{AC}$, find $m\widehat{AB}$ and $m\widehat{BC}$.

5. GIVEN: Circle B; $\widehat{AE} \cong \widehat{DC}$.
    PROVE: $\triangle ABE \cong \triangle CBD$.

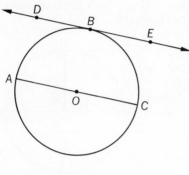

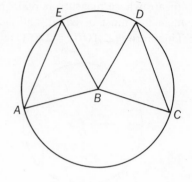

Prob. 4   Prob. 5

6. GIVEN: Circle O; $\widehat{GF} \cong \widehat{DE}$; $\widehat{DG} \cong \widehat{EF}$.
    PROVE: $DEFG$ is a parallelogram.

7. Given circle B, diameter $\overline{AC} \parallel$ chord $\overline{ED}$, and $m\widehat{ED} = 80$, find (a) $m\angle DBC$ and (b) $m\widehat{AE}$.

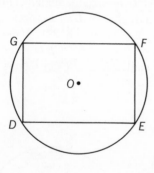

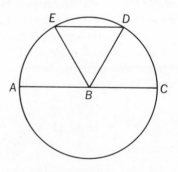

Prob. 6   Prob. 7

8. GIVEN: $\widehat{PQ} \cong \widehat{QR}$; $\widehat{QR} \cong \widehat{PR}$.
    PROVE: $\triangle PQR$ is equiangular.

9. How long is the chord of an arc whose measure is 60, if the radius of the circle is 15?

10. GIVEN: Circle C; diameter $\overline{BD}$; $\angle BCE \cong \angle BCF$.
     PROVE: $\overline{DE} \cong \overline{DF}$.

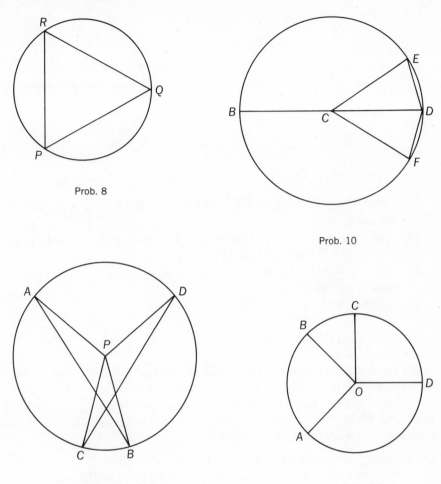

Prob. 8

Prob. 10

Prob. 11

Prob. 12

11. GIVEN: $\angle APC \cong \angle DPB$ in circle P.
    PROVE: $\overline{AB} \cong \overline{CD}$.

12. Given circle O, $m\angle AOB = 2x + 30$, $m\angle DOC = 5x - 30$, $m\angle AOD = 6x + 50$, $m\angle BOC = 3x - 10$; find (a) $m\widehat{BC}$ and (b) $m\widehat{AD}$.

(B)

13. PROVE: If A, B, C, and D, are points on a circle such that $ABCD$ is an equilateral quadrilateral, then $ABCD$ is regular.

14. PROVE: The midpoints of all chords congruent to a given chord of a circle lie on a circle concentric with the first circle.

15. GIVEN: Circle O; diameter $\overline{AB}$; chords $\overline{AC}$ and $\overline{BC}$.
    PROVE: $\angle ACB$ is a right angle. (*Hint:* Introduce $\overline{OC}$ and consider the sum of the measures of $\angle ACO$ and $\angle BCO$.)

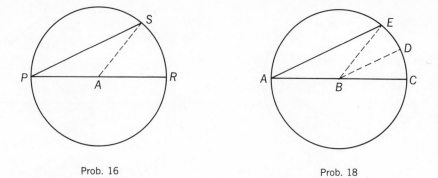

Prob. 16   Prob. 18

16. Given circle A, diameter $\overline{PR}$, and $m\angle P = 30$, find (a) $m\angle PAS$ and
(b) $m\widehat{SR}$.

17. PROVE: If A, B, C, and D are points on a circle such that $ABCD$ is a
parallelogram, then $ABCD$ is a rectangle.

18. GIVEN: Circle B; diameter $\overline{AC}$; $\overline{BD} \parallel \overline{AE}$.
PROVE: $\widehat{CD} \cong \widehat{DE}$.

19. PROVE: Thm. 11–5.

11–4 OTHER ANGLES

We have defined a central angle, and established a relationship between
the measure of the central angle and the measure of an arc. Other angles,
related to the circle, may be formed by combinations of chords, secants, and
tangents. We propose to examine relationships between such angles and arcs
of circles, and we begin with inscribed angles.

Definition 11–17: An **angle** is **inscribed** in an arc iff
(1) the two endpoints of the arc lie on the two sides of the angle, and
(2) the vertex of the angle is a point, but not an endpoint, of the arc.
(Figure 11–13.)

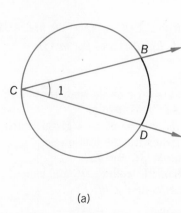

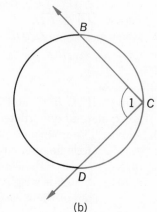

(a)   (b)

Figure 11–13

In Figure 11–13, $\angle 1$ is inscribed in $\overset{\frown}{BCD}$. Note that in Figure 11–13(a) the arc is a major arc and $\angle 1$ is acute, while in Figure 11–13(b) the arc is a minor arc and $\angle 1$ is obtuse. (Can you generalize this observation and write it in the form of a theorem?)

Definition 11–18: An angle **intercepts** an arc iff
(1) each side of the angle contains at least one endpoint of the arc, and
(2) except for its endpoints, the arc lies in the interior of the angle.
    (Figure 11–14.)

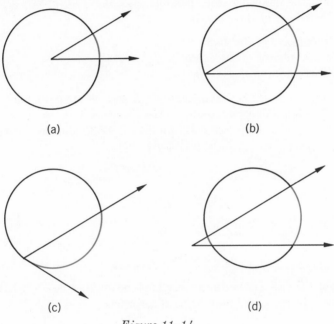

(a)   (b)

(c)   (d)

Figure 11–14

Figure 11–14 illustrates various ways in which an angle might intercept an arc on a circle. In (a) and (b), the vertex is in the interior of, or on, the circle, and each side of the angle contains one endpoint of the intercepted arc. In (c), the vertex is on the circle and one side of the angle is tangent to the circle. Again in (c), one side of the angle contains *two* endpoints of the intercepted arc. In (d), the vertex is in the exterior of the circle, and the angle intercepts *two* arcs on the circle.

One interesting relationship between an inscribed angle and its intercepted arc is indicated by Figure 11–15. As an experiment, draw a circle and several inscribed angles, each intercepting the same arc. Measure each of the inscribed angles—they should all have

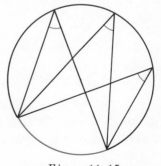

Figure 11–15

(approximately) the same measure. That they all do have exactly the same measure is a corollary of the next theorem.

Theorem 11–6: **The measure of an inscribed angle is half the measure of its intercepted arc.**

GIVEN: Inscribed $\angle B$ intercepting $\overset{\frown}{DF}$ in circle C.
PROVE: $m\angle B = \frac{1}{2}m\overset{\frown}{DF}$.

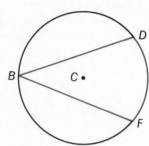

Proof: We prove this theorem by considering each of the following three possible cases in turn. The center of the circle lies:

(1) On one side of the angle.
(2) In the interior of the angle.
(3) In the exterior of the angle.

Case (1). Here $\overline{BF}$ is a diameter and $\overline{CB}$ and $\overline{CD}$ are radii, hence $CB = CD$ and $\angle B \cong \angle 2$ (Theorem 5–12). Also, since $\angle 1$ is an exterior angle of $\triangle BCD$, $m\angle 1 = m\angle B + m\angle 2$ (Corollary 8–12.3), and since $\angle 1$ is a central angle of circle C, we have $m\angle 1 = m\overset{\frown}{DF}$. Thus:

$$m\angle B + m\angle 2 = m\overset{\frown}{DF}$$

But $\qquad\qquad\qquad\quad m\angle B = m\angle 2 \qquad$ (since $\angle B \cong \angle 2$)

Then $\qquad\qquad\qquad 2(m\angle B) = m\overset{\frown}{DF}$

and $\qquad\qquad\qquad\quad m\angle B = \frac{1}{2}m\overset{\frown}{DF}$

The proof for case (1) is complete. This means that case (1) is now established as a theorem, and may be used accordingly.

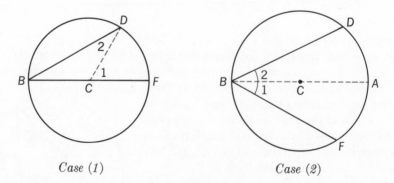

Case (1)   *Case (2)*

Case (2). Here C is in the interior of $\angle DBF$. Introduce diameter $\overline{BA}$, forming $\angle 1$ and $\angle 2$, such that $m\angle DBF = m\angle 1 + m\angle 2$ (Angle Addition Axiom, Axiom 3–9). Since $\angle 1$ and $\angle 2$ are both inscribed angles with one side of each containing the center of the circle, they both fall in the category of case (1). Therefore:

$$m\angle 1 = \tfrac{1}{2}m\widehat{FA}$$
$$m\angle 2 = \tfrac{1}{2}m\widehat{AD}$$
$$m\angle 1 + m\angle 2 = \tfrac{1}{2}m\widehat{FA} + \tfrac{1}{2}\widehat{AD}$$
$$= \tfrac{1}{2}m(\widehat{FA} + \widehat{AD}) \qquad \text{(Distributivity Axiom)}$$
$$= \tfrac{1}{2}m\widehat{FD} \qquad\qquad \text{(Axiom 11–1)}$$

and

$$m\angle BDF = \tfrac{1}{2}m\widehat{FD}$$

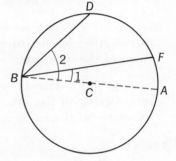

The proof for case (2) is complete.

Case (3). Here C is in the exterior of $\angle DBF$. Again we introduce diameter $\overline{BA}$, forming $\angle 1$ and $\angle 2$, each of which falls under case (1). The proof that $m\angle DBF = \tfrac{1}{2}m\widehat{DF}$ is similar to the proof for case (2), and is left as an exercise.

Theorem 11–6 has two very important corollaries. The proofs are left as exercises.

Corollary 11–6.1: An angle inscribed in a semicircle is a right angle.

Corollary 11–6.2: Angles inscribed in the same arc are congruent.

Theorem 11–7: The measure of an angle formed by a secant ray and a tangent ray, with its vertex on the circle, is half the measure of the intercepted arc.

GIVEN: Circle D; $\angle BAC$ intercepting $\widehat{AC}$; $\overrightarrow{AB}$ tangent to circle D at A.
PROVE: $m\angle BAC = \tfrac{1}{2}m\widehat{AC}$.

Proof: There are three possible cases:

(1) $\angle BAC$ is acute.
(2) $\angle BAC$ is a right angle.
(3) $\angle BAC$ is obtuse.

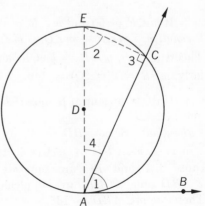

We will prove the theorem for case (1), and leave the other two cases as exercises. (See Exercise 11–4, problems 38, 39.)

Case (1). Using the notation of the figure, introduce diameter $\overline{AE}$ and chord $\overline{EC}$. By Corollary 11–6.1, $\angle 3$ is a right angle, and therefore $\triangle ACE$ is a right triangle. Thus, by Corollary 8–12.2, $\angle 2$ and $\angle 4$ are complementary. Also, by Corollary 11–1.1, $\overline{AE} \perp \overrightarrow{AB}$, and $\angle 1$ and $\angle 4$ are therefore complementary. Hence $\angle 1 \cong \angle 2$ (Theorem 4–7). $\angle 2$ is an inscribed angle, and so $m\angle 2 = \frac{1}{2}m\widehat{AC}$. Whence $m\angle 1 = \frac{1}{2}m\widehat{AC}$, which completes the proof for the case when the angle is acute.

Next we consider the situation in which angles are formed by two secants intersecting in the interior, or the exterior, of a circle. The proofs of these two theorems are also left as exercises.

Theorem 11–8: **The measure of an angle formed by two secants intersecting in the interior of a circle is half the sum of the measures of the arcs intercepted by the angle and its vertical angle.**

Theorem 11–9: **The measure of an angle formed by two secants intersecting in the exterior of a circle is half the difference of the measures of the intercepted arcs.**

EXAMPLES

1. If $m\widehat{PR} = 70$ and $m\widehat{QR} = 80$, find $m\angle P$, $m\angle Q$, and $m\angle R$.

   Solution: $m\widehat{PR} + m\widehat{QR} = 150$, and since $m\widehat{PQ} + m\widehat{QR} + m\widehat{PR} = 360$, it follows that $m\widehat{PQ} = 210$. (While it may not always be needed, it is frequently useful to determine the measures of the arcs of a circle for a particular problem.) Since $\angle P$, $\angle Q$, and $\angle R$ are inscribed angles, by Theorem 11–6 we have:

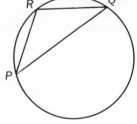

$$m\angle P = \tfrac{1}{2}m\widehat{QR} = 40$$
$$m\angle Q = \tfrac{1}{2}m\widehat{PR} = 35$$
$$m\angle R = \tfrac{1}{2}m\widehat{PQ} = 105$$

2. If $m\angle P = 50$ and $m\angle R = 60$, find $m\widehat{PR}$ and $m\widehat{QR}$.

   Solution: $m\angle P + m\angle Q + m\angle R = 180$, therefore $m\angle Q = 70$. By Theorem 11–6, $m\angle P = \frac{1}{2}m\widehat{QR}$, and thus $m\widehat{QR} = 2(m\angle P) = 100$. Similarly, $m\widehat{PR} = 2(m\angle Q) = 140$.

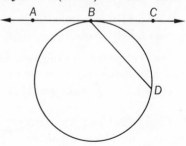

3. If $\overleftrightarrow{AC}$ is tangent at B and $m\widehat{BD} = 90$, find $m\angle ABD$.

   Solution: Since $m\widehat{BD} = 90$, by Theorem 11–7, $m\angle CBD = \frac{1}{2}m\widehat{BD} = 45$. Because $\overrightarrow{BA}$ and $\overrightarrow{BC}$ are opposite rays, $\angle ABD$ and $\angle CBD$ are supplementary. Therefore $m\angle ABD = 135$.

Exercise 11–4

(A)

In problems 1 to 4, find $m\angle B$, $m\angle C$, and $m\angle D$ under the given conditions.

1. $m\widehat{BD} = 100$, $m\widehat{BC} = 140$.   **2.** $m\widehat{DC} = 80$, $m\widehat{DB} = 60$.
3. $m\widehat{BDC} = 180$, $\widehat{BD} \cong \widehat{DC}$.   **4.** $\widehat{BD} \cong \widehat{BC} \cong \widehat{DC}$.

In problems 5 to 8, find $m\widehat{BC}$, $m\widehat{CD}$, and $m\widehat{DB}$ under the given conditions.

5. $m\angle B = 45$, $m\angle C = 55$.   **6.** $m\angle D = 60$, $m\angle B = 75$.
7. $\angle B \cong \angle C \cong \angle D$.   **8.** $m\angle B = 90$, $m\angle B = 2(m\angle C)$.

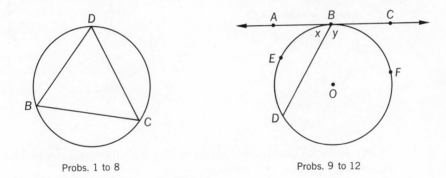

Probs. 1 to 8   Probs. 9 to 12

In problems 9 to 12, $\overleftrightarrow{AC}$ is tangent to circle O at B, and $\overline{BD}$ is a chord.

9. If $m\widehat{BED} = 80$, find $m\angle x$ and $m\angle y$.
10. If $m\widehat{BFD} = 200$, find $m\angle x$ and $m\angle y$.
11. If $m\angle y = 95$, find $m\widehat{BED}$ and $m\widehat{BFD}$.
12. If $m\angle x = 60$, find $m\widehat{BED}$ and $m\widehat{BFD}$.

13. (a) $m\angle B = ?$ (b) $m\angle C = ?$ (c) $m\angle D = ?$ (d) $m\angle A = ?$
14. (a) $m\angle S = ?$ (b) $m\angle R = ?$ (c) $m\widehat{QR} = ?$ (d) $m\angle P = ?$

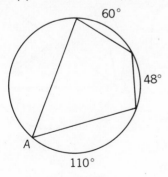

Prob. 13

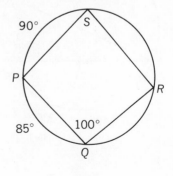

Prob. 14

15. GIVEN: Circle O; chord $\overline{AC}$; $\overleftrightarrow{DE}$ tangent at B; $\overgroup{AB} \cong \overgroup{BC}$.
   PROVE: $\overleftrightarrow{DE} \parallel \overline{AC}$.

16. GIVEN: Circles O and O' tangent internally at B; $\overline{BD}$ a chord of circle O.
   PROVE: $m\overgroup{BC} = m\overgroup{BD}$.

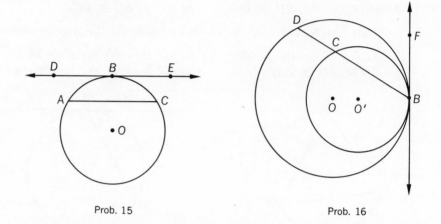

Prob. 15   Prob. 16

17. GIVEN: Circles F and D intersecting at B and E; diameters $\overline{AE}$ and $\overline{CE}$.
   PROVE: A, B, and C are collinear.

18. PROVE: If the vertices of a quadrilateral lie on a circle, each pair of nonconsecutive angles is supplementary.

19. PROVE: If the vertices of a parallelogram lie on a circle, the parallelogram is a rectangle.

20. GIVEN: A, B, C, and D lie on the circle; $\angle CAB \cong \angle DBA$.
   PROVE: $\triangle ABC \cong \triangle BAD$.

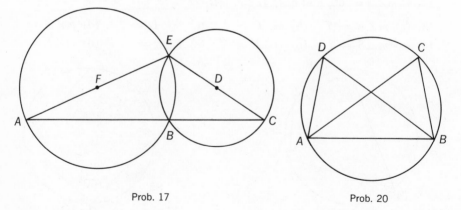

Prob. 17   Prob. 20

(B)

21. If $m\overgroup{AD} = 90$ and $m\overgroup{BC} = 60$, find $m\angle DEA$.

22. If $m\widehat{AB} = 110$ and $m\widehat{DC} = 70$, find $m\angle AEB$.

23. If $m\angle DEC = 50$ and $m\widehat{DC} = 50$, find $m\widehat{AB}$.

24. If $m\angle CEB = 80$ and $m\widehat{AD} = 100$, find $m\widehat{BC}$.

25. If $\overline{AC}$ is a diameter and $\widehat{DC} \cong \widehat{BC}$, find $m\angle AED$.

26. If $\overline{DB}$ is a diameter, $\overline{AE} \cong \overline{EC}$, and $DE < EB$, find $m\angle AEB$.

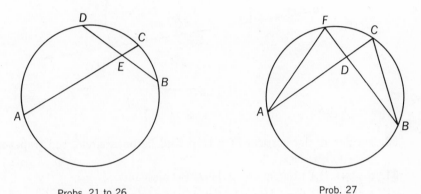

Probs. 21 to 26   Prob. 27

27. GIVEN: Intersecting chords $\overline{AC}$ and $\overline{BF}$.

   PROVE: $\triangle ADF \sim \triangle BCD$.

28. PROVE: If two chords intersect, the product of the lengths of the segments of one chord is equal to the product of the lengths of the segments of the other.

29. PROVE: The length of the perpendicular from any point on a circle to a diameter of the circle is the geometric mean between the lengths of the segments of the diameter.

30. If $m\widehat{AE} = 120$ and $m\widehat{BD} = 40$, find $m\angle C$.

31. If $m\angle C = 50$ and $m\widehat{BD} = 60$, find $m\widehat{AE}$.

32. If $\widehat{AB} \cong \widehat{DE}$, $m\widehat{AB} = 80$, and $m\widehat{DB} = 40$, find $m\angle C$.

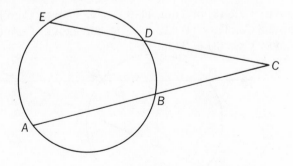

Probs. 30 to 32

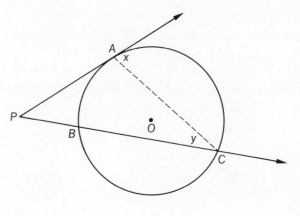

Prob. 34

33. PROVE: If the vertices of a trapezoid lie on a circle, the trapezoid is isosceles.

34. GIVEN: $\overrightarrow{PA}$ tangent to circle O; $\overrightarrow{PC}$ a secant.

PROVE: $m\angle p = \frac{1}{2}(m\widehat{AC} - m\widehat{AB})$.   (*Hint:* Introduce $\overline{AC}$ and consider $m\angle x$ and $m\angle y$.)

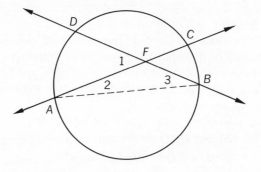

Prob. 38

35. PROVE: Case (3) of Thm. 11–6.   **36.** PROVE: Corollary 11–6.1.
37. PROVE: Corollary 11–6.2.   **38.** PROVE: Case (2) of Thm. 11–7.
39. PROVE: Case (3) of Thm. 11–7.

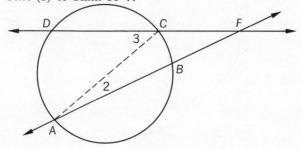

Prob. 39

40. PROVE: Thm. 11–8. (*Hint:* Introduce $\overline{AB}$ and consider $\angle 1$ as an exterior angle of $\triangle ABF$.)

41. PROVE: Thm. 11–9. (*Hint:* Introduce $\overline{AC}$ and consider $\angle 3$ as an exterior angle of $\triangle AFC$.)

11–5 TANGENT AND SECANT SEGMENTS

Definition 11–19: A segment is a **tangent segment** of a circle iff it is a subset of a tangent line, and one endpoint is the point of tangency.

As indicated in Figure 11–16, any point in the exterior of a circle can be an endpoint of two tangent segments, which have, in fact, equal lengths.

Figure 11–16

Theorem 11–10: **The two tangent segments to a circle from a given point are congruent, and form congruent angles with the line joining the point to the center of the circle.**

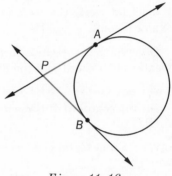

GIVEN: Circle C; tangent segments $\overline{PA}$ and $\overline{PB}$; $\overline{PC}$.

PROVE: $\overline{PA} \cong \overline{PB}$; $\angle 1 \cong \angle 2$.

Proof

STATEMENTS	REASONS
1. Tangent segments $\overline{PA}$, $\overline{PB}$.	1. Given.
2. A and B are points of tangency.	2. Why?
3. Introduce radii $\overline{CA}$ and $\overline{CB}$.	3. Why possible?
4. $CA = CB$.	4. Why?
5. $\therefore \overline{CA} \cong \overline{CB}$.	5. Why?
6. $\overline{CA} \perp \overline{PA}$, $\overline{CB} \perp \overline{PB}$.	6. Why?
7. $\therefore \angle PAC$, $\angle PBC$ are right angles.	7. Why?
8. $\overline{PC} \cong \overline{PC}$.	8. Why?
9. $\triangle PBC \cong \triangle PAC$.	9. Why?
10. $\therefore \overline{PA} \cong \overline{PB}$, $\angle 1 \cong \angle 2$.	10. Why?

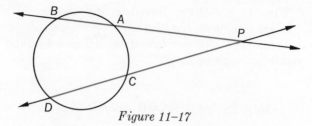

Figure 11–17

Figure 11–17 illustrates a circle intersected by two secant lines through exterior point P. $\overline{PB}$ and $\overline{PD}$ are called *secant segments* to the circle.

Definition 11–20: A segment is a **secant segment** of a circle iff the segment intersects the circle in two points, and exactly one of these points is an endpoint.

Observe that the circle further divides the secant segment into two segments, one a chord and the other a segment external to the circle.

Theorem 11–11: **If $\overline{PT}$ is a tangent segment to a circle, and $\overline{PB}$ is a secant segment intersecting the circle at A and B, then $PA \cdot PB = (PT)^2$.**

GIVEN: Circle C; tangent segment $\overline{PT}$; secant segment $\overline{PB}$.
PROVE: $PA \cdot PB = (PT)^2$.

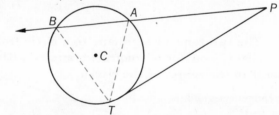

Proof

STATEMENTS	REASONS
1. Tangent segment $\overline{PT}$, secant segment $\overline{PB}$.	1. Given.
2. Introduce $\overline{AT}$ and $\overline{BT}$.	2. Why possible?
3. $m\angle ABT = \frac{1}{2}(m\widehat{AT})$.	3. Why?
4. $m\angle ATP = \frac{1}{2}(m\widehat{AT})$.	4. Why?
5. $\therefore m\angle ABT = m\angle ATP$.	5. Why?
6. $\angle ABT \cong \angle ATP$.	6. Why?
7. $\angle P \cong \angle P$.	7. Why?
8. $\therefore \triangle BTP \sim \triangle TAP$.	8. Why?
9. $\therefore \dfrac{PB}{PT} = \dfrac{PT}{PA}$	9. Why?
10. $PA \cdot PB = (PT)^2$.	10. Why?

Theorem 11–11 leads to a rather surprising result. We will show that for a given circle and a given point external to that circle, the product of the length of any secant segment and the length of its external segment is always the same!

Theorem 11–12: **Given circle Q and a point P in its exterior. Let $\overline{PB}$ and $\overline{PD}$ be any two secant segments, with external segments $\overline{PA}$ and $\overline{PC}$ respectively. Then $PB \cdot PA = PD \cdot PC$.**

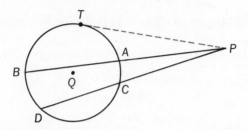

GIVEN: Circle Q; secant segments $\overline{PB}, \overline{PD}$; external segments $\overline{PA}, \overline{PC}$.
PROVE: $PB \cdot PA = PD \cdot PC$.

Proof: Introduce tangent segment $\overline{PT}$. By Theorem 11–11, $PA \cdot PB = (PT)^2$, and $(PT)^2 = PD \cdot PC$. Hence, by the Transitivity Axiom (E–3), $PA \cdot PB = PD \cdot PC$.

Theorem 11–13: **If two chords, $\overline{AB}$ and $\overline{CD}$, of the same circle intersect at P in the interior of the circle, then $AP \cdot PB = CP \cdot PD$.**

The proof of Theorem 11–13 is left as an exercise.

EXAMPLES

1. If $\overline{AD}$ and $\overline{AB}$ are tangent segments to circle C, such that $\overline{AB} \perp \overline{AD}$ and $AD = 6$, find CD.

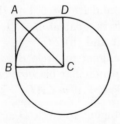

Solution: Since $\overline{AB} \perp \overline{AD}$, $m\angle DAB = 90$. Then, by Theorem 11–10, $\overline{AC}$ bisects $\angle DAB$, hence $m\angle DAC = 45$. Because $\overline{AD}$ is a tangent, and $\overline{CD}$ a radius, by Corollary 11–1.1, $\overline{AD} \perp \overline{CD}$, and $m\angle ADC = 90$. Therefore in $\triangle ACD$, $m\angle ACD = 45$, and $\triangle ACD$ is isosceles (base angles congruent). Thus $\overline{AD} \cong \overline{CD}$, and since $AD = 6$, it follows that $CD = 6$.

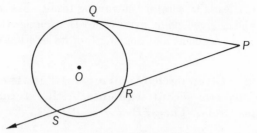

2. Given $\overline{PQ}$ tangent to circle O at Q, secant $\overrightarrow{PS}$, $PR = 9$, and $PS = 16$, find PQ.

Solution: By Theorem 11–11, $PR \cdot PS = (PQ)^2$. Therefore

$$(PQ)^2 = 9 \cdot 16$$
$$(PQ)^2 = 144$$
$$\underline{PQ = 12}$$

3. If $RB = 8$, $BT = 6$, and $WB = 12$, find BS.

Solution: By Theorem 11–13, $WB \cdot BS = RB \cdot BT$. Therefore

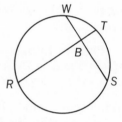

$$12 \cdot BS = 8 \cdot 6$$
$$12 \cdot BS = 48$$
$$\underline{BS = 4}$$

Exercise 11–5

(A)

In problems 1 and 2, $\overline{AC}, \overline{CE}$, and $\overline{EA}$ are tangent to circle O at B, D, and F, respectively.

1. If $CE = 12$, $EF = 3$, and $AF = 7$, find AC.
2. If $AB = 5$, $CD = 4$, and $EF = 6$, find the perimeter of $\triangle ACE$.
3. Given circles D and E tangent at B; $\overline{PA}$, $\overline{PB}$, and $\overline{PC}$ tangents; and $PB = 15$; find (a) PA and (b) PC.
4. GIVEN: $\overrightarrow{PA}$ and $\overrightarrow{PC}$ tangent to circle B at A and C.
   PROVE: $\overline{PB}$ is the perpendicular bisector of $\overline{AC}$.
5. In the figure for problem 4, if $m\angle APC = 60$ and $PB = 20$, find BC.

In problems 6 to 9, $\overline{AB}$ is tangent to circle O at B, and $\overrightarrow{AC}$ is a secant.

6. If $AC = 12$ and $AD = 3$, find AB.
7. If $AB = 8$ and $AD = 4$, find AC.
8. If $CD = 9$ and $AD = 9$, find AB.
9. If $CD = 6$ and $AB = 4$, find AD.

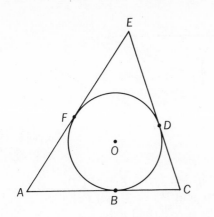

Probs. 1, 2

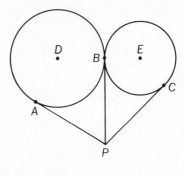

Prob. 3

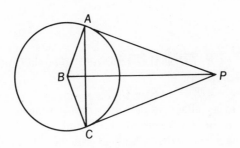

Prob. 4

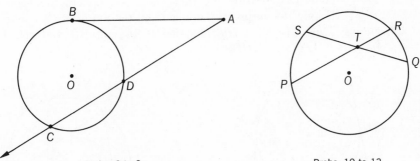

Probs. 6 to 9

Probs. 10 to 13

In problems 10 to 13, $\overline{PR}$ and $\overline{QS}$ are chords of circle O, intersecting at T.

10. If $PT = 6$, $TR = 4$, and $ST = 3$, find TQ.
11. If $PR = 12$, $TR = 4$, and $ST = 2$, find TQ.
12. If $SQ = 7$, $PT = 6$, and $TR = 2$, find ST.
13. If $PR = 9$, $ST = 2$, and $TQ = 10$, find PT.

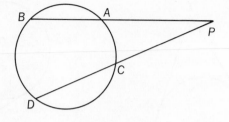

Probs. 14 to 17

14. In the figure, if $PB = 20$, $PA = 6$, and $PC = 8$, find PD.

15. In the figure, if $PA = 6$, $AB = 9$, and $PC = 8$, find PD.

16. In the figure, if $PB = PD$ and $PC = \sqrt{3}$, find PA.

17. In the figure, if $PB = 2(PD)$ and $PA = 3\sqrt{2}$, find PC.

(B)

18. GIVEN: $\overline{AC}$, $\overline{CE}$, $\overline{EG}$, and $\overline{GA}$ tangent to circle O at B, D, F, and H, respectively.

PROVE: $AC + GE = AG + CE$.

19. PROVE: If every side of a parallelogram is tangent to the same circle, then the parallelogram is a rhombus.

20. PROVE: If $\overline{AB}$ and $\overline{AC}$ are tangent segments to circle O, and $\overline{BC}$ is a chord, then $m\angle A = 2(m\angle OBC)$.

21. PROVE: If the angle formed by two tangent rays with the same endpoint has measure 60, then the circle bisects the segment joining the vertex of the angle and the center of the circle.

22. PROVE: Thm. 11–13. (*Hint:* Introduce $\overline{AC}$ and $\overline{BD}$ and consider $\triangle APC$ and $\triangle DPB$.)

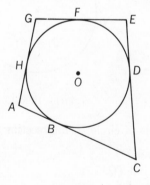

Prob. 18

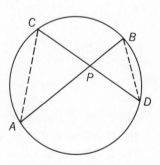

Prob. 22

Chapter 12

CHARACTERIZATIONS, CONCURRENCE, AND CONSTRUCTIONS

INTRODUCTION

Geometric problems concerning sets of points were being solved long before present-day concepts, language, and notation for sets were introduced. Instead of the phrase *set of points*, the word *locus* was frequently used. Here are two examples of such usage:

(1) In a plane, the locus of all points at a given distance from a given point is a circle, with the given point as center and the given distance as the length of its radius.

(2) In a plane, the locus of all points equidistant from the endpoints of a segment is the perpendicular bisector of the segment.

Of course, you recognize statement (1) as almost identical with the definition of a circle, and statement (2) as almost identical with Theorem 6–2. Basically, the word *locus* was used in the sense of a description of the "location" of all those points that satisfied a given condition.

We will not use the word locus. In the first place, we are already familiar with the set concept, and prefer to continue with it. In the second place, the use of the set concept is far more widespread in mathematics than that of locus. In short, there is no real need for the word, but the discussion above should help you to recognize it if you meet it again during some further study of mathematics.

12–1 CHARACTERIZATION OF SETS

Our basic concern is to define, or *characterize*, a set of points by a given condition or conditions. In somewhat more familiar language, we wish to describe a geometric figure in terms of a common property (or properties) of its points. Thus we describe a circle by the condition that all of its points shall be some given distance from a given point; and the perpendicular bisector of a segment by the condition that all of its points shall be equidistant from the endpoints of the segment.

Because the proofs of many characterization theorems are based upon the properties of equal sets, we review in a little more detail the meaning of **set equality.** Definition 2–2 defines equality of sets: $A = B$ iff the elements of A are exactly the same as the elements of B. Now, if $A = B$, then, by definition, the elements of A belong to set B. Note that this would be just as true if A were only a subset of B $(A \subset B)$. Again, if $B \subset A$, the elements of B would be elements of A. Hence, to ensure that *all* the elements of A are members of B, and *all* the elements of B are members of A, we must establish the truth of two assertions:

(1) $A \subset B$
(2) $B \subset A$

If we succeed in proving both of these assertions, then we may say $A = B$.

Let us now examine how set equality relates to geometric problems. A rereading of the two "locus" statements of the introduction indicates that, in actuality, *two* sets are being considered.

(1) The statement about the circle refers to:
  (a) The set of points constituting the circle.
  (b) The set of points equidistant from a given point.

Since the definition of a circle states that these two sets are equal, no question of proof is at issue here.

(2) The statement about the perpendicular bisector refers to:
  (a) The set of points constituting the perpendicular bisector.
  (b) The set of points equidistant from the endpoints of the segment.

Since this is not a definition but a theorem, a proof is in order, and we have supplied such a proof for Theorem 6–2. We showed that:

(1) All members of the set of points constituting the perpendicular bisector of the segment were also members of the set of points equidistant from the endpoints of the segment.

(2) All members of the set of points equidistant from the endpoints of the segment were also members of the set constituting the perpendicular bisector.

Thus we satisfied the definition of equality of sets and the theorem was proved.

Consider now the following two counterexamples.

  I. Let P be a point in a plane, and consider points of the plane 1 inch from P (Figure 12–1).
  The points Q_1 to Q_8 all satisfy the condition that they shall be 1 inch from P. Hence set $Q = \{Q_1, Q_2, \ldots, Q_8\}$ is a subset of the set of points

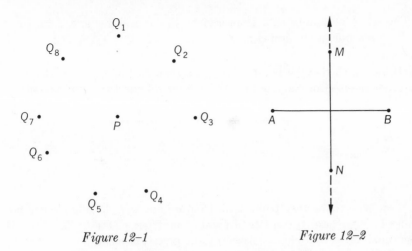

Figure 12-1   *Figure 12-2*

which is the circle with center at P and radius 1 inch. Can we say, however, that the set of all points 1 inch from P is a subset of Q? Certainly not! There are any number of points on the circle, but not in set Q. Hence set Q is *not* equal to the circle.

II. Let $\overline{AB}$ be a segment, and consider all points on the perpendicular bisector $\overline{MN}$ of $\overline{AB}$ (Figure 12-2).

Every point on $\overline{MN}$ is equidistant from A and B. Is it true that every point equidistant from A and B is on $\overline{MN}$? Again, certainly not! The *line* $\overleftrightarrow{MN}$ contains many points, all equidistant from A and B, but not all on *segment* $\overline{MN}$.

Our situation is now as follows: On the one hand we have a geometric figure which is, of course, a set of points; on the other hand we have a statement of a condition (or conditions) that describes a set of points. If we are stating a definition, e.g., a circle, then we *define* the two sets to be equal. If we are stating a theorem, then we must *prove* that the two sets are equal. We must show that:

(1) Every point of the figure satisfies the given condition.
(2) Every point that satisfies the given condition is included in the figure.

If we succeed in showing both, we have established a characterization theorem.

EXAMPLES

In examples 1 and 2, determine whether the statement below actually characterizes the given figure. If so, write *True;* if not, revise the figure or statement (or both) so that the statement is a characterization theorem illustrated by the figure. (No proofs are required.)

1. The set of all points 1 in. from a given line is another line, 1 in. from the given line, and parallel to it.

Solution

(a) If $q_1 \parallel q$, then every point of q_1 is the same distance (1 in.) from q as every other point (Corollary 8–14.1). Thus one of the two requirements is satisfied.

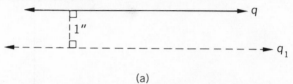

(a)

(b) Is it true that every point 1 in. from q is on q_1? The answer is no. Consider $q_2 \parallel q$, where q_2 consists of points 1 in. from q. Figure (a) above is *not* the same set as that characterized by the given statement.

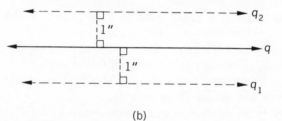

(b)

(c) We can reword the statement so as to read: "The set of all points 1 in. from a given line is *two* lines, each 1 in. away from, and parallel to, the given line." Figure (b) is the correct figure.

2. The set of all points equidistant from $\overrightarrow{AB}$ and $\overrightarrow{AC}$, the sides of $\angle BAC$, is a ray.

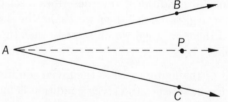

Solution: The statement is not complete. While it is true that the required figure is a ray $(\overrightarrow{AP})$, we must distinguish between the ray with which we are immediately concerned, and all other possible rays. That is, we must add to our statement some further information which distinguishes $\overrightarrow{AP}$ from other rays; in short, we must say $\overrightarrow{AP}$ is the angle bisector. The corrected statement is: "The set of all points equidistant from $\overrightarrow{AB}$ and $\overrightarrow{AC}$, the sides of $\angle BAC$, is a ray, *the angle bisector of* $\angle BAC$."

For examples 3 and 4, make a sketch of the set of points characterized by the given statement, and write a description of the required set.

3. The set of all points whose distance from a given point Q is less than or equal to 1.

Solution: We know that the set of all points 1 unit from a given point is the circle of radius 1, centered at the given point. The points less than 1 from Q lie in the interior of the circle (Definition 11–7). Hence the required set is a *circular region*, consisting of circle Q with radius $r = 1$, and all points in the interior of circle Q.

4. The set of all points equidistant from the sides of an angle *and* $\frac{1}{2}$ unit from a given line.

Solution: The set of all points equidistant from the sides of $\angle BCA$ is the angle bisector $\overrightarrow{CP}$ (see example 2). The set of all points $\frac{1}{2}$ unit from a given line, q, is two lines, q_1 and q_2, each $\frac{1}{2}$ unit from, and parallel to, q (see example 1). Now, what we are really looking for is the *intersection* of the two sets: $\overrightarrow{CP}$ and $q_1 \cup q_2$. The required intersection depends upon the positions of the given angle and line with respect to each other. In the figure,

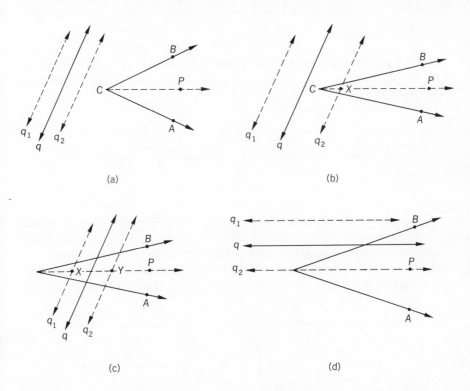

(a)

(b)

(c)

(d)

(a) shows *no* point of intersection, and the solution to the problem is the null set, $\varnothing$; (b) shows *one* point of intersection, X; (c) shows *two* points of intersection, X and Y; and (d) illustrates the possibility that line q_2 (or q_1).

contains $\overrightarrow{CP}$, and hence there are infinitely many points of intersection. In summary, the required set may have none, one, two, or infinitely many elements.

Exercise 12–1

(A)

In problems 1 to 5, determine whether the statement actually characterizes the figure. If so, write *True;* if not, revise the figure, or the statement (or both) so that the statement is a characterization theorem illustrated by the figure. (No proofs are required.)

1. The set of all points equidistant from two parallel lines two inches apart is a line parallel to the two given lines and midway between them.

Prob. 1

2. The set of all points, each of which is the center of a circle of radius 2 in., tangent to a given line q, is a line parallel to q and 2 in. from q.

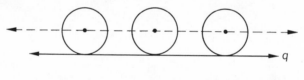

Prob. 2

3. The set of all points, each of which is the center of a circle of radius 1 in., tangent to both of two parallel lines (q_1 and q_2), is a third line parallel to the two given lines and midway between them.

4. The set of all points, each of which is the center of a circle tangent to a given line q at a given point P, is the line through P perpendicular to q.

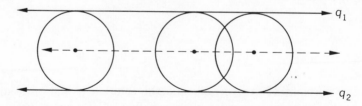

Prob. 3

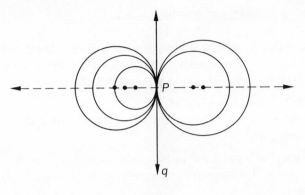

Prob. 4

5. The set of all points, each of which is the center of a circle through two given points A and B, is a ray: $\overrightarrow{CP}$.

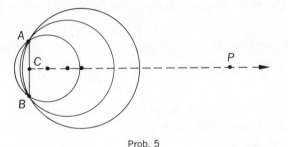

Prob. 5

For problems 6 to 17, sketch and describe the required set of points.

6. The set of all points equidistant from two given points.

7. The set of all points each of which is the vertex of an isosceles triangle with base $\overline{AB}$.

8. The set of all points 1 in. from the center of a circle of radius 2 in.

9. The set of all points each of which is the vertex of a right triangle having given segment $(\overline{BC})$ as hypotenuse.

10. The set of all points equidistant from two intersecting lines.

11. The set of all points equidistant from the points of intersection of two intersecting circles.

12. The set of midpoints of all radii of a circle of radius 2.

13. The set of all points 2 in. from each of two points 3 in. apart.

14. The set of all points in the interior of, and equidistant from the sides of, $\angle BPA$, and 1 in. from P.

15. The set of all points in the interior of circle Q, with radius $r = 2$, and equidistant from the endpoints of chord $\overline{AB}$.

16. The set of all points 1 in. from each of two intersecting lines.

17. The set of all points X for which $\triangle ABX$, which has given segment $\overline{AB}$ as base, has a given area.

12-2 CONCURRENCE THEOREMS

We now have two characterization statements. One is the definition of circle (Definition 11-1), and the other is a theorem on the perpendicular bisector of a segment (Theorem 6-2). Our next theorem is a characterization theorem.

Theorem 12-1: **The bisector of an angle is the set of all points in the interior of, or on, the angle, equidistant from the sides of the angle.**

(The vertex may be considered to be at distance *zero* from the sides of the angle.) We restate the theorem in two parts, corresponding to the discussion of Section 12-1.

(1) **Every point of the angle bisector must be in the interior of, or on, the angle, and equidistant from the sides of the angle.**

(2) **Every point in the interior of, or on, the angle, and equidistant from the sides of the angle, must be on the angle bisector.**

Proof of Statement (1)

GIVEN: $\overrightarrow{AD}$ bisects $\angle BAC$;
$P \in \overrightarrow{AD}$.

PROVE: P is in the interior of, or on, $\angle BAC$; P is equidistant from $\overrightarrow{AB}$ and $\overrightarrow{AC}$.

Proof: (If P is at A, its distance from $\overrightarrow{AB}$, as well as from $\overrightarrow{AC}$, is zero, hence $PM = PN$ and P is on the angle.)

STATEMENTS	REASONS
1. $P \in \overrightarrow{AD}$, $P \neq A$, $\overrightarrow{AD}$ bisects $\angle BAC$.	1. Given.
2. P is in the interior of $\angle BAC$, $\angle BAD \cong \angle DAC$.	2. Def. of angle bisector (Def. 5-13).
3. Introduce $\overline{PM} \perp \overrightarrow{AB}, \overline{PN} \perp \overrightarrow{AC}$.*	3. Thm. 6-3.
4. $\angle AMP, \angle ANP$ are right angles.	4. Def. 3-18, Alternate.
5. $\overline{AP} \cong \overline{AP}$.	5. Reflexive property of congruent segments (Thm. 5-1).
6. $\triangle PAN \cong \triangle PAM$.	6. Thm. 8-26.
7. $\overline{PM} \cong \overline{PN}$.	7. Def. of congruence (Def. 5-2).
8. $\therefore PM = PN$, and P is equidistant from $\overrightarrow{AB}$ and $\overrightarrow{AC}$.	8. Def. of congruent segments (Def. 4-1).

* The motivation for step 3 was Definition 7-2, the distance from a point to a line.

Proof of Statement (2)

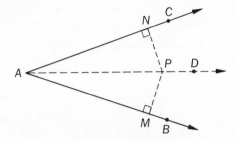

GIVEN: P is in the interior of, or on, $\angle BAC$; $\overrightarrow{AD}$ bisects $\angle BAC$; P is equidistant from $\overrightarrow{AB}$ and $\overrightarrow{AC}$.

PROVE: $P \in \overrightarrow{AD}$.

(*Note:* Angle bisector $\overrightarrow{AD}$ does not explicitly appear in the diagram. We propose to show that $\overrightarrow{AD}$ and $\overrightarrow{AP}$ are the same ray.)

Proof: (If P is zero units from $\overrightarrow{AB}$ and $\overrightarrow{AC}$, then P is the same point as vertex A, hence $P \in \overrightarrow{AD}$.)

STATEMENTS	REASONS
1. P is in the interior of $\angle BAC$.	1. Given.
2. $P \neq A$.	2. Definition of interior of an angle (Def. 3–4).
3. Introduce $\overline{PM} \perp \overrightarrow{AB}$, and $\overline{PN} \perp \overrightarrow{AC}$.	3. Thm. 6–3.
4. PM is the distance from P to $\overrightarrow{AB}$, PN the distance from P to $\overrightarrow{AC}$.	4. Def. of distance from a point to a line (Def. 7–2).
5. $PM = PN$.	5. Given.
6. $\overline{PM} \cong \overline{PN}$.	6. Def. of congruent segments (Def. 4–1).
7. $\angle ANP, \angle AMP$ are right angles.	7. Def. 3–18, Alternate.
8. $\overline{AP} \cong \overline{AP}$.	8. Reflexive property of congruent segments (Thm. 5–1).
9. $\triangle APM \cong \triangle APN$.	9. Thm. 8–27 (hyp. leg).
10. $\angle MAP \cong \angle NAP$.	10. Def. of congruence (Def. 5–2).
11. $\overrightarrow{AP}$ is the bisector of $\angle CAP$.	11. Def. of angle bisector (Def. 5–1).
12. $\overrightarrow{AP}$ is the same ray as $\overrightarrow{AD}$, and $P \in \overrightarrow{AD}$.	12. Uniqueness of angle bisector, (Ax. 5–1).

It is not at all unusual to find *two* coplanar lines concurrent (having a point in common)—we almost expect this to be the case. The concurrence

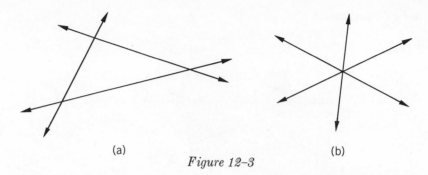

(a)   (b)

Figure 12–3

of *three* lines is another matter. We are certainly more accustomed to seeing three lines determine a triangle [Figure 12–3(a)] rather than being concurrent [Figure 12–3(b)].

Definition 12–1: Two or more lines are **concurrent** iff there is a single point which lies on all of them.

We shall now see how characterization theorems may be used in proofs.

Theorem 12–2: The angle bisectors of a triangle are concurrent in a point equidistant from the three sides of the triangle.

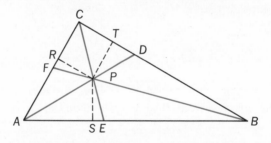

GIVEN: $\triangle ABC$; angle bisectors $\overline{AD}$, $\overline{CE}$, $\overline{BF}$.
PROVE: $P \in \overline{AD}$; $P \in \overline{CE}$; $P \in \overline{BF}$; P is equidistant from $\overline{AB}$, $\overline{BC}$, and $\overline{CA}$.

Proof: Let P be the point of intersection of $\overline{AD}$ and $\overline{CE}$. (Proof that they do intersect is left as an exercise.) Then P lies on the bisector of $\angle A$, and also on the bisector of $\angle C$. By Theorem 12–1, it follows that P is equidistant from $\overline{AB}$ and $\overline{AC}$ (that is, $PS = PR$), as well as from $\overline{AC}$ and $\overline{CB}$, ($PR = PT$). By the Transitivity Axiom (E–3), $PS = PT$, hence P is equidistant from $\overline{AB}$ and $\overline{BC}$. By Theorem 12–1, it follows that P lies on the bisector of $\angle B$, that is, $P \in \overline{BF}$. Thus P is on $\overline{AD}$, $\overline{CE}$, and $\overline{BF}$; and P is equidistant from $\overline{AB}$, $\overline{BC}$, and $\overline{CA}$.

Theorem 12–3: The perpendicular bisectors of the sides of a triangle are concurrent in a point equidistant from the three vertices of the triangle.

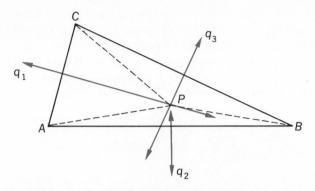

GIVEN: $\triangle ABC$; perpendicular bisectors q_1, q_2, and q_3.
PROVE: $P \in q_1$; $P \in q_2$; $P \in q_3$; $PA = PB = PC$.

Proof: Let q_1 and q_3 intersect at P. (Proof that they do intersect is left as an exercise.) Hence $P \in q_1$ and $P \in q_3$. But then it follows by Theorem 6–2, that P is equidistant from A and C, and also, from C and B. Thus $PA = PC$ and $PC = PB$. By the Transitivity Axiom (E–3), $PA = PB$, and so P must lie on the perpendicular bisector of $\overline{AB}$, that is: $P \in q_2$. Hence the three lines are concurrent, and $PA = PB = PC$.

Corollary 12–3.1: There is one and only one circle through three noncollinear points.

Proof: The three noncollinear points will always determine a triangle. Since Theorem 12–3 establishes the existence and uniqueness of a point (P) equidistant from the three vertices of a triangle, it follows that P determines the center of the circle containing the three points. The radius of the circle is the length of the segment from P to any of the three given points.

Corollary 12–3.1 is often stated as: **Three noncollinear points determine a circle.**

Corollary 12–3.2: Two distinct circles can intersect in at most two points.

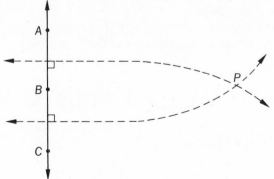

Proof: If two distinct circles intersected in three or more *noncollinear* points, this would contradict Corollary 12–3.1, hence two distinct circles cannot intersect in three noncollinear points. Suppose next that two distinct circles intersected in three *collinear* points, say A, B, and C. Then $\overline{AB}$ and $\overline{BC}$ would be chords of the circles, and the perpendicular bisectors of $\overline{AB}$ and $\overline{BC}$ would pass through the centers of the circles (Corollary 11–1.5). But then there would be *two* perpendiculars to a given line ($\overleftrightarrow{AC}$) through a given point (the center of a circle), which is a contradiction; and the Corollary is proved.

EXAMPLES

1. Given an arc of a circle, containing points A, B, and C, show how to locate the center of the circle.

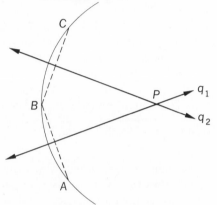

Solution: We know that the desired center must be a point equidistant from the three given points. This suggests Theorem 12–3 which tells us that the point of concurrency of the perpendicular bisectors of the sides of a triangle is equidistant from the three vertices of the triangle. So, introduce $\overline{AB}$ and $\overline{BC}$, two sides of $\triangle ABC$, as well as q_1 and q_2, the perpendicular bisectors of $\overline{AB}$ and $\overline{BC}$, respectively, intersecting at P. (Note that it is not necessary to introduce the third perpendicular bisector.) By Theorem 12–3, P is the center of the circle.

2. PROVE: The perpendicular bisectors of the sides of a right triangle are concurrent at the midpoint of the hypotenuse.

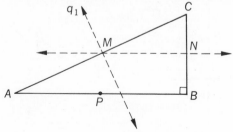

Proof: Let $\triangle ABC$ be a right triangle, with $\overline{AB} \perp \overline{BC}$. Let M, N, and P be the midpoints of the three sides. Introduce $\overleftrightarrow{MN}$. Then $\overleftrightarrow{MN} \parallel \overline{AB}$ (Theorem 8–21). Since $\overline{BC} \perp \overline{AB}$, it follows that $\overline{BC} \perp \overleftrightarrow{MN}$ (Theorem 8–11), and so $\overleftrightarrow{MN}$ is the perpendicular bisector of $\overline{BC}$. Through midpoint M introduce q_1 so that $q_1 \perp \overline{AC}$. Then q_1 is the perpendicular bisector of $\overline{AC}$. Now, q_1 and $\overleftrightarrow{MN}$ intersect at M. By Theorem 12–3, all three perpendicular bisectors are concurrent. Hence the perpendicular bisector of $\overline{AB}$ must also contain M, and the theorem is proved.

Exercise 12–2

(A)

1. If the point of concurrency of the angle bisectors of a triangle is 6 in. from one side, how far is the point from each of the other sides?
2. If the point of concurrency, P, of the perpendicular bisectors of the sides of $\triangle ABC$ is $2\frac{1}{3}$ in. from A, how far is P from B? From C?

Draw an acute triangle, a right triangle, and an obtuse triangle. Use a ruler and a protractor to draw the perpendicular bisectors of the sides of each of the triangles. (The point of concurrency of the perpendicular bisectors is called the **circumcenter.**) Use these figures to help answer questions 3 to 6.

3. Do you think the circumcenter of a triangle must be in its interior?
4. What kind of triangle appears to have its circumcenter on a side?
5. What kind of triangle appears to have its circumcenter in its exterior?
6. Can you explain why the circumcenter cannot be at a vertex of a triangle?

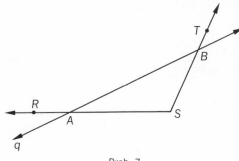

Prob. 7

7. Line q intersects the sides of $\angle RST$ in A and B as shown. Explain how to find a point P on q such that P will be equidistant from $\overrightarrow{SR}$ and $\overrightarrow{ST}$.
8. Given three noncollinear points. Where is the point in their plane equidistant from all three points? Why must the points be noncollinear?

Given convex quadrilateral $ABCD$ (9 to 12):

9. Explain how to find a point equidistant from A, B, and C.

10. Explain how to find a point equidistant from $\overleftrightarrow{AD}$, $\overleftrightarrow{AB}$, and $\overleftrightarrow{BC}$.

11. Explain how to find a point equidistant from $\overleftrightarrow{CB}$ and $\overleftrightarrow{DC}$, and also equidistant from A and B.

12. Explain how to find a point equidistant from D and C, and also equidistant from $\overleftrightarrow{BC}$ and $\overleftrightarrow{AB}$.

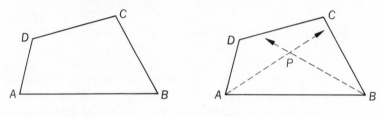

Probs. 9 to 12   Prob. 13

13. GIVEN: $ABCD$; $\overrightarrow{AP}$ bisects $\angle DAB$; $\overrightarrow{BP}$ bisects $\angle ABC$.
PROVE: P is equidistant from $\overleftrightarrow{AD}$ and $\overleftrightarrow{BC}$.

14. PROVE: If the angle bisectors of three of the angles of a quadrilateral are concurrent, then all four angle bisectors are concurrent.

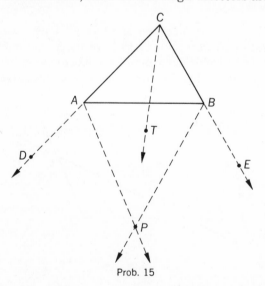

Prob. 15

15. GIVEN: $\triangle ABC$; $\overrightarrow{AP}$ bisects $\angle DAB$; $\overrightarrow{BP}$ bisects $\angle ABE$; $\overrightarrow{CT}$ bisects $\angle ACB$.
PROVE: $\overrightarrow{AP}$, $\overrightarrow{BP}$, and $\overrightarrow{CT}$ are concurrent at P.

16. PROVE: If the four vertices of a quadrilateral lie on a circle, then the perpendicular bisectors of its sides are concurrent.

(B)

17. PROVE: The bisectors of two consecutive angles of a parallelogram intersect at a point equidistant from a pair of opposite sides.

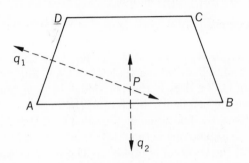

Prob. 18

18. GIVEN: Trapezoid $ABCD$; $\overline{AD} \cong \overline{BC}$; q_1 and q_2 are perpendicular bisectors of $\overline{AD}$ and $\overline{AB}$, respectively, intersecting at P.
    PROVE: P is equidistant from A, B, C, and D.
19. In the proof of Thm. 12–3, it was asserted that the perpendicular bisectors of *two* of the sides intersected. Prove this assertion. (*Hint:* Write an indirect proof, using Thm. 8–11.)
20. In the proof of Thm. 12–2 it was asserted that *two* of the angle bisectors of a triangle intersect. Prove this assertion. (*Hint:* Write an indirect proof, using Thm. 8–8.)

12–3 FURTHER CONCURRENCE THEOREMS

Theorem 12–4: **The altitudes of a triangle are concurrent.**

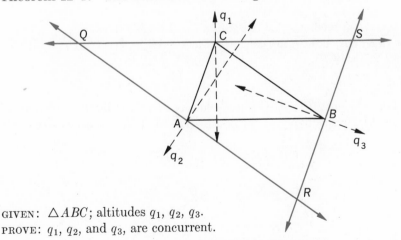

GIVEN: $\triangle ABC$; altitudes q_1, q_2, q_3.
PROVE: q_1, q_2, and q_3, are concurrent.

DISCUSSION: The proof hinges upon two features. First, we use the word "altitude" to mean the line containing the altitude. (See the discussion following Definition 5–14, page 118.) Second, we introduce certain auxiliary sets, which make the proof quite simple.

Proof: Through each of the vertices of $\triangle ABC$ introduce a line parallel to the opposite side, as shown in the sketch. These three lines determine $\triangle QSR$. Now, $ABSC$ and $ABCQ$ are parallelograms. Hence $\overline{CS} \cong \overline{AB}$, and $\overline{AB} \cong \overline{QC}$. Then $CS = AB$ and $AB = QC$, so that $CS = QC$. But this means that C is the midpoint of $\overline{QS}$, and q_1 is the perpendicular bisector of $\overline{QS}$. In the same way, q_2 is the perpendicular bisector of $\overline{QR}$ and q_3 is the perpendicular bisector of $\overline{RS}$. Now, by Theorem 12–3 applied to $\triangle QRS$, q_1, q_2, and q_3 are concurrent. But q_1, q_2, and q_3 are the altitudes of $\triangle ABC$, hence the altitudes are concurrent and the theorem is proved. (The point of concurrency of the altitudes is called the **orthocenter.**)

The next theorem completes our list of concurrency theorems. We shall divide the proof into three parts for ease of reading. (We suggest that you refer freely to the list of theorems provided in the Appendix, pages 425–29.)

Theorem 12–5: **The medians of a triangle are concurrent, and the point of concurrency is two-thirds of the distance from any vertex to the midpoint of the opposite side.**

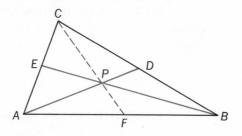

GIVEN: $\triangle ABC$; medians $\overline{AD}$, $\overline{BE}$, and $\overline{CF}$.
PROVE: $\overline{AD}$, $\overline{BE}$, and $\overline{CF}$ are concurrent at P; $AP = \frac{2}{3}(AD)$; $BP = \frac{2}{3}(BE)$; $CP = \frac{2}{3}(CF)$.

Proof

(1) Let $\overline{AD}$ and $\overline{BE}$ intersect at P, and let M and N be the midpoints of $\overline{AP}$ and $\overline{BP}$, respectively. Introduce $\overline{MN}$ and $\overline{ED}$. Then $\overline{ED} \parallel \overline{AB}$,

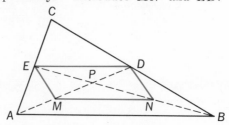

$\overline{MN} \parallel \overline{AB}$, $MN = \frac{1}{2}(AB)$, and $ED = \frac{1}{2}(AB)$ (Theorem 8–21 applied to $\triangle ABC$ and $\triangle ABP$). So, $MN = ED$, and by Theorem 8–10, $\overline{ED} \parallel \overline{MN}$. It follows, by Theorem 8–19, that $MNDE$ is a parallelogram. Hence (Theorem 8–17) the diagonals $\overline{MD}$ and $\overline{EN}$ bisect each other, or $MP = PD$ and $NP = PE$. Now M and N are midpoints, hence $AM = MP$ and $BN = NP$. Summing up, we have:

$$AM = MP = PD \quad \text{and} \quad BN = NP = PE$$

Therefore

$$AP = \tfrac{2}{3}(AD) \quad \text{and} \quad BP = \tfrac{2}{3}(BE)$$

(2) Let $\overline{AD}$ and $\overline{CF}$ intersect in P'. By the same chain of reasoning as used in part (1), we establish:

$$CP' = \tfrac{2}{3}(CF)$$

and

$$AP' = \tfrac{2}{3}(AD)$$

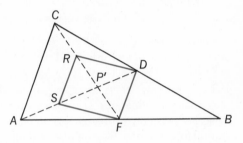

(3) Consider now the following two results:

(a) $AP = \tfrac{2}{3}(AD)$.
(b) $AP' = \tfrac{2}{3}(AD)$.

Statement (a) says that on $\overrightarrow{AD}$ there is a point P such that AP is a number equal to two-thirds of AD. Statement (b) says that on $\overrightarrow{AD}$ there is a point P' such that AP' is a number equal to two-thirds of AD. But Axiom 2–4 states that there is exactly *one* point on $\overrightarrow{AD}$ such that its distance from A is a given positive number. Hence P and P' must be the same point. Thus P lies on all the medians, i.e., the medians are concurrent; $AP = \tfrac{2}{3}(BE)$, $BP = \tfrac{2}{3}(BE)$, and $CP = \tfrac{2}{3}(CF)$, as was to be proved.

The point of concurrency of the medians of a triangle is called the **centroid** of the triangle. It is the point of "balance"; if you were to cut a triangle out of a piece of cardboard, draw the medians carefully, and place a pencil point at the centroid, the triangular region would balance on the pencil point.

EXAMPLES

Given $\triangle ABC$ with medians $\overline{AN}$ and $\overline{BM}$ (1 to 5):

1. Explain why P is the centroid.
2. If $AP = 12$, find PN.
3. If $MB = 25$, find PB.
4. If median $\overline{CD}$ were introduced, then $P \in \overline{CD}$. Explain.
5. If $CD = 14$, find PD.

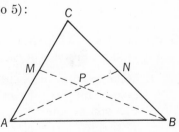

Solutions

1. Since $\overline{AN}$ and $\overline{BM}$ are medians, they must intersect at the centroid (Theorem 12–5). Since two lines may intersect in at most one point, P *is* the point of intersection, and so P is the centroid.

2. The centroid is $\frac{2}{3}$ of the distance from any vertex to the midpoint of the opposite side. Then: $AP = \frac{2}{3}(AN)$, so $PN = \frac{1}{3}(AN)$. Now, $AP = 12$. Therefore $\frac{2}{3}(AN) = 12$, so $\frac{1}{3}(AN) = \frac{1}{2}(12) = 6$. Hence $PN = 6$.

3. $PB = \frac{2}{3}(MB); PB = \frac{2}{3}(25); \underline{PB = \frac{50}{3}}$ or $16\frac{2}{3}$.

4. Since the medians concur at the centroid, and P is the centroid, $P \in \overline{CD}$.

5. $PD = \frac{1}{3}(CD); PD = \frac{1}{3}(14); \underline{PD = \frac{14}{3}}$ or $4\frac{2}{3}$.

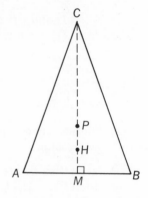

6. GIVEN: Isosceles $\triangle ABC$ (base $\overline{AB}$).
   PROVE: The centroid (P), the orthocenter (H), and the vertex (C) are collinear.

Proof: Introduce $\overline{CM} \perp \overline{AB}$. Then $H \in \overline{CM}$, since $\overline{CM}$ is an altitude, and the altitudes are concurrent at orthocenter H. Now, if the centroid is to lie on $\overline{CM}$, then the medians must be concurrent at a point on $\overline{CM}$. Past experience with isosceles triangle problems brings to mind that the altitude to the base is also a median. Since $\triangle AMC$ and $\triangle BMC$ are right triangles, $\overline{CA} \cong \overline{CB}$, and $\angle A \cong \angle B$, and so $\triangle AMC \cong \triangle BMC$ (Theorem 8–26). Then $\overline{AM} \cong \overline{MB}$, $AM = MB$, M is a midpoint, and $\overline{CM}$ *is* a median. Since the medians are concurrent, centroid P must lie on $\overline{CM}$. Hence C, H, and P are collinear.

Exercise 12–3

(A)

Draw three triangles—an acute triangle, a right triangle, and an obtuse triangle. Using a protractor, draw the three altitudes of each triangle. Use your drawings to help with problems 1 to 3.

1. Do you think the orthocenter is always in the interior of a triangle?
2. Where is the orthocenter of a right triangle?
3. What kind of triangle has its orthocenter exterior to the triangle?

For problems 4 and 5, draw three triangles (acute, right, and obtuse), and draw the three medians of each triangle.

4. Make a conjecture as to where the centroid of a triangle always seems to be. (Interior? Exterior? On the triangle?)
5. Can you explain why the centroid cannot be on a side (including the vertices) of a triangle?

In the figure, $\overline{AE}$, $\overline{BD}$, and $\overline{CF}$ are the medians of $\triangle ABC$ (6 to 11):

6. If $AE = 9$, find AP.   7. If $PD = 4$, find BP.
8. If $BP = 11$, find PD.   9. If $CP = 10$, find CF.
10. If $DB = 15$, find DP and PB.
11. If $CF = (12x + 3)$, express CP and PF in terms of x.

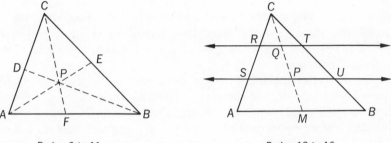

Probs. 6 to 11   Probs. 12 to 16

Given $\triangle ABC$, median $\overline{CM}$, centroid P, and Q the midpoint of $\overline{CP}$ (12 to 16):

12. If $CM = 21$, find CQ, QP, and PM.
13. If $\overleftrightarrow{RT} \parallel \overleftrightarrow{SU} \parallel \overline{AB}$, state a reason to justify $\overline{CR} \cong \overline{RS} \cong \overline{SA}$ and $\overline{CT} \cong \overline{TU} \cong \overline{UB}$.
14. If $\overleftrightarrow{RT} \parallel \overleftrightarrow{SU} \parallel \overline{AB}$, and the altitude from Q to $\overline{AB}$ is 8, how long is the altitude from P to $\overline{AB}$?
15. If the altitude from P to $\overline{AB}$ is 4, how long is the altitude from C to $\overline{AB}$?
16. PROVE: The altitude from P to $\overline{AB}$ is one-third the altitude from C to $\overline{AB}$. (Hint: Consider the results of problems 12 to 15.)

17. Draw $\triangle PQR$. Draw the three altitudes, and label the orthocenter E. Verify that P is the orthocenter of $\triangle QER$ and that R is the orthocenter of $\triangle PEQ$.
18. GIVEN: $\triangle ABC$; altitudes $\overline{AD}$, $\overline{BE}$, $\overline{CF}$; orthocenter P.
    PROVE: $\angle ACB \cong \angle BPD$.

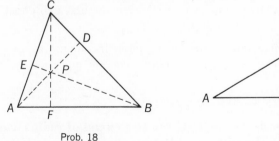

(B)   Prob. 18   Probs. 19, 20

Given $\triangle BCD$, median $\overline{CM}$, centroid P, altitude $\overline{CH}$ (19, 20):

19. If $PM = 5$ and $MH = 9$, find CH.
20. If $PC = \frac{26}{3}$ and $CH = 12$, find MH.

12-4 CONSTRUCTIONS

Up to now, you have drawn many figures, using ruler, protractor, and compass freely. The major concern was not great accuracy, but only to have the figure represent the given information and not be grossly misleading. You are probably aware that many refined and sensitive drawing instruments are available which enable us to make drawings to almost any desired degree of accuracy. You may be surprised to learn that it is possible to make many geometric drawings using only two devices—a compass and unmarked straightedge—and achieve as good or better accuracy than that afforded by ruler and protractor.

The matter of making drawings using only a compass and straightedge dates back to the days of the ancient Greeks. They looked upon such problems as intellectual exercises—one might say "puzzles"—and a great amount of effort was expended on them. Among the many problems studied over the years are some that they could not solve. One example is the problem of trisecting an angle; that is, given any angle, to divide it into three congruent angles—using only a compass and unmarked straightedge. In the pursuit of solutions to such problems, many useful theorems were discovered. Today we can *prove* that, using only a compass and unmarked straightedge, it is not possible to trisect every angle. (Certain particular angles *can* be trisected in this manner, for example, a 90° angle and a 45° angle; on the other hand, a 60° angle *cannot*.)

We refer to compass-straightedge drawings as **constructions**. Thus, when we say *draw* a figure, we mean, as earlier, use any of the tools you may have. When we say **construct** a given figure, we mean use an unmarked straightedge and compass only; measuring, such as with ruler and protractor, is not to be done. To sum up:

(1) The straightedge is to be used only to draw straight lines.

(2) A compass can be used for drawing circles with a given radius and a given center.

Most of our constructions depend upon the possible intersections between two lines, a line and a circle, and two circles. For the first two possibilities we have:

(1) Two coplanar lines intersect either in one point, or not at all.

(2) In a plane, a line intersects a circle in two points, one point, or not at all.

For the third possibility we state an axiom:

Axiom 12-1 (Two-Circle Axiom): **Given two circles of radius a and b, respectively, and c the distance between their centers. If each of the numbers a, b, and c, is less than the sum of the other two, then the circles intersect in two points, one on each side of the line determined by the two centers.**

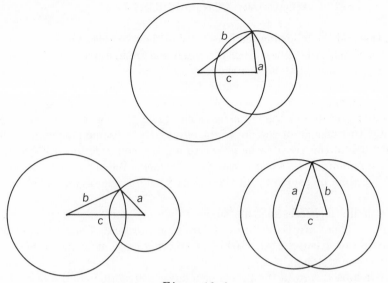

Figure 12–4

Figure 12–4 illustrates situations in which the inequalities are satisfied, and the circles intersect in two points.

Figure 12–5 illustrates situations in which the circles do not intersect, since the inequalities are not satisfied.

$c > a + b$

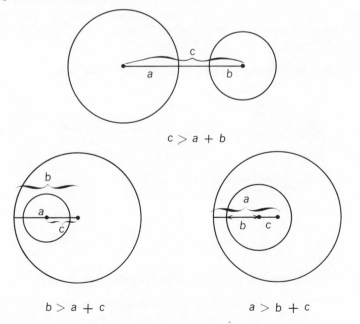

$b > a + c$ $a > b + c$

Figure 12–5

12–5 ELEMENTARY CONSTRUCTIONS I

In this and the following sections, we show how to make various elementary constructions. All of these basic constructions are in a plane, and can be used as steps in more difficult constructions.

In order that you shall be able to follow the procedures described, we first explain the language to be used. When we say "construct" a circle, we do not necessarily mean construct the *entire* circle; on the contrary we are content to draw just enough of the arc of the circle to serve some particular purpose. How much of the arc is to be drawn in a given construction will usually become apparent as the construction is performed. When we say "center of an arc," we shall of course mean the center of the circle of which the arc is a part.

We shall use phrases such as "sufficiently long" and "radius any convenient length." There are no definitions for these phrases. Careful study of the constructions discussed below will help to bring more meaning to these necessarily vague statements.

A much-used step in the proofs of many constructions is the fact that, by the definition of circle, radii of the same (or congruent) circles are congruent. We use this concept freely, but shall not specifically state the reason each time it is used. If you are in doubt as to why two segments are congruent in a given proof, examine the steps of the construction and determine whether they are radii of the same, or of congruent circles.

As a final word, it is recommended that you actually perform the constructions as you study them. Try to use segments at least $1\frac{1}{2}$ in. in length whenever possible, and draw all circles with a compass having a well sharpened pencil.

Construction 1: To copy a given angle on either side of a given ray.

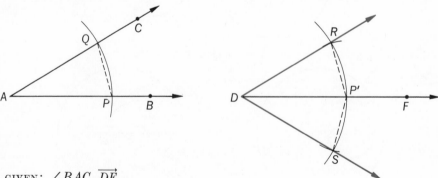

GIVEN: $\angle BAC$, $\overrightarrow{DF}$.

CONSTRUCT: An angle, with $\overrightarrow{DF}$ as a side, congruent to $\angle ABC$.

Step 1. With A as center, and with any convenient length radius, r_1, construct a circle intersecting $\overrightarrow{AB}$ and $\overrightarrow{AC}$ in P and Q respectively.

Step 2. With D as center, and radius $r_1 = AP \ (= AQ)$, construct a sufficiently long arc, intersecting $\overrightarrow{DF}$ in P'.

Step 3. With P' as center and radius $r_2 = PQ$, construct an arc intersecting circle D in points R and S.

Step 4. Draw $\overrightarrow{DR}$ and $\overrightarrow{DS}$. Then $\angle SDP'$ (or $\angle P'DR$) is the required angle. (If there is no need for both angles, either may be omitted.)

Proof: $\overline{QA} \cong \overline{RD}$, $\overline{PA} \cong \overline{P'D}$, and $\overline{QP} \cong \overline{RP'}$. Hence $\triangle APQ \cong \triangle DP'R$, SSS Axiom (Axiom 5–4), and it follows that $\angle P'DR \cong \angle BAC$. In the same way, $\angle SDP' \cong \angle BAC$.

Construction 2: To bisect a given angle.

GIVEN: $\angle BAC$.
CONSTRUCT: $\overrightarrow{AP}$, the bisector of $\angle BAC$.

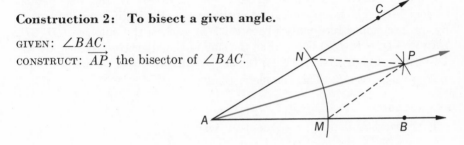

Step 1. With A as center and any convenient radius, construct a circle intersecting $\overrightarrow{AB}$ and $\overrightarrow{AC}$ at M and N respectively.

Step 2. With centers at M and at N, construct circles with radius r_2, where $r_2 > \frac{1}{2}(MN)$. By the Two-Circle Axiom (Axiom 12.1), these circles intersect in two points, one on each side of $\overleftrightarrow{MN}$. Let P be the point on the side opposite A.

Step 3. Construct $\overrightarrow{AP}$. $\overrightarrow{AP}$ is the required angle bisector.

Proof: $\overline{AM} \cong \overline{AN}$, $\overline{PN} \cong \overline{PM}$, and $\overline{AP} \cong \overline{AP}$. Hence $\triangle AMP \cong \triangle ANP$, SSS Axiom (Axiom 5–4); and $\angle NAP \cong \angle MAP$. It follows, by Definition 5–1, that $\overrightarrow{AP}$ is the bisector of $\angle BAC$.

Construction 3: To copy a given triangle.

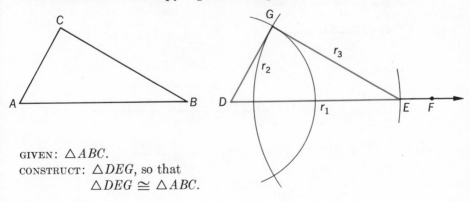

GIVEN: $\triangle ABC$.
CONSTRUCT: $\triangle DEG$, so that
$\qquad \triangle DEG \cong \triangle ABC$.

Step 1. Construct $\overrightarrow{DF}$.

Step 2. With D as center and radius $r_1 = AB$, construct a circle intersecting $\overrightarrow{DF}$ at E.

Step 3. With D as center and radius $r_2 = AC$, construct a circle.

Step 4. With E as center and radius $r_3 = BC$, construct a circle.

Step 5. These last two circles intersect at G and G'.

Step 6. Either G or G' may be used as the third vertex for the triangle. Draw $\overline{GD}$ and $\overline{GE}$ (or $\overline{G'D}$ and $\overline{G'E}$). $\triangle DEG$ (or $\triangle DEG'$) is the desired triangle.

Proof: Plainly, $\triangle ABC \cong \triangle DEG$ (or $\triangle DEG'$) by the SSS Axiom (Axiom 5–4). The less obvious part of the proof is the justification for step 5. By the Triangular Inequality (Theorem 7–5), each of the numbers GD, GE, DE (or $G'D$, $G'E$, DE) is less than the sum of the other two. Hence, by the Two-Circle Axiom (Axiom 12–1), the circles must intersect in two points on opposite sides of $\overrightarrow{DF}$. This completes the proof.

EXAMPLES

1. Construct a segment congruent to $\overline{AB}$.

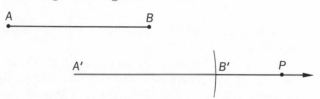

Solution: Draw any ray to use as a "construction base," say $\overrightarrow{A'P}$. Place your compass on $\overline{AB}$ so that one point of the compass is at A, and open the compass until the second point falls on B. Now, with center A' and radius $r = AB$, construct circle A'. Mark the point of intersection (B') of circle A' with $\overrightarrow{A'P}$. Then $\overline{A'B'} \cong \overline{AB}$.

2. Construct a segment $\overline{RS}$ such that $RS = a + b$, where a and b are lengths of two given segments.

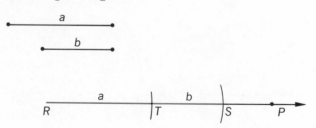

Solution: Draw $\overrightarrow{RP}$. With R as center and radius $r_1 = a$, construct circle R. Mark the point of intersection (T) of circle R with $\overrightarrow{RP}$. With T as center and radius $r_2 = b$, construct circle T. Mark the point of intersection (S) of circle T with $\overrightarrow{RP}$ so that T is between R and S. Then $RS = a + b$.

3. Construct a triangle with sides 1 in., $1\frac{1}{2}$ in., and 2 in.

Solution: Since the sum of any two of the three lengths is greater than the third, the Triangular Inequality (Theorem 7–5) tells us that such a triangle exists. Draw three segments, one for each of the given lengths. Now, except for the fact that the three given segments are not already arranged to form a triangle, this construction can be accomplished by following Construction 3.

4. Construct a triangle with sides of lengths 3 in., 1 in., and 1 in.

Solution: This triangle does not exist, as the lengths of the three sides do not satisfy the requirements of the Triangular Inequality. (Plainly, $1 + 1 = 2$, and $2 \not> 3$.) You may find it instructive to attempt to construct the triangle.

Exercise 12–5

(A)

For construction problems use compass and straightedge only. If a problem suggests segments of specific length, this is for convenience only. (Obviously you will need to use a ruler to measure the suggested lengths.)

Construct a triangle, if possible, with sides having the following lengths (1 to 8):

1. 2 in., 3 in., 4 in.	**2.** 3 in., 3 in., 4 in.	**3.** 2 in., 3 in., 6 in.
4. 2 in., 3 in., 5 in.	**5.** 3 in., 3 in., 3 in.	**6.** 3 in., 4 in., 5 in.
7. 3 in., 3 in., 5 in.	**8.** $1\frac{1}{4}$ in., 3 in., $3\frac{1}{4}$ in.	

In problems 9 and 10, given $DE = m(\overline{DE})$.

9. Construct $\overline{MN}$ so that
   $MN = DE + DE + DE$.

10. Construct $\overline{RT}$ so that $RT = 2(DE)$.

Probs. 9, 10

11. Draw $\triangle ABC$ with sides no shorter than $1\frac{1}{2}$ in. Use Construction 3 to construct $\triangle AB'C$, using $\overline{AC}$ as one side, such that $\triangle AB'C \cong \triangle ABC$.

12. Draw $\triangle DEF$ with no side shorter than $1\frac{1}{2}$ in. Use Construction 1 twice to construct $\triangle DE'F \cong \triangle DEF$, with $\overline{DF}$ as one side.

13. Draw $\triangle ABC$, and a segment $\overline{RS}$ with length $RS = AB + AB$ [or $RS = 2(AB)$]. With R as vertex, construct $\angle SRT \cong \angle A$. With S as vertex, construct $\angle RST \cong \angle B$. Answer the following questions:

   (a) $\angle T \cong \angle \underline{\ ?\ }$ (b) $\dfrac{AB}{RS} = \dfrac{?}{?} = \dfrac{?}{?}$

14. Draw $\triangle DEF$ and construct the three angle bisectors. (Are your bisectors concurrent?)

15. Draw a segment, $\overline{AB}$. Construct an equilateral triangle with $\overline{AB}$ as one side.

16. Construct a 60° angle. (*Hint:* See problem 15.)
17. Construct a 30° angle. (*Hint:* See problems 15 and 16.)
18. Explain how to construct a 15° angle.

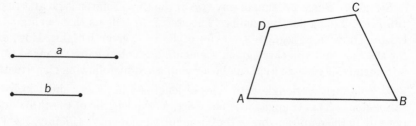

Prob. 19   Prob. 20

19. Given the figure, construct an isosceles triangle with base of length b, and sides of length a.
20. Copy, by construction methods, $ABCD$.

12–6 ELEMENTARY CONSTRUCTIONS II

Construction 4: **To construct the perpendicular bisector of a given segment.**

GIVEN: $\overline{AB}$.

CONSTRUCT: $\overleftrightarrow{PQ}$ so that $\overleftrightarrow{PQ} \perp \overline{AB}$, and $\overleftrightarrow{PQ}$ bisects $\overline{AB}$.

Step 1. With A as center and r as radius $[r > \frac{1}{2}(AB)]$, construct a circle.

Step 2. With B as center and the same radius, r, construct a circle.

Step 3. Circle A and circle B intersect at P and Q. Construct $\overleftrightarrow{PQ}$. $\overleftrightarrow{PQ}$ is the perpendicular bisector of $\overline{AB}$.

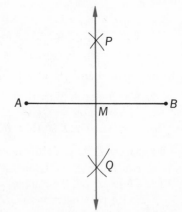

Proof: $PA = PB$ and $QA = QB$. Hence, by Corollary 6–2.1, $\overleftrightarrow{PQ}$ is the perpendicular bisector of $\overline{AB}$.

Observe that Construction 4 furnishes a *perpendicular* to a segment as well as a *bisector* of the segment. Many construction problems require a right angle. This can often be accomplished by using Construction 4, or the following Construction 5, which is simply a variation of Construction 4.

Construction 5: To construct a perpendicular from a given point to a given line. The given point may be on, or not on, the given line.

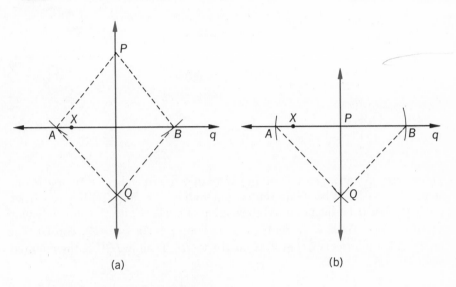

(a)   (b)

GIVEN: Line q: (a) $P \notin q$, (b) $P \in q$.

CONSTRUCT: A line through P, perpendicular to q.

Step 1. Let X be any point on q ($X \neq P$). With P as center and radius r_1 ($r_1 > PX$), construct a circle intersecting q in A and B.

Step 2. With A as center, and radius r_2 [$r_2 > \frac{1}{2}(AB)$], construct a circle.

Step 3. With B as center, and the same radius, r_2, construct a circle intersecting circle A at Q.

Step 4. Construct $\overleftrightarrow{PQ}$. $\overleftrightarrow{PQ}$ is the desired perpendicular to q.

Proof: $PA = PB$ and $AQ = BQ$. Hence, by Corollary 6–2.1, $\overleftrightarrow{PQ} \perp \overline{AB}$ and therefore $\overleftrightarrow{PQ} \perp q$.

EXAMPLE

1. Construct a right triangle, given that its legs are $\frac{1}{2}b$ and $2a$, respectively.

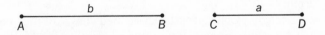

Solution: We bisect $\overline{AB}$ in order to obtain the length of one of the legs ($AM = \frac{1}{2}b$), and we add $CD + CD$ to obtain $2a$, the length of the second leg ($FE = 2a$):

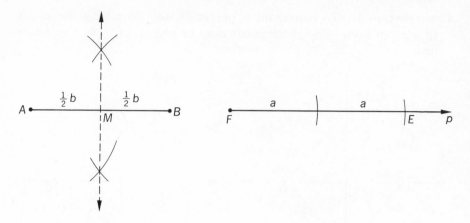

Draw $\overleftrightarrow{RQ}$. At any point G of $\overleftrightarrow{RQ}$ construct a perpendicular to $\overleftrightarrow{RQ}$ (Construction 5(b)). With G as center and radius $r = \frac{1}{2}b$ $(= AM)$, construct circle G. Let H be the point of intersection of circle G with the perpendicular to $\overleftrightarrow{RQ}$ at G. With G as center and radius $r_2 = 2a$ $(= FE)$, construct a circle which intersects $\overleftrightarrow{RQ}$ at J. Construct $\overline{JH}$. Then $\triangle JGH$ is the required right triangle.

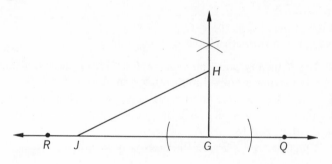

Exercise 12–6

(A)

1. Draw an acute triangle with sides no shorter than $1\frac{1}{2}$ in. Construct the three altitudes of the triangle. Are your constructed altitudes concurrent?

2. Draw an obtuse triangle, and construct the three altitudes. Are they concurrent?

3. Draw a triangle. Construct the three medians. Are they concurrent?

4. Construct a right triangle, given legs of lengths a and b, respectively.

Prob. 4

5. Construct an isosceles right triangle, given that each leg is half the length of $\overline{RS}$.
6. Construct a rectangle, given one side, $\overline{ST}$, and that the second side is three times as long as $\overline{ST}$.
7. Construct a square, given that each side is of length s.

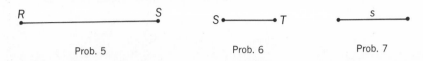

R _____ S   S •————• T   •——— s ———•

Prob. 5   Prob. 6   Prob. 7

8. Explain how you would divide a segment into 4 congruent segments.
9. Construct a square, given that its perimeter is the length of $\overline{PQ}$. (*Hint:* See problem 8.)

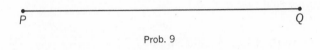

P •———————————————————————• Q

Prob. 9

10. Construct a 90° angle, and use it to construct a 45° angle.
11. Construct a rhombus, given the lengths of both diagonals. (*Hint:* See Thm. 8–23.)
12. Construct right $\triangle ABC$, given one of its acute angles, and the length of the hypotenuse ($\overline{AC}$).
13. Construct an isosceles triangle, given the base and the altitude to the base.
14. Construct a line tangent to a given circle at a given point of contact.
15. Construct a parallelogram, given the lengths of two consecutive sides, and the angle included by the given sides. (*Hint:* See Thm. 8–18.)

12–7 ELEMENTARY CONSTRUCTIONS III

Construction 6: To construct a line parallel to a given line through a given point not on the given line.

GIVEN: Line q, $P \notin q$.
CONSTRUCT: $\overleftrightarrow{PQ} \parallel q$.

Step 1. Choose any point $T \in q$, and construct $\overleftrightarrow{TP}$.

Step 2. Construct $\angle RPT$, such that $\angle RPT \cong \angle PTS$ (see Construction 1), with R and S on opposite sides of $\overleftrightarrow{TP}$.

Step 3. Construct $\overleftrightarrow{RP}$. $\overleftrightarrow{RP}$ is the desired line, parallel to q.

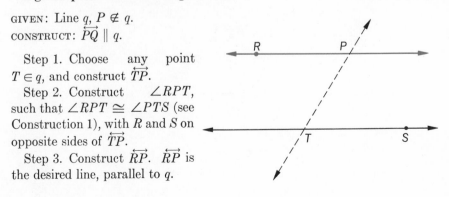

Proof: By Theorem 8–4, $\overleftrightarrow{RP} \parallel q$.

Construction 7: To divide a segment into a given number of congruent segments.

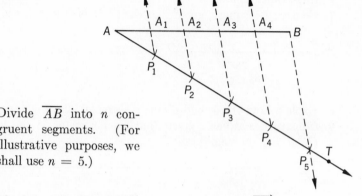

GIVEN: $\overline{AB}$.

CONSTRUCT: Divide $\overline{AB}$ into n congruent segments. (For illustrative purposes, we shall use $n = 5$.)

Step 1. With A as endpoint, draw any convenient ray $(\overrightarrow{AT})$.

Step 2. With compass, mark off n congruent segments on $\overrightarrow{AT}$: $\overline{AP_1}$, $\overline{P_1P_2}, \ldots, \overline{P_{n-1}P_n}$. (*Caution:* Do not have too large an opening of your compass.)

Step 3. Draw $\overrightarrow{BP_n}$. ($\overrightarrow{BP_5}$ in the illustration.)

Step 4. Using Construction 6, through each of $P_1, P_2, \ldots, P_{n-1}$, construct a ray parallel to $\overrightarrow{BP_n}$.

Step 5. These rays intersect $\overline{AB}$ in $A_1, A_2, \ldots, A_{n-1}$. Then $\overline{AA_1} \cong \overline{A_1A_2} \cong \cdots \cong \overline{A_{n-1}A_n}$, and these are the required n congruent segments.

Proof: By Corollary 8–25.1, the n parallel rays of the construction intercept congruent segments on $\overrightarrow{AT}$, hence they intercept congruent segments on $\overline{AB}$.

EXAMPLE

1. Given $\triangle ABC$, through each vertex construct a line parallel to the opposite side.

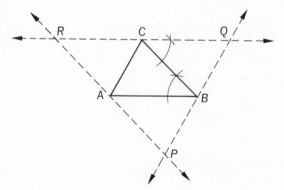

Solution: This construction may be accomplished by applying Construction 6 at each of the three vertices. For example, at C, use $\overline{BC}$ as a transversal, and construct $\angle QCB \cong \angle ABC$. (You will recall that this construction was part of the proof of Theorem 12–3.)

Exercise 12–7

(A)

1. Construct a line through a vertex of a triangle, parallel to the opposite side.
2. Trisect a given line segment.
3. Construct an equilateral triangle, given a segment of length equal to the perimeter of the triangle. (*Hint:* See problem 2.)
4. Construct a triangle whose sides are respectively $\frac{2}{5}$, $\frac{3}{5}$, and $\frac{4}{5}$ the length of a given segment.
5. Construct trapezoid $ABCD$, given bases $\overline{AB}$ and $\overline{CD}$, one nonparallel side $\overline{AD}$, and a diagonal $\overline{BD}$.
6. Construct two parallel lines, then construct the set of all points in the plane equidistant from these two lines.
7. Construct the set of all points in the plane at a distance of 1 in. from a given line.
8. Construct the set of all points that are $\frac{1}{2}$.in. from both sides of, and in the interior of, a given angle.
9. Draw $\angle RST$ and locate H approximately as shown. Construct two rays, having H as endpoint, parallel to $\overrightarrow{ST}$ and $\overrightarrow{SR}$, respectively. How many possibilities are there? What is the relation between $\angle H$ and $\angle S$?

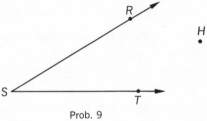

Prob. 9

10. Divide given segment $\overline{AB}$ into two segments such that the lengths of the segments shall have the ratio $\frac{2}{3}$.
11. Divide a given segment into 3 segments, such that the length of the second segment is twice that of the first, and the length of the third segment is three times that of the first.

12–8 INSCRIBED AND CIRCUMSCRIBED CIRCLES

The last two constructions to be described relate circles and triangles. Figure 12–6 shows $\triangle ABC$, and circles C_1 and C_2. After two further definitions, we shall see how circles C_1 and C_2 may be constructed.

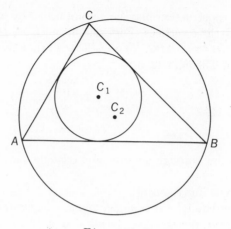

Figure 12–6

Definition 12–2: A circle is **inscribed in a triangle,** or a triangle is **circumscribed about a circle,** iff each side of the triangle is tangent to the circle.

Definition 12–3: A circle is **circumscribed about a triangle,** or a triangle is **inscribed in a circle,** iff each vertex of the triangle lies on the circle.

(These definitions generalize at once to *polygons*—we need only to replace "triangle" by "polygon.")

Now, for Figure 12–6, we can say:

1. $\triangle ABC$ is circumscribed about circle C_1, and circle C_1 is inscribed in $\triangle ABC$.

2. $\triangle ABC$ is inscribed in circle C_2, and circle C_2 is circumscribed about $\triangle ABC$.

Construction 8:   To circumscribe a circle about a given triangle.

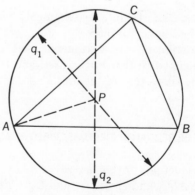

GIVEN: $\triangle ABC$.

CONSTRUCT: Circle P circumscribed about $\triangle ABC$.

Step 1. Construct the perpendicular bisectors, q_1 and q_2, of any two of the three sides of $\triangle ABC$ (see Construction 4). Let P be the point of intersection of q_1 and q_2.

Step 2. With P as center, and radius $r = PA$, construct circle P. Circle P is the required circumscribed circle.

Proof: By Theorem 12–3, P also lies on the perpendicular bisector of the third side of $\triangle ABC$ ($\overline{BC}$). Also by Theorem 12–3, P is equidistant from A, B, and C; that is, $PA = PB = PC$. Hence circle P passes through B and C, and is the required circle.

Construction 9: To inscribe a circle in a given triangle.

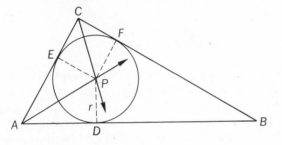

GIVEN: $\triangle ABC$.
CONSTRUCT: Circle P inscribed in $\triangle ABC$.

Step 1. Construct the bisectors of $\angle A$ and of $\angle C$ (see Construction 2). Let P be the point of intersection of angle bisectors $\overrightarrow{AP}$ and $\overrightarrow{CP}$.

Step 2. Construct a perpendicular from P to $\overline{AB}$ (see Construction 5). Then $\overline{PD} \perp \overline{AB}$.

Step 3. With P as center, and radius $r = PD$, construct circle P, which is the required circle.

Proof: Since $\overline{PD} \perp \overline{AB}$ and $\overline{PD}$ is a radius of circle P, by Corollary 11–1.2, $\overline{AB}$ is tangent to circle P. By Theorem 12–2, P is equidistant from $\overline{AC}$ and $\overline{AB}$. Therefore E, the foot of the perpendicular from P to $\overline{AC}$, lies on the circle. Hence the circle is tangent to $\overline{AC}$. In the same manner, the circle is tangent to $\overline{BC}$. Then circle P is tangent to all three sides of $\triangle ABC$, and is therefore the inscribed circle.

EXAMPLES

1. Inscribe a circle in a square.

Solution: We require a point, if it exists, that shall be equidistant from all four sides of the square. What do we know about points equidistant from sides? The points on an angle bisector are equidistant from the sides of the angle. What do we know about the angle bisectors of a square? The diagonals bisect the angles whose vertices are the endpoints of the diagonals. The point of intersection of the diagonals lies on the bisectors of all four angles, hence the point of intersection of the diagonals is the required point—that is, the center of the inscribed circle. We can now proceed. First, construct a square, then construct its diagonals. Point A is the center of the desired circle. A way to obtain the required radius is to drop a perpendicular from A to any one of the four sides. With A as center, and the length of the perpendicular segment as radius, construct the required circle.

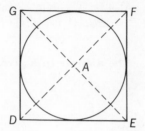

2. Construct a right triangle given the hypotenuse and a leg.

Solution: We can construct a segment which is the hypotenuse, at once. The real problem is locating the third vertex of the desired triangle. We ask: Where are all the possible vertices of a right triangle having the given segment as base? Since we know that every angle inscribed in a semicircle is a right angle, this suggests that we examine a circle to seek an answer. In fact, if $\overline{AB}$ is the diameter of a circle, then any angle with vertex X on the circle, and sides $\overline{XA}$ and $\overline{XB}$, will be a right angle. How shall we choose the particular point on the circle which leads to the desired right triangle, from among the many that are possible? Since we have been given the length of a leg, we shall use that segment to locate the desired third vertex.

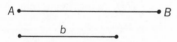

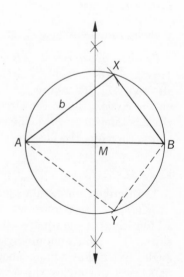

Step 1. Construct $\overline{AB}$, the given hypotenuse.

Step 2. Bisect $\overline{AB}$, label the midpoint M, and construct a circle with center M and radius $r_1 = \frac{1}{2}(AB)$.

Step 3. Let b be the length of the given leg. With A as center and radius $r_2 = b$, construct a circle intersecting circle M at X (or Y).

Step 4. Construct $\overline{AX}$ and $\overline{BX}$ (or $\overline{AY}$ and $\overline{BY}$). Then $\triangle AXB$ (or $\triangle AYB$) is the required triangle.

Exercise 12–8

These exercises are to be done using compass and straightedge. Use segments at least $1\frac{1}{2}$ in. in length.

(A)

1. Given a scalene triangle, construct its circumscribed circle.
2. Given a scalene triangle, construct its inscribed circle.
3. Construct an equilateral triangle. Construct its inscribed and circumscribed circles.
4. How are the centers of the inscribed and circumscribed circles of an equilateral triangle related?
5. Construct an isosceles right triangle.
6. Where is the center of the circumscribed circle of a right triangle?
7. Construct the circumscribed circle of an isosceles right triangle.
8. Construct a rhombus, given a side, and construct its inscribed circle.
9. Construct a rhombus, not a square, and construct its inscribed circle.
10. How are the centers of the inscribed and circumscribed circles of a square related?
11. Circumscribe a circle about a square.
12. Construct an isosceles right triangle given the radius of the circumscribed circle.
13. Construct a right triangle, given the radius of the circumscribed circle, and one of the acute angles.
14. Given an arc of a circle, locate the center of the circle.

(B)

15. Construct an equilateral triangle given the radius of the circumscribed circle.
16. Construct an equilateral triangle given the radius of the inscribed circle.
17. Construct a right triangle, given a leg and the radius of the circumscribed circle.

Chapter **13**

AREA OF CIRCULAR REGIONS

13–1   REGULAR POLYGONS

In Chapter 8 we introduced definitions for polygon, and convex polygon (Definitions 8–6 and 8–11). In this chapter polygons are used to study further properties of circles, namely circumferences and areas. In particular, we use a polygon classified as *regular*. First we shall define regular polygon, and then discuss a method for constructing such a polygon.

Definition 13–1:   A convex polygon is a **regular polygon** iff all of its sides are congruent, and all of its angles are congruent.

Our particular concern here is with regular polygons inscribed in circles.

Definition 13–2:   A polygon is **inscribed** in a circle iff its vertices lie on the circle.   The circle is **circumscribed** about the polygon.

Consider now a circle with center C and radius r.   Divide the circle into n congruent arcs.   (Figure 13–1 illustrates the case for $n = 6$.)   Next, introduce the chords joining consecutive points of division of the circle.   The resulting polygon, $ABDEFG$ (Figure 13–1), is regular. To prove this, we must show that the requirements of Definition 13–2 are satisfied. Since the arcs are all congruent, their corresponding chords are congruent (Theorem 11–5).   Since each angle of the polygon is inscribed in the circle, its measure is half the measure of its intercepted arc (Theorem 11–6).   For example, $m\angle B = \frac{1}{2}m\widehat{AFD}$, and $m\angle A = \frac{1}{2}m\widehat{GEB}$.   Now, because $\widehat{AFD}$ and

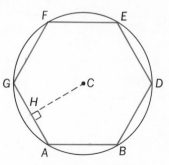

Figure 13–1

366

$\overparen{GEB}$ contain the same number of congruent arcs, we have $m\overparen{AFD} = m\overparen{GEB}$, and therefore $\angle A \cong \angle B$. In a similar way, we can show that all of the angles of the polygon are congruent. Thus, since all the sides are congruent, and all the angles are congruent, polygon $ABDEFG$ is regular.

It can be shown that every regular polygon can be inscribed in a circle, but we shall not include the proof. We require regular polygons only in the study of circles, and the regular polygons we shall use will be inscribed in circles by the method described above.

Observe $\overline{CH}$ in Figure 13–1, and note that $\overline{CH} \perp \overline{GA}$. This segment plays a special role in what follows, and its length is called the "apothem."

Definition 13–3: The **apothem** of a regular polygon is the distance from the center of the circumscribed circle to a side of the polygon.

Recall that the perimeter of a polygon is the sum of the lengths of its sides (Definition 8–20). In the case of the regular polygon, a simple formula can be found for computing the perimeter. Let a side of the regular polygon have length s, and let the polygon have n sides. Then the perimeter P is:

$$P = ns$$

There are certain commonly used names for polygons with a given number of sides. (The polygons do not have to be regular.) We list some of these names here. Note that if the number of sides is given by the number n, the polygon is referred to as an n-gon.

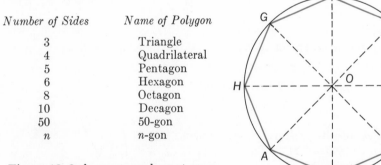

Number of Sides	Name of Polygon
3	Triangle
4	Quadrilateral
5	Pentagon
6	Hexagon
8	Octagon
10	Decagon
50	50-gon
n	n-gon

Figure 13–2

Figure 13–2 shows a regular octagon inscribed in a circle. Also shown are the radii drawn to each vertex of the octagon, forming eight central angles. It is not difficult to show that the eight triangles formed by the chords and the radii are all congruent, SSS Axiom (Axiom 5–4); and therefore the eight central angles are congruent. Then each central angle of the regular octagon has measure $\frac{360}{8}$, since $\frac{360}{8}$ is the measure of the intercepted arc. (For example, in Figure 13–2, $m\angle AOB = \frac{360}{8} = 45$.) More generally, each central angle of a regular n-gon has measure $\dfrac{360}{n}$, because $\dfrac{360}{n}$ is the measure of the intercepted arc.

Definition 13–4: The **center of a regular polygon** is the center of its circumscribed circle.

Definition 13–5: An angle is a **central angle of a regular polygon** iff its vertex is the center of the polygon and its sides include consecutive vertices of the polygon.

EXAMPLES

1. Find the measure of a central angle of a regular 12-gon.

Solution: By Definitions 13–4 and 13–5, the central angle of a regular polygon is also a central angle of the circumscribed circle. Therefore the measure of the central angle is equal to the measure of its intercepted arc. Now, since our n-gon has 12 congruent sides, the circumscribed circle is divided into 12 congruent arcs, each with a measure $\frac{360}{12} = 30$. Therefore, a central angle of a regular 12-gon has measure 30.

2. How many sides has a regular polygon whose central angle has measure 24?

Solution: From the solution for example 1, we see that $\dfrac{360}{n}$ is the measure of each central angle. Therefore

$$\frac{360}{n} = 24$$

$$n = \frac{360}{24}$$

$$n = 15$$

3. Find the apothem of an equilateral triangle inscribed in a circle of radius 4.

Solution: Since $\triangle AFH$ is equilateral,

$$m\angle HAF = 60.$$

Radius $\overline{CA}$ bisects $\angle HAF$ (see problem 19), making $m\angle CAD = 30$. Thus, $\triangle ADC$ is a 30°–60° right triangle, and $a = \frac{1}{2}AC = 2.$

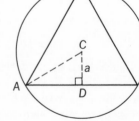

Exercise 13–1

(A)

Find the measure of a central angle of each of the following regular polygons (1 to 6):

1. Equilateral triangle.   2. Square.
3. Hexagon.   4. Octagon.
5. Decagon.   6. Pentagon.

How many sides has a regular polygon whose central angle has measure (7 to 10)?

7. 20   **8.** 40   **9.** 15   **10.** 12

Find the apothem of each of the following regular polygons, if each is inscribed in a circle of radius 1 (11 and 12):

11. Square   **12.** Hexagon.
13. Use compass and straightedge to inscribe a square in a given circle.
14. Use compass and straightedge to inscribe a regular octagon in a given circle.

Find the perimeter of each of the following regular polygons (15 to 18):

15. A square whose apothem is 2.
16. A square inscribed in a circle of radius 2.
17. An equilateral triangle inscribed in a circle of radius 2.
18. An equilateral triangle whose apothem is 2.

19. PROVE: An interior angle of an inscribed regular polygon is bisected by the radius to the vertex of the angle.
20. PROVE: The perpendicular from the center to the side of a regular polygon bisects a central angle.

(B)

21. PROVE: If a circle is divided into five congruent arcs, the chords of these arcs form a regular pentagon.
22. PROVE: If a circle is divided into five congruent arcs, the tangents at the points of division form a regular pentagon.
23. PROVE: The measure of an interior angle of a regular n-gon is $\dfrac{(n-2)180}{n}$.

In problems 24 to 31 use the formula given in problem 23 to find the measure of an interior angle of a regular polygon with the indicated number of sides.

24. 3   **25.** 4   **26.** 5   **27.** 6
28. 8   **29.** 10   **30.** 12   **31.** 15

13–2 THE CIRCUMFERENCE OF A CIRCLE

The circumference of a circle is sometimes described as the *perimeter* of the circle. This is not too bad as a description, since it does indicate the strong analogy between the circumference of a circle and the perimeter of a polygon. However, great difficulty is encountered if one tries to define circumference in the same way we defined perimeter. The definition of perimeter calls for a sum of lengths of segments. Since a circle is not composed of segments, this type of definition would not be satisfactory.

It sometimes seems strange that the circle, a figure with which we are so familiar, can be so troublesome. Nevertheless, the circumference is quite awkward to define, basically because it requires mathematics beyond the scope of this book. We shall simply indicate a general line of attack, and rely upon an "intuitive" definition.

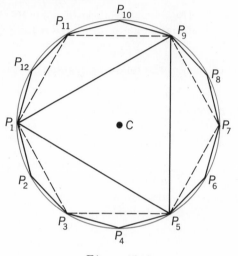

Figure 13–3

Our plan is based on comparing the perimeters of inscribed regular polygons, of increasing number of sides, with the circumference of the circle in which they are inscribed. We begin by considering a regular triangle (i.e., an equilateral triangle), $\triangle P_1 P_5 P_9$, inscribed in circle C (Figure 13–3). Locate the midpoints of the arcs determined by the sides of this triangle, and join consecutive points, as shown, to form $\overline{P_1 P_3}$, $\overline{P_3 P_5}$, $\overline{P_5 P_7}$, $\overline{P_7 P_9}$, $\overline{P_9 P_{11}}$, and $\overline{P_{11} P_1}$, the sides of regular hexagon $P_1 P_3 P_5 P_7 P_9 P_{11}$. Now, by Theorem 7–5:

$$P_1 P_3 + P_3 P_5 > P_1 P_5$$
$$P_5 P_7 + P_7 P_9 > P_5 P_9$$
$$P_9 P_{11} + P_{11} P_1 > P_9 P_1$$

By repeated applications of Axiom O–2 (Addition Axiom), we have:

$$P_1 P_3 + P_3 P_5 + P_5 P_7 + P_7 P_9 + P_9 P_{11} + P_{11} P_1 > P_1 P_5 + P_5 P_7 + P_7 P_9$$

In words, the perimeter of the inscribed regular hexagon is greater than the perimeter of the inscribed regular triangle.

In exactly the same manner, by locating midpoints of arcs and joining them as described above, we obtain a regular inscribed 12-gon,

$$P_1 P_2 P_3 P_4 P_5 P_6 P_7 P_8 P_9 P_{10} P_{11} P_{12}.$$

Repeated applications of Theorem 7–5 and Axiom O–2 show that the perimeter of the 12-gon is greater than the perimeter of the hexagon.

It seems evident that we could continue in this manner indefinitely, forming next a 24-gon, then a 48-gon, a 96-gon, etc. The perimeter of each newly formed inscribed regular n-gon can be shown to be greater than the perimeter of each of the preceding n-gons (Axiom O–2 as applied above, and Axiom O–4). Intuitively then, it seems that the more sides the n-gon has, the more nearly it "fits" the circle—that is, the increasing perimeter seems to differ by smaller and smaller amounts from the circumference of the circle. We describe this mathematically by saying that the perimeter of the n-gons approaches the circumference of the circle as a "limit" as the number of sides, n, increases. This suggests our next definition.

Definition 13–6: The **circumference** of a circle is the limit of the perimeters of the inscribed regular polygons.

We now state a relationship between the circumference and the diameter of a circle that has been known for many centuries.

Theorem 13–1: **The ratio of the circumference to the diameter is the same for all circles.**

We do not include a proof of this theorem, since the mathematics involved, again, is beyond the scope of this book. The theorem tells us that for a circle of radius r, circumference C, and diameter $2r$, the ratio $\dfrac{C}{2r}$ is constant. This constant number is traditionally designated by the Greek letter π (pi). Thus we have the familiar formula:

$$\frac{C}{2r} = \pi \quad \text{or} \quad C = 2\pi r$$

This same formula is sometimes stated as $C = \pi d$, where $d = 2r$ is the diameter of the circle.

Although π is readily defined as the ratio $\dfrac{C}{2r}$, computing its numerical value is quite another matter. Part of the difficulty stems from the fact that π is an irrational number; it cannot be expressed as a common fraction or as an exact decimal. To be sure, $3\frac{1}{7}$, 3.14, and even 3.1416 are commonly used as values for π, but π is not exactly equal to any of these numbers. Archimedes (ca. 225 B.C.) determined that π was between $3\frac{10}{71}$ and $3\frac{1}{7}$. Vieta (ca. 1593) refined this to:

$$3.1415926535 < \pi < 3.1415926537$$

Recently, with the aid of an electronic digital computer, π was computed to over 100,000 decimal places!

It is possible to define the length of a circular arc as a certain limit, in much the same way as we defined the circumference of a circle.

Consider $\overset{\frown}{AB}$ (Figure 13–4), an arc of circle C. Locate points A, P_1, $P_2, \ldots, P_{n-1}$, B on $\overset{\frown}{AB}$ so that, when radii are introduced, the corresponding central angles will have equal measure. There will be n such angles (in Figure 13–4, $n = 5$), and each will have measure $\frac{1}{n}\,(m\overset{\frown}{AB})$. Hence

$$\overset{\frown}{AP_1} \cong \overset{\frown}{P_1P_2} \cong \cdots \cong \overset{\frown}{P_{n-1}B}$$

and

$$\overline{AP_1} \cong \overline{P_1P_2} \cong \cdots \cong \overline{P_{n-1}B}$$

Therefore

$$AP_1 = P_1P_2 = \cdots = P_{n-1}B$$

We continue to increase the number of division points, and use the Triangular Inequality (Theorem 7–5) to show that the sum

$$AP_1 + P_1P_2 + \cdots + P_{n-1}B$$

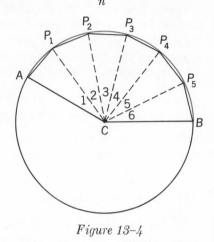

Figure 13–4

increases accordingly. This sum approaches closer and closer to what would seem to be the "length" of $\overset{\frown}{AB}$.

Definition 13–7: The **length of $\overset{\frown}{AB}$** is the limit of $AP_1 + P_1P_2 + \cdots + P_{n-1}B$ as n, the number of chords, increases. (Figure 13–4.)

Intuitively, it would seem that if two arcs have equal radii, and the measure of the first arc is twice the measure of the second arc, then the length of the first should be twice the length of the second. That is, if the measures of the two arcs have the ratio $\frac{2}{1}$, then the lengths should have the same ratio, $\frac{2}{1}$.

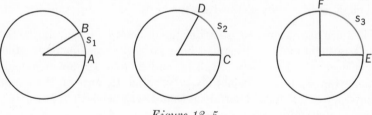

Figure 13–5

In Figure 13–5, s_1, s_2, and s_3 represent the lengths of $\overset{\frown}{AB}$, $\overset{\frown}{CD}$, and $\overset{\frown}{EF}$, respectively, and the circles are congruent. If $m\overset{\frown}{AB} = 30$, $m\overset{\frown}{CD} = 60$, and $m\overset{\frown}{EF} = 90$, it should follow that: $s_2 = 2s_1$; $s_3 = 3s_1$; and $s_3 = \frac{2}{3}s_2$. In terms of ratio:

$$\frac{s_2}{s_1} = \frac{2}{1} \qquad \frac{s_3}{s_1} = \frac{3}{1} \qquad \text{and} \qquad \frac{s_3}{s_2} = \frac{3}{2}$$

The following theorem, presented without proof, states this idea formally.

Theorem 13–2: **If two arcs have equal radii, then their lengths are proportional to their measures.**

In applying Theorem 13–2, it is convenient to consider a circle as an arc with measure 360. This can be somewhat justified by thinking of a circle as an arc with its endpoints coinciding, and as the union of two semicircles, each with measure 180.

EXAMPLES

1. Find (a) the exact, and (b) an approximate, value of the circumference of a circle with a radius of 4 inches.

Solution

(a) The exact value of the circumference is found by using the symbol π, and not a numerical value in its place. Therefore,

$$C = 2\pi r$$
$$C = 2\pi \cdot 4$$
$$C = 8\pi \text{ in.}$$

(b) To obtain an approximate value for the circumference, we must assign a numerical value to π, and since π is an irrational number, any such numerical value must necessarily be approximate. The particular value used is determined by the accuracy required in the problem at hand. Here we will use 3.14 for π.

$$C = 2\pi r$$
$$C \approx 2 \cdot 3.14 \cdot 4$$
$$C \approx 25.12 \text{ in.}$$

2. Find the radius of a circle having a circumference of 16π cm.
Solution: Since we are given $C = 16\pi$, we have:

$$2\pi r = 16\pi$$
$$r = \frac{16\pi}{2\pi}$$
$$r = 8 \text{ cm.}$$

3. If the radius of a circle is 4 in., what is the approximate length of an arc whose measure is 30?
Solution: By Theorem 13–2, the circumference of the circle and the length of the arc have the same ratio as their measures, if we consider the circle as

an arc whose measure is 360. Thus, if C represents the circumference and s the arc length,

$$\frac{s}{C} = \frac{30}{360}$$

$$\frac{s}{C} = \frac{1}{12}$$

$$s = \tfrac{1}{12}C$$

and since $C = 2\pi r \approx 2 \cdot 3.14 \cdot 4$,

$$s \approx \tfrac{1}{12} \cdot 2 \cdot 3.14 \cdot 4$$

$$s \approx \tfrac{1}{3} \cdot 2 \cdot 3.14$$

$$s \approx 2.09 \text{ in.}$$

Exercise 13–2

(A)

In problems 1 to 4, find the *exact* value of the circumference of a circle with the indicated radius.

1. 3 in.   **2.** 5 ft.   **3.** $5a$ **4.** $3b$

In problems 5 to 8, find an approximate value of the circumference of a circle with the indicated radius: (*Note:* Use 3.14 for π for all approximations.)

5. 2.12 in.   **6.** 3.25 cm.   **7.** 1.06 cm.   **8.** 4.21 in.

In problems 9 to 12, find the radius of a circle having the given circumference:

9. 12π cm.   **10.** 8π in.   **11.** $4\pi\sqrt{3}$ ft.   **12.** $6\pi\sqrt{2}$ ft.

In problems 13 to 16, find an approximate value for the radius of a circle having the given circumference:

13. 6.28 ft.   **14.** 9.42 in.   **15.** 7.85 in.   **16.** 10.99 ft.

17. Approximately how many feet does an automobile wheel with 28 in. diameter travel in 10 revolutions?

18. Find the exact circumference of a circle circumscribed about a square with a side 2 in. long.

19. The earth travels in a nearly circular orbit with the sun at the center. If the radius of the path is 93,000,000 miles, approximately how far does the earth travel each year in this orbit? If there are 365 days in a year, what is our approximate speed in miles per hour?

The radius of a circle is 10 in. What is the approximate length of an arc whose measure is (20 to 23):

20. 60   **21.** 45   **22.** 72   **23.** 20

24. If a 60° arc has a length of 2 in., find (a) the radius and (b) the length of the chord of the arc.

25. Given circle B, tangents $\overrightarrow{AD}$ and $\overrightarrow{AF}$, $m\angle A = 60$, and $BD = 5$, find the approximate length of $\overset{\frown}{DF}$.

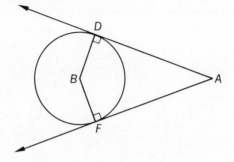

Prob. 25

26. A continuous belt runs around two pulleys of radii 5 in. and 25 in. The centers of the pulleys are 40 in. apart. Find the approximate length of the belt.

27. A track has the dimensions shown. Find the approximate distance around the track in yards.

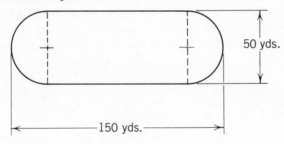

Prob. 27

28. PROVE: The circumferences of two circles have the same ratio as their radii.

29. Find the exact ratio of the circumference of a circle to the perimeter of an inscribed square.

13–3 AREA OF CIRCLE AND SECTOR

In Chapter 9 we introduced the idea of a polygonal region. Here is a similar concept regarding a circle and its interior.

Definition 13–8: A **circular region** is the union of a circle and its interior.

Just as we mean "area of a polygonal region" when we say "area of a polygon," we shall mean "area of a circular region" when we say "area of a circle."

The development of a formula to compute the area of a circle presents the same problems as the development of the formula for its circumference. A proof requires a knowledge of mathematics beyond this text, and what follows is intended only to point the way.

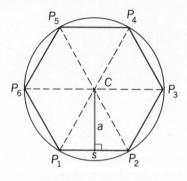

Figure 13–6

Consider a regular n-gon inscribed in circle C (in Figure 13–6, $n = 6$). As shown in the figure, each side of the n-gon forms, with two radii as the sides, an isosceles triangle. It is readily seen that we have n congruent triangles. Now, if s represents the length of a side, and a the apothem, then

$$\text{area}(\triangle P_1 P_2 C) = \tfrac{1}{2}as$$

Since the region $P_1 P_2 P_3 \cdots P_n$ is divided into n congruent triangles, we have:

$$A_p = \text{area of polygon}$$
$$A_p = \tfrac{1}{2}as + \tfrac{1}{2}as + \cdots + \tfrac{1}{2}as \qquad (n \text{ terms})$$
$$\therefore \qquad A_p = n(\tfrac{1}{2}as)$$
$$\text{or} \qquad A_p = \tfrac{1}{2}a \cdot ns$$

Since the n-gon is regular, its perimeter P is equal to ns, therefore:

$$A_p = \tfrac{1}{2}aP$$

Now, as the number of sides increases, the perimeter of the polygon approaches the circumference of the circle, while the apothem approaches the length of the radius. At the same time, it is evident that the area of the polygon differs from the area of the circle by smaller and smaller amounts. This suggests the definition:

Definition 13–9: The **area of a circle** is the limit of the areas of the inscribed regular polygons.

Now let us see how our formula for the area of a regular polygon is affected as the number of sides, n, increases. Let us use A to represent the area of the circle. The following pairs of numbers differ by increasingly smaller amounts as the number of sides of the polygon is increased: A_p and A; apothem a and radius r; perimeter P and circumference C. Hence we say, in the limit, the formula $A_p = \frac{1}{2}aP$ becomes:

$$A = \tfrac{1}{2}rC$$

But $C = 2\pi r$ by Theorem 13-1. Hence we obtain the familiar area formula:

$$A = \pi r^2$$

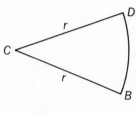

We complete this chapter with a discussion of "sector," a geometric figure closely resembling the shape of a slice of pie (Figure 13-7). A more precise definition follows.

Figure 13-7

Definition 13-10: A **sector** of a circle is a region bounded by two radii and an arc of the circle.

The illustrations in Figure 13-8 are intended to suggest that the area of a sector of a given circle is very directly related to the measure of its boundary arc. In Figure 13-8(a), the circle has been divided into three congruent arcs, each with measure 120. The area of sector CBD appears to be one-third the area of the circle. Notice that $\frac{120}{360} = \frac{1}{3}$.

In Figure 13-8(b), $m\widehat{BD} = 90$. Here the area of sector CBD seems to be one-fourth the area of the circle. Notice that $\frac{90}{360} = \frac{1}{4}$.

In Figure 13-8(c), $\dfrac{m\widehat{BD}}{360} = \dfrac{60}{360} = \dfrac{1}{6}$, and the area of the sector is one-sixth the area of the circle.

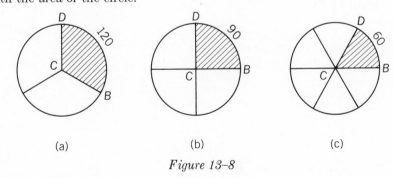

| (a) | (b) | (c) |

Figure 13-8

Theorem 13-3: **The ratio of the area of a sector of circle to the area of the circle is equal to the ratio of the measure of the arc of the sector to 360.**

We close with the now familiar refrain: the mathematics for the proof of this theorem is beyond the scope of this book.

EXAMPLES

1. Find (a) the exact, and (b) an approximate, value for the area of a circle with radius of 4 in. (See example 1, Section 13–2, page 373 for a discussion of "exact" and "approximate" values for π.)

Solution
(a) Since $r = 4$ in., we have

$$A = \pi r^2$$
$$A = 16\pi \text{ sq. in.}$$

(b) Using 3.14 for π, we have

$$A \approx 16 \cdot 3.14$$
$$A \approx 50.24 \text{ sq. in.}$$

2. Find the radius of a circle having an area of 49π sq. cm.
Solution: Since $A = 49\pi$, the formula gives us:

$$\pi r^2 = 49\pi$$
$$r^2 = 49$$
$$r = \sqrt{49} \qquad \text{(We have no need here for the negative square root.)}$$
$$r = 7$$

3. If the radius of a circle is 5 in., find the area of a sector whose arc has measure 30.
Solution: If A represents the area of the circle and S the area of the sector, by Theorem 13–3

$$\frac{S}{A} = \frac{30}{360} = \frac{1}{12}$$
$$S = \tfrac{1}{12}A$$

and since

$$A = \pi r^2 = 25\pi$$

then

$$S = \tfrac{1}{12} \cdot 25\pi$$
$$S = \frac{25\pi}{12} \qquad \text{(exact)}$$
$$S \approx \frac{25 \cdot 3.14}{12}$$
$$S \approx 6.54 \qquad \text{(approximate)}$$

Exercise 13–3

(A)

In problems 1 to 4, find the *exact* value of the area of a circle with the indicated radius:

1. 3 in.   **2.** 5 ft.   **3.** $5a$ **4.** $3b$

In problems 5 to 8, find an *approximate* value for the area of a circle with the indicated radius:

5. 2.12 in.   **6.** 3.25 cm.   **7.** 1.06 cm.   **8.** 4.21 in.

In problems 9 to 12, find the radius of a circle having the given area.

9. 16π sq. in.   **10.** 25π sq. cm.   **11.** 12π sq. cm.   **12.** 27π sq. ft.

13. Find the exact area of a circle circumscribed about a square with a side 2 in. long.

14. Find the exact area of a circle inscribed in an equilateral triangle of side 18 in.

15. Given a square of side $2s$; find the ratio of the area of the inscribed circle to the area of the circumscribed circle.

The radius of a circle is 10 in. What is the approximate area of a sector whose arc has the indicated measure (16 to 19)?

16. 60   **17.** 45   **18.** 72   **19.** 20

20. If a 60° arc has a chord of length 2 in., find the area of the corresponding sector.

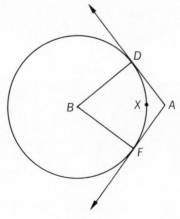

Prob. 21

21. Given circle B, tangents $\overrightarrow{AD}$ and $\overrightarrow{AF}$, $m\angle A = 135$, and $BD = 5$, find area of sector $DBFX$.

In problems 22 and 23, find the approximate area of the shaded portion of each figure.

22.

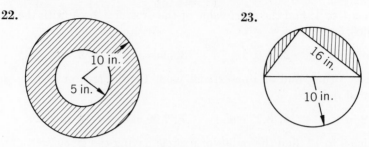

23.

24. PROVE: If d represents the length of a diameter of a circle, the area is given by the formula: $A = \dfrac{\pi d^2}{4}$.

25. PROVE: The areas of two circles have the same ratio as the squares of their radii and also as the squares of their diameters.

26. PROVE: The area of a circle constructed upon the hypotenuse of a right triangle as a diameter is equal to the sum of the areas of the circles constructed upon the legs as diameters.

27. PROVE: The areas of two circles have the same ratio as the squares of their circumferences.

(B)

28. Find the exact radius of a circle whose area is equal to the sum of the areas of two circles with radii 2 and 3, respectively.

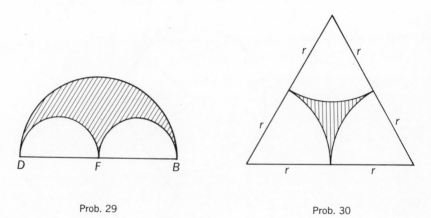

Prob. 29   Prob. 30

29. If $DF = FB$, prove that the area of the shaded portion is equal to the sum of the areas of the smaller semicircles.

30. Find the exact area of the shaded portion:

Chapter 14

ANALYTIC GEOMETRY

INTRODUCTION

The first significant advance in geometry since the time of Euclid occurred only three centuries ago, with the development of a new method, called **coordinate geometry.** This method was discovered by René Descartes (1596–1650), a French mathematician. A thorough study of this method goes well beyond the scope of this text, but enough can be presented so that some insight may be gained as to what it is like, and how it works.

14-1 COORDINATE SYSTEMS IN THE PLANE

You will recall, from Chapter 2, how coordinate systems are constructed on a line. For convenience, we reprint an axiom and two definitions:

Axiom 2–2 (Ruler Axiom): The points of a line can be placed in correspondence with the real numbers in such a way that:

(1) To every point on the line there corresponds exactly one real number, and
(2) To every real number there corresponds exactly one point on the line, and
(3) The distance between two points equals the absolute value of the difference between the corresponding numbers.

Definition 2–9: A correspondence of the sort described by the Ruler Axiom is a **coordinate system on a line.**

Definition 2–10: The number corresponding to a point is the **coordinate** of the point.

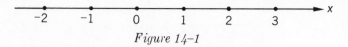

Figure 14–1

These three concepts enabled us to establish a coordinate system on a line. We now propose to establish a coordinate system in a plane. As you will see, the same three concepts help us to construct such a system.

We begin with a line (line x, Figure 14–1) on which we set up a coordinate system. This line is called the x-axis. It is customary to indicate the positive direction along this axis by an arrowhead, as shown.

Next, a second line is introduced (line y, Figure 14–2), perpendicular to the x-axis at the point on the x-axis with coordinate 0. This line is called the y-axis. Starting with the point of intersection corresponding to the number zero, a coordinate system is set up on the y-axis. Again the positive direction is indicated by the arrowhead. The point of intersection is called the *origin;* it has coordinate 0 on both axes.

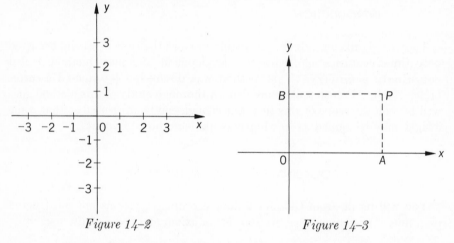

Figure 14–2   *Figure 14–3*

We are now prepared to set up the scheme for describing any point in a plane. Consider P (Figure 14–3). From P drop a perpendicular to the x-axis, and name the foot of the perpendicular, A. Then A is the projection of P on the x-axis (see Definitions 10–4 and 10–5). Let x be the coordinate of A on the x-axis. The number x is called the *x-coordinate* of P. Next, by dropping a perpendicular, we obtain the projection, B, of P, on the y-axis. Let y be the coordinate of B on the y-axis. Then y is called the *y-coordinate* of P. Thus it becomes evident that a pair of numbers must be associated with a point in a plane, rather than just one number as in the case of points on a line. The two numbers are called the *coordinates* of P.

Figure 14–4 illustrates several points in a plane. We can read off the coordinates of these points by following the "dashed" lines to the axes: $P_1(1,3); P_2(3,1); P_3(-1,4); P_4(-4,3); P_5(-4,-3); P_6(4,-2); P_7(-2,4); P_8(\frac{3}{2}, -\pi)$.

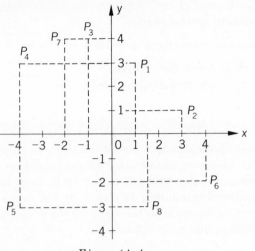

Figure 14–4

Examining this list of points, it appears that the *order* in which the co-ordinates are listed makes a difference. $P_1(1, 3)$ and $P_2(3, 1)$ are different points; $P_6(4, -2)$ and $P_7(-2, 4)$ are different points. Thus the coordinates of a point form an **ordered pair** of real numbers. It is customary to arrange the coordinates of a point with the x-coordinate first, and the y-coordinate second. We shall follow this convention in this text.

The above discussion is summarized as:

Definition 14–1: The **x-coordinate** (x) of a point P is the coordinate of the projection of P on the x-axis. The **y-coordinate** (y) of P is the coordinate of the projection of P on the y-axis. The numbers x and y are the *coordinates* of P. (Notation: $P(x, y)$.)

We have now achieved this much: To each point in a plane we associate an ordered pair of numbers—the coordinates of the point. We raise the question: Given a pair of numbers (a, b), can a point be found such that a and b are its coordinates? If we erect a line perpendicular to the x-axis at $x = a$, and another line perpendicular to the y-axis at $y = b$, the point of intersection of these two lines will be a point with the given coordinates (a, b); in fact, there is exactly one such point (Figure 14–5). Thus there is an ordered pair of numbers associated with every point in a plane, and a point in the plane associated with every ordered pair of numbers. To sum up, we now have a one-to-one correspondence be-tween the set of points in a plane, and

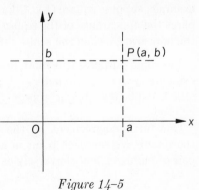

Figure 14–5

the set of ordered pairs of real numbers. Such a correspondence is called a
coordinate system in the plane.

The formal requirements for a coordinate system in a plane are these:

(1) Choice of an x-axis and a y-axis.
(2) Choice of a positive direction on each axis.
(3) Choice of a unit measure of distance on each axis.

Certain features of these requirements are discussed briefly:

(1) For our purposes, the two axes will always be perpendicular lines. It
is not incorrect to use curves or lines, perpendicular or not. In advanced
fields of mathematics other kinds of axes are sometimes used.

(2) The positive direction may be chosen at will. As a matter of convention, the customary choice is to the right on the x-axis, and upward on the
y-axis, a convention that we will follow.

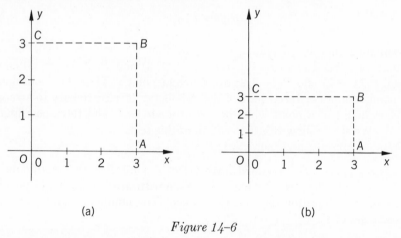

(a)   (b)

Figure 14–6

(3) Most often, the choice of unit of length is the same on each axis; that
is, the same scale is used on both axes. Since these scales are used in geometry
to measure distances, diagrams would be distorted if the scales differed. For
example, suppose square $OABC$ has sides 3 units in length. Figure 14–6 com-
pares the appearance of the square when the scales are the same, at (a), with
the appearance when the scales differ, at (b).

For some purposes it is more practical to use different scales. If we had to
compare *years* with *numbers of people*, points with coordinates such as
(1950, 10,000,000) might appear. Scales such as those in Figure 14–7 could
be used.

One further agreement on the use of language is needed. For a given
coordinate system, each point in a plane corresponds to exactly one ordered
pair of numbers, and conversely each ordered pair of numbers corresponds to

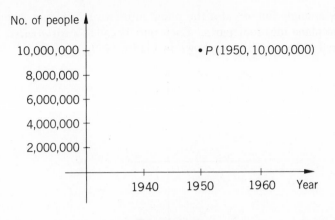

Figure 14-7

exactly one point: hence we shall make such statements as: "point $(1, 3)$" and "point (x, y)"; rather than "the point with coordinates $(1, 3)$" or "the point with coordinates (x, y)."

Figure 14–4 shows dashed lines sketched in perpendicular to the axes, to aid in reading coordinates. This is not always desirable—it is much more convenient to use graph paper. You are advised to have a supply of graph paper during your study of this chapter. With graph paper, axes may be .drawn anywhere on the sheet, depending upon the use to be made of them. When labeling axes, it is not considered necessary to label every single unit indicated on the axes. Figure 14–8 illustrates two useful arrangements. The axes should be labeled x and y; the arrowheads should be included; and enough points should be numbered on the axes so that coordinates may be read off with relative ease.

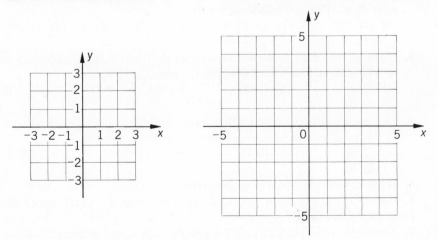

Figure 14-8

Just as a single line divides the plane into two half-planes, the two axes divide the plane into four parts. Each part is called a **quadrant,** and they are referred to by number, as shown in Figure 14–9.

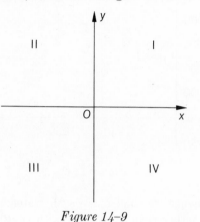

Figure 14–9

Exercise 14–1

(A)

You will find graph paper very helpful for these problems.

1. Draw and label a pair of axes as shown in the text. Plot the following points:
   (a) $(1, 3)$ (b) $(-2, 1)$ (c) $(-3, -5)$ (d) $(0, -6)$
   (e) $(0, 0)$ (f) $(5, 5)$ (g) $(-5, -5)$.   (h) $(5, -5)$
   (i) $(-5, 5)$ (j) $(-6, 0)$

2. Draw a pair of axes. Examine the numbers used for coordinates of points to be plotted, and then decide on the units to be marked on your axes. Plot the following points:
   (a) $(10, 20)$ (b) $(-40, 0)$ (c) $(-30, -30)$ (d) $(0, 20)$
   (e) $(40, -10)$

3. Plot each point on a coordinate system, and then make a conjecture as to where all points with x-coordinate zero may be found.
   (a) $(0, 1)$ (b) $(0, 3)$ (c) $(0, -4)$ (d) $(0, -6)$
   (e) $(0, 5)$

4. Plot each point on a coordinate system, and then make a conjecture as to where all points with y-coordinate zero may be found.
   (a) $(1, 0)$ (b) $(3, 0)$ (c) $(-4, 0)$ (d) $(-6, 0)$
   (e) $(5, 0)$

5. What are the coordinates of the origin?

6. Which pair of points do you think are closer together: $(3, 1)$ and $(3, 2)$; or $(3, 2)$ and $(3, 0)$?

7. Name the quadrant in which each of the following points lies:
   (a) $(6, -2)$ (b) $(-6, 2)$ (c) $(-6, -2)$ (d) $(6, 2)$

8. Given u a positive number and v a negative number, name the quadrant in which each of the following points lies:
   (a) (u, v) (b) $(-u, v)$ (c) $(u, -v)$ (d) $(-u, -v)$
   (e) (v, u) (f) $(-v, -u)$ (g) $(v, -u)$ (h) $(-v, u)$

9. Name the point which is the projection of each of the following points on the x-axis:
   (a) $(2, 4)$ (b) $(2, 5)$ (c) $(-2, 4)$ (d) $(-2, -4)$
   (e) $(4, -2)$

10. Name the point which is the projection of each of the points of problem 9 on the y-axis.

11. The following points are projected on the x-axis. Write them in such an order that their projections will be in order from left to right.

$$A(5, -1), \quad B(-3, 4), \quad C(0, 3), \quad D(-4, 0).$$

12. If the points of problem 11 are projected on the y-axis, arrange them so their projections will be in order from below to above.

13. State the coordinate of the point that is the projection of each of the following points on the x-axis:
    $(3, 0), \quad (3, -2), \quad (3, 6), \quad (3, 1), \quad (3, -6), \quad (3, -5), \quad (3, 3).$

14. State the coordinate of the point that is the projection of each of the following points on the y-axis:
    $(6, 3), \quad (-2, 3), \quad (4, 3), \quad (1, 3), \quad (-6, 3), \quad (-5, 3), \quad (3, 3).$

15. Plot the following pairs of points:
    $(1, 3), \quad (3, 1); \quad (-2, -4), \quad (-4, -2); \quad (3, -1), \quad (-1, 3).$
    Decide whether interchanging the x-coordinate and the y-coordinate of a given ordered pair changes the given point.

16. Will interchanging the coordinates of the origin change the point? State the coordinates of at least two more points such that interchanging the order of the coordinates will not matter.

14–2 SLOPE

For descriptive purposes, we adapt two words, *horizontal* and *vertical*, by narrowing their usual meaning. Given a pair of axes, we say that the x-axis and all lines parallel to it are **horizontal;** the y-axis and all lines parallel to it are **vertical.** (This statement applies to segments and rays as well.) The words vertical and horizontal will be used only as defined here—that is, only with respect to a given coordinate system.

One property of horizontal and vertical lines is readily seen. In Figure 14–10, q_1 is a horizontal line. The projection of every point of q_1 on the y-axis is the point $(0, b)$; hence every point on q_1 has the same y-coordinate, b. By similar reasoning, all points on the vertical line q_2 have the same x-coordinate, a. More generally, all points on horizontal lines have the same y-coordinate, and all points on vertical lines have the same x-coordinate.

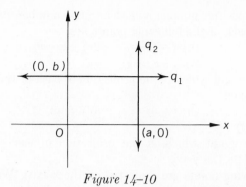

Figure 14–10

Not all lines are vertical or horizontal. Figure 14–11 displays three distinct lines that appear to be situated "differently" from each other with respect to the axes. To make this idea more precise, we introduce the concept of *slope*.

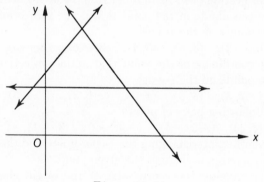

Figure 14–11

To begin, let us look more closely at the length of a horizontal segment, $\overline{AB}$ (Figure 14–12). The projection of $\overline{AB}$ on the x-axis is $\overline{A'B'}$. The figure $A'B'BA$ is a rectangle, hence $AB = A'B'$. Recall that the length of a segment is computed by finding the absolute value of the difference between the coordinates of the endpoints of the segment (Definition 2–10). Thus $A'B' = |x_2 - x_1| = AB$. Suppose we did *not* take the absolute value of the difference between the coordinates. If $x_2 > x_1$, then $(x_2 - x_1)$ represents a positive number. If $x_2 < x_1$, then $(x_2 - x_1)$ represents a negative number. Since the positive direction on the x-axis is to the right, we can tell when the difference between the coordinates is positive or negative by observing which of the two coordinates is to the right of the other.

Reasoning in the same manner, we have $D'C' = |y_2 - y_1| = DC$ (Figure 14–13). On the y-axis, upward is the positive direction. Hence, if $y_2 > y_1$, then $(y_2 - y_1)$ represents a positive number; if $y_2 < y_1$, then $(y_2 - y_1)$ represents a negative number. We can tell when the difference between two y-coordinates is positive or negative by observing which of the two coordinates is above the other.

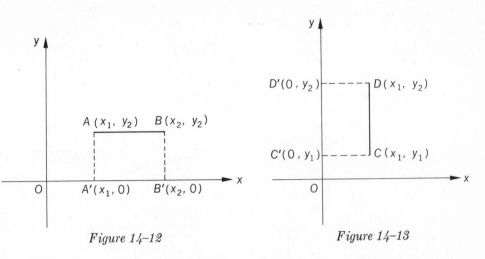

Figure 14–12

Figure 14–13

We are now prepared to define slope, following which we examine related facts.

Definition 14–2: If $\overline{P_1 P_2}$, with endpoints $P_1(x_1, y_1)$ and $P_2(x_2, y_2)$, is nonvertical, then the **slope** of $\overline{P_1 P_2}$ is:

$$m = \frac{y_2 - y_1}{x_2 - x_1}$$

Many basic facts follow directly from this definition:

(1) If a segment is nonvertical, then $x_2 \neq x_1$. Hence the slope formula always determines a number, since the denominator $(x_2 - x_1) \neq 0$.

(2) If a segment is horizontal, then $y_2 = y_1$, and $(y_2 - y_1) = 0$, while the denominator is not zero. Hence the slope of a horizontal segment is 0 [Figure 14–14(c)].

(3) If a segment is vertical, $x_2 = x_1$ and the denominator is zero. The fraction $\dfrac{y_2 - y_1}{0}$ is meaningless, hence a vertical segment has no slope.

(4) If the order of the endpoints is reversed, the slope is not changed. For if $(y_2 - y_1)$ is a positive number, then $(y_1 - y_2)$ is negative. Hence $-(y_2 - y_1) = (y_1 - y_2)$. Similarly, $-(x_2 - x_1) = (x_1 - x_2)$. Therefore:

$$\frac{y_1 - y_2}{x_1 - x_2} = \frac{-(y_2 - y_1)}{-(x_2 - x_1)} = \frac{y_2 - y_1}{x_2 - x_1} = m$$

(5) If a segment rises from left to right, its slope is positive [Figure 14–14(a)]. Since y_2 is above y_1, $(y_2 - y_1) > 0$, and since x_2 is to the right of x_1, $(x_2 - x_1) > 0$. Hence m is the quotient of two positive numbers, and is therefore positive.

(6) If a segment descends from left to right, its slope is negative [Figure 14–14(b)]. Here $(y_2 - y_1) > 0$, but since x_1 is to the right of x_2, $(x_2 - x_1) < 0$. Hence m is the quotient of a positive and a negative number, and is therefore negative.

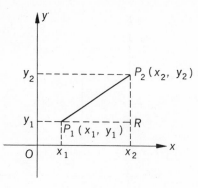

(a)

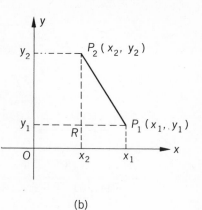

(b)

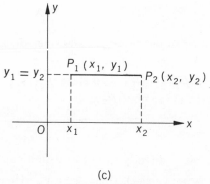

(c)

Figure 14–14

A useful geometric form for the slope, in terms of projections of segments, may be obtained from statements (5) and (6) and by inspection of Figure 14–14. (P_1R is the length of $\overline{P_1R}$, where $\overline{P_1R}$ is the projection of $\overline{P_1P_2}$ on a horizontal line through P_1: similarly $\overline{RP_2}$ is the projection of $\overline{P_1P_2}$ on a vertical line through P_2.) Observe first (Figure 14–14(a)) that $P_1R = (x_2 - x_1)$, and $RP_2 = (y_2 - y_1)$. Then:

$$m = \frac{y_2 - y_1}{x_2 - x_1} = \frac{PR_2}{P_1R}$$

Next note (Figure 14–14(b)) that in the case of a negative slope, $P_1R = (x_1 - x_2)$ and $PR_2 = (y_2 - y_1)$. But $(x_1 - x_2) = -(x_2 - x_1)$. Then:

$$m = \frac{y_2 - y_1}{-(x_2 - x_1)} = -\frac{y_2 - y_1}{x_2 - x_1} = -\frac{RP_2}{P_1R}$$

Thus for $m > 0$, $m = \dfrac{RP_2}{P_1R}$; and for $m < 0$, $m = -\dfrac{RP_2}{P_1R}$.

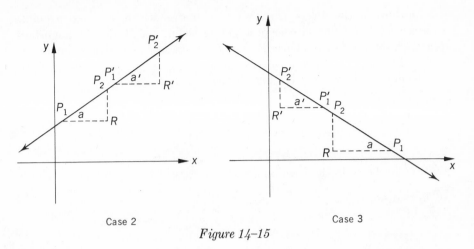

Case 2

Case 3

Figure 14–15

Theorem 14–1: **All segments on a nonvertical line have the same slope.**

Proof: Since the line is nonvertical, it may be horizontal, or it may slope upward from left to right, or it may slope downward from left to right. We consider each of the three possibilities.

Case 1. If the line is horizontal, every segment has slope zero, and the theorem is obvious.

Cases 2 and 3. In both illustrations, $\angle a \cong \angle a'$ (Figure 14–15). $\triangle P_1 R P_2$ and $\triangle P_1' R' P_2'$ are right triangles. Hence $\triangle P_1 R P_2 \sim \triangle P_1' R' P_2'$. Therefore:

$$\frac{RP_2}{R'P_2'} = \frac{P_1R}{P_1'R'}$$

or

$$\frac{RP_2}{P_1R} = \frac{R'P_2'}{P_1'R'} \tag{1}$$

In case 2, the slopes of $\overline{P_1P_2}$ and $\overline{P_1'P_2'}$ are the same as the two fractions of equation (1); hence the slopes are equal. In case 3, the slopes of $\overline{P_1P_2}$ and $\overline{P_1'P_2'}$ are the negatives of the same two fractions, hence the slopes are equal.

Definition 14–3: The **slope** of a nonvertical line is the number which is the slope of every segment of the line.

EXAMPLES

1. Compute the slope of the line through $A(9, 3)$ and $B(-4, -7)$.

Solution: The slope of a line is given by the formula:

$$m = \frac{y_2 - y_1}{x_2 - x_1} = \frac{(-7) - (3)}{(-4) - (9)} = \frac{-10}{-13} = \frac{10}{13}$$

or

$$m = \frac{(3) - (-7)}{(9) - (-4)} = \frac{10}{13}$$

Note that the same slope is obtained no matter which of the two points is chosen as P_2 for the purpose of applying Definition 14–2. The important thing is to be consistent. . Once P_2 is chosen, its coordinates must be chosen first in the numerator *and* in the denominator.

2. Compute the slope of the line through $S(11, 3)$ and $T(11, -4)$.

Solution

$$m = \frac{(-4) - (3)}{(11) - (11)}$$

Since $11 - 11 = 0$, the fraction becomes $\dfrac{-7}{0}$, which is meaningless. Hence $\overleftrightarrow{ST}$ has no slope; it is a vertical line.

Exercise 14–2

1. Find the missing coordinate (indicated by ?) so that the line determined by the two points will be horizontal.
   (a) $(2, 5)$ and $(-2, ?)$.   (b) $(3, -4)$ and $(0, ?)$.
   (c) $(-3, -2)$ and $(3, ?)$.   (d) (x_1, y_1) and $(x_2, ?)$.
2. Find the missing coordinate so that the line determined by the two points will be vertical.
   (a) $(?, 3)$ and $(5, 2)$.   (b) $(-2, -4)$ and $(?, 5)$.
   (c) $(5, a)$ and $(?, b)$.   (d) (x_1, y_1) and $(?, y_2)$.
3. Sketch segments with the following pairs of points as endpoints. State the length of each segment.
   (a) $(3, 0)$ and $(6, 0)$.   (b) $(1, 1)$ and $(9, 1)$.
   (c) $(-3, 0)$ and $(6, 0)$.   (d) $(-2, -5)$ and $(-7, -5)$.
   (e) (x_1, y_1) and (x_2, y_1).
   (f) Examine a, b, c, d, e and decide what is alike for each pair of points.
   (g) Can you state a rule for finding the distance between such pairs of points?
   (h) Does your rule apply to $(2, 6)$ and $(2, -6)$?
4. Sketch segments with the following pairs of points as endpoints. State the length of each segment.
   (a) $(0, 3)$ and $(0, 6)$.   (b) $(1, 1)$ and $(1, 9)$.
   (c) $(0, -3)$ and $(0, 6)$.   (d) $(-5, -2)$ and $(-5, -7)$.
   (e) (x_1, y_1) and (x_1, y_2).
   (f) Examine a, b, c, d, e and decide what is alike for each pair of points.
   (g) Can you state a rule for finding the distance between such pairs of points?
5. From the figures shown opposite, find the coordinates of $A, B, C,$ and D.
6. Determine, from problem 5, the following distances:
   (a) AP_1 (b) AP_2 (c) BP_1 (d) P_2B
   (e) CP_1 (f) P_2C (g) DP_1 (h) P_2D

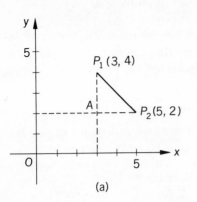

(a)

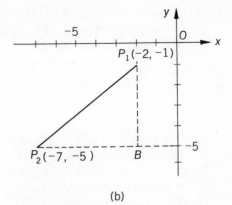

(b)

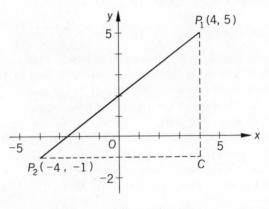

(c)

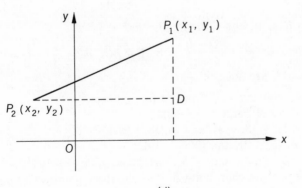

(d)

Prob. 5

7. Compute the slope of $\overline{P_1P_2}$ for each part of problem 5.

8. Compute the slope of $\overline{AP_2}$, $\overline{P_2B}$, and $\overline{P_2C}$, of problem 5.

9. A frequently used definition for slope is: the ratio of the change in the y direction (or vertical direction), to the change in the x direction (or horizontal direction); sometimes indicated as:

$$m = \frac{\text{change in } y}{\text{change in } x}$$

If a road rises 30 ft. vertically over a horizontal distance of 600 ft., what is the slope of the road?

10. A balloon rises 2000 ft. while being blown over the ground a distance of 25,000 ft. Find the slope of the path of the balloon.

11. Given the two points $A(3, 7)$ and $B(-2, 5)$.

   (a) Compute the slope of $\overline{AB}$ using: $\dfrac{(7) - (5)}{(3) - (-2)}$.

   (b) Compute the slope of $\overline{AB}$ using: $\dfrac{(5) - (7)}{(-2) - (3)}$.

12. Compute the slope of the segment whose endpoints are:

   (a) $(3, 1)$ and $(0, 0)$.   (b) $(2, 5)$ and $(4, -6)$.

   (c) $(0, 0)$ and $(1, -4)$.   (d) $(\frac{2}{3}, \frac{1}{2})$ and $(\frac{5}{6}, \frac{3}{8})$.

13. Compute the slope of the segment whose endpoints are:

   (a) $(0, 0)$ and $(-2, -3)$.   (b) $(0, 0)$ and $(2, 3)$.

   (c) (a, b) and (c, d).   (d) (x_1, y_1) and $(3, -2)$.

   (e) (r, s) and (r, t).   (f) (r, s) and (t, r).

14. Find the missing coordinate. (Hint: Substitute in the slope formula.)

   (a) $(2, 5)$, $(6, ?)$, $m = 1$.   (b) $(3, 2)$, $(?, 6)$, $m = \frac{2}{3}$.

Slope may be used to determine collinearity of three points. Three points (A, B, and C) are collinear iff the slope of $\overline{AB}$ is equal to the slope of $\overline{BC}$ ($\overline{AB}$ and $\overline{BC}$ nonvertical).

EXAMPLE

Are $A(1, 0)$, $B(2, 3)$, and $C(3, 4)$ collinear?

Solution: For $\overline{AB}$: $m = \dfrac{3 - 0}{2 - 1} = 3$. For $\overline{BC}$: $m = \dfrac{4 - 3}{3 - 2} = 1$. $3 \neq 1$.

Hence A, B, and C are not collinear.

15. Test the following sets of points for collinearity:

   (a) $(1, 1)$, $(2, 2)$, and $(-5, -5)$.

   (b) $(-1, 1)$, $(-3, -3)$, and $(5, 13)$.

   (c) $(2, 4)$, $(6, -2)$, and $(306, -197)$.

   (d) $(0, -5)$, $(2, 3)$, and $(-5, -31)$.

16. Find the missing coordinate so that the three points shall be collinear.

   (a) $(2, 0)$, $(7, 1)$, and $(-3, ?)$.

   (b) $(0, \frac{3}{2})$, $(5, 4)$ and $(?, -\frac{1}{2})$.

17. Determine the slope of the segment joining:
    (a) $(0, a)$ and $(a, 0)$ (b) $(0, b)$ and $(2b, -2b)$.
    (c) $(r, r + s)$ and $(s, r - s)$.
18. The vertices of a triangle are $R(-2, 3)$, $S(5, -4)$, and $T(1, 8)$. Find the slope of each side.
19. The vertices of a quadrilateral are $A(0, 0)$, $B(8, 0)$, $C(10, 4)$, and $D(2, 4)$. Find the slope of each side. Can you tell if this is a particular type of quadrilateral?
20. A quadrilateral has vertices $A(0, 0)$, $B(a, 0)$, $C(c + a, d)$, and $D(c, d)$. Find the slope of each side. Can you tell if this is a particular type of quadrilateral?

14–3 PARALLEL AND PERPENDICULAR LINES

You will recall that a considerable amount of study was devoted to the concepts of parallelism and perpendicularity of lines. We shall see how co-ordinate geometry techniques can be used to deal with these concepts.

We consider first parallelism of two nonvertical lines.

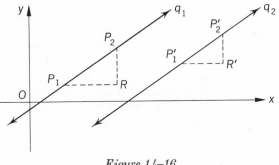

Figure 14–16

(1) If two nonvertical lines are parallel, their slopes are equal. It is simple to show that $\triangle P_1 R P_2 \sim \triangle P_1' R' P_2'$ (Figure 14–16). Therefore:

$$\frac{RP_2}{R'P_2'} = \frac{P_1 R}{P_1' R'}$$

or

$$\frac{RP_2}{P_1 R} = \frac{R'P_2'}{P_1' R'}$$

and the slopes are equal.

(2) If two distinct nonvertical lines intersect, then their slopes are not equal. Let the two lines intersect at $P_1(x_1, y_1)$. Since the lines are distinct, $P_2(x_2, y_2)$ and $P_2'(x_2, y_3)$ are distinct points, and so $y_2 \neq y_3$. Let m_1 denote

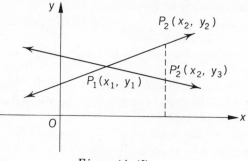

Figure 14–17

the slope of $\overline{P_1P_2}$ and m_2 the slope of $\overline{P_1P_2'}$. Then

$$m_1 = \frac{y_2 - y_1}{x_2 - x_1} \qquad m_2 = \frac{y_3 - y_1}{x_2 - x_1}$$

Since the denominators of these two fractions are the same, but the numerators are different, the two fractions cannot be equal. Hence $m_1 \neq m_2$. We combine statements (1) and (2) above into the following theorem.

Theorem 14–2: **Two nonvertical lines are parallel iff they have the same slope.**

Next we consider perpendicularity of nonvertical lines.

(1) Let q_1 and q_2 intersect at P, q_1 and q_2 nonvertical, and $q_1 \perp q_2$ (Figure 14–18). As in the figure, choose any point S on q_2, above and to the left of P. Through P introduce a line parallel to the x-axis. Complete right $\triangle SRP$ by introducing $\overline{SR}$ so that $\overline{SR} \perp \overleftrightarrow{RP}$. Next, introduce S' on q_1, above and to the right of P, so that $PS' = PS$, and complete right $\triangle S'R'P$ by dropping a perpendicular from S' to $\overleftrightarrow{RP}$. It is easy to prove that $\triangle SRP \cong \triangle PR'S'$. Then $SR = PR'$, and $RP = R'S'$. By the Division

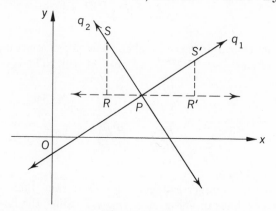

Figure 14–18

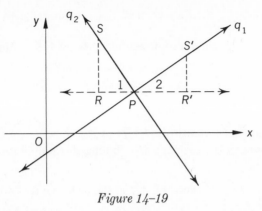

Figure 14–19

Axiom (E–7), $\dfrac{SR}{RP} = \dfrac{PR'}{R'S'}$. But the slope of q_1 is $m_1 = \dfrac{R'S'}{PR'}$; and the slope

of q_2 is $m_2 = -\dfrac{SR}{RP}$. Observing that $\dfrac{PR'}{R'S'}$ is the reciprocal of $\dfrac{R'S'}{PR'}$, we have

$\dfrac{PR'}{R'S'} = \dfrac{1}{m_1}$. But $\dfrac{PR'}{R'S'} = \dfrac{SR}{RP} = -m_2$. Hence, $-m_2 = \dfrac{1}{m_1}$ or $m_2 = -\dfrac{1}{m_1}$.

In words, the slope of each of two perpendicular lines is the **negative reciprocal** of the slope of the other.

(2) As in (1), let q_1 and q_2 intersect at P, q_1 and q_2 nonvertical, and

$m_2 = -\dfrac{1}{m_1}$. We shall show that $q_1 \perp q_2$ (Figure 14–19). As before, complete right $\triangle SRP$. Next, introduce R' on $\overrightarrow{RP}$ so that $PR' = RS$. Complete right $\triangle PR'S'$ by introducing $\overline{R'S} \perp \overrightarrow{RP}$. Now

$$m_2 = -\frac{SR}{RP} \qquad \text{or} \qquad -m_2 = \frac{SR}{RP}$$

Also

$$m_1 = \frac{S'R'}{PR'} \qquad \text{or} \qquad \frac{1}{m_1} = \frac{PR'}{S'R'}$$

Since $-m_2 = \dfrac{1}{m_1}$, we have $\dfrac{SR}{RP} = \dfrac{PR'}{S'R'}$. Since $SR = PR'$, it follows that

$\dfrac{PR'}{RP} = \dfrac{PR'}{S'R'}$, or $RP = S'R'$, and $\overline{RP} \cong \overline{S'R'}$. Thus we can prove that

$\triangle SRP \cong \triangle PR'S'$. It can then readily be shown that $\angle 1$ and $\angle 2$ are complementary, and therefore $q_2 \perp q_1$. This discussion is summarized by

Theorem 14–3: Two nonvertical lines are perpendicular iff their slopes are negative reciprocals of each other.

To complete this section, we consider the trivial cases to which Theorems 14–2 and 14–3 do not apply: if one of the two given lines is vertical.

(1) If q_1 is vertical, then all vertical lines are parallel to q_1. No slopes exist.

(2) If q_1 is vertical, then all horizontal lines are perpendicular to q_1, and have slope zero.

EXAMPLES

$A(2, 5)$, $B(0, 6)$, and $C(3, 8)$ are vertices of a triangle.

1. Find the slope of the altitude $(\overline{AH})$ to $\overline{BC}$.
2. Find the slope of the segment $\overline{MN}$ joining the midpoints of $\overline{AC}$ and $\overline{AB}$.

Solutions

1. Since $\overline{AH} \perp \overline{BC}$, the slope of $\overline{AH}$ is the negative reciprocal of the slope of $\overline{BC}$. For $\overline{BC}$:

$$m = \frac{8 - 6}{3 - 0} = \frac{2}{3}$$

Hence for $\overline{AH}$: $m = -\frac{3}{2}$.

2. The segment joining the midpoints of a triangle is parallel to the third side. Hence $\overline{MN} \parallel \overline{BC}$, and the slope of $\overline{MN}$ is equal to the slope of $\overline{BC}$. Thus the slope of $\overline{MN}$ is $\frac{2}{3}$.

Exercise 14–3

1. Show that the points $A(-1, 5)$, $B(5, 1)$, $C(6, -2)$, and $D(0, 2)$ determine segments forming $\square ABCD$. (*Hint:* Use definition of parallelogram, Def. 8–15.)

Without plotting, determine whether the four given points may be vertices of a parallelogram (2 and 3).

2. $A(-5, -2)$, $B(-4, 2)$, $C(4, 6)$, $D(3, 1)$.
3. $R(-2, -2)$, $S(4, 2)$, $T(9, 1)$, $V(3, -3)$.
4. Lines q_1, q_2, q_3, q_4 have slopes $\frac{2}{5}$, -5, $-2\frac{1}{2}$, and $\frac{1}{5}$, respectively. Which pairs of lines are perpendicular?
5. The vertices of a triangle are $P(16, 0)$, $O(0, 0)$, and $R(9, 2)$. Find the slope of each side. Find the slope of each altitude.
6. Find the slope of each side and each altitude of $\triangle ABC$ if $A(-3, 0)$, $B(-5, -4)$, and $C(-7, 0)$ are its vertices.
7. Given $A(-3, 0)$, $B(3, -6)$, and $C(5, 8)$, show that $\triangle ABC$ is a right triangle.
8. Given $A(-2, 2)$, $B(2, -2)$, $C(4, 2)$, and $D(2, 4)$, show that the diagonals of $ABCD$ are perpendicular.
9. Four points taken in pairs determine six segments. Which pairs of segments determined by the following four points are parallel? $R(3, 6)$, $S(5, 9)$, $T(8, 2)$, $P(6, -1)$.
10. The line through $(4, k - 1)$ and $(6, 5)$ is parallel to the line through $(2, k)$ and $(3, -6)$. Find the value of k.

11. Given $A(1, 2)$, $B(3, -4)$, and $C(k, 5)$, find a value of k so that $\overline{AB} \perp \overline{BC}$.

12. Given $P_1(1, 2)$, $P_2(5, -6)$, and $P_3(k, k)$, find the value of k so that $\angle P_1P_2P_3$ is a right angle.

13. Given $R(-5, 4)$, $S(3, 5)$, $T(7, -2)$, and $P(-1, -3)$, show that $RSTP$ is a parallelogram with perpendicular diagonals.

14–4 THE DISTANCE FORMULA

Suppose we have a coordinate system established in a plane. Then, if we know two pairs of coordinates, two points in the plane are determined: $P_1(x_1, y_1)$ and $P_2(x_2, y_2)$. Therefore, by Axiom 2–2 and Definition 2–10, the distance P_1P_2 between P_1 and P_2 is determined. We shall now derive a formula that provides a way to calculate this distance in terms of the coordinates of the points (Figure 14–20).

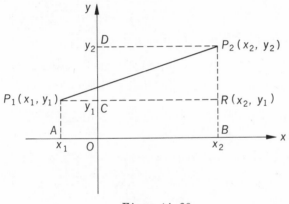

Figure 14–20

Let A and B be the projections on the x-axis of P_1 and P_2, respectively. Let C and D be their projections on the y-axis. Let R be the point where $\overleftrightarrow{P_1C}$ intersects $\overleftrightarrow{P_2B}$. Since $\triangle P_1RP_2$ is a right triangle, by the Pythagorean Theorem, $(P_1R)^2 + (RP_2)^2 = (P_1P_2)^2$. Now $ABRP_1$ is a rectangle, hence $\overline{AB} \cong \overline{P_1R}$ and $AB = P_1R$. Again, CRP_2D is a rectangle, hence $\overline{RP_2} \cong \overline{CD}$ and $RP_2 = CD$. Hence:

$$(AB)^2 + (CD)^2 = (P_1P_2)^2$$

By Definition 2–10, $AB = |x_2 - x_1|$ and $CD = |y_2 - y_1|$. Hence:

$$(P_1P_2)^2 = |x_2 - x_1|^2 + |y_2 - y_1|^2$$

Since the square of a number is equal to the square of its absolute value (see Exercise 14–4, problem 14), we may write:

$$(P_1P_2)^2 = (x_2 - x_1)^2 + (y_2 - y_1)^2$$

Since P_1P_2 is either positive or zero, we have:

$$P_1P_2 = \sqrt{(x_2 - x_1)^2 + (y_2 - y_1)^2}$$

We repeat this result as the following theorem.

Theorem 14–4 (The Distance Formula): The distance between two points with coordinates (x_1, y_1) and (x_2, y_2), respectively, is given by

$$\sqrt{(x_2 - x_1)^2 + (y_2 - y_1)^2}$$

EXAMPLES

1. Show that the triangle whose vertices are $A(-1, 0)$, $B(7, -8)$, and $C(-2, -9)$ is isosceles.

Solution: A triangle is isosceles if the lengths of two of its sides are equal. We compute the lengths, and examine them.

$$AB = \sqrt{(7 - (-1))^2 + (-8 - 0)^2} = \sqrt{64 + 64} = \sqrt{128} = 8\sqrt{2}$$

$$BC = \sqrt{(-2 - 7)^2 + (-9 - (-8))^2} = \sqrt{81 + 1} = \sqrt{82}$$

$$CA = \sqrt{(-2 - (-1))^2 + (-9 - 0)^2} = \sqrt{1 + 81} = \sqrt{82}$$

Since $\sqrt{82} = \sqrt{82}$, $BC = CA$, and the triangle is isosceles.

2. Find a point on the y-axis that is equidistant from $D(-2, -3)$ and $E(6, 1)$.

Solution: Every point on the y-axis has x-coordinate zero. Let $P(0, b)$ be the point required. Then $DP = PE$.

$$DP = \sqrt{(-2 - 0)^2 + (-3 - b)^2} = \sqrt{4 + 9 + 6b + b^2}$$

$$PG = \sqrt{(6 - 0)^2 + (1 - b)^2} = \sqrt{36 + 1 - 2b + b^2}$$

Since $DP = PE$,

$$\sqrt{4 + 9 + 6b + b^2} = \sqrt{36 + 1 - 2b + b^2}$$

$$b^2 + 6b + 13 = b^2 - 2b + 37$$

$$8b = 24$$

$$b = 3$$

Hence the point equidistant from D and E is the point $P(0, 3)$.

Exercise 14–4

1. Use the Distance Formula (Thm. 14–4) to find the distance between:
   (a) $(0, 0)$ and $(3, 4)$.   (b) $(0, 0)$ and $(3, -4)$.
   (c) $(1, 2)$ and $(6, 14)$.   (d) $(8, 11)$ and $(15, 35)$.
   (e) $(3, 8)$ and $(-5, -7)$.   (f) $(-2, 3)$ and $(-1, 4)$.
   (g) $(10, 1)$ and $(40, 81)$.   (h) $(-6, 3)$ and $(4, -2)$.

2. Find the perimeter of the triangle having vertices $A(5, 7)$, $B(1, 10)$, and $C(-3, -8)$.

3. Show that the triangle with vertices $P(0, 0)$, $Q(3, 4)$, and $R(-1, 1)$ is an isosceles triangle.

4. The vertices of $ABCD$ are $A(-1, -1)$, $B(1, 0)$, $C(2, 2)$, and $D(0, 1)$. Show that $ABCD$ is equilateral.

5. The vertices of $MNPQ$ are $M(-3, -2)$, $N(0, -3)$, $P(1, 0)$, and $Q(-2, 1)$. Show that:
   (a) $MNPQ$ is equilateral.   (b) $MP = NQ$.

6. Rectangle $ABCD$ has vertices: $A(0, 0)$, $B(a, 0)$, and $D(0, b)$.
   (a) What are the coordinates of C?
   (b) Show that $AC = BD$.

7. Without using slopes, show that $\triangle GHK$ is a right triangle. $G(1, 1)$, $H(3, 0)$, and $K(4, 7)$. (*Hint:* Use the converse of the Pythagorean Theorem.)

8. Without using slopes, show that $\triangle ABC$ is a right triangle. $A(-3, 0)$, $B(3, -6)$, and $C(5, 8)$ (see problem 7).

9. Prove, without plotting, that $B(1, 4)$ is *between* $A(-1, 6)$ and $C(7, -2)$.

10. One vertex of a triangle is at the origin, the other two are $(1, 12)$ and $(11, -1)$. Show that the triangle *is*, or *is not*, a right triangle.

11. A quadrilateral has vertices $A(-1, 3)$, $B(5, 7)$, $C(9, 1)$, and $D(3, -3)$. Prove that the quadrilateral is, or is not, a rectangle.

12. Find a point on the x-axis that is equidistant from $A(-4, 6)$ and $B(14, -2)$.

13. Find the point on the y-axis that is equidistant from $P(-4, 6)$ and $Q(14, -2)$.

14. PROVE: If x denotes any number, then $x^2 = |x|^2$. (*Hint:* See Def. 2–7.)

14–5 THE MIDPOINT FORMULA

Consider a segment $\overline{AC}$ on an x-axis with midpoint B (Figure 14–21). By the definition of midpoint of a segment, $AB = BC$. If the methods of coordinate geometry are to be applied to the problems of geometry, we shall need to have some way of expressing the coordinates of the midpoint of a segment in terms of the coordinates of the endpoints.

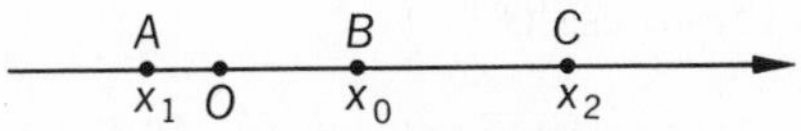

Figure 14–21

In the case illustrated by Figure 14–21, C is to the right of B, and B is to the right of A ($x_1 < x_0 < x_2$). Hence $AB = (x_0 - x_1)$ and $BC = (x_2 - x_0)$.

Since $AB = BC$,

$$x_0 - x_1 = x_2 - x_0$$

$$2x_0 = x_1 + x_2$$

$$x_0 = \frac{x_1 + x_2}{2}$$

In the same manner, if the two points are on a y-axis, we obtain:

$$y_0 = \frac{y_1 + y_2}{2}$$

We use these formulas to derive midpoint formulas for a segment that is neither horizontal nor vertical.

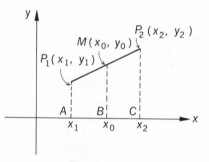

Figure 14–22

Let M be the midpoint of $\overline{P_1P_2}$, with projections A, B, and C on the x-axis as shown (Figure 14–22). Now $\overline{P_1A} \parallel \overline{MB} \parallel \overline{P_2C}$ (why?). Furthermore, $\overline{P_1M} \cong \overline{MP_2}$. Hence, by Theorem 8–22, $\overline{AB} \cong \overline{BC}$ and $AB = BC$, or B is the midpoint of $\overline{AC}$. Now $\overleftrightarrow{MB}$ is a vertical line, hence the x-coordinate of every point on it is the same, namely x_0. But, by our derivation for a horizontal segment, $x_0 = \frac{x_1 + x_2}{2}$. Therefore the x-coordinate of M is also $\frac{x_1 + x_2}{2}$.

If we take projections of P_1, M, and P_2, on the y-axis, and follow the same line of reasoning, we find that the y-coordinate of M is $\frac{y_1 + y_2}{2}$. The following theorem sums up these results.

Theorem 14–5 (The Midpoint Formula): If $P_1(x_1, y_1)$ and $P_2(x_2, y_2)$ are two points, then the midpoint of $\overline{P_1P_2}$ is the point

$$M\left(\frac{x_1 + x_2}{2}, \frac{y_1 + y_2}{2}\right).$$

This result is sometimes remembered more readily by thinking of the midpoint coordinates as the "**average**" of the endpoint coordinates. That is, add the x-coordinates, divide by **2**; add the y-coordinates, and divide by 2.

EXAMPLE

The vertices of a triangle are $D(2, 3)$, $E(12, 4)$, and $F(6, 8)$. Find the length of the median to $\overline{EF}$.

Solution: The median of a triangle is the segment from a vertex of the triangle to the midpoint of the opposite side. Hence we require the coordinates of the midpoint of $\overline{EF}$. Let $X(x_0, y_0)$ be the midpoint of $\overline{EF}$. Then

$$x_0 = \frac{12 + 6}{2} = 9, \text{ and } y_0 = \frac{8 + 4}{2} = 6. \quad \text{Hence the midpoint of } \overline{EF} \text{ is}$$

$X(9, 6)$. By the Distance Formula:

$$DX = \sqrt{(9 - 2)^2 + (6 - 3)^2} = \sqrt{49 + 9} = \sqrt{58}$$

Exercise 14–5

Compute the coordinates of the midpoints of the segments whose endpoints are (1 to 10):

1. $(0, 0)$, $(12, 0)$.   **2.** $(-5, 0)$, $(0, 0)$.   **3.** $(2, 0)$, $(8, 0)$.

4. $(5, 5)$, $(-5, -5)$.   **5.** $(6, 8)$, $(12, 10)$.   **6.** $(-2, -6)$, $(-9, 3)$.

7. $(\frac{1}{2}, \frac{1}{8})$, $(\frac{1}{5}, \frac{1}{3})$.   **8.** $(0, 0)$, $(96, 96)$.   **9.** $(a, 0)$, (b, c).

10. $\left(\dfrac{a}{2}, b\right)$, $(a, 0)$.

11. One endpoint of a segment is $A(3, 4)$ and the midpoint is $M(5, -5)$. Find the coordinates of the other endpoint. (Hint: Use the midpoint formulas.)

12. Find the coordinates of a point equidistant from $R(14, 12)$ and $T(-24, -40)$.

13. Two segments bisect each other if the midpoint of the first segment is also the midpoint of the second segment. Given $A(3, 5)$, $B(7, 1)$, $C(-6, 2)$, and $D(16, 4)$, show that $\overline{AB}$ and $\overline{CD}$ bisect each other.

14. Given $A(12, 4)$ and $B(4, -8)$, find the coordinates of a point $\frac{1}{4}$ of the distance from A to B.

15. Given $A(2, 1)$, $B(7, 4)$, $C(4, 9)$, and $D(-1, 6)$, the vertices of a quadrilateral, show that the diagonals of this quadrilateral are congruent, bisect each other, and are perpendicular.

16. Given $A(3, -2)$, $B(-3, 4)$, $C(1, 8)$, and $D(7, 4)$, the vertices of a quadrilateral, show that the quadrilateral formed by joining the midpoints of each side is a parallelogram.

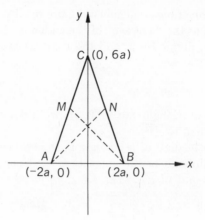

Prob. 17

17. Using coordinate methods, show that the two medians, $\overline{AN}$ and $\overline{BM}$, are perpendicular.

18. The vertices of a triangle are $A(5, -1)$, $B(1, 5)$, and $C(-3, 1)$. Find the lengths of its medians.

14–6 PROOFS BY COORDINATE METHODS

We now put coordinate systems to work proving theorems and solving problems. The emphasis here is chiefly on the methods used in proving, rather than the content of, the theorems. There are no hard and fast rules as to how to solve a problem by coordinate methods, but, as always, practice and experience help to develop skill.

The first step in applying coordinate methods is to introduce a coordinate system, and thus furnish coordinates for points. A guiding principle for the placement of a set of axes in a problem is to obtain the greatest simplification of algebra that we can. The following two examples should help you to become familiar with the approach.

EXAMPLES

1. *A Triangle.* Figure 14–23(a) shows $\triangle ABC$ in a plane. The position of the axes is such that no algebraic simplifications are evident. The six coordinates involved are all different. This choice is least desirable.

Next consider Figure 14–23(b). The axes are so situated that $\overline{AB}$ is parallel to the x-axis. Hence the y-coordinate of B is the same as that of A. This is a small improvement.

Much more advantage can be gained by placing the axes so that $\overline{AB}$ is on the x-axis, and A coincides with the origin O (Figure 14–23(c)). The coordinates of the three vertices now involve zero and only three other numbers. In a given problem, the choice illustrated by Figure 14–23(c) would be most desirable.

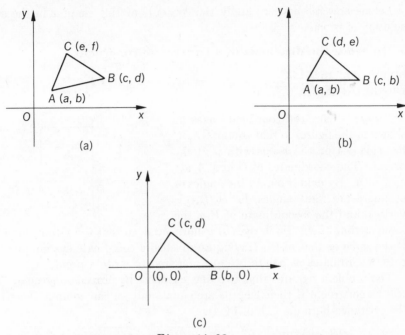

Figure 14-23

2. *A Parallelogram.* Since it is usually desirable to place the origin at one point of a figure, and the x-axis to include a segment, if possible, we nearly always place the axes for a parallelogram problem as shown in Figure 14-24(a). We may also avail ourselves of any properties of the given figure that are *defined.* For example, by definition the opposite sides of a parallelogram are parallel. Then $\overline{CB}$ is parallel to the x-axis, and the y-coordinate of C is the same as the y-coordinate of B. Figure 14-24(b) shows the corresponding coordinates.

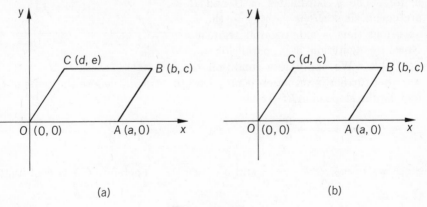

Figure 14-24

Let us now see how we apply the concepts of this chapter in the actual solution of problems.

1. To prove the diagonals of a square are congruent.

GIVEN: Square $OABC$.
PROVE: $\overline{OB} \cong \overline{CA}$.

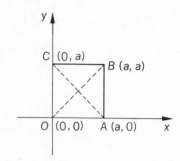

Proof: Place the coordinate axes as shown in the figure, so that square $OABC$ has side $\overline{OA}$ on the x-axis with O at the origin. The coordinates of O and A are as shown. By definition, all the angles of a square are right angles, hence $\overline{BA}$ is vertical and the x-coordinate of B is the same as that of A. Similarly, $\overline{CB}$ is horizontal, so that the y-coordinate of B is the same as that of C. Having established a coordinate system, and indicated coordinates of points, we are prepared to write a proof.

The problem requires that two line segments be proved congruent. They will be congruent if their lengths are equal, and we can compute lengths by the Distance Formula (Thm. 14-4).

$$OB = \sqrt{(a - 0)^2 + (a - 0)^2} = \sqrt{a^2 + a^2} = \sqrt{2a^2}$$
$$CA = \sqrt{(0 - a)^2 + (a - 0)^2} = \sqrt{a^2 + a^2} = \sqrt{2a^2}$$

Hence $OB = CA$ and $\overline{OB} \cong \overline{CA}$. The problem is completed.

2. To prove that if the diagonals of a parallelogram are congruent, the parallelogram is a rectangle.

GIVEN: $\Box OABC$; $\overline{OB} \cong \overline{CA}$.
PROVE: $OABC$ is a rectangle.

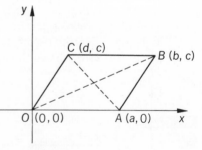

Proof: Choose axes as shown in the figure. The y-coordinates of C and B are equal, since $\overline{CB}$ is parallel to the x-axis, and thus is a horizontal segment. Now, by definition of a parallelogram, $\overline{OC} \parallel \overline{AB}$. We apply this condition to see what further information it may lead to. Let m_1 denote the slope of $\overline{OC}$ and m_2 the slope of $\overline{AB}$. Then

$$m_1 = \frac{c - 0}{d - 0} = \frac{c}{d} \quad \text{and} \quad m_2 = \frac{c - 0}{b - a} = \frac{c}{b - a}$$

Since $m_1 = m_2$, $\dfrac{c}{d} = \dfrac{c}{b - a}$ and $b - a = d$. Therefore C has coordinates $(b - a, c)$.

Now we use the hypothesis, $\overline{OB} \cong \overline{CA}$, or $OB = CA$.

$OB = \sqrt{(b-0)^2 + (c-0)^2}$ 	 $CA = \sqrt{(d-a)^2 + (c-0)^2}$

$OB = \sqrt{b^2 + c^2}$ 	 $CA = \sqrt{(b-a-a)^2 + c^2}$

$CA = \sqrt{(b-2a)^2 + c^2}$

$CA = \sqrt{b^2 - 4ab + 4a^2 + c^2}$

Since $OB = CA$:

$$\sqrt{b^2 + c^2} = \sqrt{b^2 - 4ab + 4a^2 + c^2}$$

Squaring

$$b^2 + c^2 = b^2 - 4ab + 4a^2 + c^2$$

$$0 = 4a^2 - 4ab$$

$$4ab = 4a^2$$

Dividing by $4a$ $(a > 0)$:

$$b = a$$

This means that the x-coordinate of B is the same as the x-coordinate of A, hence $\overline{AB}$ is vertical. Then $\angle OAB$ is a right angle. Since nonconsecutive angles of a parallelogram are congruent, it is readily seen that all the angles of $OABC$ are right angles, and so $OABC$ is a rectangle (Definition 8–17).

Exercise 14–6

(A)

Prove the following theorems by coordinate methods.

1. The midpoint of the hypotenuse of a right triangle is equidistant from the vertices.
2. The diagonals of a rectangle have equal lengths.
3. The segment joining the midpoints of the nonparallel sides of a trapezoid is parallel to the bases.
4. The segments joining the midpoints of successive sides of a quadrilateral form a parallelogram.
5. Every point on the perpendicular bisector of a segment is equidistant from the endpoints of the segment.
6. The diagonals of a rhombus are perpendicular to each other.
7. The segment joining the midpoints of two sides of a triangle is parallel to the third side, and its length is half the length of the base.
8. The line segments joining the midpoints of the nonconsecutive sides of any quadrilateral bisect each other.
9. If two medians of a triangle are congruent, the triangle is isosceles.
10. The sum of the squares of the lengths of the sides of a parallelogram is equal to the sum of the squares of the lengths of the diagonals.

14-7 **THE GRAPH OF A CONDITION**

The term *graph* is used to mean a figure in a plane; that is, a set of points. Angles, quadrilaterals, half-planes, and in fact any of the figures used heretofore, are examples of graphs. Graphs may be described by stating a condition which is satisfied by all the points of the figure, and by no other points. In particular, the use of a coordinate system often enables us to describe the condition conveniently in terms of the coordinates of the points. Here are some examples (see Figure 14-25).

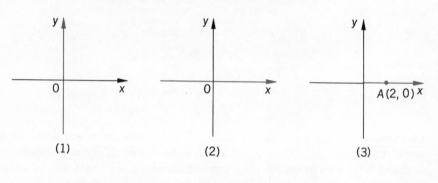

    (1)   (2)   (3)

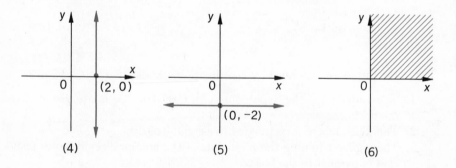

    (4)   (5)   (6)

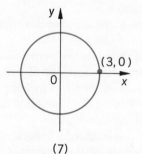

(7)

Figure 14-25

Condition	*Graph*
1. The x-coordinate of every point is zero ($x = 0$).	1. The y-axis.
2. The y-coordinate of every point is zero ($y = 0$).	2. The x-axis.
3. The y-coordinate is zero, the x-coordinate is greater than or equal to zero ($y = 0$, $x \geq 0$).	3. $\overrightarrow{OA}$, where A is the point with coordinates $(2, 0)$.
4. $x = 2$.	4. The vertical line through $(2, 0)$.
5. $y = -2$.	5. The horizontal line through $(0, -2)$.
6. $x > 0$, $y > 0$.	6. The first quadrant.
7. All points at a distance 3 units from the origin.	7. The circle with center at the origin and radius 3.

Very often the condition describing a graph is in the form of an equation or an inequality. We shall then say that the graph is *the graph of the equation*, or *the graph of the inequality*.

To sum up; the graph of a condition is the set of *all* points that satisfy the condition.

EXAMPLES

Sketch the graphs of the following conditions.

1. $-1 < x \leq 2$.   2. $x > 2$ and $y < 1$.   3. $|x| = 4$.

Solutions

1. ($-1 < x \leq 2$). We first locate the set of points for which $x = 2$, and draw it [the vertical line through $(2, 0)$]. Next we sketch the set of points for which $x = -1$. (This line is "dashed" to indicate that the points on it are *not* part of the graph.) The shaded area is the required graph. You should check several points of the graph, and points *not* of the graph, to convince yourself that the conditions are satisfied.

2. ($x > 2$ and $y < 1$). As shown on page 410, we draw a dashed line for $x = 2$, and hatch the half-plane on the right. This is the graph of the condition $x > 2$. Next we draw a dashed line for $y = 1$, and hatch the half-plane below it in the opposite direction. This is the graph of the condition $y < 1$. The cross-hatched region is the intersection of these two graphs, and it is the required graph.

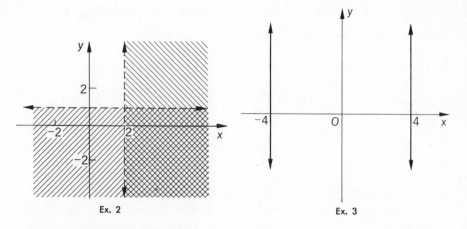

Ex. 2   Ex. 3

3. ($|x| = 4$). We know that $|4| = 4$ and also $|-4| = 4$. Hence all points satisfying the condition $x = 4$ must be part of the graph. Further, all points satisfying the condition $x = -4$ must also be part of the graph. The graph of $|x| = 4$, then, consists of two parallel lines whose equations are $x = 4$ and $x = -4$.

Exercise 14–7

(A)

Sketch the graphs of the conditions stated below. Use a "dashed" line when necessary (see example 1).

1. $x = 5$.	**2.** $x = -5$.	**3.** $|x| = 5$.	**4.** $x > 5$.
5. $x < 5$.	**6.** $y = 2$.	**7.** $y = -2$.	**8.** $y > 3$.
9. $|y| = 3$.	**10.** $|y| > 3$.	**11.** $|x| < 5$.	

12. $x < 0$ and $y > 0$.
13. $-3 \leq x < 4$.
14. $4 < x \leq 7$.
15. $-2 \leq x \leq 3$.
16. $|x| < 2$ and $y > 0$.
17. $1 \leq x \leq 3$ and $1 \leq y \leq 5$.
18. $|x| = 2$ and $y > 3$.
19. $|y| = 2$ and $x > 3$.
20. $|x| < 2$ and $|y| < 2$.

14–8   DESCRIPTION OF A LINE BY AN EQUATION

In this section we shall show that any line in the plane is the graph of a certain type of equation. We begin by pointing out that the situation with respect to a vertical line is almost obvious. If a vertical line passes through the point $(a, 0)$, then every point on the line has its x-coordinate equal to a. Thus the line is the graph of $x = a$.

For nonvertical lines, the situation is not at all obvious. Our general plan is this: Given a nonvertical line, q, with slope m, passing through a point

$P_1(x_1, y_1)$, we will produce an equation such that:

(1) The coordinates of every point of q satisfy the equation.

(2) Every pair of numbers that satisfies the equation are the coordinates of a point on q.

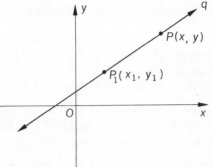

Proof of statement *(1):*   Let q be a nonvertical line with slope m, and $P_1(x_1, y_1)$ a point on q. Now, the slope of a line is equal to the slope of any segment of the line (Theorem 14–2). Then, if $P(x, y)$ is any point on q (distinct from P_1):

$$\frac{y - y_1}{x - x_1} = m \tag{1}$$

Observe that equation (1) is not satisfied by (x_1, y_1), since then $\dfrac{y - y_1}{x - x_1}$ becomes $\dfrac{0}{0}$, which is meaningless. But, multiplying both members of equation (1) by $(x - x_1)$, we get:

$$y - y_1 = m(x - x_1) \tag{2}$$

Equation (2) *is* satisfied by (x_1, y_1), since $y_1 - y_1 = m(x_1 - x_1)$, or $0 = m(0)$, a true statement. In effect we have restored the missing point $P_1(x_1, y_1)$ to the set. Hence every point on q satisfies equation (2).

Proof of statement *(2):*   Here we show that if the coordinates of a point satisfy equation (2), then the point lies on q.

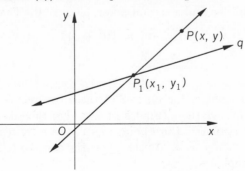

Let $P(x, y)$ be a point distinct from P_1 such that:

$$y - y_1 = m(x - x_1)$$

Since P is distinct from P_1, $x \neq x_1$ and $(x - x_1) \neq 0$. Then $\overline{P_1P}$ has slope $\dfrac{y - y_1}{x - x_1}$. But $m = \dfrac{y - y_1}{x - x_1}$ is the slope of q. Hence either $\overleftrightarrow{P_1P} \parallel q$, or $\overleftrightarrow{P_1P}$ and q are the same line. If $\overleftrightarrow{P_1P} \parallel q$, then they must have no points in common. But $P_1 \in \overleftrightarrow{P_1P}$ and $P_1 \in q$, hence $\overleftrightarrow{P_1P} \not\parallel q$. So $\overleftrightarrow{P_1P}$ and q are the same line, and P lies on q.

Statements (1) and (2) are combined in Theorem 14–6.

Theorem 14–6: **Let q be a nonvertical line with slope m, passing through $P_1(x_1, y_1)$. Then $P(x, y)$ lies on q iff the coordinates of P satisfy the equation $y - y_1 = m(x - x_1)$.**

The equation of Theorem 14–6 is called the **point-slope form** of the equation of the line. Here is an example of its use. Suppose we want the equation of the line determined by $P_1(1, 3)$ and $P_2(-3, 6)$. The slope of the line is $m = \dfrac{6 - 3}{-3 - 1} = -\dfrac{3}{4}$. Using $P_1(1, 3)$ and the point-slope form, we have:

$$y - 3 = -\frac{3}{4}(x - 1) \qquad (3)$$

Of course, equation (3) may be simplified to:

$$-4y + 12 = 3x - 3$$
$$3x + 4y = 15 \qquad (4)$$

Notice, however, that while equation (4) appears simpler, equation (3) has the advantage of being able to be "read geometrically." That is, the "trained eye" can discern at once that the slope of the line is $-\frac{3}{4}$, and the line passes through the point $(1, 3)$. As an exercise, you can verify that equation (4) can be derived using $P_2(-3, 6)$ as the fixed point rather than P_1.

The point-slope form simplifies the sketching of the graph. For example, consider: $y - 2 = \frac{1}{3}(x + 3)$. We know at once that the line passes through the point $(-3, 2)$. To find a second point, let $x = 0$. Then:

$$y - 2 = \tfrac{1}{3}(0 + 3)$$
$$y - 2 = 1$$
$$y = 3$$

$(0, 3)$ is a second point of the line. Plot these two points on a set of axes, and draw a line through them (Figure 14–26). For the sake of accuracy, it is good practice to compute a third point to serve as a "check" point. For example, if $x = 3$, then $y = 4$. As closely as the eye can tell, the point $(3, 4)$ does lie on the graph.

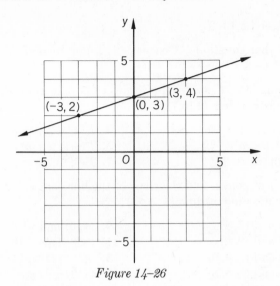

Figure 14-26

As one consequence of Theorem 14–6, consider a horizontal line—that is, a line with slope $m = 0$—and suppose it passes through $P_1(x_1, y_1)$. Then

$$y - y_1 = 0(x - x_1)$$
$$y - y_1 = 0$$
$$y = y_1$$

This means that the equation of a horizontal line has the simple form: $y = b$ (b denotes a constant), where b is the y-coordinate of the point of intersection of the line with the y-axis.

A second consequence of Theorem 14–6 is an extremely useful form for the equation of the line.

Definition 14–4:   The y-coordinate of the point where a line intersects the y-axis is called the **y-intercept.**

Theorem 14–7:   The graph of the equation $y = mx + b$ is the line with y-intercept b, and slope m.

Proof: By Theorem 14–6:

$$y - b = m(x - 0)$$

or
$$y - b = mx$$

Hence
$$y = mx + b$$

The form developed by Theorem 14–7 is called the **slope-intercept form** of the equation of a line, and is probably one of the most convenient forms available.

Exercise 14-8

1. Show that equation (4) on page 412 may be derived using the slope and $P_2(-3, 6)$ instead of $P_1(1, 3)$.

Write an equation in point-slope form of the line through P and having slope m, as given below (2 to 7):

2. $P(-1, 2)$, $m = 4$.
3. $P(2, -2)$, $m = -1$.
4. $P(-4, 0)$, $m = \frac{5}{4}$.
5. $P(-3, 2)$, $m = 0$.
6. $P(0, 0)$, $m = 3$.
7. $P(0, 6)$, $m = -5$.

For each pair of points, find the slope of the line containing them, and then write an equation for the line (8 to 15):

8. $(3, 4)$ and $(7, 8)$.
9. $(4, 5)$ and $(2, 4)$.
10. $(0, 0)$ and $(2, 6)$.
11. $(3, -4)$ and $(0, 0)$.
12. $(0, 4)$ and $(-6, 0)$.
13. $(8, -14)$ and $(11, -17)$.
14. $(2, 7)$ and $(-8, 5)$.
15. $(\sqrt{2}, \sqrt{8})$ and $(-\sqrt{8}, -\sqrt{2})$.

For each of the following equations, state the slope, and find the coordinates of *two* points of its graph (16 to 21):

16. $y - 2 = 3(x - 4)$.
17. $y - 2 = 3(x + 4)$.
18. $y + 1 = \frac{3}{2}(x - 2)$.
19. $y = \frac{4}{3}(x - 3)$.
20. $y = -\frac{2}{5}(x + \frac{15}{2})$.
21. $y - \frac{2}{3} = -\frac{1}{2}(x + 6)$.

Each of the equations below is written in slope-intercept form. State the y-intercept, and the slope, and sketch the graph (22 to 27):

22. $y = 2x + 4$.
23. $y = -3x - 2$.
24. $y = \frac{2}{3}x - 3$.
25. $y = -\frac{3}{2}x + 4$.
26. $y = \frac{3}{4}x$.
27. $y = -\frac{2}{5}x$.

28. Sketch the graph of $y = x$.
29. Sketch the graph of $y = -x$.

Rewrite the following equations in slope-intercept form, and then state the slope of each line (30 to 33):

30. $5x - 2y - 6 = 0$.
31. $3x + 4y - 2 = 0$.
32. $15x - 6y - 14 = 0$.
33. $45x + 10y + 16 = 0$.

34. Find an equation of the line through $P(2, 3)$ and parallel to $y = \frac{3}{4}x + 2$.
35. Find an equation of the line through $P(3, -5)$ and perpendicular to $y = \frac{2}{3}x - 1$.
36. Find an equation of the line through $(0, -6)$ and perpendicular to $3x + 4y - 9 = 0$.

For problems 37 and 38, find an equation of the line through $(-3, 4)$ that also meets the given condition.

37. Parallel to $5x - 6y + 15 = 0$.
38. Perpendicular to $x + 12y - 48 = 0$.

APPENDIX

TABLE OF TRIGONOMETRIC FUNCTIONS

Angle	Sine	Cosine	Tangent	Angle	Sine	Cosine	Tangent
0	0.000	1.000	0.000				
1	.017	1.000	.017	46	0.719	0.695	1.036
2	.035	0.999	.035	47	.731	.682	1.072
3	.052	.999	.052	48	.743	.669	1.111
4	.070	.998	.070	49	.755	.656	1.150
5	.087	.996	.088	50	.766	.643	1.192
6	.105	.995	.105	51	.777	.629	1.235
7	.122	.993	.123	52	.788	.616	1.280
8	.139	.990	.141	53	.799	.602	1.327
9	.156	.988	.158	54	.809	.588	1.376
10	.174	.985	.176	55	.819	.574	1.428
11	.191	.982	.194	56	.829	.559	1.483
12	.208	.978	.213	57	.839	.545	1.540
13	.225	.974	.231	58	.848	.530	1.600
14	.242	.970	.249	59	.857	.515	1.664
15	.259	.966	.268	60	.866	.500	1.732
16	.276	.961	.287	61	.875	.485	1.804
17	.292	.956	.306	62	.883	.469	1.881
18	.309	.951	.325	63	.891	.454	1.963
19	.326	.946	.344	64	.899	.438	2.050
20	.342	.940	.364	65	.906	.423	2.145
21	.358	.934	.384	66	.914	.407	2.246
22	.375	.927	.404	67	.921	.391	2.356
23	.391	.921	.424	68	.927	.375	2.475
24	.407	.914	.445	69	.934	.358	2.605
25	.423	.906	.466	70	.940	.342	2.747
26	.438	.899	.488	71	.946	.326	2.904
27	.454	.891	.510	72	.951	.309	3.078
28	.469	.883	.532	73	.956	.292	3.271
29	.485	.875	.554	74	.961	.276	3.487
30	.500	.866	.577	75	.966	.259	3.732
31	.515	.857	.601	76	.970	.242	4.011
32	.530	.848	.625	77	.974	.225	4.331
33	.545	.839	.649	78	.978	.208	4.705
34	.559	.829	.675	79	.982	.191	5.145
35	.574	.819	.700	80	.985	.174	5.671
36	.588	.809	.727	81	.988	.156	6.314
37	.602	.799	.754	82	.990	.139	7.115
38	.616	.788	.781	83	.993	.122	8.144
39	.629	.777	.810	84	.995	.105	9.514
40	.643	.766	.839	85	.996	.087	11.43
41	.656	.755	.869	86	.998	.070	14.30
42	.669	.743	.900	87	.999	.052	19.08
43	.682	.731	.933	88	.999	.035	28.64
44	.695	.719	.966	89	1.000	.017	57.29
45	.707	.707	1.000	90	1.000	.000	

TABLE OF SQUARE ROOTS OF NUMBERS 1–300

N	$\sqrt{N}$	N	$\sqrt{N}$	N	$\sqrt{N}$	N	$\sqrt{N}$	N	$\sqrt{N}$	N	$\sqrt{N}$
1	1.000	51	7.141	101	10.050	151	12.288	201	14.177	251	15.843
2	1.414	52	7.211	102	10.100	152	12.329	202	14.213	252	15.875
3	1.732	53	7.280	103	10.149	153	12.369	203	14.248	253	15.906
4	2.000	54	7.348	104	10.198	154	12.410	204	14.283	254	15.937
5	2.236	55	7.416	105	10.247	155	12.450	205	14.318	255	15.969
6	2.449	56	7.483	106	10.296	156	12.490	206	14.353	256	16.000
7	2.646	57	7.550	107	10.344	157	12.530	207	14.387	257	16.031
8	2.828	58	7.616	108	10.392	158	12.570	208	14.422	258	16.062
9	3.000	59	7.681	109	10.440	159	12.610	209	14.457	259	16.093
10	3.162	60	7.746	110	10.488	160	12.649	210	14.491	260	16.125
11	3.317	61	7.810	111	10.536	161	12.689	211	14.526	261	16.155
12	3.464	62	7.874	112	10.583	162	12.728	212	14.560	262	16.186
13	3.606	63	7.937	113	10.630	163	12.767	213	14.595	263	16.217
14	3.742	64	8.000	114	10.677	164	12.806	214	14.629	264	16.248
15	3.873	65	8.062	115	10.724	165	12.845	215	14.663	265	16.279
16	4.000	66	8.124	116	10.770	166	12.884	216	14.697	266	16.310
17	4.123	67	8.185	117	10.817	167	12.923	217	14.731	267	16.340
18	4.243	68	8.246	118	10.863	168	12.961	218	14.765	268	16.371
19	4.359	69	8.307	119	10.909	169	13.000	219	14.799	269	16.401
20	4.472	70	8.367	120	10.954	170	13.038	220	14.832	270	16.432
21	4.583	71	8.426	121	11.000	171	13.077	221	14.866	271	16.462
22	4.690	72	8.485	122	11.045	172	13.115	222	14.900	272	16.492
23	4.796	73	8.544	123	11.091	173	13.153	223	14.933	273	16.523
24	4.899	74	8.602	124	11.136	174	13.191	224	14.967	274	16.553
25	5.000	75	8.660	125	11.180	175	13.229	225	15.000	275	16.583
26	5.099	76	8.718	126	11.225	176	13.266	226	15.033	276	16.613
27	5.196	77	8.775	127	11.269	177	13.304	227	15.067	277	16.643
28	5.292	78	8.832	128	11.314	178	13.342	228	15.100	278	16.673
29	5.385	79	8.888	129	11.358	179	13.379	229	15.133	279	16.703
30	5.477	80	8.944	130	11.402	180	13.416	230	15.166	280	16.733
31	5.568	81	9.000	131	11.446	181	13.454	231	15.199	281	16.763
32	5.657	82	9.055	132	11.489	182	13.491	232	15.232	282	16.793
33	5.745	83	9.110	133	11.533	183	13.528	233	15.264	283	16.823
34	5.831	84	9.165	134	11.576	184	13.565	234	15.297	284	16.852
35	5.916	85	9.220	135	11.619	185	13.601	235	15.330	285	16.882
36	6.000	86	9.274	136	11.662	186	13.638	236	15.362	286	16.912
37	6.083	87	9.327	137	11.705	187	13.675	237	15.395	287	16.941
38	6.164	88	9.381	138	11.747	188	13.711	238	15.427	288	16.971
39	6.245	89	9.434	139	11.790	189	13.748	239	15.460	289	17.000
40	6.325	90	9.487	140	11.832	190	13.784	240	15.492	290	17.029
41	6.403	91	9.539	141	11.874	191	13.820	241	15.524	291	17.059
42	6.481	92	9.592	142	11.916	192	13.856	242	15.556	292	17.088
43	6.557	93	9.644	143	11.958	193	13.892	243	15.588	293	17.117
44	6.633	94	9.695	144	12.000	194	13.928	244	15.620	294	17.146
45	6.708	95	9.747	145	12.042	195	13.964	245	15.652	295	17.176
46	6.782	96	9.798	146	12.083	196	14.000	246	15.684	296	17.205
47	6.856	97	9.849	147	12.124	197	14.036	247	15.716	297	17.234
48	6.928	98	9.899	148	12.166	198	14.071	248	15.748	298	17.263
49	7.000	99	9.950	149	12.207	199	14.107	249	15.780	299	17.292
50	7.071	100	10.000	150	12.247	200	14.142	250	15.811	300	17.321

LIST OF DEFINITIONS

2–1: A set R is a **subset** of the set S if and only if every element of R is also an element of S. (p. 9)

2–2: Two sets are **equal** iff the two sets contain exactly the same elements. (p. 10)

2–3: The **intersection** of two sets is the set whose elements are all the elements common to both sets. (p. 10)

2–4: The **union** of two sets R and S is the set whose elements are all of the elements in R or in S or in both. (p. 10)

2–5: The set with no elements is called the **empty** or **null** set. (p. 10)

2–6: If $x \in R$, then $\sqrt{x^2} = x$ iff $x \geq 0$, and $\sqrt{x^2} = -x$ iff $x < 0$. (p. 24)

2–7: If $x \in R$, then $|x| = x$ iff $x \geq 0$, $|x| = -x$ iff $x < 0$. (p. 25)

2–8: The **distance** between two points on a line is the unique number of Axiom 2–1, and is given by the absolute value of the difference between their coordinates. (p. 28)

2–9: A correspondence of the sort described in the Ruler Axiom is a **coordinate system on a line.** (p. 28)

2–10: The number corresponding to a point is the **coordinate** of the point. (p. 28)

2–11: The point Q is **between** the points P and R iff (1) P, Q, and R are three different points on a line and (2) $PR = PQ + QR$. (p. 29)

2–12: The **segment** $\overline{XY}$, or $\overline{YX}$, is the set of points whose elements are the points X and Y, together with all the points of the line $\overleftrightarrow{XY}$ that lie between X and Y. (p. 32)

2–13: The points X and Y are the **endpoints** of $\overline{XY}$. (p. 32)

2–14: The number XY is the **length** of $\overline{XY}$, or the **measure** of $\overline{XY}$. (p. 32)

2–15: Two points, B and C, are on the **same side of point** A iff A, B, and C are distinct points on the same line and A is *not* between B and C. (p. 32)

2–16: **Ray** $\overrightarrow{AB}$ is the set of points which is the union of A and all points on the same side of A as B. (p. 32)

2–17: The point A is the **endpoint** of $\overrightarrow{AB}$. (p. 33)

2–18: Two rays are **opposite rays** iff they are subsets of the same line and their intersection consists of a single point. (p. 33)

2–19: Q is the **midpoint** of $\overline{PR}$ iff Q is between P and R and $PQ = QR$. (p. 37)

2–20: A point **bisects** a segment iff it is the midpoint of the segment. (p. 37)

3–1: A set of points is **collinear** iff they all lie on the same straight line. (p. 41)

3–2: A set of points is **coplanar** iff they all lie in the same plane. (p. 41)

3–3: A figure is an **angle** iff it is the union of two rays with the same endpoint. The two rays are the **sides** of the angle, and their common endpoint is the **vertex.** (p. 45)

3–4: The **interior** of $\angle RST$ is the set of all points B such that B and R lie on the same side of $\overleftrightarrow{ST}$ and B and T lie on the same side of $\overleftrightarrow{SR}$. (p. 47)

3–5: The set of all points not in the interior of an angle, nor on the angle, is the **exterior** of the angle. (p. 47)

419

3–6: The union of segments $\overline{AB}$, $\overline{AC}$, and $\overline{BC}$ is a **triangle** iff A, B, and C are any three noncollinear points. A, B, and C are **vertices**; $\overline{AB}$, $\overline{AC}$, and $\overline{BC}$ are **sides.** (p. 47)

3–7: A point lies in the **interior** of a triangle iff it is an element of the set of all points lying in the intersection of the interiors of the three angles of the triangle. A point lies in the **exterior** of a triangle iff it is an element of the set of all points neither in the interior nor on the triangle. (p. 48)

3–8: The number specified by the Angle Measurement Axiom (Axiom 3–7) is the **measure** of the angle. (p. 51)

3–9: An angle is **acute** iff its measure is less than 90. (p. 54)

3–10: An angle is a **right angle** iff its measure is 90. (p. 54)

3–11: An angle is **obtuse** iff its measure is greater than 90 but less than 180. (p. 54)

3–12: An angle is a **straight angle** iff its measure is 180. (p. 54)

3–12 (Alternate): An angle is a **straight angle** iff its sides are opposite rays. (p. 54)

3–13: Two angles are **adjacent** iff they lie in the same plane, have a common vertex and a common side, and the intersection of their interiors is empty. The sides **not common** to both angles are **exterior sides.** (p. 55)

3–14: Two angles formed by two intersecting straight lines are **vertical angles** iff their sides form two pairs of opposite rays. (p. 55)

3–15: Two angles are **complementary angles** iff the sum of their measures is 90. Each angle is the **complement** of the other. (p. 55)

3–16: Two angles are **supplementary angles** iff the sum of their measures is 180. Each angle is the **supplement** of the other. (p. 55)

3–17: Two angles are **congruent** iff their measures are equal. (p. 56).

3–18: Two intersecting lines are **perpendicular** iff they form congruent adjacent angles. (p. 60)

3–18 (Alternate): Two intersecting straight lines are **perpendicular** iff they form a right angle. (p. 60)

4–1: Two line segments are **congruent** iff their measures are equal. (p. 83)

5–1: $\overrightarrow{BD}$ is the **bisector** of $\angle ABC$ iff D is in the interior of $\angle ABC$ and $\angle ABD \cong \angle DBC$. (p. 92)

5–2: A one-to-one correspondence between the vertices of two triangles is a **congruence between the triangles** iff every pair of corresponding sides are congruent and every pair of corresponding angles are congruent. (p. 96)

5–3: An **angle** is **included between two sides** of a triangle iff the two sides of the triangle are subsets of the sides of the angle. (p. 97)

5–4: A **side** of a triangle is **included between two angles** of the triangle iff the endpoints of the side are the vertices of the angles. (p. 97)

5–5: An **angle** of a triangle is **opposite a side** of a triangle (and that **side is opposite the angle**) iff the vertex of the angle is not an endpoint of the side. (p. 97)

5–6: A triangle is **scalene** iff no two sides are congruent. (p. 105)

5–7: A triangle is **isosceles** iff at least two sides are congruent. The **vertex** is the common endpoint of the two congruent sides. The **vertex angle** is the angle included between the two congruent sides. The **base** is the side opposite the vertex angle. The **base angles** are the angles opposite the congruent sides. (p. 105)

5–8: A triangle is **equilateral** iff three sides are congruent. (p. 106)

5–9: A triangle is **equiangular** iff its three angles are congruent. (p. 106)

5–10: A triangle is **acute** iff each of its angles is acute. (p. 106)

5–11: A triangle is **obtuse** iff one of its angles is obtuse. (p. 106)

5–12: A segment is a **median** of a triangle iff its endpoints are a vertex of the triangle and the midpoint of the opposite side. (p. 117)

5–13: A segment is an **angle bisector of a triangle** iff it is a subset of the bisector of one of the angles of the triangle and its endpoints are the vertex of the angle and the point of intersection of the angle bisector and the opposite side. (p. 117)

5–14: A segment is an **altitude** of a triangle iff it is a perpendicular from a vertex to the line containing the opposite side. (p. 118)

6–1: In a plane, a line is the **perpendicular bisector** of a segment iff it is perpendicular to the segment and contains the midpoint of the segment. (p. 130)

6–2: A triangle is a **right triangle** iff one of its angles is a right angle. The sides which include the right angle are called the **legs,** and the side opposite the right angle is called the **hypotenuse.** (p. 135)

7–1: $\angle DCE$ is an **exterior angle** of $\triangle BCD$ iff C is between B and E. (p. 148)

7–2: The **distance from a point to a line** (the point not in the line) is the length of the perpendicular segment from the point to the line. If the point is in the line, the distance is defined to be zero. (p. 157)

8–1: Two lines are **skew** iff they are not coplanar. (p. 162)

8–2: Two lines are **parallel** iff they are coplanar and do not intersect. (p. 162)

8–3: A line is a **transversal** of two coplanar lines iff it intersects them in two different points. (p. 164)

8–4: Let t be a transversal of q_1 and q_2, intersecting them at A and B, respectively. Let X be a point of q_1 and Y a point of q_2 such that X and Y are on opposite sides of t. Then $\angle XAB$ and $\angle YBA$ are **alternate interior angles.** (p. 168)

8–5: If two lines are cut by a transversal so that $\angle 5$ and $\angle 3$ are alternate interior angles, and if $\angle 5$ and $\angle 7$ are vertical angles, then $\angle 3$ and $\angle 7$ are **corresponding angles.** (p. 168)

8–6: Let $P_1, P_2, P_3, \ldots, P_n$ be n distinct coplanar points ($n \geq 3$). Let the n segments $\overline{P_1P_2}, \overline{P_2P_3}, \ldots, \overline{P_{n-1}P_n}, \overline{P_nP_1}$ be such that:

    (1) No two segments intersect except at their endpoints.

    (2) No two segments with a common endpoint are collinear.

The union of these n segments is a **polygon.** (p. 187)

8–7: The n segments of a polygon are the **sides** of the polygon. Intersecting segments are called **consecutive sides.** (p. 188)

8–8: The n points of intersection of the sides of a polygon are its **vertices.** The endpoints of each side are called **consecutive vertices.** (p. 188)

8–9: A **diagonal** of a polygon is a segment with nonconsecutive vertices as endpoints. (p. 188)

8–10: An **angle of a polygon** is an angle determined by a pair of consecutive sides. Angles of a polygon whose vertices are consecutive vertices of the polygon are **consecutive angles.** (p. 188)

8–11: A polygon is a **convex polygon** iff no two of its vertices lie on opposite sides of a line containing any side of the polygon. (p. 189)

8–12: A set of points is a **quadrilateral** iff it is a polygon and the number of its sides is four. (p. 189)

8–13: A set of points is a **trapezoid** iff it is a quadrilateral with one and only one pair of parallel sides. The parallel sides are called **bases.** (p. 191)

8–14: A trapezoid is an **isosceles trapezoid** iff the nonparallel sides are congruent. (p. 191)

8–15: A set of points is a **parallelogram** iff it is a quadrilateral with both pairs of nonconsecutive sides parallel. (p. 191)

8–16: A set of points is a **rhombus** iff it is a parallelogram all of whose sides are congruent. (p. 191)

8–17: A set of points is a **rectangle** iff it is a parallelogram all of whose angles are right angles. (p. 191)

8–18: A set of points is a **square** iff it is a rectangle all of whose sides are congruent. (p. 191)

8–19: The **distance between two parallel lines** is the distance from any point on one line to the other line. (p. 193)

8–20: The **perimeter** of a polygon is the sum of the lengths of its sides. (p. 193)

8–21: If a transversal t intersects two lines q_1 and q_2 in points A and B, respectively, then we say that q_1 and q_2 **intercept** $\overline{AB}$ on t. (p. 199)

9–1: A **triangular region** is the union of a triangle and its interior. (p. 212)

9–2: A **polygonal region** is the union of a finite number of coplanar triangular regions such that if any two triangular regions intersect, the intersection is either a segment or a point. (p. 213)

9–3: The **area** of a polygonal region is the unique number associated with it by Axiom 9–1. (p. 213)

10–1: Two sequences of positive numbers $a, b, c, \ldots$ and $p, q, r, \ldots$ are **proportional** iff: $\dfrac{a}{p} = \dfrac{b}{q} = \dfrac{c}{r} = \cdots = k;$ or $\dfrac{p}{a} = \dfrac{q}{b} = \dfrac{r}{c} = \cdots = \dfrac{1}{k}$ $(k \neq 0)$. (p. 235)

10–2: A one-to-one correspondence between the vertices of two polygons is a **similarity between the polygons** iff:
    (1) Corresponding sides are proportional.
    (2) Corresponding angles are congruent. (p. 239)

10–3: If a, b, and c are positive numbers, b is the **geometric mean** of a and c iff $\dfrac{a}{b} = \dfrac{b}{c}$. (p. 275)

10–4: The **projection of a point on a line** is the foot of the perpendicular from the point to the line. (p. 276)

10–5: The **projection of a given segment on a line** in the same plane is the segment whose endpoints are the projections of the endpoints of the given segment. (p. 276)

11–1: A **circle** is the set of all points in a plane which are a given distance from a given point in the plane. The given point is called the **center,** and the given distance is the **radius,** of the circle. (p. 298)

11–2: Two or more circles are **concentric** iff they have the same center. (p. 298)

11–3: A segment is a **chord** of a circle iff its endpoints are points of the circle. (p. 298)

11–4: A line is a **secant** iff it contains a chord. (p. 298)

11–5: A chord is a **diameter** iff it includes the center of the circle. (p. 299)

11–6: A segment is a **radius** iff one of its endpoints is the center and the other a point of the circle. The endpoint on the circle is the **outer end** of the radius (p. 299)

11–7: The **interior** of a circle is the union of its center and the set of all points in the plane of the circle whose distances from the center are less than the radius. The **exterior** of a circle is the set of all points in the plane of the circle whose distances from the center are greater than the radius. (p. 300)

11–8: A line is **tangent** to a circle iff it is in the plane of the circle and intersects the circle in only one point. The point of intersection is the **point of tangency,** or **point of contact.** The line and the circle are **tangent** to each other. (p. 301)

11–9: Two **circles** are **congruent** iff they have congruent radii. (p. 305)

11–10: Two **circles** are **tangent** iff they are each tangent to the same line at the same point. Two circles are **internally tangent** iff their centers are on the same side of the common tangent line, and **externally tangent** iff their centers lie on opposite sides of the common tangent line. (p. 305)

11–11: An angle is a **central angle** of a circle iff its vertex is the center of the circle. (p. 310)

11–12: A set of points is a **minor arc** of a circle iff it is the union of two points of a circle, not the endpoints of a diameter, and all the points on the circle which lie in the interior of the central angle whose sides contain the two points. The two points are the **endpoints** of the arc. (p. 310)

11–13: A set of points is a **major arc** of a circle iff it is the union of two points of the circle and all points of the circle in the exterior of the central angle whose sides contain the two points. The two points are the **endpoints** of the arc. (p. 310)

11–14: A set of points is a **semicircle** iff it is the union of the endpoints of a diameter and all points of the circle that lie on the same side of the diameter. (p. 311)

11–15: The **degree measure of an arc** is

  (1) the measure of the central angle iff the arc is a minor arc,
  (2) 180 if the arc is a semicircle,
  (3) 360 minus the measure of the corresponding minor arc iff the arc is a major arc. (p. 311)

11–16: Two **arcs** are **congruent** iff they are arcs of the same, or congruent, circles, and have equal measures. (p. 312)

11–17: An **angle** is **inscribed** in an arc iff

  (1) the two endpoints of the arc lie on the two sides of the angle, and
  (2) the vertex of the angle is a point, but not an endpoint, of the arc. (p. 316)

11–18: An angle **intercepts** an arc iff

  (1) each side of the angle contains at least one endpoint of the arc, and
  (2) except for its endpoints, the arc lies in the interior of the angle. (p. 317)

11–19: A segment is a **tangent segment** of a circle iff it is a subset of a tangent line and one endpoint is the point of tangency. (p. 325)

11–20: A segment is a **secant segment** of a circle iff the segment intersects the circle in two points, and exactly one of these points is an endpoint. (p. 326)

12–1: Two or more lines are **concurrent** iff there is a single point which lies on all of them. (p. 340)

12–2: A circle is **inscribed in a triangle,** or a triangle is **circumscribed about a circle,** iff each side of the triangle is tangent to the circle. (p. 362)

12–3: A circle is **circumscribed about a triangle,** or a triangle is **inscribed in a circle,** iff each vertex of the triangle lies on the circle. (p. 362)

13–1: A convex polygon is a **regular polygon** iff all of its sides are congruent and all of its angles are congruent. (p. 366)

13–2: A polygon is **inscribed** in a circle iff its vertices lie on the circle. (p. 366)

13–3: The **apothem** of a regular polygon is the distance from the center of the circumscribed circle to a side of the polygon. (p. 367)

13–4: The **center of a regular polygon** is the center of its circumscribed circle. (p. 368)

13–5: An angle is a **central angle of a regular polygon** iff its vertex is the center of the polygon and its sides contain consecutive vertices of the polygon. (p. 368)

13–6: The **circumference** of a circle is the limit of the perimeters of the inscribed regular polygons. (p. 371)

13–7: The **length** of $\overset{\frown}{AB}$ is the limit of $AP_1 + P_1P_2 + \cdots + P_{n-1}B$ as n, the number of chords, increases. (p. 372)

13–8: A **circular region** is the union of a circle and its interior. (p. 375)

13–9: The **area of a circle** is the limit of the areas of the inscribed regular polygons. (p. 376)

13–10: A **sector** of a circle is a region bounded by two radii and an arc of the circle. (p. 377)

14–1: The **x-coordinate** (x) of a point P is the coordinate of the projection of P on the x-axis. The **y-coordinate** (y) of P is the coordinate of the projection of P on the y-axis. The numbers x and y are the **coordinates** of P. (Notation: $P(x, y)$.) (p. 383)

14–2: If $\overline{P_1P_2}$ with endpoints $P_1(x_1, y_1)$ and $P_2(x_2, y_2)$ is nonvertical, then the **slope** of $\overline{P_1P_2}$ is:

$$ m = \frac{y_2 - y_1}{x_2 - x_1} \qquad\qquad \text{(p. 389)} $$

14–3: The **slope** of a nonvertical line is the number which is the slope of every segment of the line. (p. 391)

14–4: The y-coordinate of the point where a line intersects the y-axis is the **y-intercept.** (p. 413)

4–1: Every angle is congruent to itself. (p. 71)

4–2: Any two right angles are congruent. (p. 72)

4–3: Any two straight angles are congruent. (p. 72)

4–4: If two angles are congruent and supplementary, then each angle is a right angle. (p. 72)

4–5: If two angles are adjacent, and their exterior sides are contained in two perpendicular lines, then they are complementary. (p. 72)

4–6: If two angles are adjacent, and their exterior sides are contained in a straight line, then they are supplementary. (p. 72)

4–7: Complements of the same angle are congruent. (p. 74)

4–8: Supplements of congruent angles are congruent. (p. 75)

4–9: Complements of congruent angles are congruent. (p. 76)

4–10: Supplements of the same angle are congruent. (p. 76)

4–11: If two lines intersect, then the vertical angles formed are congruent. (p. 76)

4–12: If two intersecting lines are perpendicular, then they form four right angles. (p. 76)

5–1 (Reflexive property): Every segment is congruent to itself. (p. 89)

5–2 (Symmetry property): If $\overline{AB} \cong \overline{CD}$, then $\overline{CD} \cong \overline{AB}$. (p. 89)

5–3 (Transitive property): If $\overline{AB} \cong \overline{CD}$ and $\overline{CD} \cong \overline{EF}$, then $\overline{AB} \cong \overline{EF}$. (p. 89)

5–4 (Addition property): If B is between A and C, S is between R and T, $\overline{AB} \cong \overline{RS}$, and $\overline{BC} \cong \overline{ST}$, then $\overline{AC} \cong \overline{RT}$. (p. 89)

5–5 (Subtraction property): If $\overline{AC} \cong \overline{RT}$, B is between A and C, S is between R and T, and $\overline{AB} \cong \overline{RS}$ then $\overline{BC} \cong \overline{ST}$. (p. 90)

5–6 (Symmetry property): If $\angle A \cong \angle B$, then $\angle B \cong \angle A$. (p. 90)

5–7 (Transitive property): If $\angle A \cong \angle B$ and $\angle B \cong \angle C$, then $\angle A \cong \angle C$. (p. 90)

5–8 (Addition property): If D is in the interior of $\angle ABC$, P is in the interior of $\angle RST$, $\angle ABD \cong \angle RSP$ and $\angle DBC \cong \angle PST$, then $\angle ABC \cong \angle RST$. (p. 90)

5–9 (Subtraction property): If $\angle ABC \cong \angle RST$, D is in the interior of $\angle ABC$, P is in the interior of $\angle RST$, and $\angle ABD \cong \angle RSP$, then $\angle DBC \cong \angle PST$. (p. 90)

5–10: If $\overline{AC} \cong \overline{RT}$, B is the midpoint of $\overline{AC}$ and S is the midpoint of $\overline{RT}$, then $\overline{AB} \cong \overline{RS}$. (p. 91)

5–11: If $\angle ABC \cong \angle RST$, $\overrightarrow{BD}$ is the bisector of $\angle ABC$, and $\overrightarrow{SP}$ is the bisector of $\angle RST$, then $\angle ABD \cong \angle RSP$. (p. 92)

5–12: If two sides of a triangle are congruent, the angles opposite these sides are congruent. (p. 106)

5–12.1: Every equilateral triangle is equiangular. (p. 107)

5–13: If two angles of a triangle are congruent, the sides opposite these angles are congruent. (p. 107)

5–13.1: Every equiangular triangle is equilateral. (p. 107)

6–1: In a plane, through a given point on a given line, there is one and only one line perpendicular to the given line. (p. 129)

6–2: In a plane, a line is the perpendicular bisector of a segment iff it is the set of all points equidistant from the endpoints of the segment. (p. 131)

6–2.1: In a plane, if two points are each equidistant from the endpoints of a segment, then the line determined by the two points is the perpendicular bisector of the segment. (p. 132)

6–3: In a plane, through a given point not on a given line, there is one and only one line perpendicular to the given line. (p. 133)

6–4: No triangle has more than one right angle. (p. 135)

7–1: If $a = b + c$ and $c > 0$, then $a > b$. (p. 145)

7–2 (Exterior Angle Theorem): The measure of an exterior angle of a triangle is greater than the measure of either of the nonadjacent interior angles of the triangle. (p. 148)

7–2.1: If a triangle has one right angle, then its other angles are acute. (p. 149)

7–3: If two sides of a triangle are not congruent, then the angles opposite them are not congruent, and the angle whose measure is the greater is opposite the longer side. (p. 152)

7–4: If two angles of a triangle are not congruent, then the sides opposite them are not congruent, and the longer side is opposite the angle whose measure is the greater. (p. 154)

7–5 (Triangle Inequality): The sum of the lengths of any two sides of a triangle is greater than the length of the third side. (p. 156)

7–6: The shortest segment joining a point to a line is the perpendicular segment. (p. 157)

7–7: If two sides of one triangle are congruent respectively to two sides of a second triangle, and the measure of the included angle of the first triangle is greater than the measure of the included angle of the second triangle, then the third side of the first triangle is longer than the third side of the second. (p. 159)

7–8: If two sides of one triangle are congruent respectively to two sides of a second triangle, and the third side of the first triangle is longer than the third side of the second, then the measure of the angle opposite the third side of the first triangle is greater than the measure of the angle opposite the third side of the second triangle. (p. 160)

8–1: If two lines are parallel, they lie in exactly one plane. (p. 163)

8–2: If two coplanar lines are perpendicular to the same line, they are parallel. (p. 163)

8–3: Through a given point not on a given line, there exists at least one line parallel to the given line. (p. 164)

Lemma 8–1: If two lines are cut by a transversal so that one pair of alternate interior angles are congruent, then the other pair of alternate interior angles are congruent. (p. 169)

8–4: If two lines are cut by a transversal so that a pair of alternate interior angles are congruent, then the lines are parallel. (p. 169)

8–5: If two lines are cut by a transversal so that a pair of corresponding angles are congruent, the lines are parallel. (p. 170)

8–6: If two parallel lines are cut by a transversal, then alternate interior angles are congruent. (p. 170)

8–7: If two parallel lines are cut by a transversal, each pair of corresponding angles are congruent. (p. 171)

8–8: If two parallel lines are cut by a transversal, interior angles on the same side of the transversal are supplementary. (p. 171)

8–9: If two lines are cut by a transversal so that interior angles on the same side of the transversal are supplementary, the lines are parallel. (p. 171)

8–10: In a plane, two lines parallel to a third line are parallel to each other. (p. 171)

8–11: In a plane, if a line is perpendicular to one of two parallel lines, it is perpendicular to the other. (p. 172)

8–12: The sum of the measures of the angles of a triangle is 180. (p. 179)

8–12.1: If two angles of one triangle are congruent, respectively, to two angles of another, the third angles are congruent. (p. 180)

8–12.2: The acute angles of a right triangle are complementary. (p. 181)

8–12.3: The measure of an exterior angle of a triangle is equal to the sum of the measures of the two nonadjacent interior angles. (p. 181)

8–12.4: The measure of each of the angles of an equilateral triangle is 60. (p. 181)

8–13: Either diagonal separates a parallelogram into two congruent triangles. (p. 192)

8–14: Any two nonconsecutive sides of a parallelogram are congruent. (p. 192)

8–14.1: If $q_1 \parallel q_2$, and P and R are any two points on q_1, then the distances of P and R from q_2 are equal. (p. 192)

8–15: In a parallelogram, any two consecutive angles are supplementary. (p. 192)

8–16: In a parallelogram, any two nonconsecutive angles are congruent. (p. 192)

8–17: The diagonals of a parallelogram bisect each other. (p. 192)

8–18: If both pairs of nonconsecutive sides of a quadrilateral are congruent, the quadrilateral is a parallelogram. (p. 192)

8–19: If two nonconsecutive sides of a quadrilateral are both congruent and parallel, the quadrilateral is a parallelogram. (p. 192)

8–20: If the diagonals of a quadrilateral bisect each other, the quadrilateral is a parallelogram. (p. 192)

8–21: The segment joining the midpoints of two sides of a triangle is parallel to the third side, and is half as long as the third side. (p. 192)

8–22: If a parallelogram has one right angle, then it has four right angles and the parallelogram is a rectangle. (p. 193)

8–23: The diagonals of a rhombus are perpendicular to each other. (p. 193)

8–24: If the diagonals of a quadrilateral bisect each other, and are perpendicular, then the quadrilateral is a rhombus. (p. 193)

8–25: If three parallel lines intercept congruent segments on one transversal, then they intercept congruent segments on any other transversal. (p. 200)

8–25.1: If three or more parallel lines intercept congruent segments on one transversal, then they intercept congruent segments on any other transversal. (p. 201)

8–26: If the hypotenuse and an acute angle of one right triangle are congruent to the corresponding parts of a second right triangle, then the triangles are congruent. (p. 205)

8–27: If the hypotenuse and one leg of one right triangle are congruent to the corresponding parts of a second right triangle, then the triangles are congruent. (p. 206)

8–28: The length of the median to the hypotenuse of a right triangle is one half the length of the hypotenuse. (p. 206)

8–29: If an acute angle of a right triangle has measure 30, then the side opposite it is half as long as the hypotenuse. (p. 207)

9–1: The area of a square is the square of the length of a side. (Formula: $A = s^2$.) (p. 216)

9–2: The area of a right triangle is half the product of the lengths of its legs. (Formula: $A = \frac{1}{2}ba$.) (p. 219)

9–3: The area of a triangle is half the product of any base and the corresponding altitude. (Formula: $A = \frac{1}{2}bh$.) (p. 219)

9–4: The area of a parallelogram is the product of a base and the corresponding altitude. (p. 221)

9–5: The area of a trapezoid is half the product of its altitude and the sum of its bases. (p. 222)

9–6: If two triangles have equal altitudes, then the ratio of their areas is equal to the ratio of their bases. (p. 222)

9–7: If two triangles have equal bases, then the ratio of their areas is equal to the ratio of their altitudes. (p. 223)

9–8: If two triangles have equal altitudes and equal bases, then they have equal areas. (p. 223)

9–9: The area of a rhombus is half the product of the lengths of the diagonals. (p. 223)

9–10 (The Pythagorean Theorem): In a right triangle, the square of the length of the hypotenuse is equal to the sum of the squares of the lengths of the legs. (p. 228)

9–11: If the square of the length of one side of a triangle is equal to the sum of the squares of the lengths of the other two sides, then the triangle is a right triangle, with the right angle opposite the first side. (p. 229)

9–12: If one leg of a right triangle is half as long as the hypotenuse, the angle opposite that leg has measure 30. (p. 230)

9–13: The hypotenuse of an isosceles right triangle is $\sqrt{2}$ times as long as a leg. (p. 230)

10–1: If a line parallel to one side of a triangle intersects the other two sides in distinct points, it divides the other two sides proportionally. (p. 247)

10–2: If a line intersects two sides of a triangle, and divides those two sides proportionally, then the line is parallel to the third side. (p. 248)

10–3: If corresponding angles of two triangles are congruent, the triangles are similar. (p. 253)

10–3.1 (AA Similarity Corollary): If two pairs of corresponding angles of two triangles are congruent, the triangles are similar. (p. 255)

10–3.2: If a line parallel to one side of a triangle intersects the other two sides in distinct points, then it determines a triangle similar to the given triangle. (p. 255)

10–4: If one triangle is similar to a second, and the second triangle is similar to a third, then the first triangle is similar to the third. (p. 259)

10–5: If two triangles are congruent, they are similar. (p. 259)

10–6 (SAS Similarity Theorem): If two pairs of corresponding sides of two triangles are proportional, and the included angles are congruent, the triangles are similar. (p. 260)

10-7   (SSS Similarity Theorem): If corresponding sides of two triangles are proportional, the triangles are similar. (p. 260)

10-8:   In any right triangle, the altitude to the hypotenuse separates the triangle into two triangles which are similar to each other, and to the original triangle. (p. 275)

10-9:   Given a right triangle and an altitude to the hypotenuse:
  (1)   The altitude is the geometric mean of the lengths of the projections of the legs on the hypotenuse.
  (2)   The length of either leg is the geometric mean of the length of the hypotenuse and the length of the projection of that leg on the hypotenuse. (p. 276)

10-10: If two triangles are similar, then the ratio of their areas is the square of the ratio of the lengths of any two corresponding sides. (p. 282)

10-11: Areas of similar polygons have the same ratio as the squares of the lengths of any pair of corresponding sides. (p. 283)

10-12: If an acute angle of one right triangle is congruent to an acute angle of a second right triangle, the triangles are similar. (p. 287)

11-1:   If a line and a circle are in the same plane, and if P is the foot of the perpendicular from the center of the circle to the line, then:
  (1)   Every point of the line is outside the circle, or
  (2) P is on the circle and the line is tangent to the circle, or
  (3) P is inside the circle, and the line intersects the circle in two points which are equidistant from P. (p. 302)

11-1.1: Every line tangent to a circle is perpendicular to the radius drawn to the point of contact. (p. 304)

11-1.2: Any line perpendicular to a radius at its outer end is tangent to the circle. (p. 304)

11-1.3: Any perpendicular from the center of a circle to a chord bisects the chord. (p. 304)

11-1.4: The segment joining the center of the circle to the midpoint of a chord is perpendicular to the chord. (p. 304)

11-1.5: The perpendicular bisector of a chord passes through the center of the circle. (p. 305)

11-1.6: If a line intersects the interior of a circle, then it intersects the circle in exactly two points. (p. 305)

11-2:   In the same circle, or in congruent circles, chords equidistant from the center are congruent. (p. 305)

11-3:   In the same circle, or in congruent circles, any two congruent chords are equidistant from the center. (p. 305)

11-4:   In the same circle, or in congruent circles, if two chords are congruent, the corresponding minor arcs are congruent. (p. 312)

11-5:   In the same circle, or in congruent circles, if two arcs are congruent, then so are the corresponding chords. (p. 312)

11-6:   The measure of an inscribed angle is half the measure of its intercepted arc. (p. 318)

11-6.1: An angle inscribed in a semicircle is a right angle. (p. 319)

11-6.2: Angles inscribed in the same arc are congruent. (p. 319)

11–7: The measure of an angle formed by a secant ray and a tangent ray, with its vertex on the circle, is half the measure of the intercepted arc. (p. 319)

11–8: The measure of an angle formed by two secants intersecting in the interior of a circle is half the sum of the measures of the arcs intercepted by the angle and its vertical angle. (p. 320)

11–9: The measure of an angle formed by two secants intersecting in the exterior of a circle is half the difference of the measures of the intercepted arcs. (p. 320)

11–10: The two tangent segments to a circle from a given point are congruent, and form congruent angles with the line joining the point to the center of the circle. (p. 325)

11–11: If $\overline{PT}$ is a tangent segment to a circle, and $\overline{PB}$ is a secant segment intersecting the circle at A and B, then

$$PA \cdot PB = (PT)^2. \quad \text{(p. 326)}$$

11–12: Given circle Q and a point P in its exterior. Let $\overline{PB}$ and $\overline{PD}$ be any two secant segments, with external segments $\overline{PA}$ and $\overline{PC}$, respectively. Then

$$PB \cdot PA = PD \cdot PC. \quad \text{(p. 327)}$$

11–13: If two chords, $\overline{AB}$ and $\overline{CD}$, of the same circle intersect at P in the interior of the circle, then

$$AP \cdot PB = CP \cdot PD. \quad \text{(p. 327)}$$

12–1: The bisector of an angle is the set of all points in the interior of, or on, the angle, equidistant from the sides of the angle. (p. 338)

12–2: The angle bisectors of a triangle are concurrent in a point equidistant from the three sides of the triangle. (p. 340)

12–3: The perpendicular bisectors of the sides of a triangle are concurrent in a point equidistant from the three vertices of the triangle. (p. 340)

12–3.1: There is one and only one circle through three noncollinear points. (p. 341)

12–3.2: Two distinct circles can intersect in at most two points. (p. 341)

12–4: The altitudes of a triangle are concurrent. (p. 345)

12–5: The medians of a triangle are concurrent, and the point of concurrency is two-thirds of the distance from any vertex to the midpoint of the opposite side. (p. 346)

13–1: The ratio of the circumference to the diameter is the same for all circles. (p. 371)

13–2: If two arcs have equal radii, then their lengths are proportional to their measures. (p. 373)

13–3: The ratio of the area of a sector of a circle to the area of the circle is equal to the ratio of the measure of the arc of the sector to 360. (p. 377)

14–1: All segments on a nonvertical line have the same slope. (p. 391)

14–2: Two nonvertical lines are parallel if and only if they have the same slope. (p. 396)

14–3: Two nonvertical lines are perpendicular if and only if their slopes are negative reciprocals of each other. (p. 397)

14–4 (Distance Formula): The distance between two points with coordinates (x_1, y_1) and (x_2, y_2), respectively, is given by:

$$\sqrt{(x_2 - x_1)^2 + (y_2 - y_1)^2}.$$ (p. 400)

14–5 (Midpoint Formula): If $P_1(x_1, y_1)$ and $P_2(x_2, y_2)$ are two points, then the midpoint of $\overline{P_1P_2}$ is the point

$$M\left(\frac{x_1 + x_2}{2},\ \frac{y_1 + y_2}{2}\right)$$ (p. 402)

14–6: Let q be a nonvertical line with slope m, passing through $P_1(x_1, y_1)$. Then $P(x, y)$ lies on q if and only if the coordinates of P satisfy the equation $y - y_1 = m(x - x_1)$. (p. 412)

14–7: The graph of the equation $y = mx + b$ is the line with y-intercept b, and slope m. (p. 413)

Equality Axioms

E–1 (Reflexive Axiom): $a = a$. (p. 20)
E–2 (Symmetric Axiom): If $a = b$, then $b = a$. (p. 20)
E–3 (Transitivity Axiom): If $a = b$ and $b = c$, then $a = c$. (p. 20)
E–4 (Addition Axiom): If $a = b$ and $c = d$, then $a + c = b + d$. (p. 20)
E–5 (Subtraction Axiom): If $a = b$ and $c = d$, then $a - c = b - d$. (p. 20)
E–6 (Multiplication Axiom): If $a = b$ and $c = d$, then $ac = bd$. (p. 20)
E–7 (Division Axiom): If $a = b$ and $c = d \neq 0$, then $\dfrac{a}{c} = \dfrac{b}{d}$. (p. 20)
E–8: If $a = b$ and $b > 0$, then $\sqrt{a} = \sqrt{b}$. (p. 24)

Order Axioms

O–1 (Trichotomy Axiom): For every pair of real numbers a and b, exactly one of the following is true: $a < b$, $a = b$, $a > b$. (p. 21)
O–2 (Addition Axiom): If $a < b$ and $c \leq d$, then $a + c < b + d$. (p. 21)
O–3 (Multiplication Axiom): If $a < b$ and $c > 0$, then $ac < bc$. (p. 21)
O–4 (Transitivity Axiom): If $a < b$ and $b < c$, then $a < c$. (p. 21)
S–1 (Substitution Axiom): If x and y are two symbols for the same real number, then either may be substituted for the other in any equation or inequality, without changing the truth or falsity of the statement. (p. 21)
F–1 (Closure law for addition): If $a, b \in R$, then $a + b \in R$. (p. 21)
F–2 (Associative law for addition): If $a \in R$, $b \in R$, and $c \in R$, then $(a + b) + c = a + (b + c)$. (p. 21)
F–3 (Commutative law for addition): If $a, b \in R$, then $a + b = b + a$. (p. 21)
F–4 (Additive identity law): There exists a real number 0 (zero) such that if $a \in R$, then $0 + a = a$. (p. 21)
F–5 (Additive inverse law): If $a \in R$, then there exists an element $(-a) \in R$ such that $a + (-a) = 0$. (p. 21)
F–6 (Closure law for multiplication): If $a, b \in R$, then $ab \in R$. (p. 21)
F–7 (Associative law for multiplication): If a, b, and $c \in R$, then $(ab)c = a(bc)$. (p. 21)
F–8 (Commutative law for multiplication): If $a, b \in R$, then $ab = ba$. (p. 21)
F–9 (Multiplicative identity law): There exists a real number 1 (one) such that if $a \in R$, then $1 \cdot a = a$. (p. 21)
F–10 (Multiplicative inverse law): If $a \in R$, $a \neq 0$, then there exists an element $\dfrac{1}{a} \in R$, such that $a \cdot \dfrac{1}{a} = 1$. (p. 21)
F–11 (Distributive law): If a, b, and $c \in R$, then $a(b + c) = ab + ac$. (p. 21)
R–1: Every positive number has a positive square root. (p. 24)
2–1: To every pair of different points there corresponds a unique positive number. (p. 28)

2–2 (Ruler Axiom): The points of a line can be placed in correspondence with the real numbers in such a way that:

  (1) To every point of the line there corresponds exactly one real number, and

  (2) To every real number there corresponds exactly one point of the line, and

  (3) The distance between two points equals the absolute value of the difference between the corresponding numbers. (p. 28)

2–3: For every two distinct points there is exactly one line that contains both points. (p. 31)

2–4 (Point-Plotting Axiom): If x denotes a positive number and $\overrightarrow{PR}$ is a ray, then there is exactly one point Q of $\overrightarrow{PR}$ such that $PQ = x$. (p. 36)

2–5: Every segment has exactly one midpoint. (p. 37)

3–1: If two different lines intersect, they intersect in at most one point. (p. 41)

3–2: If two points lie in a plane, then the line determined by the two points lies entirely in the plane. (p. 43)

3–3: Any three points lie in at least one plane; if the three points are noncollinear, they lie in exactly one plane. (p. 43)

3–4: A line and a point not on the line determine exactly one plane. (p. 43)

3–5: If two different lines intersect, they determine exactly one plane. (p. 43)

3–6: If two different planes intersect, then their intersection is a straight line. (p. 43)

3–7 (Angle Measurement Axiom): To every angle there corresponds a real number from 0 to 180 inclusive. (p. 51)

3–8 (Angle Construction Axiom): Let $\overrightarrow{AB}$ be a ray on the edge of a half-plane. For every number r, $(0 < r < 180)$ there is exactly on ray $\overrightarrow{AP}$, with P in that half-plane, such that $m\angle PAB = r$. For $r = 0$, P lies on $\overrightarrow{AB}$; for $r = 180$, P lies on the ray opposite to $\overrightarrow{AB}$. (p. 51)

3–9 (Angle Addition Axiom): If P is a point in the interior of $\angle ABC$, then $m\angle ABC = m\angle ABP + m\angle PBC$. (p. 51)

5–1: Every angle has exactly one bisector. (p. 92)

5–2 (The SAS Axiom): Two triangles are congruent if two sides and the included angle of one are congruent to the corresponding sides and included angle of the second. (p. 100)

5–3 (The ASA Axiom): Two triangles are congruent if two angles and the included side of one are congruent to the corresponding angles and included side of the second. (p. 101)

5–4 (The SSS Axiom): Two triangles are congruent if three sides of one are congruent to the corresponding sides of the second. (p. 101)

8–1 (The Parallel Axiom): Through a given point not on a given line there is at most one line parallel to the given line. (p. 164)

9–1: To every polygonal region there corresponds a unique positive real number. (p. 213)

9–2: If two triangles are congruent, then the triangular regions determined by them have equal areas. (p. 213)

9–3: If R is the union of regions R_1 and R_2 and if R_1 and R_2 intersect in at most a finite number of segments and points, then: area(R) = area(R_1) + area(R_2). (p. 214)

9–4: The area of a rectangle is the product of the length of its base and the length of its altitude. (Formula: $A = bh$). (p. 216)

11–1: If $\widehat{AB}$ and $\widehat{BC}$ are arcs of the same circle, having only point B in common, and if their union is $\widehat{AC}$, then $m\widehat{AB} + m\widehat{BC} = m\widehat{AC}$. (p. 312)

12–1 (Two-Circle Axiom): Given two circles of radius a and b, respectively, and c the distance between their centers. If each of the numbers a, b, and c, is less than the sum of the other two, then the circles intersect in two points, one on each side of the line determined by the two centers. (p. 350)

Exercise 1–1

3. (2) **5.** (a) Two teams have one and only one game in common. (b) Every game in the system "lies in" two and only two teams. (c) There are exactly four teams in the system. **9.** Violates axiom (b). **11.** Violates axiom (b). **13.** None **15.** None **17.** Violates axioms (a) and (c). **19.** (a) 4 (b) 6

Exercise 2–1

1. $\{1, 2, 3, 4, 5, 6\}$ **3.** $\{6\}$ **5.** $\{2, 4, 5, 6\}$ **7.** $\{6\}$ **9.** $\{1, 2, 3, 4, 5, 6, 7\}$ **11.** $\varnothing$ **13.** $\{2, 4\}$ **15.** $\{a, b, c, d\}$, $\{a, b, c\}$, $\{a, b, d\}$, $\{a, c, d\}$, $\{b, c, d\}$, $\{a, b\}$, $\{a, c\}$, $\{a, d\}$, $\{b, c\}$, $\{b, d\}$, $\{c, d\}$, $\{a\}$, $\{b\}$, $\{c\}$, $\{d\}$, $\varnothing$. **17.** Never **19.** Never **21.** Sometimes **23.** Always **27.** Never **29.** Never. **31.** $\{x \mid x + 4n, \ n$ any positive integer$\}$ **33.** $\{x \mid x = n^2, \ n$ any positive integer$\}$ **35.** Yes **37.** No

Exercise 2–2

1. False **3.** True **5.** True **7.** True **9.** True **11.** $\{-5, 0, 1, \sqrt{4}\}$ **13.** $\{\pi, -\sqrt{2}\}$ **15.** False **17.** True **19.** True **21.** Always **23.** Sometimes **25.** Always **27.** Sometimes **29.** Always **31.** Sometimes **33.** Always

Exercise 2–3

1. As many as you please. **3.** Not necessarily. **5.** 1, 4, or 6

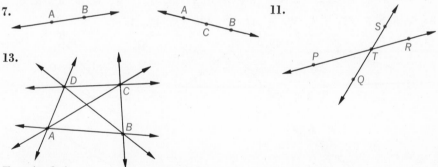

7. **11.** **13.**

Exercise 2–4

1. 3.029, 3.07, 3.1, $\sqrt{10}$ **3.** $-1, -\frac{3}{4}, -\frac{5}{6}$ **5.** x is less than y. **7.** p is less than q is less than r. **9.** 5 is greater than n, and n is greater than or equal to 3. **11.** Sometimes **13.** Never **15.** Sometimes **17.** $y > 0$ **19.** $n > 0$ or $n \neq 0$ **21.** $a \leq b$ **23.** $5 > 4$ **25.** $x \leq 3$ **27.** $a \nleq b$ **29.** $a \nless b$

Exercise 2–5

1. E–5 (or E–4) **3.** E–4 (or E–5) **5.** F–11 **7.** E–7 (or E–6) **9.** O–2 **11.** F–10 **13.** F–1 **15.** F–8 **17.** 4 **19.** $-3\frac{1}{4}$ **21.** $-\frac{1}{4}$ **23.** $\frac{4}{13}$ **25.** Additive inverse law **27.** Associative law for multiplication **29.** Additive identity law **31.** Subtraction Ax., Addition Ax., Division Ax. **33.** Distributive law, Subtraction Ax., Subtraction Ax., Division Ax. **35.** $\dfrac{-9}{\sqrt{5}}, \dfrac{\sqrt{5}}{9}$ **37.** $\dfrac{\sqrt{3}}{2}, \dfrac{-2}{\sqrt{3}}$

Exercise 2–6

1. 4 **3.** x^2 **5.** x **7.** $(x-1)$ **9.** $x \geq -1$ **11.** 4 **13.** $|a|$ **15.** $-(x-1)$
17. $x < 2$ **19.** False **21.** True **23.** False **25.** $2, \sqrt{11}, 4$ **27.** $-6, 0, \sqrt{(-5)^2}$
29. All values of x **31.** None **33.** None

Exercise 2–7

1. -5 **3.** 0 **5.** 4 **7.** -2 **9.** 2 **11.** 2 **13.** C $(AC + CD = AD)$ **15.** C
$(AC + CF = AF)$ **17.** -3 **19.** $-\frac{3}{2}$ **21.** -2 **23.** $-\frac{5}{3}$ **25.** 8 **27.** 4 **29.** 6.4
31. 6, 4 **33.** 12, -2 **35.** 908, -898 **37.** $\{x \mid -1 < x < 3\}$ **39.** $\{x \mid 2 \leq x \leq 4\}$
41. $\{x \mid -3 < x < 1\}$ **43.** $\{x \mid -4 < x < -2\}$ **45.** $\{x \mid \frac{4}{3} < x < \frac{8}{3}\}$
47. $\{x \mid 3 - \sqrt{2} < x < 3 + \sqrt{2}\}$ **49.** $\{x \mid x > 5 \text{ or } x < -1\}$

Exercise 2–8

1. 2 **3.** A line has no endpoints, a ray has one endpoint, a segment has two
endpoints. **5.** Yes **7.** No **9.** Yes, by Def. 2–11 **11.** $\overrightarrow{PA}$ or $\overrightarrow{PQ}$

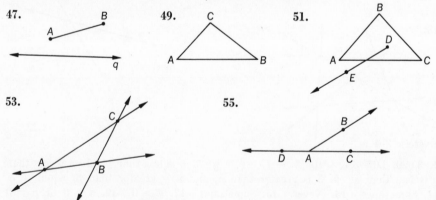

25. **27.** P, Q, R, S, T **29.** Q, P **31.** Q, R **33.** R, S, T
35. Q, R, S, T **37.** S, T **39.** A **41.** $\emptyset$ **43.** $\overline{AF}$ **45.** A

57. $\overline{AB} \cup \overrightarrow{AC} \cup \overleftarrow{BC}$ **59.** $\overline{AB} \cup \overline{AC}$ **61.** $\overrightarrow{AC} \cup \overline{CB} \cup \overline{BA}$ **63.** $\overleftrightarrow{AB} \cup \overline{BC} \cup \overleftrightarrow{CD} \cup \overline{DA}$
65. $\overleftrightarrow{AB} \cup \overleftrightarrow{BC} \cup \overleftrightarrow{CD} \cup \overleftrightarrow{DA}$

Exercise 2–9

1. 5 **3.** 2 **5.** 5 **7.** -6 **9.** $6\frac{1}{4}$ **11.** -6 **13.** y **15.** x **17.** $M, \overrightarrow{PR}, \overrightarrow{MX}, n$
19. No (Ax. 2–1) **21.** No (Ax. 2–5) **23.** No; C is not between A and B. **25.** No;
M must be on $\overleftrightarrow{AB}$.

Exercise 3–1

1. If a set of points all lie on the same line, they are collinear. If a set of points are collinear, they all lie on the same line. **3.** Yes (Ax. 2–3), yes (Ax. 3–2), no, yes

(Ax. 3–3) **5.**  **7.** A, B, C **9.** Yes, no, yes, no

11. Yes (Ax. 3–1) **13.** Exactly one **15.** Exactly one

Exercise 3–2

1. Ax. 3–3 **3.** An infinite number. Only one, if they are noncollinear; otherwise an infinite number. **5.** A line (or segment). Ax. 3–6. **9.** 4 **11.** 6 **13.** 14

Exercise 3–3

1. $\overline{AB}$, $\overline{BD}$, $\overline{DA}$; A, B, D. $\overline{BC}$, $\overline{CD}$, $\overline{DB}$; B, C, D. **3.** $\angle A$, $\angle C$, $\angle ADC$

5. $\angle APB$, $\angle APD$, $\angle DPC$, $\angle CPB$, none

7. (a)   (b)

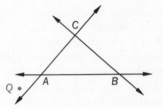

11. No. Sides of angles are rays. **13.** G, F **15.** C, P, D, E

Exercise 3–4

1. 50 **3.** 120 **5.** 15 **7.** 70 **9.** 55 **11.** 90 **15.** MNP **17.** ANP **21.** 155
23. $12\frac{1}{2}$ **25.** $107\frac{1}{2}$ **27.** $s + r$ **29.** $110 - s$ **31.** 120 **33.** 132

Exercise 3–5

1. 2, 4 **3.** (a) 130 (b) 60 (c) $157\frac{1}{2}$ (d) $180 - x$ (e) x **5.** (a) $\angle CPA$ (b) 180
(c) CPA (d) $\angle 2$ (e) Def. 3–12 Alternate, and Def. 3–12 (f) 130 (g) Def. 3–12
Alternate (h) Yes; Def. 3–12 (i) 50 (j) Yes (k) 130 (l) $\angle 1$, $\angle 3$; $\angle 2$, $\angle 4$
(m) Congruent **7.** No; intersection of interiors is not empty. **9.** No; no common
vertex. **11.** (a) If the sum of the measures of two angles is 180, the angles are
supplementary. (b) If two angles are supplementary the sum of their measures is
180. **13.** (a) If the sides of an angle are opposite rays, the angle is a straight
angle. (b) If an angle is a straight angle, its sides are opposite rays. **15.** $\angle APB$
acute, $\angle BPC$ acute, $\angle APC$ right, $\angle APD$ obtuse, $\angle BPE$ obtuse, $\angle CPE$ right,
$\angle CPD$ acute **17.** $\angle EPC$, $\angle CPA$; $\angle EPD$, $\angle DPA$ **19.** 75 **21.** No
23. $\angle BAE$, $\angle FED$

Exercise 3–6

1. *Def. 3–18:* If two intersecting lines form congruent adjacent angles, they are
perpendicular. If two intersecting lines are perpendicular, they form congruent
adjacent angles. *Def. 3–18 (Alt):* If two intersecting lines form a right angle, they
are perpendicular. If two intersecting lines are perpendicular, they form a right

angle. **3.** (a) Def. 3–6 (b) Yes; Def. 3–18 (c) 90, 90; Def. 3–18 (Alt.) and Def. 3–10 **7.** $\overrightarrow{PC} \perp \overleftrightarrow{AB}$ **9.** $\overleftrightarrow{AB} \perp \overrightarrow{PC}$ **13.** $\angle BPE, \angle DPA$ **15.** None

Exercise 4–1

5. (a) 15 (b) 820 (c) $\dfrac{n(n+1)}{2}$ **7.** $\angle 1$

Exercise 4–2

1. If I go outdoors during a rainstorm, then I get wet. **3.** If two even integers are multiplied, then the product is an even integer. **5.** If two lines intersect, then they are not parallel. **7.** If all three angles of a triangle are congruent, then all three sides are congruent. **9.** If two intersecting lines are perpendicular, then they form four right angles. **11.** If two numbers are multiplied, then their product is positive.

Exercise 4–3

1. *Hypothesis:* A student is registered with the admissions office, and has filed his complete program. *Conclusion:* He may attend classes. **3.** *Hypothesis:* Two of the angles of a triangle are congruent. *Conclusion:* The sides opposite these angles are congruent. **5.** (a) No; angles not adjacent. (b) Yes (c) No; exterior sides not contained in a line. (d) No; angles not adjacent. **7.** *Hypothesis:* Two lines intersect. *Conclusion:* They are not parallel. **9.** *Hypothesis:* All three angles of a triangle are congruent. *Conclusion:* All three sides are congruent.

Exercise 4–4

1. Ax. E–5 **3.** Def. 3–15 **5.** Thm. 4–2 **7.** Ax. O–1 **9.** Def. 3–11 **11.** Ax. E–3 **13.** Thm. 4–4 **15.** Ax. E–1 **17.** 80 **19.** 120 **21.** 50 **23.** 60

Exercise 4–5

1. 25, 65, 65 **3.** 90, 90, 45, 45, 45, 45 **5.** (a) $\angle BPC$ (b) $\angle APB, \angle DPC$ (c) $\angle APB, \angle BPD$; $\angle DPC, \angle CPA$ **17.** (1) Thm. 4–6, (2) Def. 3–16, (3) Ax. 3–9, (4) Given, (5) Def. 3–18 (Alt.), (6) Def. 3–10, (7) Ax. S–1, (8) Ax. S–1, (9) Ax. E–5

Exercise 5–1

1. $\angle ABD \cong \angle RSP$, $\angle ABC \cong \angle RST$, $\angle DBC \cong \angle PST$ **3.** Thm. 5–2 **5.** Thm. 5–3 **7.** Thm. 5–5 **9.** Thm. 5–4 **11.** Thm. 5–1 **13.** Thm. 5–6 **15.** Thm. 5–7 **17.** Thm. 5–9 **19.** Thm. 5–8 **21.** Thm. 4–1

Exercise 5–2

1. (a), (e); (b), (c); (d), (f); (h), (l); (j), (k) **3.** $\triangle ABE \cong \triangle CBD$ **5.** $\triangle PQT \cong \triangle RQS$ **7.** $\triangle GDE \cong \triangle GFE$ **9.** $\triangle ADB \cong \triangle CDB$ **11.** $\overline{BD}$ **13.** $\angle D$ **15.** $\angle C$ **17.** $\overline{AC}$ **19.** $\angle A$ **21.** $\overline{EB}$ **23.** $\angle EBD$ **25.** $\overline{PU} \cong \overline{ST}$, $\overline{UR} \cong \overline{TQ}, \overline{PR} \cong \overline{SQ}, \angle P \cong \angle S, \angle U \cong \angle T, \angle URP \cong \angle TQS$ **27.** $\overline{DE} \cong \overline{AE}$, $\overline{EC} \cong \overline{EB}, \overline{DC} \cong \overline{AB}, \angle CDE \cong \angle BAE, \angle DEC \cong \angle AEB, \angle DCE \cong \angle ABE$ **29.** $\overline{AC} \cong \overline{BD}$, $\overline{AD} \cong \overline{BC}$, $\overline{CD} \cong \overline{DC}$, $\angle DAC \cong \angle CBD$, $\angle DCA \cong CDB$, $\angle CDA \cong \angle BCD$ **31.** $\overline{AB} \cong \overline{AB}$, $\overline{AE} \cong \overline{BC}$, $\overline{EB} \cong \overline{AC}$, $\angle EAB \cong \angle CBA$, $\angle E \cong \angle C, \angle CAB \cong \angle EBA$ **33.** $\overline{PQ} \cong \overline{XY}$, $\overline{QR} \cong \overline{YW}$, $\overline{PR} \cong \overline{XW}$, $\angle P \cong \angle X, \angle Q \cong \angle Y, \angle R \cong \angle W$ **35.** $\overline{PQ} \cong \overline{YW}, \overline{QR} \cong \overline{WX}, \overline{PR} \cong \overline{YX}$, $\angle P \cong \angle Y, \angle Q \cong \angle W, \angle R \cong \angle X$

Exercise 5–3

1. SAS Ax. **3.** SSS Ax. **5.** None **7.** SAS Ax. **9.** None **11.** None

Exercise 5–4

1. Isosceles, acute **3.** Equiangular, equilateral, acute **5.** Right, scalene **7.** Isosceles, right **9.** Obtuse, scalene **13.** $m\angle 2 = 120$, $m\angle 3 = 30$, $m\angle 5 = 60$, $m\angle 6 = 60$, $m\angle 7 = 90$, $m\angle 8 = 120$ **17.** $m\angle 2 = 40$, $m\angle 4 = 80$, $m\angle 5 = 100$, $m\angle 6 = 80$, $m\angle 8 = 40$

Exercise 5–5

1. Yes **3.** Yes **5.** Yes **7.** No **9.** No **11.** D between C, E; B between C, A **13.** None **15.** B between C, A **17.** B, C, D all lie between points on both sides.

Exercise 6–1

1. $\sqrt{3}$ is either rational or irrational. **3.** The lines are perpendicular or they are not perpendicular. **5.** $\angle R < \angle S$ **7.** $\overline{AC} \not\cong \overline{BC}$

Exercise 6–2

1. (a) $\triangle ADC$; $\triangle BDC$ (b) $\overline{AC}$, $\overline{AD}$, $\overline{DC}$; $\overline{BC}$, $\overline{BD}$, $\overline{DC}$ **3.** Uniqueness. No. **7.** $BC = CD = DA = 12$ **9.** $x = 6, 7 = 7, z = 9$ **11.** $\overline{MP}$ **13.** $\overline{AB}$ would be the perpendicular bisector of $\overline{CD}$.

Exercise 6–3

1. Yes, Ax. 2–3 **3.** No; the two sets are not necessarily the same set. **5.** Yes, Thm. 6–3 **7.** Yes, Thm. 6–3 **9.** (a) $\overline{DB}$, $\overline{PR}$ (b) $\overline{PR}$

Exercise 7–1

1. Ax. O–1 **3.** Ax. O–2 **5.** Ax. O–4 **7.** Thm. 7–1 **9.** >, Ax. O–2 **11.** >, Ax. O–2 **13.** =, Ax. O–1 **15.** <, Ax. O–2 **17.** >, Ax. O–2 **19.** >, Ax. O–1 **21.** >, Thm. 7–1 **23.** >, Ax. O–2 **25.** <, Ax. O–1

Exercise 7–2

1. 1, 3, 6, 8, 10, 12 **3.** 1 and 3 **5.** 1, 3; 6, 8; 10, 12 **7.** $\angle FCD$ **9.** $\angle E$ (or $\angle EDC$) **11.** $\angle C$ or $\angle DBC$ **13.** 90 **15.** 110 **17.** > 100 **19.** < 90

Exercise 7–3

1. If a man lives in California, then he lives in Los Angeles. False. **3.** If a triangle is equiangular, then it is equilateral. True. **5.** If the sum of the measures of two angles is 180, then the angles are supplementary. True. **7.** If the sum of the measures of three angles is 180, then the angles are the angles of a triangle. False. **9.** $\overline{BC}$ **11.** $\angle G$, $\angle F$, $\angle H$ **13.** (a) $\angle R$ (b) $\angle Q$

Exercise 7–4

1. Yes **3.** No **5.** No **7.** Yes **9.** $\overline{AE}$, $\overline{AC}$ **11.** 12 **13.** 9 **15.** 7 **17.** 20 **19.** 15

Exercise 7–5

3. No

Exercise 8–1

1. Coplanar and nonintersecting **3.** No; the two lines may be skew. **5.** (a) No. No. (b) No. No. (c) No. No. **7.** q_3, q_4; none; none; q_4; q_3; q_2 **9.** (1) Given, (2) Def. 5–7, (3) Def. 4–1, (4) Given, (5) Def. 5–12, (6) Def. 2–19, (7) Cor. 6–2.1, (8) Given, (9) Thm. 8–2.

Exercise 8–2

1. 4, 6; 3, 5 **3.** 1, 5; 2, 6; 4, 8; 3, 7; **5.** Alternate interior **7.** Alternate exterior **9.** Alternate exterior **11.** Corresponding **13.** Corresponding **15.** True **17.** False **19.** False **21.** True **23.** $m\angle 2 = 40$, $m\angle 3 = 50$, $m\angle 4 = 90$, $m\angle 5 = 40$, $m\angle 6 = 40$, $m\angle 7 = 50$, $m\angle 8 = 140$ **25.** $\overline{DA}$ and $\overline{CB}$, transversal $\overline{DC}$ **27.** $\overline{DA}$ and $\overline{CB}$, transversal $\overline{AC}$ **29.** $\overline{DA} \parallel \overline{BC}$ **31.** None **33.** $\overline{DA} \parallel \overline{CB}$ **35.** 180 **37.** 60, 50, 70

Exercise 8–3

1. (a) 130 (b) $180 - 2r$ (c) 90 (d) 31 (e) 60 (f) 90 **3.** 110 **5.** 70 **7.** 60 **9.** $m\angle 1 = 70$, $m\angle 2 = 45$, $m\angle 3 = 65$, $m\angle 4 = 110$, $m\angle 7 = 115$ **11.** 45, 135, 45 **13.** 36, 72, 72 **15.** $x = 45$

Exercise 8–4

1. $\overline{AB}$, $\overline{BC}$, $\overline{CD}$, $\overline{DE}$, $\overline{EA}$ **3.** $\angle A$, $\angle B$; $\angle B$, $\angle C$; $\angle C$, $\angle D$ **5.** $\overline{AC}$, $\overline{AD}$ **7.** No **9.** Yes **11.** $\overline{BD}$, $\overline{AC}$ **13.** 43, 43 **15.** (a) 2 (b) 3 **17.** (a) The number of triangles is two less than the number of sides. (b) $(n-2)$ triangles **19.** 720; 1080; 1440; 3240 **21.** 13 **23.** No. n must be an integer, thus $(n-2)180 \neq 920$ **25.** 14 **27.** 156 **29.** 12

Exercise 8–5

1. Always **3.** Never **5.** Sometimes **7.** Never **9.** Never **11.** Never **13.** Never **15.** Never **17.** Never **19.** (a) 25, 25, 130 (b) 50, 65, 65 **21.** 6, 6, 8, 8 **23.** 10, 12, 6 **25.** 60, 120, 60, 120 **27.** No

Exercise 8–6

1. 10 **7.** 10 **9.** 9, 9, 3 **11.** 8, 4, 4, 3 **13.** 20

Exercise 8–7

1. 16 **3.** $5\frac{1}{2}$ **5.** 21 **7.** 9 **9.** 14 **11.** 6 **13.** $10\frac{1}{2}$ **15.** 45, 45 **17.** 22 **19.** 24 **21.** 135 **23.** 18

Exercise 9–1

13. 18 sq. ft. **15.** $12\frac{1}{2}$ sq. in. **17.** 12.15 sq. cm. **19.** 30.25 sq. in. **21.** ≈ 151.3 sq. mi. **23.** 11 ft. **25.** 18 sq. in. **27.** 14 sq. in. **29.** (c) **31.** False **33.** False **35.** True

Exercise 9–2

1. 56 **3.** 16.64 **5.** 36 **7.** 99 **9.** 30 **11.** 40 **13.** 75 **15.** 64 **17.** 18 **19.** 66 **21.** 66 **23.** (a) 16 (b) $\frac{240}{17}$ **25.** 6 **27.** 60 **31.** The altitude of the triangle is twice the altitude of the parallelogram. **33.** $\frac{1}{1}$ **35.** $\frac{1}{2}$ **37.** $32\sqrt{3}$ **39.** 50

Exercise 9–3

1. 5 **3.** 7 **5.** 6 **7.** $3\sqrt{2}$ **9.** 2 **11.** Yes **13.** No **15.** Yes **17.** Yes **19.** Yes

21. $s = 8, t = 4\sqrt{3}$ **23.** $r = \frac{5}{2}, t = \frac{5\sqrt{3}}{2}$ **25.** $r = 2, s = 4$ **27.** $q = 4, r = 4\sqrt{2}$

29. $p = q = 7$ **31.** $4\sqrt{3}$ **33.** $7 + 3\sqrt{3}$ **35.** $100\sqrt{3}$ **37.** 144 **39.** $144\sqrt{3}$ **41.** 20

43. $\frac{20}{\sqrt{3}}$ or $\frac{20\sqrt{3}}{3}$ **45.** 10 **47.** $5\sqrt{2}$ **49.** 240 **51.** $\frac{9\sqrt{3}}{4}$ **53.** $\frac{7\sqrt{3}}{4}$ **55.** 10 **57.** 12

59. $50\sqrt{3}$

Exercise 10–1

1. $\frac{1}{3}$ **3.** $\frac{1}{4}$ **5.** $\frac{2}{1}$ **7.** $\frac{3}{2}$ **9.** $\frac{x}{3y}$ **11.** (a)-(f), (a)-(i), (f)-(i), (b)-(d), (b)-(e), (d)-(e),

(c)-(g), (c)-(h), (g)-(h) **13.** $x = 1, y = \frac{5}{3}, z = \frac{13}{3}$ **15.** $\frac{5}{2}$ **17.** $\frac{33}{2}$ **19.** (a) 3 (b) b

(c) n **21.** $\frac{b + 5}{5}$ **23.** $\frac{15 - 12}{12}$ **25.** $\frac{a}{b}$ **27.** $\frac{9}{18}$ **29.** Correct **31.** Not correct

33. Not correct

Exercise 10–2

1. $\frac{AB}{RS} = \frac{BC}{ST} = \frac{CD}{TU} = \frac{DE}{UV} = \frac{EF}{VW} = \frac{FA}{WR}$ **3.** $\frac{3}{1}$ or $\frac{1}{3}$ **5.** $RS = \frac{2}{3}, ST = \frac{2}{3},$

$TU = 1, \quad UV = 1, \quad VW = \frac{2}{3}, \quad WR = \frac{1}{3}$ **7.** $AB = \frac{8}{3}, \quad BC = \frac{8}{3}, \quad CD = \frac{4}{3},$

$DE = 1, \; EF = \frac{2}{3}, \; FA = \frac{2}{3}$ **9.** 87 **11.** $AB = \frac{BC}{EF} \cdot DE$ **13.** $CA = \frac{AB}{DE} \cdot FD$

15. $DE = \frac{FD}{CA} \cdot AB$ **17.** $\frac{25}{3}, \frac{40}{3}$ **19.** Yes. Not necessarily. $\frac{1}{1}$ **21.** Yes. Both

squares. **23.** $\frac{AD}{CD} = \frac{DC}{DB} = \frac{CA}{BC}, \angle A \cong \angle DCB, \angle ACD \cong \angle B, \angle ADC \cong \angle BDC$

25. $\frac{168}{5}, \frac{144}{5}, \frac{54}{5}, m\angle A = r, m\angle B = s$

Exercise 10–3

1. 8 **7.** 11 **9.** 10 **11.** $\frac{MQ}{QP}$ **13.** $\frac{MP}{MQ}$ **15.** $\frac{MP}{QP}$ **17.** Yes **19.** No **21.** $\frac{a}{b}$ **23.** $\frac{m}{a}$

25. n **29.** 12 **33.** 3, 12

Exercise 10–4

1. Yes. $ABC \leftrightarrow FDE$ **3.** No **7.** 40, 40 **9.** $\triangle ABC \sim \triangle DEC$

21. $\triangle APB \sim \triangle CPD$

Exercise 10–5

1. Yes **3.** Yes **5.** No **7.** $\triangle RST \sim \triangle CAB$ (Thm. 10–7) **9.** $\triangle XYZ \sim \triangle ACB,$
(Thm. 10–7) **11.** (a) Yes (Thm. 10–7) (b) No (c) Yes (Cor. 10–3.2) (d) Yes
(Cor. 10–3.1) (e) No (f) Yes (Cor. 10–3.2) **13.** Thm. 10–6 **15.** 12, 20, 28
17. (a) Thm. 10–7 (b) $\frac{1}{4}$ or $\frac{4}{1}$ (c) 18, 72 (d) $\frac{1}{4}$ or $\frac{4}{1}$ **21.** 50 **23.** 55 mi., 165 mi.,
220 mi., 330 mi. **25.** 240 ft. **27.** 6 and 2, $\frac{15}{2}$ and $\frac{5}{2}$ **31.** $\frac{36}{7}, \frac{48}{7}$ **33.** $\frac{1}{2}$

Exercise 10–6

3. Yes **7.** $\overline{HG}, \overline{GF}, \overline{FE}, \overline{FE}, \overline{GF}, \overline{HG}$. Thm. 8–25 **9.** 6 **11.** $5\sqrt{3}$ **13.** $16, 4\sqrt{5}$, $8\sqrt{5}$ **15.** 15, 20; 9, 16 **17.** $3\sqrt{10}, 9\sqrt{10}, 30$ **19.** $4, 4\sqrt{3}, 8\sqrt{3}$ **21.** $18, 6\sqrt{3}$ **23.** $4b$ **25.** $13, \frac{60}{13}$

Exercise 10–7

1. $\frac{3}{4}, \frac{3}{4}, \frac{9}{16}$ **3.** $\frac{3}{4}, \frac{3}{4}, \frac{9}{16}$ **5.** $\frac{x}{y}, \frac{x}{y}, \frac{x^2}{y^2}$ **7.** $\frac{5}{16}$ **9.** $\frac{1}{100}$ **11.** 8 **13.** 25 in. **15.** $\frac{9}{16}$

17. $\frac{16}{25}$ **19.** 32 **21.** 324, 729 **23.** $\frac{5}{4}$ **25.** 12 **27.** 4 ft., 6 ft. **29.** 3 **33.** $\frac{3\sqrt{3}}{4}$

35. $\frac{4}{3}$ **37.** 16, 48, 80, 112

Exercise 10–8

1. $\frac{5}{13}, \frac{12}{13}, \frac{5}{12}$ **3.** $\frac{3}{5}, \frac{4}{5}, \frac{3}{4}$ **5.** $\frac{\sqrt{3}}{2}, \frac{1}{2}, \frac{\sqrt{3}}{1}$ **7.** $a\sqrt{3}, \frac{1}{2}, \frac{\sqrt{3}}{2}, \frac{1}{\sqrt{3}}$ or $\frac{\sqrt{3}}{3}$ **9.** $\frac{1}{\sqrt{5}}$ or $\frac{\sqrt{5}}{5}$

11. $\frac{\sqrt{5}}{5}$ **13.** 2 **15.** $\frac{12}{13}$ **17.** $\frac{5}{13}$ **19.** $\frac{5}{12}$

Exercise 10–9

1. .259, .966, .268 **3.** .777, .629, 1.235 **5.** .985, .174, 5.671 **7.** 3 **9.** 3 **11.** 0 **13.** 83.9 ft. **15.** 76.9 ft. **17.** 39.4 ft., 3152 sq. ft. **19.** $164\sqrt{3} \approx 284$ **21.** 8.2, 11.3 **23.** 41°, 41°, 98° **25.** 154 ft., 194.7 ft.

Exercise 11–1

1. **3.**

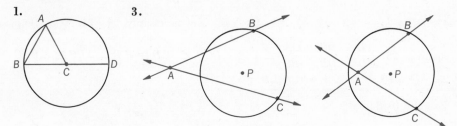

5. **7.**

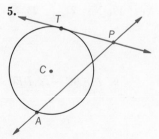

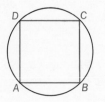

Exercise 11–2

1. Yes **7.** 8 **9.** $8\sqrt{2}$ **17.** 26 **19.** M **21.** C **23.** C

Exercise 11–3

1. No. Yes **3.** (a) 40 (b) 140 (c) 180 (d) 220 (e) 130 **7.** 50, 50 **9.** 15

Exercise 11–4

1. 60, 50, 70 **3.** 45, 45, 90 **5.** 160, 90, 110 **7.** 120, 120, 120 **9.** 40, 140 **11.** 170, 190 **13.** 101, 126, 79, 54 **21.** 75 **23.** 50 **25.** 90 **31.** 160

Exercise 11–5

1. 16 **3.** 15, 15 **5.** 10 **7.** 16 **9.** 2 **11.** 16 **13.** 4 or 5 **15.** $\frac{4.5}{4}$ **17.** $6\sqrt{2}$

Exercise 12–1

1. True **3.** True

Exercise 12–2

1. 6 in. **3.** No (see the obtuse triangle) **5.** Obtuse **7.** The intersection of q with the bisector of $\angle RST$. **9.** Draw the perpendicular bisectors of $\overline{AB}$ and $\overline{BC}$. **11.** Draw the bisector of $\angle C$ and the perpendicular bisector of $\overline{AB}$.

Exercise 12–3

1. No (see the obtuse triangle) **3.** Obtuse **7.** 8 **9.** 15 **11.** $(8x+2), (4x+1)$ **13.** Thm. 8–25 **15.** 12 **19.** 12

Exercise 12–5

1. Possible **3.** Not possible **5.** Possible **7.** Possible **13.** (a) $\angle C$ (b) $\dfrac{AC}{RT} = \dfrac{BC}{ST}$

Exercise 12–7

9.

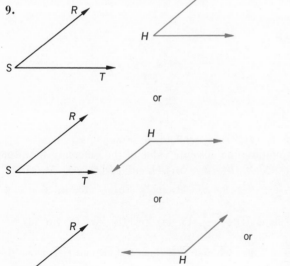

or

or

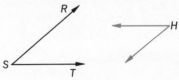

Exercise 13–1

1. 120 **3.** 60 **5.** 36 **7.** 18 **9.** 24 **11.** $\dfrac{\sqrt{2}}{2}$ **15.** 16 **17.** $6\sqrt{3}$ **25.** 90 **27.** 120 **29.** 144 **31.** 156

Exercise 13–2

1. 6π in.   **3.** $10a\pi$ **5.** 13.3 in.   **7.** 6.66 cm.   **9.** 6 cm.   **11.** $2\sqrt{3}$ ft.   **13.** 1.0 ft.
15. 1.25 in.   **17.** 73.3 ft.   **19.** 584,040,000 mi., 66,670 m.p.h.   **21.** 7.85 in.
23. 3.49 in.   **25.** 10.5   **27.** $(200 + 50\pi) \approx 357$ yd.   **29.** $\dfrac{\pi\sqrt{2}}{4}$

Exercise 13–3

1. 9π sq. in.   **3.** $25a^2\pi$ **5.** 14.1 sq. in.   **7.** 3.53 sq. cm.   **9.** 4 in.   **11.** $2\sqrt{3}$ cm.
13. 2π sq. in.   **15.** $\frac{1}{2}$ **17.** 39.3 sq. in.   **19.** 17.4 sq. in.   **21.** 9.81
23. $(50\pi - 96) \approx 61$ sq. in.

Exercise 14–1

1.

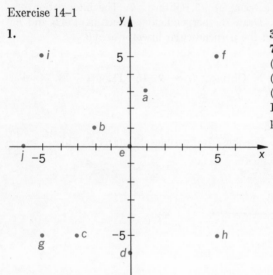

3. On the y-axis   **5.** $(0, 0)$
7. (a) IV   (b) II   (c) III
(d) I   **9.** (a) $(2, 0)$ (b) $(2, 0)$
(c) $(-2, 0)$ (d) $(-2, 0)$
(e) $(4, 0)$ **11.** D, B, C, A
13. 3   **15.** Yes, for these given
points.

Exercise 14–2

1. (a) 5 (b) -4 (c) -2 (d) y **3.** (a) 3 (b) 8 (c) 9 (d) 5 (e) $|x_2 - x_1|$ or $|x_1 - x_2|$
(f) Same y-coordinates (g) Compute the absolute value of the difference between
the x-coordinates. (h) No   **5.** $A(3, 2), B(-2, -5), C(4, -1), D(x_1, y_2)$ **7.** (a) -1
(b) $\frac{4}{5}$ (c) $\frac{3}{4}$ (d) $\dfrac{y_1 - y_2}{x_1 - x_2}$ or $\dfrac{y_2 - y_1}{x_2 - x_1}$ **9.** $\frac{1}{20}$ **11.** (a) $\frac{2}{5}$ (b) $\frac{2}{5}$ **13.** (a) $\frac{3}{2}$ (b) $\frac{3}{2}$
(c) $\dfrac{d - b}{c - a}$ (d) $\dfrac{y_1 + 2}{x_1 - 3}$ (e) No slope (f) $\dfrac{r - s}{t - r}$ **15.** (a) Yes (b) Yes (c) No (d) No
17. (a) -1 (b) $-\frac{3}{2}$ (c) $\dfrac{2s}{r - s}$ **19.** $\overline{AD}$ and $\overline{BC}$: slope 2; $\overline{AB}$ and $\overline{CD}$: slope 0;
parallelogram.

Exercise 14–3

3. Yes   **5.** $\overline{PO}$: 0, altitude to $\overline{PO}$: no slope; $\overline{OR}$: $\frac{2}{9}$, altitude to $\overline{OR}$: $\dfrac{-9}{2}$; $\overline{RP}$: $\dfrac{-2}{7}$,
altitude to $\overline{RP}$: $\frac{7}{2}$ **7.** $\overline{CA} \perp \overline{BA}$ **9.** $\overline{RS} \parallel \overline{TP}, \overline{ST} \parallel \overline{RP}$ **11.** 30

Exercise 14–4

1. (a) 5 (b) 5 (c) 13 (d) 25 (e) 17 (f) $\sqrt{2}$ (g) $10\sqrt{73}$ (h) $5\sqrt{5}$ **3.** $PQ = QR = 5$
5. $MN = NP = PQ = QM = \sqrt{10},\ MP = NQ = 2\sqrt{5}$ **7.** $GH = \sqrt{5}, HK = \sqrt{50},$
$KG = \sqrt{45}$ **9.** See Def. 2–11 **11.** It is. **13.** $\left(0, \dfrac{-37}{4}\right)$

Exercise 14–5

1. $(6, 0)$ **3.** $(5, 0)$ **5.** $(9, 9)$ **7.** $(\tfrac{7}{20}, \tfrac{11}{48})$ **9.** $\left(\dfrac{a+b}{2}, \dfrac{c}{2}\right)$ **11.** $(7, -14)$
13. At $(5, 3)$ **15.** $AC = BD = 2\sqrt{17}$; common midpoint $(3, 5)$; slopes 4 and $-\tfrac{1}{4}$
17. $N(a, 3a),\ M(-a, 3a)$

Exercise 14–7

1.

3.

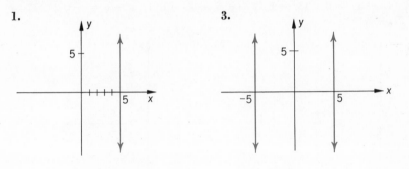

5.

7.

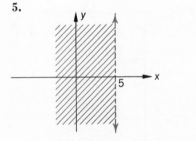

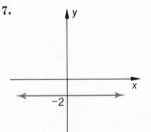

9.   **11.**   **13.**

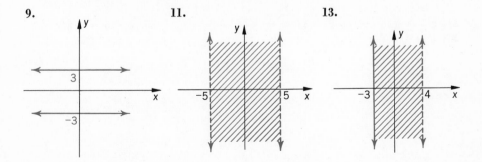

15.   **17.**   **19.**

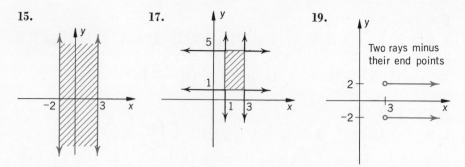

Two rays minus their end points

Exercise 14–8

3. $y + 2 = (-1)(x - 2)$ **5.** $y - 2 = 0$ **7.** $y - 6 = -5x$ **9.** $\frac{1}{2}, x - 2y = -6$
11. $-\frac{4}{3}, 4x + 3y = 0$ **13.** $-1, x + y = -6$ **15.** $1, x - y = -\sqrt{2}$ **17.** 3
19. $\frac{4}{3}$ **21.** $-\frac{1}{2}$

23.   **25.**

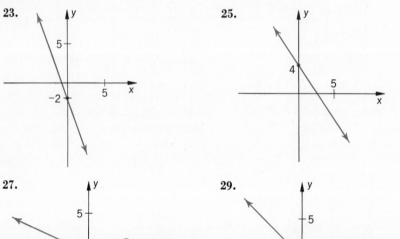

27.   **29.**

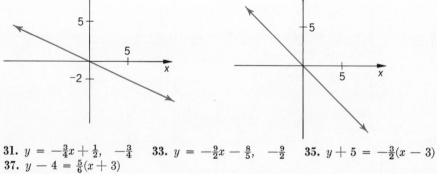

31. $y = -\frac{3}{4}x + \frac{1}{2}, \quad -\frac{3}{4}$ **33.** $y = -\frac{9}{2}x - \frac{8}{5}, \quad -\frac{9}{2}$ **35.** $y + 5 = -\frac{3}{2}(x - 3)$
37. $y - 4 = \frac{5}{6}(x + 3)$

INDEX

AA Similarity Corollary, 255
Absolute value, 24–28
Acute angles, 54, 149–50, 181, 205, 207, 287
Acute triangles, 106
Addition Axioms, 20–22, 145
  Angle, 51, 72
Addition Property Theorems, 89–90
Additive Identity Law, 21
Additive Inverse Law, 21
Adjacent angles, 55–56, 72–73, 84, 108
Algebraic Properties of Proportion, 236–37
Alternate exterior angles, 168–69
Alternate interior angles, 168–71
Altitudes, 118–19, 141, 215–16, 219–23
  concurrent, 345–46
  of similar right triangles, 274–77
Angle Addition Axiom, 51, 72
Angle bisectors, 117–19, 338–40
Angle Construction Axiom, 51, 129–30, 140, 171
Angle Measurement Axiom, 51
Angles, 45–60, 188, 191
  acute, 54, 149–50, 181, 205, 207, 287
  adjacent, 55–56, 72–73, 84, 108
  base, 106
  bisection of, 92–93, 112, 117–19, 140, 338–40, 353
  central, 310, 368

complementary, 55–57, 72, 74–76, 181
consecutive, 188, 192
construction of, 352–53
corresponding, 168–71, 234–35, 239–41, 253–55, 260
exterior, 112, 148–52, 168–69, 181
exteriors of, 47
inscribed, 316–19
interior, 112, 168–71, 181
interiors of, 47, 51, 90–92, 338–40
measures of, 49–54, 160, 179–82, 194, 317–20
obtuse, 54
parallel lines and, 167–79
right, 54, 72, 76–77, 97, 229–30, 319
straight, 54–55, 72
supplementary, 55–56, 72–76, 78, 84, 171, 192
trisection of, 350
vertex, 106
vertical, 55, 76–77, 168, 320
See also Congruent angles
Apothems, 367
Arcs, 310–12, 316–20, 352, 372–74, 377–78
Areas, 212–33
  of circles, 375–80
  of triangles, 219–23, 281–87
ASA Axiom, 101–102, 107

447

Associative Law for Addition, 21
Associative Law for Multiplication, 21
Auxiliary sets, 140–44
Axioms, defined, 4

Base angles, 106
Bases, 215–17, 219–23
Betweenness, 26–31, 83, 90–91
Bisection, 37, 91–93, 112, 192–93,
  304–305
  of angles, 92–93, 112, 117–19, 140,
    338–40, 353
  concurrent, 338–41
  See also Perpendicular bisectors

Centers of circles, 298, 304–305, 310,
  350–52, 367–68
Central angles, 310, 368
Centroids, 347
Characterization of sets, 331–37
Chords, 298–99, 304–305, 312, 327
Circular regions, 375–76
Circles, 325–30, 361–69
  areas of, 375–80
  centers of, 298, 304–305, 310, 350–52,
    367–68
  circumferences of, 371–75
  congruent, 305, 312–13, 352
  tangent, 305
Circumcenters, 343
Circumferences, 369–75
Circumscribed circles, 361–69
Closure Law for Addition, 21
Closure Law for Multiplication, 21
Collinearity, 41, 112–13
Commutative Law for Addition, 21
Commutative Law for Multiplication, 21
Complementary angles, 55–57, 72,
  74–76, 181
Completeness, criterion of, 64
Concentric circles, 298
Conclusions, 69–70
Concurrence, 338–49
  points of, 346–47
Conditions, graphs of, 408–10
Congruent angles, 85, 90–92, 169–71,
  192, 194, 319, 366
  corresponding, 239–41, 253–55, 261

defined, 56
supplementary, 71–72, 74–76, 78, 84,
  171
of triangles, 95–97, 100–102, 106,
  152–54, 180, 205, 287–88
Congruent arcs, 312
Congruent chords, 312
Congruent circles, 305, 312–13, 352
Congruent diagonals, 406–407
Congruent radii, 352
Congruent segments, 83, 89–92, 95,
  200–201, 360–61
Congruent sides, 105–107, 152–54,
  159–60, 192, 366
Congruent triangles, 94–105, 126,
  141–42, 152–54, 192
  areas of, 213
  defined, 96
  right, 205–206
  similar, 259
Consecutive angles, 188, 192
Consecutive sides, 188
Consecutive vertices, 188
Consistency, criterion of, 64–65
Constant of proportionality, 236
Constructions, 350–65
  of perpendiculars, 356–59
Continued proportions, 236
Converses, defined, 152
Convex polygons, 188–89
Coordinate geometry, 381
Coordinate systems, 28, 381–87, 404–407
Coordinates, 18–19, 28, 381
  See also x-coordinates; y-coordinates
Coplanar lines, 162–64, 350
Coplanar points, 186–87
Coplanar sets, 41
Corollaries, defined, 106
Corresponding angles, 168–71, 234–35,
  239–41, 253–55, 260
Corresponding sides, 239–40, 260–61,
  283–84
Cosines, 288–97
  table of, 293

Deductive reasoning, 68–71, 124
Degrees, 49, 311
Descartes, René, 381

Diagonals, 188, 192–93, 223, 406–407
Diameters, 299, 371–72
Direct method, 124
Direction, 33
Distance, 26–29, 157
    equal, 130–33, 192, 305, 338–41
Distance Formula, 399–401
Distributive Law, 21
Division Axiom, 20, 22, 72

Edges, 46
Elements, defined, 8
Empty sets, 10, 41
Endpoints, 32–33, 50, 131, 187–88, 276,
    310–11
    See also Vertices
Equalities, 10, 19, 332–33
Equality axioms, 20, 24–25, 73
Equiangular polygons, 187
Equiangular triangles, 106–108
Equidistance, 130–33, 192, 305, 338–41
Equilateral polygons, 187
Equilateral triangles, 106–108, 181
Euclid, 1–2, 14–15
Exterior Angle Theorem, 148–49
Exterior angles, 112, 148–52, 168–69, 181
Exterior sides, 55, 72–73
Exteriors
    of angles, 47
    of circles, 300, 302, 327
Externally tangent circles, 305

Falsity, 67–68
Field properties, 20–24
Formal proofs, 71, 74–82

Garfield, James A., 228
Geometric means, 275–77
Goldbach Conjecture, 65
Graphs, 18, 408–10, 412–13

Half-planes, 46, 50–51, 188
Horizontal lines, 387–89, 413
Hypotenuses, 135, 205–208, 228, 230,
    275–77, 289
Hypotheses, 68–70, 111–12

Identity congruence, 97

Independence, criterion of, 64
Indirect proofs, 124–28, 130
Inductive reasoning, 65–67, 69–70
Inequalities, 19–21, 145–61
    of triangles, 156–61
Infinite sets, 9, 12
Informal proofs, 71–74
Inscribed angles, 316–19
Inscribed circles, 361–65
Inscribed polygons, 366–67, 371, 376–77
Integers, 12, 18
Interception, 199–201, 317–20, 413
Interior angles, 112, 168–71, 181
Interiors
    of angles, 47, 51, 90–92, 338–40
    of circles, 300, 302, 305, 327
Internally tangent circles, 305
Intersection, 10, 43, 47, 187–88, 214,
    247–49, 255, 382
    of circles, 300–303, 305, 326–27,
    341–42, 350–51
    of lines, 41, 55, 59–60, 76, 85, 350
Intuitive similarity, 234–39, 281–82
Irrational numbers, 12
Isosceles trapezoids, 191
Isosceles triangles, 105–106, 230

Laws, 21
Legs, 206, 219, 228, 230, 276–77, 289
    defined, 135
Lemmas, defined, 169
Length, defined, 32
Lines, 14–16, 40, 112, 118
    concurrent, 339–40
    coplanar, 162–64, 350
    described by equations, 410–14
    horizontal, 387–89, 413
    intersection of, 41, 55, 59–60, 76, 85,
    350
    nonvertical, 389–91, 395–99, 410–13
    number, 18–20
    in planes, 43
    points on, 26–29, 31–33, 276, 381–82
    secant, 298, 301, 319–20, 326–27
    tangent, 300–310, 319–20, 325–27
    vertical, 287–89, 410
    See also Parallel lines; Perpendicular
    lines

Listing method, 8
Loci, 331

Major arcs, 310–12
Mean proportionals, 275–77
Measures, 32, 112, 311–12, 372–74
    of angles, 49–54, 160, 179–82, 194, 317–20
Medians, 117, 119, 141, 206–207, 346–47
Members of sets, 8
Midpoint Formula, 401–404
Midpoints, 36–39, 91, 112, 130, 192–94, 304, 346–47
Minor arcs, 310–12
Multiplication Axioms, 20–22, 72, 145
Multiplicative Identity Law, 21
Multiplicative Inverse Law, 21

Natural numbers, 12
Negative reciprocals, 397–98
Noncollinear points, 43, 341
Noncollinear sets, 41
Nonvertical lines, 389–91, 395–99, 410–13
Notation (symbols), 5, 3–12
Null (empty) sets, 10, 41
Number lines, 18–20
Numbers, *see* Integers; *specific types of numbers*
Numerical trigonometry, 292–97

Obtuse angles, 54
Obtuse triangles, 106, 118
One-to-one correspondence, 18, 50–51, 95
Opposite rays, 33
Order, 18–20, 187, 383
Order axioms, 21
Ordered pairs, 383–85
Origin, 18, 382
Orthocenters, 346
Outer ends, 299

Parallel Axiom, 164–65, 171
Parallel lines, 162–79, 192, 247–48, 255, 395–97
    angles and, 167–79
    construction of, 359–60

Parallelograms, 191–94, 215, 221, 405
Perimeters, 193, 283, 369–71
Perpendicular bisectors, 130–33, 136, 140–41, 305, 332–33, 340–41, 356
Perpendicular lines, 59–63, 72, 85, 112, 119–20, 128–40, 382
    nonvertical, 397–98
    parallel lines and, 163–64, 172
    in right angles, 76–77
    in right triangles, 135–36
    segments as, 157, 304
    tangency and, 301–305
Planes, 15–16, 40–41, 112, 381–87
    half-planes, 46, 50–51, 133
    parallel lines in, 162–63, 171–72
    points in, 43, 382–85
Point-Plotting Axiom, 64, 140
Point-slope form, 412
Points, 14–18, 32, 164–65, 399–400
    of concurrence, 346–47
    coplanar, 186–87
    on a line, 26–29, 31–33, 276, 381–82
    noncollinear, 43, 341
    in planes, 43, 382–85
    sets of, 14–17
    of tangency (contact), 300, 304
    See also Endpoints; Midpoints
Polygonal regions, 212–19
Polygons, 186–91, 239–45, 283–84, 376–77
    circumscribed circles and, 362, 366–69, 371
    See also Quadrilaterals; *specific polygons*
Positive numbers, 24, 28, 235–36
Prime numbers, 65
Projection, 275–77
Proofs, 64–68, 71–88, 129–30, 133–34
    formal, 71, 74–82
    indirect, 124–28, 130
    inductive, 65–67, 69–70
    informal, 71–74
    writing of, 82–88, 111–17
Proportion, 235–37, 239–40, 246–53, 260–61
Pythagorean Theorem, 228–33

Quadrants, 386

Quadrilaterals, 189, 191–99

Radii, 298–99, 304–305, 352, 373–74
Rational numbers, 12
Ratios, 236, 282–84, 371–72
  areas and, 222–23, 282–83, 377–78
  of corresponding sides, 240, 283–84
  trigonometric, 287–97
Rays, 32–33, 164–65, 300–301, 319–20
  of angles, 45, 50–51, 129–30, 140
Real numbers, 13, 24, 28, 51, 213,
  383–85
Rectangles, 191, 193, 215–17
Reflexive Axiom, 20, 73
Reflexive Property Theorems, 89–90
Regular polygons, 366–69, 371, 376–77
Rhombuses, 191, 193, 223
Right angles, 54, 72, 76–77, 97, 229–30,
  319
Right triangles, 118, 135–36, 205–11,
  274–81
  acute angles of, 149–50, 181
  areas of, 219–20, 228–30
Ruler Axiom, 26–31, 43, 381

SAS Axiom, 100–102
SAS Similarity Theorem, 260
Scalene triangles, 105, 126–27
Secants, 298, 301, 319–20, 326–27
Sectors, 375–80
Segments, 40, 59, 89–90, 112, 117–23,
  140, 192–94
  congruent, 83, 89–92, 95, 200–201,
    360–61
  defined, 32
  midpoints of, 37
  parallel, 164
  perpendicular, 157, 304
  perpendicular bisectors of, 131–33, 356
  in polygons, 186–88
  proportional division of, 246–53
  secant, 326–27
  similar, 234–35, 239–40
  slopes of, 388–92
  tangent, 300–301, 325–27
Semicircles, 311
Set-builder notation, 8–9

Sets, 8–17, 331–37
  auxiliary, 140–44
  empty, 10, 41
  of numbers, 12–14
  of points, 14–17
Sides, 188–89, 193
  of angles, 45, 50–51, 55, 72–73,
    338–39
  congruent, 105–107, 152–54, 159–60,
    192, 366
  consecutive, 188
  corresponding, 239–40, 260–61,
    283–84
  of squares, 216–17
  of triangles, 95–98, 100–102, 135, 207,
    229–30, 247–49, 255, 340–41
  See also Bases; Hypotenuses; Legs
Similar triangles, 241, 253–87
  areas of, 281–87
  right, 274–81
Similarities, 234–45
  intuitive, 234–39, 281–82
Sines, 288–97
  table of, 293
Skew lines, 162
Slope-intercept form, 413
Slopes, 387–98, 410–13
  defined, 389
Space, 40
Square roots, 24–26
Squares, 191, 406–407
SSS Axiom, 101–102
SSS Similarity Theorem, 260–61
Straight angles, 54–55, 72
Subsets, 9, 40
Substitution Axiom, 21, 145
Subtraction Axiom, 20, 22, 145
Subtraction Property theorems, 90–92
Supplementary angles, 55–56, 72–76,
  78, 84, 171, 192
Symbols (notation), 5, 8–12
Symmetric Axiom, 20, 25
Symmetry Property Theorems, 89–90

Tangency, 300–310, 319–20, 325–27
Tangents (trigonometric ratios), 288–97
  table of, 293
Theorems, defined, 4

Theories, 5
Transitive Property Theorems, 89–90
Transitivity Axioms, 20–21, 72–73, 145
Transversals, 165, 167–71, 199–201, 247
Trapezoids, 191, 215, 222
Triangle Inequality Theorem, 156–57
Triangles, 105–23, 179–86, 192–94,
        404–405
    acute, 106
    areas of, 219–23, 281–87
    concurrent parts of, 340–41, 345–47
    construction of, 353–54, 361–65
    defined, 47
    drawing of circles and, 361–65
    equiangular, 106–108
    equilateral, 106–108, 181
    exterior angles of, 148–49
    inequalities of, 156–61
    obtuse, 106, 118
    proportional division and, 246–49
    scalene, 105, 126–27
    See also Congruent triangles; Right
        triangles; Similar triangles;
        Trigonometry
Triangular regions, 212–13
Trichotomy Axiom, 21, 59, 126, 145

Trigonometric ratios, 387–97
    table of, 293
Trigonometry, 287–97
Trisection of angles, 350
Truth, 67–68
Two-Circle Axiom, 350–51

Union of sets, 10
Unique positive real numbers, 213

Vertex angles, 106
Vertical angles, 55, 76–77, 168, 320
Vertical lines, 387–89, 410
Vertices, 45, 310, 319–20, 368
    of polygons, 188–89, 239, 366
    of triangles, 95–97, 105, 117, 274,
        340–41, 346–47

x-axes, 382–88, 404–406, 409
x-coordinates, 382–88, 399–400, 402,
        406–407, 409–12

y-axes, 382–88, 401–403, 409, 413
y-coordinates, 382–88, 399–400, 402,
        404–406, 409, 412–13
y-intercepts, 413